Thousand Year Canon of
Lunar Eclipses
1501 to 2500

Fred Espenak

Edition 1.0
July 2014

Thousand Year Canon of Lunar Eclipses 1501 to 2500

Astropixels Publishing
P.O. Box 16197
Portal, AZ 85632

www.astropixels.com/pubs

Printed in the United States of America

ISBN 978-1-941983-01-0

Astropixels Publication: AP002

First Edition (Version 1.0)

Front Cover Photo: The total lunar eclipse of 2014 April 15 was well placed for observers in North and South America. This photo is a composite of three separate images showing the Moon near the beginning, middle and end of totality. Photo copyright ©2014 by Fred Espenak. More images of this eclipse can be seen at *www.mreclipse.com/main/photoindex.html#lunar*

Back Cover Photo: Copyright ©2014 by Babak Tafreshi

Preface

With the publication of the *Five Millennium Canon of Lunar Eclipses* (Espenak & Meeus, 2009a) and its companion volume the *Five Millennium Catalog of Lunar Eclipses* (Espenak & Meeus, 2009b), there was no plan to produce any future canons. But in the years that followed, it became evident that the 1000–year period encompassing the present era of these two publications was being used far more often than the rest. For this reason, it would be convenient to have a subset of the *Canon* and *Catalog* in a single smaller volume.

As the design of the *Thousand Year Canon of Lunar Eclipses* took shape, new features were developed to distinguish it from the *Five Millennium* publication. Most importantly, the figures would be ~60% larger with 12 per page instead of 20. This increase in map size makes it easier to discern regions of eclipse visibility. Larger figures also allow the addition of more parameters including ΔT (Delta T) and the lunar node of the eclipse. The narrative and explanatory sections of the *Thousand Year Canon* are newly written and include detailed eclipse statistics for the 1000-year period containing 2,424 lunar eclipses. In addition to the *standard edition* of the *Canon* (published in blank and white), there is a *color edition* that makes the 201 pages of eclipse maps and diagrams easier to interpret.

The *Thousand Year Canon of Lunar Eclipses* uses the Jet Propulsion Lab's DE406 — the same ephemeris used in their online HORIZONS service for dates thousands of years in the past or future. The *Five Millennium* publications are based on the older VSOP87 and ELP-2000/82 ephemerides for the Sun and Moon. There is excellent agreement in the eclipse predictions between these publications in spite of using widely different methods of calculating the positions of the Sun and the Moon. In this respect, the new canon serves as a robust consistency check with the earlier *Five Millennium* publications over the period 1501 through 2500.

To compliment the new canon of lunar eclipses, the *Thousand Year Canon of Solar Eclipses 1501 to 2500* (Espenak, 2014) is being published in parallel. It covers the same period and includes a catalog and larger maps than the those in the *Five Millennium Canon of Solar Eclipses* (Espenak & Meeus, 2006).

The figures, maps and catalogs in the two *Thousand Year Canons* are the basis of a new website on solar and lunar eclipse predictions: *www.EclipseWise.com*. A plain text file containing the entire lunar eclipse catalog appearing in *Appendix A* can be downloaded from this website at: *www.EclipseWise.com/lunar/LEpubs/TYCLEcatalog.txt*.

The NASA *Five Millennium* publications had a single printing with a limited distribution. In contrast, the two *Thousand Year Canons* are being published via print-on-demand so they will be available to a wider audience for many years to come.

The lessons learned from print-on-demand publishing will assist in developing new and expanded replacements of the *Fifty Year Canon of Solar Eclipses* (Espenak , 1987) and *Fifty Year Canon of Lunar Eclipses* (Espenak , 1989), as well as specialized publications on individual eclipses similar to the NASA Eclipse Bulletin series.

— *Fred Espenak*
July 2014

Acknowledgments

I am profoundly grateful my wife Patricia Totten Espenak, for tirelessly editing the manuscript at multiple stages of its development. Her insightful comments and suggestions have been a major asset in creating the final version of the *Canon*. Any remaining typographical, grammatical, or technical errors are solely my responsibility. I also want to thank Michael Zeiler and Xavier Jubier for productive discussions about the jungle of self publishing, print-on-demand, ISBN numbers, etc.. Finally, I want to thank my mentor, colleague, co-author and friend Jean Meeus for a lifetime of inspiration, technical expertise and fascination in the calculation of solar system phenomena. His 1966 *Canon of Solar Eclipses* started me down the road of eclipse predictions shortly after viewing my first total solar eclipse in 1970.

Dedication

To Patricia Totten Espenak, my wife and best friend. We first met in the shadow of the Moon nearly twenty years ago and half a world away, and we've been chasing eclipses together ever since.

To Valerie Anne and Maggie Marie Delos-Reyes, my granddaughters who might see their very first total solar eclipse from their back yard in 2017.

And in loving memory of my parents Fred and Asie Espenak who always encouraged me to follow my own path, and of my sister Nancy J. Davies. I miss you all.

Table of Contents

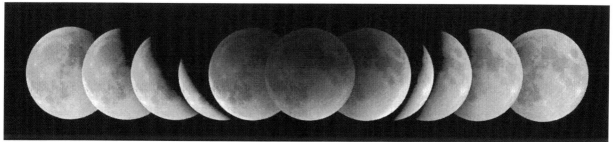

Photo 1–1 shows various phases of the total lunar eclipse of 2001 Jan 21. ©2001 F. Espenak

Section 1: Lunar Eclipse Fundamentals

1.1 Introduction

The Moon orbits Earth once every 29.5306 days with respect to the Sun. Over the course of its orbit, the Moon's changing position relative to the Sun results in its familiar phases: New Moon > New Crescent > First Quarter > Waxing Gibbous > Full Moon > Waning Gibbous > Last Quarter > Old Crescent > New Moon. The New Moon phase is not visible because the illuminated side of the Moon points away from Earth. The other phases are easily seen as the Moon cycles through them month after month.

During Full Moon, the Moon appears opposite the Sun in the sky. It rises as the Sun sets and is visible throughout the night. The Full Moon sets in the morning just as the Sun rises. This unique geometry occurs when the Moon is 180° from the Sun as seen from Earth. This is also the direction that Earth casts its shadow into space.

The Moon's orbit is tilted about 5.1° to Earth's orbit around the Sun. The apparent points where the two orbits cross are called the nodes. When the Full Moon occurs near one of these nodes, Earth's shadow can sometimes fall on some portion of the Moon and a lunar eclipse takes place.

Earth's shadow is composed of two cone-shaped components, one nested inside the other. The outer or penumbral shadow is a zone where the Sun's rays are partially blocked. In contrast, the inner or umbral shadow is a region where direct rays from the Sun are completely blocked.

1.2 Classification of Lunar Eclipses

There are three basic types of lunar eclipses:

1. **Penumbral Lunar Eclipse** — The Moon passes through Earth's faint penumbral shadow. Penumbral eclipses are of minor interest since they are quite difficult to observe. Although rare, a penumbral eclipse can occur in which the Moon's entire disk is enveloped within the penumbra. Such events are called total penumbral eclipses.

2. **Partial Lunar Eclipse** — A portion of the Moon passes through Earth's dark umbral shadow. The remaining part of the Moon appears bright even though it lies deep within the penumbra. Partial eclipses are easy to see, even with the unaided eye.

3. **Total Lunar Eclipse** — The entire Moon passes through Earth's umbral shadow. Total eclipses are quite striking for the vibrant range of colors the Moon can take on during the total phase, referred to as totality.

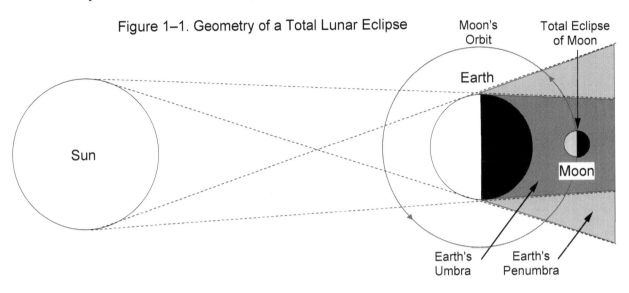

Figure 1–1. Geometry of a Total Lunar Eclipse

Figure 1–1 illustrates the geometry of a total lunar eclipse. A partial eclipse is visible if only part of the Moon enters Earth's umbral shadow. If the Moon passes through the penumbral shadow but misses the umbral shadow, then a penumbral eclipse occurs.

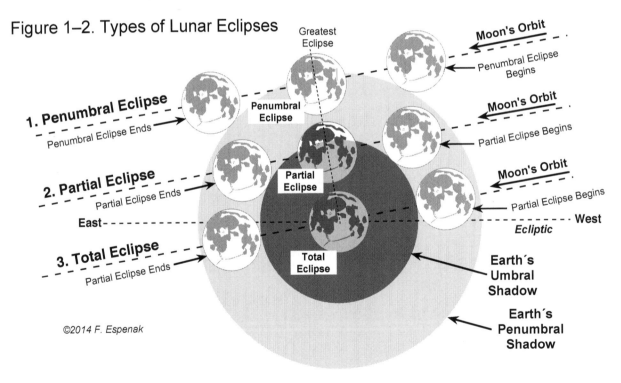

Figure 1–2. Types of Lunar Eclipses

©2014 F. Espenak

Figure 1–2 illustrates the three types of lunar eclipses as seen from Earth. 1. A penumbral eclipse occurs when the Moon passes through the penumbra but completely misses the umbra. 2. A partial eclipse occurs if some portion of the Moon enters the umbra. 3. A total lunar eclipse takes place when the entire disk of the Moon enters the umbral shadow.

1.3 Visual Appearance of Penumbral Lunar Eclipses

The visual appearance of penumbral, partial and total lunar eclipses differs significantly. While penumbral eclipses are pale and difficult to see, partial eclipses are easy naked-eye events while total eclipses are colorful and dramatic.

Earth's penumbral shadow forms a diverging cone that expands into space in the anti-solar direction. From within this zone, Earth blocks part but not all of the Sun's disk. Thus, some portion of the Sun's direct rays continues to reach the Moon during a penumbral eclipse.

The early and late stages of a penumbral eclipse are completely invisible to the eye. It is only when about 2/3 of the Moon's disk has entered the penumbral shadow that a skilled observer can detect a faint shading across the Moon.

Even when 90% of the Moon is immersed in the penumbra, approximately 10% of the Sun's rays still reach the Moon's deepest limb. Under such conditions, the Moon remains relatively bright with only a subtle shadow gradient across its disk.

1.4 Visual Appearance of Partial Lunar Eclipses

Compared to penumbral eclipses, partial eclipses are easy to see with the naked eye. The lunar limb that extends into the umbral shadow appears very dark or black. This is due to a contrast effect since the remaining portion of the Moon in the penumbra may be 500x brighter. Because the umbral shadow's diameter is about 2.7x times the Moon's diameter, it appears as though a semi-circular bite has been taken out of the Moon.

Aristotle (384–322 BCE) first proved that Earth was round using the curved umbral shadow seen at partial eclipses. In comparing observations of several eclipses, he noted that Earth's shadow was round no matter where the eclipse took place, whether the Moon was high in the sky or low near the horizon. Aristotle correctly reasoned that only a sphere casts a round shadow from every angle.

1.5 Visual Appearance of Total Lunar Eclipses

The total lunar eclipse is the most dramatic and visually compelling type of lunar eclipse. The Moon's appearance can vary enormously throughout the period of totality and from one eclipse to the next. The geometry of the Moon's path through the umbra plays a significant role in determining the appearance of totality. The effect that Earth's atmosphere has on a total eclipse is not as apparent. Although the physical mass of Earth blocks all direct sunlight from the umbra, the planet's atmosphere filters, attenuates and bends some of the Sun's rays into the shadow.

The molecules in Earth's atmosphere scatter short wavelength light (i.e., yellow, green, blue) more than long wavelength light (i.e., orange, red). The same process responsible for making sunsets red also gives total lunar eclipses their characteristic ruddy color. The exact appearance can vary considerably in both hue and brightness.

Because the lowest layers of the atmosphere are the thickest, they absorb more sunlight and refract it through larger angles. About 75% of the atmosphere's mass is concentrated in the bottom 10 kilometers (troposphere) as well as most of the water vapor, which can form massive clouds that block even more light. Just above the troposphere lies the stratosphere (10 to 50 kilometers), a rarified zone above most of the planet's weather systems. The stratosphere is subject to important photochemical reactions due to the high level of solar ultraviolet radiation that penetrates the region. The troposphere and stratosphere act together as a ring-shaped lens that refracts heavily reddened sunlight into Earth's umbral shadow. Since the higher stratospheric layers contain less gas, they refract sunlight through progressively smaller angles into the outer parts of the umbra. In contrast, denser tropospheric layers refract sunlight through larger angles to reach the inner parts of the umbra.

Photo 1–2 captures the beginning, middle and end of totality during the total lunar eclipse of 2004 October 27. ©2004 F. Espenak

Because of this lensing effect, the amount of light refracted into the umbra tends to increase radially from center to edge. Inhomogeneities due to asymmetric amounts of cloud and dust at differing latitudes can cause significant variations in brightness throughout the umbra.

Besides water (clouds, mist, precipitation), Earth's atmosphere also contains aerosols or tiny particles of organic debris, meteoric dust, volcanic ash and photochemical droplets. This material attenuates sunlight before it is refracted into the umbra. For instance, major volcanic eruptions in 1963 (Agung) and 1982 (El Chichon) each dumped huge quantities of gas and ash into the stratosphere and were followed by several years of very dark eclipses (Keen, 1983).

The 1991 eruption of Pinatubo in the Philippines had a similar effect. While most of the solid ash fell to Earth several days after circulating through the troposphere, a sizable volume of sulphur dioxide (SO_2) reached the stratosphere where it combined with water vapor to produce sulphuric acid (H_2SO_4). This high-altitude volcanic haze layer severely attenuates sunlight that must travel several hundred kilometers horizontally through the layer before being refracted into the umbral shadow. Thus, total eclipses following large volcanic eruptions are particularly dark. The total lunar eclipse of 1992 Dec 09 (1½ years after Pinatubo) was so dark that it was difficult to see the Moon's dull gray disk with the naked eye.

All total eclipses begin with penumbral and partial phases. After the total phase, the eclipse ends with partial followed by penumbral phases. While *solar* eclipses require special filters for safe viewing, no such precautions are needed to watch *lunar* eclipses. The best views of a lunar eclipse are with binoculars and the naked eye.

1.6 Danjon Scale of Lunar Eclipse Brightness

The French astronomer A. Danjon proposed a useful five-point scale for evaluating the visual appearance and brightness of the Moon during a total lunar eclipse. The L values for various luminosities are defined in Table 1–1.

Table 1–1. Danjon Brightness Scale for Total Lunar Eclipses

Danjon Value	Visual Description
L=0	Very dark eclipse (Moon is almost invisible, especially at mid-totality)
L=1	Dark eclipse, grey or brownish in coloration (details are distinguishable only with difficulty)
L=2	Deep red or rust-colored eclipse (very dark central shadow, while outer umbra is relatively bright)
L=3	Brick-red eclipse (umbral shadow usually has a bright or yellow rim)
L=4	Very bright copper-red or orange eclipse (umbral shadow has a bluish, very bright rim)

The Danjon scale is a useful tool to characterize the range of colors and brightness the Moon takes on during a total lunar eclipse. Assigning an L value is best done with the naked eye or binoculars near the time of mid-totality. The Moon's appearance should also be evaluated just after the start and before the end of totality. The Moon is then near the edge of the shadow, providing an opportunity to assign an L value to the outer umbra. In making such determinations, the instrumentation and the time should be recorded.

Photo 1–3 Various phases of the total lunar eclipse of 2000 January 20–21 appear in this composite image. ©2000 F. Espenak

Section 2: Lunar Eclipse Predictions

2.1 Lunar Eclipse Contacts

During the course of a lunar eclipse, the instants when the Moon's disk becomes tangent to Earth's shadows are known as eclipse contacts. They mark the primary stages or phases of a lunar eclipse.

Penumbral lunar eclipses have two major contacts although neither of these events is observable.

> **P1** — Instant of first exterior tangency of the Moon with the Penumbra
> (Penumbral Eclipse Begins)
> **P4** — Instant of last exterior tangency of the Moon with the Penumbra
> (Penumbral Eclipse Ends)

Partial lunar eclipses have four contacts. As the Moon's limb enters and exits the umbral shadow, contacts U1 and U4 mark the instants when the partial eclipse phase begins and ends, respectively.

> **P1** — Instant of first exterior tangency of the Moon with the Penumbra
> (Penumbral Eclipse Begins)
> **U1** — Instant of first exterior tangency of the Moon with the Umbra
> (Partial Umbral Eclipse Begins)
> **U4** — Instant of last exterior tangency of the Moon with the Umbra
> (Partial Umbral Eclipse Ends)
> **P4** — Instant of last exterior tangency of the Moon with the Penumbra
> (Penumbral Eclipse Ends)

Total lunar eclipses have six contacts. Contacts U2 and U3 mark the instants when the Moon's entire disk is first and last internally tangent to the umbra. These are the times when the total phase of the eclipse begins and ends, respectively.

> **P1** — Instant of first exterior tangency of the Moon with the Penumbra
> (Penumbral Eclipse Begins)
> **U1** — Instant of first exterior tangency of the Moon with the Umbra
> (Partial Umbral Eclipse Begins)
> **U2** — Instant of first interior tangency of the Moon with the Umbra
> (Total Umbral Eclipse Begins)
> **U3** — Instant of last interior tangency of the Moon with the Umbra
> (Total Umbral Eclipse Ends)
> **U4** — Instant of last exterior tangency of the Moon with the Umbra
> (Partial Umbral Eclipse Ends)
> **P4** — Instant of last exterior tangency of the Moon with the Penumbra
> (Penumbral Eclipse Ends)

The instant of greatest eclipse occurs when the Moon passes closest to the shadow axis. This corresponds to the maximum phase of the eclipse when the Moon is at its deepest position within either the penumbral or umbral shadow.

13

Figure 2–1. Lunar Eclipse Contacts

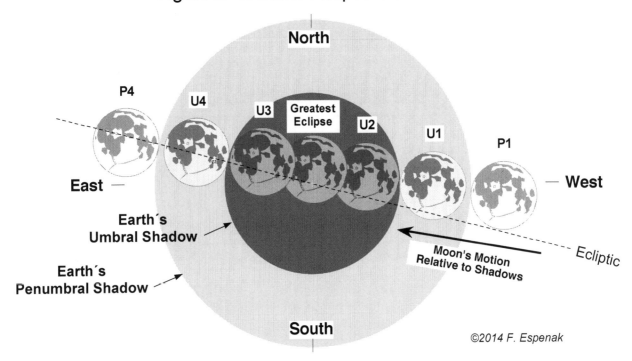

©2014 F. Espenak

Figure 2–1 illustrates the six contacts for a total lunar eclipse. These correspond to the instants when the Moon's disk is tangent to the penumbral or umbral shadows. Partial eclipses do not have contacts U2 and U3, while penumbral eclipses only have contacts P1 and P4.

2.2 Enlargement of Earth's Shadows

In 1707, Philippe de La Hire made a curious observation about Earth's umbra. The predicted radius of the shadow needed to be enlarged by about 1/41 in order to fit timings made during a lunar eclipse. Additional observations over the next two centuries revealed that the shadow enlargement was somewhat variable from one eclipse to the next. According to William Chauvenet (1891):

"This fractional increase of the breath of the shadow was given by Lambert as 1/40, and by Mayer as 1/60. Beer and Maedler found 1/50 from a number of observations of eclipses of lunar spots in the very favorable eclipse of December 26, 1833."

Chauvenet adopted a value of 1/50, which has become the standard enlargement factor for lunar eclipse predictions published by many national institutes worldwide. The enlargement enters into the definitions of the penumbral and umbral shadow radii as follows.

penumbral radius: $\quad R_p = 1.02 \times (0.998340 \times P_m + S_s + P_s)$ (2–1)

umbral radius: $\quad R_u = 1.02 \times (0.998340 \times P_m - S_s + P_s)$ (2–2)

Where: $\quad P_m$ = Equatorial horizontal parallax of the Moon
S_s = Geocentric semi-diameter of the Sun
P_s = Equatorial horizontal parallax of the Sun

The factor 1.02 is the enlargement of the shadows by 1/50. Earth's true figure approximates that of an oblate ellipsoid with a flattening of ~1/300. Furthermore, the degree of axial tilt of the planet towards or away from the Sun throughout the year means the shape of the penumbral and umbral shadows varies by a small amount. It is sufficient to use a mean radius of Earth at latitude 45° to approximate the departure from perfectly circular shadows. The *Astronomical Almanac* uses a factor of 0.998340 to scale the Moon's equatorial horizontal parallax to account for this (0.998340 ≈ 1.0 – 0.5 × 1/300).

In an analysis of 57 eclipses over 150 years, Link (1969) found a mean shadow enlargement of 2.3%. Timings of crater entrances and exits through the umbra during four lunar eclipses from 1972 to 1982 (Table 2–1) closely support the Chauvenet value of 2%.

Table 2–1. Umbral Shadow Enlargement From Craters Timings*

Lunar Eclipse Date	Crater Entrances % Enlargement	Crater Exits % Enlargement	Sky & Telescope Reference
1972 Jan 30	1.69 [420]	1.68 [295]	Oct 1972, p.264
1975 May 24	1.79 [332]	1.61 [232]	Oct 1975, p.219
1982 Jul 05	2.02 [538]	2.24 [159]	Dec 1982, p.618
1982 Dec 30	1.74 [298]	1.74 [90]	Apr 1983, p.387

* Values in square brackets are the number of observations included in each measurement.

From a physical point of view, there is no abrupt boundary between the umbra and penumbra. The shadow density varies continuously as a function of radial distance from the central axis out to the extreme edge of the penumbra. The density variation is most rapid near the theoretical edge of the umbra. Kuhl's (1928) contrast theory demonstrates that the edge of the umbra is perceived at the point of inflexion in the shadow density. This point appears to be equivalent to a layer in Earth's atmosphere at an altitude of about 120–150 kilometers. The net enlargement of Earth's radius of 1.9% to 2.4% corresponds to an umbral shadow enlargement of 1.5% to 1.9%, in good agreement with the conventional value.

Some authorities dispute Chauvenet's shadow enlargement convention. Danjon (1951) notes the only reasonable way of accounting for a layer of opaque air surrounding Earth is to increase the planet's radius by the altitude of the layer. This is accomplished by proportionally increasing the parallax of the Moon. The radii of the umbral and penumbral shadows are then subject to the same absolute correction and not the same relative correction employed in the traditional Chauvenet 1/50 convention. Danjon estimates the thickness of the occulting layer to be 75 kilometers and this results in an enlargement of Earth's radius and the Moon's parallax of about 1/85.

In 1951, the French almanac *Connaissance des Temps* adopted Danjon's method for the enlargement of Earth's shadows in their eclipse predictions as shown below.

penumbral radius: $Rp = 1.01 \times Pm + Ss + Ps$ (2–3)
umbral radius: $Ru = 1.01 \times Pm - Ss + Ps$ (2–4)

Where: Pm = Equatorial horizontal parallax of the Moon
Ss = Geocentric semi-diameter of the Sun
Ps = Equatorial horizontal parallax of the Sun

and $1.01 \approx 1 + 1/85 - 1/594$

15

The factor 1.01 combines the 1/85 shadow enlargement term with a 1/594 term to correct for Earth's oblateness at a latitude of 45°.

Danjon's method correctly models the geometric relationship between an enlargement of Earth's radius and the corresponding increase in the size of its shadows. Meeus and Mucke (1979) and Espenak & Meeus (2009a) both use Danjon's method. However, the resulting umbral and penumbral eclipse magnitudes are smaller by approximately 0.006 and 0.026, respectively, as compared to predictions using the traditional Chauvenet convention of 1/50.

For instance, the umbral magnitude of the partial lunar eclipse of 2008 Aug 16 was 0.813 according to the *Astronomical Almanac for 2008* (2008) using Chauvenet's method, but only 0.8076 according to Espenak & Meeus (2009a) using Danjon's method.

Of course, the small magnitude difference between the two methods is difficult to observe because the edge of the umbra is poorly defined. The choice of shadow enlargement method has its largest effect in certain limiting cases where a small change in magnitude can shift an eclipse from one type to another. An eclipse that is barely total according to Chauvenet's method will be a large magnitude partial eclipse if calculated using Danjon's method. Table 2–2 shows 4 instances where a shallow total eclipse calculated with Chauvenet becomes a deep partial eclipse using Danjon.

Table 2–2. Total (Chauvenet) vs. Partial (Danjon) Lunar Eclipses: 1501 to 2500

Calendar Date	Umbral Magnitude (Chauvenet)	Umbral Magnitude (Danjon)	Magnitude Difference
1540 Sep 16	1.0007	0.9947	0.0060
1856 Oct 13	1.0017	0.9960	0.0057
2196 Jul 10	1.0007	0.9960	0.0047
2413 Nov 08	1.0042	0.9993	0.0049

Similarly, small umbral magnitude partial eclipses using Chauvenet must be reclassified as penumbral eclipses of large penumbral magnitude when calculated with Danjon's method. A recent example was the eclipse of 1988 Mar 03, which was partial with an umbral magnitude of 0.0028 according to the Chauvenet's method, but was penumbral with an umbral magnitude –0.0017 by Danjon's method. A similar case will occur on 2042 September 29. Table 2–3 lists all such cases from 1501 through 2500.

Table 2–3. Partial (Chauvenet) vs. Penumbral (Danjon) Lunar Eclipses: 1501 to 2500

Calendar Date	Umbral Magnitude (Chauvenet)	Umbral Magnitude (Danjon)	Magnitude Difference
1513 Sep 15	0.0036	–0.0003	0.0039
1900 Jun 13	0.0012	–0.0040	0.0052
1988 Mar 03	0.0028	–0.0017	0.0045
2042 Sep 29	0.0027	–0.0031	0.0058
2429 Dec 11	0.0020	–0.0033	0.0053

In some cases the shadow enlargement convention can make the difference between a shallow penumbral eclipse (Chauvenet) or no eclipse at all (Danjon). Table 2–4 lists nine small magnitude penumbral eclipses over a 500-year interval as determined using Chauvenet's method. When the eclipse predictions are repeated using Danjon's method, no lunar eclipses are found on these dates.

Table 2–4. Penumbral Lunar Eclipses (Chauvenet): 1801 to 2300

Calendar Date	Penumbral Magnitude (Chauvenet)
1864 Apr 22	0.0237
1872 Jun 21	0.0008
1882 Oct 26	0.0059
1951 Feb 21	0.0068
2016 Aug 18	0.0165
2042 Oct 28	0.0077
2194 Mar 07	0.0085
2219 Apr 30	0.0008
2288 Feb 18	0.0204

Practically speaking, the faint and indistinct edge of the penumbral shadow makes the penumbral eclipse contacts (P1 and P4) completely unobservable. So the small magnitude differences discussed here are of academic interest. Still, it is important to note which shadow enlargement convention is used since it is critical in comparing predictions from different sources.

In the *Canon*, Earth's penumbral and umbral shadow sizes have been calculated using Danjon's enlargement method. Other sources using Danjon's method include Meeus and Mucke (1979), Espenak and Meeus (2009a) and *Connaissance des Temps*. Several sources using Chauvenet's method are the *Astronomical Almanac*, Liu and Fiala (1992), and Espenak (1989).

2.3 Solar and Lunar Coordinates

The coordinates of the Sun and the Moon used in the eclipse predictions presented here have been calculated with the JPL DE406 (Jet Propulsion Laboratory Developmental Ephemeris 406). The DE406 is based upon the International Celestial Reference Frame (ICRF), the adopted reference frame of the International Astronomical Union (IAU). The DE406 is often referred to as the "JPL long ephemeris" because it covers a 6000-year period from –3000 Feb 23 (JED 0625360.50) to +3000 May 06 (JED 02816912.50). While based on the DE405, the accuracy of the interpolating polynomials of the DE406 has been lessened in order to cover the much larger time span. The DE406 does not include nutation or libration.

The interpolating accuracy of the DE406 is within 25 meters for any planet and 1 meter for the Moon. Since the absolute accuracy of the DE405 is several kilometers for planetary positions, the difference between the DE405 and DE406 is of no consequence in the predictions presented in the *Canon*. The DE406 is used by JPL's online HORIZONS ephemeris service for dates in the distant past or future.

2.4 Secular Acceleration of the Moon

Ocean tides are caused by the gravitational pull of the Moon (and, to a lesser extent, the Sun). The resulting tidal bulge in Earth's oceans is dragged ahead of the Moon in its orbit because of the daily rotation of Earth. As a consequence, the ocean mass offset from the Earth–Moon line exerts a pull on the Moon and accelerates it in its orbit. Conversely, the Moon's gravitational tug on this mass exerts a torque that decelerates the rotation of Earth. The length of the day gradually increases as energy is transferred from Earth to the Moon and the lunar orbit and period of revolution about Earth increases.

The tides are not the only factor changing Earth's rotation rate. The melting of continental ice sheets at the end of the last glacial period result in the rise of land masses that were depressed by the enormous weight of the ice sheets. This "post-glacial rebound" of the land allows the return flow of mantle material back under the de-glaciated landmasses particularly in the polar regions. Through conservation of angular momentum, the resulting shift in mass from the equator to the poles will cause Earth's rotation to slow down. However, it will take many thousands of years for the land to reach an equilibrium level because of the extreme viscosity of the mantle.

The secular acceleration of the Moon is small, but it has a cumulative effect on the Moon's position when extrapolated over many centuries. Direct measurements of the acceleration have only been possible since 1969 using the Apollo retro-reflectors (LLR) left on the Moon. The results from LLR show that the Moon's mean distance from Earth is increasing by 3.8 centimeters per year (Dickey, et al., 1994). The corresponding acceleration in the Moon's ecliptic longitude is –25.858 arc-seconds/century^2 (Chapront, Chapront-Touzé, and Francou, 2002).

The value of the Moon's secular acceleration over long time spans is unknown. Careful records for its derivation only go back a century. Before then, spurious and incomplete eclipse and occultation observations from medieval and ancient manuscripts comprise the database. In any case, the current value implies an increase in the length of day (LOD) of ~ 2.3 milliseconds/century. Such a small amount may seem insignificant, but it has very measurable cumulative effects. For instance, time as measured with Earth's rotation during the 20th century lost 64 seconds when compared to atomic time.

2.5 Measurement of Time

The system of time measurement is crucial to the prediction of eclipses. Over the past several centuries, the way we measure time has changed significantly as our understanding of solar system dynamics and sub-atomic physics has developed.

The most natural form of time measurement is the solar day (usually measured from solar noon to solar noon). Unfortunately, the length of the solar day varies during the year because of the eccentricity of Earth's orbit around the Sun. Mean solar time resolves this problem by using an average to define the mean solar day.

In 1884, Greenwich Mean Time (GMT) — the mean solar time on the Greenwich Meridian (0° longitude) — was adopted as the standard reference time for clocks around the world. A fundamental basis of GMT is the assumption that Earth's rotation on its axis is constant. It wasn't until the mid-twentieth century that astronomers realized the rotation period is gradually increasing. Earth is slowing down because of tidal friction with the Moon (Sect. 2.4).

For purposes of orbital calculations, time using Earth's rotation was abandoned for a more uniform time scale based on Earth's orbit about the Sun. In 1952, Ephemeris Time was introduced to address the problem. The ephemeris second was defined as a fraction of the tropical year for 1900 Jan 01 as calculated from Newcomb's *Tables of the Sun* (1895). Ephemeris Time was used for Solar System ephemeris calculations until 1979.

Terrestrial Dynamical Time (TD) is the modern replacement for Ephemeris Time and is used in theories of planetary motion in the Solar System. TD is based on International Atomic Time (TAI), which is a high-precision standard using several hundred atomic clocks worldwide. To ensure continuity with Ephemeris Time, TD was defined to match ET for the date 1977 Jan 01. In 1991, the IAU refined the definition of TD to make it more precise. It was also renamed Terrestrial Time (TT) although the author prefers to use the older name Terrestrial Dynamical Time.

Civilian time used throughout the world is still based on mean solar time, although indirectly. While Greenwich Mean Time was determined though observations of the Sun, its modern day replacement, Universal Time (actually UT1) is based on Earth's rotation using observations of distant quasars. UT1 is a nonuniform time because Earth is gradually slowing down at an irregular rate. At present (2014), the accumulated error in the rotation of Earth in the course of one year is ~0.3 seconds.

Coordinated Universal Time (UTC) is derived from International Atomic Time (TAI). The length of the UTC second is defined in terms of an atomic transition of cesium and is accurate to approximately one nanosecond (billionth of a second) per day. UTC was defined to closely parallel UT1. However, the two time systems are intrinsically incompatible since UTC is uniform while UT1 is based on Earth's rotation, which is gradually slowing. In order to keep the two times within 0.9 seconds of each other, a leap second is added to UTC as needed (currently once every few years).

Today, UTC is the time standard used to define time zones around the world. It is the time reference for GPS satellites and aviation, and is used to synchronize the clocks of computers across the Internet.

2.6 ΔT (Delta T)

The orbital positions of the Sun and the Moon, required by eclipse predictions, are calculated using Terrestrial Dynamical Time (TD) because it is a uniform time scale. However, world time zones and daily life are based on Universal Time[1] (UT1). In order to convert eclipse predictions from TD to UT1, the difference between these two time scales must be known. The parameter ΔT (Delta T) is the arithmetic difference, in seconds, between the two as:

$$\Delta T = TD - UT1 \tag{2-1}$$

Past values of ΔT can be deduced from historical records. In spite of their relatively low precision, these data represent the only evidence for the value of ΔT prior to 1600. In the centuries following the introduction of the telescope (circa 1609), thousands of high quality observations have been

---

[1] World time zones are actually based on Coordinated Universal Time (UTC). It is an atomic time synchronized and adjusted to stay within a second of astronomically determined Universal Time (UT1) through the addition of an occasional "leap second" to compensate for the gradual slowing of Earth's rotation.

made of lunar occultations of stars. The number and accuracy of these timings increase from the seventeenth through the twentieth century, affording valuable data in the determination of ΔT.

The estimated uncertainty in the value of ΔT is 20 seconds in the year 1500, but it drops to 1 second by 1800. A detailed analysis of historical measurements for ΔT from 1500 to +1950 is presented in Table 2–1 and includes the standard error for each value (Morrison and Stephenson, 2004).

Table 2–1: Values of ΔT Derived from Historical Records

Year	ΔT (seconds)	Standard Error (seconds)
1500	200	20
1600	120	20
1700	9	5
1750	13	2
1800	14	1
1850	7	<1
1900	–3	<1
1950	29	<0.1

In modern times, the determination of ΔT is made using atomic clocks and radio observations of quasars. Table 2–2 gives the value of ΔT every five years from 1955 to 2010 (*Astronomical Almanac for 2011*, page K9) and the most recent value in 2014.

Table 2–2: Recent Values of ΔT from Direct Observations

Year	ΔT (seconds)	5-Year Change (seconds)	Average 1-Year Change (seconds)
1955.0	+31.1	—	—
1960.0	+33.2	2.1	0.42
1965.0	+35.7	2.5	0.50
1970.0	+40.2	4.5	0.90
1975.0	+45.5	5.3	1.06
1980.0	+50.5	5.0	1.00
1985.0	+54.3	3.8	0.76
1990.0	+56.9	2.6	0.52
1995.0	+60.8	3.9	0.78
2000.0	+63.8	3.0	0.60
2005.0	+64.7	0.9	0.18
2010.0	+66.1	1.4	0.28
2014.0	+67.3	1.5	0.30

As revealed in Table 2–2, the average 1-year change in ΔT ranges from 0.18 seconds to 1.06 seconds. Future changes in ΔT are unknown since theoretical models of the physical causes are imprecise. Extrapolations from the table weighted by the long period trend from tidal braking of the Moon offer estimates of +70 seconds in 2020, +85 seconds in 2050, +127 seconds in 2100, and +271 seconds in the year 2200. It should be noted that extrapolations of future values of ΔT are little more than educated guesses due to the inherent uncertainties in the tidal breaking and glacial rebound of Earth's rotation.

2.7 Polynomial Expressions for ΔT

Using the ΔT values obtained from the historical record and from direct observations (Tables 2–1 and 2–2, respectively), a series of polynomial expressions were created to simplify the evaluation of ΔT for any time during the interval 1501 to 2500. The decimal year "y" is defined as follows:

$$y = year + (month - 0.5)/12$$

This gives "y" for the middle of the month, which is accurate enough given the precision in the known values of ΔT. The following table of polynomial expressions can be used to calculate the value of ΔT (in seconds) over the interval of the *Canon*.

Table 2–3 lists twelve polynomial expression for ΔT, each one covering a specific range of dates. The time in the third column is calculated from the decimal year as defined above. The first ten expressions covering the years 500 to 2005 are from the *Five Millennium Canon of Solar Eclipses* (Espenak & Meeus, 2006). The eleventh expression covering the period 2005 to 2015 was derived for this publication from the most recent values of ΔT. The last expression covering the years 2015 and beyond is an extrapolation based on recent values of ΔT combined with the long term trend obtained by fitting a quadratic function to the values of ΔT from the historic records. It is an updated expression based on van der Sluys (2010).

Table 2–3: Polynomial Expressions for ΔT

Date Range*	Polynomial Expression for Delta T (ΔT)	Time**
500 to 1600	$\Delta T = 1574.2 - 556.01 \times u + 71.23472 \times u^2 + 0.319781 \times u^3 - 0.8503463 \times u^4 - 0.005050998 \times u^5 + 0.0083572073 \times u^6$	$u = (y-1000)/100$
1600 to 1700	$\Delta T = 120 - 0.9808 \times t - 0.01532 \times t^2 + t^3 / 7129$	$t = y - 1600$
1700 to 1800	$\Delta T = 8.83 + 0.1603 \times t - 0.0059285 \times t^2 + 0.00013336 \times t^3 - t^4 / 1174000$	$t = y - 1700$
1800 to 1860	$\Delta T = 13.72 - 0.332447 \times t + 0.0068612 \times t^2 + 0.0041116 \times t^3 - 0.00037436 \times t^4 + 0.0000121272 \times t^5 - 0.0000001699 \times t^6 + 0.000000000875 \times t^7$	$t = y - 1800$
1860 to 1900	$\Delta T = 7.62 + 0.5737 \times t - 0.251754 \times t^2 + 0.01680668 \times t^3 - 0.0004473624 \times t^4 + t^5 / 233174$	$t = y - 1860$
1900 to 1920	$\Delta T = -2.79 + 1.494119 \times t - 0.0598939 \times t^2 + 0.0061966 \times t^3 - 0.000197 \times t^4$	$t = y - 1900$
1920 to 1941	$\Delta T = 21.20 + 0.84493 \times t - 0.076100 \times t^2 + 0.0020936 \times t^3$	$t = y - 1920$
1941 to 1961	$\Delta T = 29.07 + 0.407 \times t - t^2 / 233 + t^3 / 2547$	$t = y - 1950$
1961 to 1986	$\Delta T = 45.45 + 1.067 \times t - t^2 / 260 - t^3 / 718$	$t = y - 1975$
1986 to 2005	$\Delta T = 63.86 + 0.3345 \times t - 0.060374 \times t^2 + 0.0017275 \times t^3 + 0.000651814 \times t^4 + 0.00002373599 \times t^5$	$t = y - 2000$
2005 to 2015	$\Delta T = 64.69 + 0.2930 \times t$	$t = y - 2000$
2015 to 2500	$\Delta T = 67.62 + 0.3645 \times t + 0.0039755 \times t^2$	$t = y - 2015$

* The calendar date for each year in the *Date Range* corresponds to Jan 01 at 00:00:00.
** The variable *y* in the *Time* corresponds to the decimal year.

21

The largest deviation in the value of ΔT between the polynomial expressions in Table 2–3 and the historically derived values in Table 2–1 occurs in the period 500 to 1600 and is less than 4 seconds. This accuracy is acceptable so the polynomial expressions have been used in evaluating ΔT for all eclipses in the *Thousand Year Canon*.

2.8 Date Format

There are a number of ways to write the calendar date through variations in the order of day, month, and year. The International Organization for Standardization's (ISO) 8601 uses a numeric date representation, which organizes the elements from largest to smallest. The format is YYYY–MM–DD where YYYY is the calendar year, MM is the month of the year between 01 (January) and 12 (December), and DD is the day of the month between 01 and 31. For example, the 27th day of April in the year 1943 would then be expressed as 1943-04-27. The ISO convention is adopted here, but the month number has been replaced with the three-letter English abbreviation of the month name for additional clarity. From the previous example, the date then is expressed as 1943 Apr 27.

2.9 Calendar Date

The Gregorian calendar is the civil calendar currently used throughout most of the world. The older Julian calendar was used until 1582 Oct 04. As a consequence of the Gregorian Calendar Reform, the day following 1582 Oct 04 (Julian calendar) is 1582 Oct 15 (Gregorian calendar).

Pope Gregory XIII decreed the use of the Gregorian calendar in 1582 in order to correct a problem in a drift of the seasons. It adopts the convention of a year containing 365 days. Every fourth year is a leap year of 366 days if it is divisible by 4 (e.g., 2004, 2008, etc.). However, whole century years (e.g., 1700, 1800, 1900) are excluded from the leap year rule unless they are also divisible by 400 (e.g., 2000). This dating scheme was designed to keep the vernal equinox on or within a day of March 21. Precession of the equinoxes will eventually produce an error of one day in the Gregorian calendar in about 7700 years.

Prior to the Gregorian Calendar Reform of 1582, the Julian calendar was in wide use. It was less complicated in that all years divisible by 4 were counted as 366-day leap years, but this simplicity came at a cost. After more than 16 centuries of use, the Julian calendar date of the vernal equinox had drifted 11 days from March 21. It was this failure in the Julian calendar that prompted the Gregorian Calendar Reform.

2.10 Statistical Comparison with Five Millennium Canon of Lunar Eclipses

As discussed in section 2.3, the *Thousand Year Canon* uses the JPL DE406, a numerically integrated ephemeris for the Sun and the Moon. In comparison, the *Five Millennium Canon of Lunar Eclipses* (Espenak & Meeus, 2009a) uses the older analytical ephemerides VSOP87 (Bretagnon & Francou, 1988) and ELP-2000/82 (Chapront-Touze and Chapront, 1983) for the Sun and the Moon, respectively.

Table 2–3 presents a statistical comparison between the two canons for several parameters over a range of years. The tabulated values are averages of the differences between the *Thousand Year Canon* minus the *Five Millennium Canon* for ten 50-year periods.

The average difference in the instant of *Greatest Eclipse* ranges from 0.01 to –1.58 seconds. The average difference in *Gamma²* ranges from 260.8 to 289.6 meters while the *Umbral Magnitude* spans 20.8×10^6 to 36.8×10^6. The average differences for Besselian elements X and Y range from 120.5 to 216.6 meters and 98.8 to 275.4 meters, respectively.

Table 2–3: Statistical Comparison with the *Five Millennium Canon of Lunar Eclipses*

Years	Greatest Eclipse (seconds)	Gamma (meters)	Umbral Magnitude (x 10⁶)	X (meters)	Y (meters)
1501–1551	–1.58 [0.073]	±289.1 [3.6]	22.3 [6.6]	±156.2 [10.7]	±231.2 [12.1]
1601–1651	–1.05 [0.004]	±293.3 [14.6]	25.1 [4.9]	±188.6 [4.1]	±227.5 [15.2]
1701–1751	–0.47 [0.008]	±279.4 [19.6]	34.7 [0.7]	±220.0 [19.2]	±231.3 [13.1]
1801–1851	–0.25 [0.133]	±270.3 [21.4]	36.4 [0.7]	±206.5 [28.6]	±196.9 [4.7]
1901–1951	–0.02 [0.004]	±260.8 [5.3]	25.8 [2.6]	±153.7 [11.7]	±134.5 [12.1]
2001–2051	0.03 [0.003]	±279.3 [7.8]	20.8 [1.6]	±120.5 [9.5]	±98.8 [9.0]
2101–2151	0.01 [0.005]	±285.5 [27.6]	23.5 [0.5]	±150.8 [11.7]	±125.9 [5.7]
2201–2251	–0.17 [0.012]	±281.8 [21.1]	34.8 [0.8]	±195.9 [12.9]	±212.6 [8.3]
2301–2351	–0.66 [0.021]	±286.9 [12.6]	36.5 [5.8]	±216.6 [7.6]	±275.4 [17.0]
2401–2451	–0.87 [0.075]	±289.6 [12.3]	27.8 [6.6]	±196.0 [10.3]	±269.9 [17.0]

*Table 2–3 presents a statistical comparison between the two canons for several parameters over a range of years. The tabulated values are averages of the differences between the **Thousand Year Canon** minus the **Five Millennium Canon** for ten 50-year periods. The values in square brackets are the standard deviations of the average differences.*

In all cases, the best agreement between the two canons occurs during the present era (2001–2051), while the largest differences arise hundreds of years in the past or future. This is excellent agreement, considering the computational differences between the numerically integrated and analytical ephemerides.

---

2 Gamma is the minimum distance of the Moon's center from the shadow axis measured in units of Earth's equatorial radius. This instant occurs at greatest eclipse.

2.11 Map Accuracy

The accuracy of the eclipse maps depends principally on two factors. The first is the rigorousness of the solar and lunar ephemerides used in the calculations (Sect. 2.3). These ephemerides are accurate to approximately 1 arc-second over the entire span of the *Canon*. The agreement with predictions in the *Five Millennium Canon* using different ephemerides illustrates the level of accuracy (Sect. 2.10).

The second and greater source of error is due to the uncertainty in ΔT (Sect. 2.6). This parameter is the arithmetic difference between Terrestrial Dynamical Time (TD) and Universal Time (UT1). TD can be thought of as time measured with an idealized or perfect clock. In contrast, UT1 is based on Earth's rotation, which is gradually slowing down. TD is used to calculate solar system ephemerides and eclipse predictions, but UT1 is used for defining world time and longitudes.

Earth rotated faster in the past so eclipse predictions generated in TD must be converted to UT1 (UT1 = TD – ΔT) before the geographic visibility of a lunar eclipse can be determined. In other words, the physical impact of ΔT on eclipse predictions is to the shift zone of visibility east, relative to the position calculated from TD. Because 1° in longitude corresponds to 4 minutes of time, a ΔT value of 240 seconds shifts a zone 1° east of its TD position. The maps in the *Canon* already include the ΔT translation from TD to UT1 and depict the actual regions of visibility of each eclipse.

The largest uncertainty in ΔT (20 seconds in 1501) corresponds to an error in longitude of the visibility zone of 0.08°. Such a small error is not visible on the scale of the maps in the *Canon*.

Photo 2–1 The total lunar eclipse of 2000 July 16 was shot in Maui. ©2000 F. Espenak

Section 3: Lunar Eclipse Statistics

3.1 Statistical Distribution of Eclipse Types

There are three basic types of lunar eclipses:

1. **Penumbral** — The Moon passes partially or completely into Earth's penumbral shadow
2. **Partial** — The Moon passes through Earth's penumbral shadow and partially into the umbral shadow
3. **Total** — The Moon passes through Earth's penumbral shadow and completely into the umbral shadow

During the 1000-year period from 1501 to 2500, Earth experiences 2,424 eclipses of the Moon. The statistical distribution of the three eclipse types over this interval is shown in Table 3–1.

Table 3–1. Distribution of Basic Lunar Eclipse Types

Eclipse Type	Abbreviation	Number	Percent
All Eclipses	–	2424	100.0%
Penumbral	N	883	36.4%
Partial	P	856	35.3%
Total	T	685	28.3%

During most penumbral eclipses, only part of the Moon passes through Earth's penumbral shadow. Examples of such *partial* penumbral eclipses include: 2012 Nov 28, 2013 Oct 18, 2016 Mar 23 and 2016 Sep 16. It is also possible to have a penumbral eclipse in which the Moon passes completely within Earth's penumbral shadow while not entering the inner umbral shadow. Such *total* penumbral eclipses are quite rare compared the typical *partial* penumbral eclipses. During the 21st century, there are 87 *partial* penumbral eclipses, but only 5 *total* penumbral eclipses: 2006 Mar 14, 2053 Aug 29, 2070 Apr 25, 2082 Aug 08, and 2099 Sep 29. Table 3–2 shows the distribution of the two penumbral eclipse types during the period covered by the *Canon*. For more on total penumbral eclipses, see Section 3.11.

Table 3–2. Statistics of Penumbral Lunar Eclipses

Eclipse Type	Number	Percent
All Penumbral Eclipses	883	100.0%
Partial Penumbral	850	96.3%
Total Penumbral	33	3.7%

While there are no special classifications for partial eclipses, total lunar eclipses through Earth's umbral shadow can be categorized into two types:

1. **Central** — The Moon passes through the central axis of Earth's umbral shadow
2. **Non-Central** — The Moon misses the central axis of Earth's umbral shadow

Using these categories, the distribution of the 685 total eclipses in the *Canon* is shown in Table 3–3.

Table 3–3. Statistics of Total Lunar Eclipses

Eclipse Type	Number	Percent
All Total Eclipses	685	100.0%
Central Total	432	63.1%
Non-Central Total	253	36.9%

Examples of central total eclipses include: 2000 Jul 16, 2011 Jun 15, 2018 Jul 27 and 2022 May 16. Several examples of non-central total eclipses are: 2010 Dec 21, 2011 Dec 10, 2014 Apr 15 and 2014 Oct 08.

3.2 Distribution of Lunar Eclipse Types by Century

Table 3–4 summarizes 1000 years of eclipses by eclipse type in 100-year intervals. The average century contains 242 lunar eclipses of which 88 are penumbral, 86 are partial and 69 are total. Individual centuries deviate from these mean values in interesting ways. For instance, the number of eclipses in a century varies from a minimum of 228 to a maximum of 256. The number of penumbral eclipses varies from 81 to 98 while the number of partial eclipses ranges from 57 to 98. Finally, the number of total lunar eclipses per century varies from 60 to 85.

The last column lists the number of total lunar eclipse tetrads per century. A tetrad is a grouping of four consecutive total lunar eclipses each separated by six lunations. Their frequency ranges from 0 to 8 per century. For more information on tetrads, see Section 3–16.

Table 3–4. Number of Lunar Eclipse Types by Century: 1501 to 2500

Century Interval	All Lunar Eclipses	All Pen. Eclipses	Partial Pen. Eclipses	Total Pen. Eclipses	All Partial Eclipses	All Total Eclipses	Central Total Eclipses	Non-Central Total Eclipses	Total Eclipse Tetrads
1501 to 1600	233	82	79	3	74	77	39	38	6
1601 to 1700	249	91	88	3	97	61	11	50	0
1701 to 1800	256	98	98	0	98	60	13	47	0
1801 to 1900	249	90	88	2	97	62	11	51	0
1901 to 2000	229	83	74	9	65	81	48	33	5
2001 to 2100	228	86	81	5	57	85	61	24	8
2101 to 2200	238	81	77	4	88	69	24	45	4
2201 to 2300	252	94	93	1	97	61	11	50	0
2301 to 2400	253	95	95	0	98	60	12	48	0
2401 to 2500	237	83	77	6	85	69	23	46	4

There is a periodic oscillation in the total number of lunar eclipses as well as in the individual types. By inspection, the period is about 600 years. Using tables from von Oppolzer's *Canon der Finsternisse* (1887) the Dutch astronomer G. Van den Bergh (1954) calculated a period of 586 years. By studying the distributions of tetrad eclipse groups (Section 3.16), Meeus derived an empirical expression showing that this period is slowly decreasing (Meeus 2004). While its current value is actually 565 years, the period was 618 years in –1999 and it will decrease to 552 years by 3000.

A theoretical study by Hughes (2004) demonstrates that the period is caused by the eccentricity of Earth's orbit, which is currently decreasing.

There are other interesting features in the distribution of eclipse types per century. For instance, the number of total lunar eclipses as well as deep central total eclipses is highest when the overall number of lunar eclipses is at a minimum. In contrast, numbers of penumbral eclipses, partial eclipses and non-central total eclipses all appear to be directly correlated with the overall number of lunar eclipses. Finally, the number of total penumbral eclipses, and total lunar eclipse tetrads are most frequent during epochs when the overall number of lunar eclipses is at a minimum.

3.3 Distribution of Lunar Eclipse Types by Month

Table 3–5 summarizes 1000 years of eclipses by eclipse type in each month of the year. The first value in each column is the number of eclipses of a given type for the corresponding month. The second value in square brackets is the number of eclipses divided by the number of days in that month. This normalization allows direct comparison of eclipse frequencies in different months.

The normalized values in the column "Number of All Lunar Eclipses" shows that eclipses are equally distributed around the year. The same is true for partial eclipses; however, the columns for penumbral and total eclipses reveal something interesting. Penumbral eclipses are about 9% more likely during December–January–February compared to the months June–July–August. This effect is attributed to Earth's elliptical orbit. Earth currently reaches perihelion in early January and aphelion in early July. Consequently, the Sun's apparent diameter varies from 1,952 to 1,887 arc-seconds between perihelion and aphelion. The Sun's larger apparent diameter at perihelion makes Earth's penumbral shadow larger so penumbral eclipses are more frequent at that time.

The opposite argument holds true for total eclipses which are 16% more likely during the period June–July–August compared to the months December–January–February. In this case, the Sun's smaller apparent size around aphelion increases the diameter of Earth's umbral shadow so the frequency of total eclipses is slightly higher at that time.

Table 3–5. Lunar Eclipse Types by Month: 1501 to 2500

Month	Number of All Lunar Eclipses	Number of Penumbral Eclipses	Number of Partial Eclipses	Number of Total Eclipses
January	208 [6.71]	81 [2.61]	69 [2.23]	58 [1.87]
February	180 [6.43]	68 [2.43]	64 [2.29]	48 [1.71]
March	211 [6.81]	79 [2.55]	75 [2.42]	57 [1.84]
April	201 [6.70]	73 [2.43]	74 [2.47]	54 [1.80]
May	208 [6.71]	76 [2.45]	74 [2.39]	58 [1.87]
June	200 [6.67]	68 [2.27]	68 [2.27]	64 [2.13]
July	197 [6.35]	69 [2.23]	63 [2.03]	65 [2.10]
August	205 [6.61]	75 [2.42]	70 [2.26]	60 [1.94]
September	205 [6.83]	76 [2.53]	73 [2.43]	56 [1.87]
October	204 [6.58]	73 [2.35]	76 [2.45]	55 [1.77]
November	201 [6.70]	67 [2.23]	78 [2.60]	56 [1.87]
December	204 [6.58]	78 [2.52]	72 [2.32]	54 [1.74]

3.4 Lunar Eclipse Frequency and the Calendar Year

There are two to five lunar eclipses in every calendar year. Table 3–6 shows the distribution in the number of eclipses per year for the 1000 years covered in the *Canon*.

Table 3–6. Number of Lunar Eclipses per Year

Number of Eclipses per Year	Number of Years	Percent
2	710	71.0%
3	163	16.3%
4	120	12.0%
5	7	0.7%

When two eclipses occur in one calendar year, they can be in any combination of penumbral, partial, or total (N, P, or T, respectively). Table 3–7 lists the frequency of each eclipse combination along with five examples nearest the present when the combination occurs. The table makes no distinction in the order of any two eclipses. For example, the eclipse combination PT includes all years where the order is either PT or TP.

Of the 710 years containing two eclipses, 78% of them are divided between the combinations PP (39.6%) and TT (38.4%). The NT pair is the rarest combination with no instances in the *Canon*.

Table 3–7. Two Lunar Eclipses in One Year

Eclipse Combinations*	Number of Years	Percent	Examples (Years)
NN	23	3.2%	..., 1987, 2016, 2042, 2045, 2053, ...
NP	56	7.9%	..., 2005, 2006, 2012, 2017, 2023, ...
NT	0	0.0%	—
PP	281	39.6%	..., 1980, 2039, 2041, 2046, 2057, ...
PT	77	10.8%	..., 2008, 2010, 2019, 2021, 2026, ...
TT	273	38.4%	..., 2007, 2011, 2014, 2015, 2018, ...

* N = Penumbral, P = Partial, and T = Total.

There are 163 years containing three eclipses in the *Canon* that occur in any of nine possible combinations of N, P, or T. Table 3–8 lists the frequency of each eclipse combination along with five examples nearest the present when each combination occurs. The table makes no distinction in the order of eclipses in any combination. For example, the eclipse combination NPT includes all years where the order is NPT, NTP, PNT, PTN, TPN, and TNP. The NTT combination occurs only once, while there are no instances of NNT or PPP combinations.

Table 3–8. Three Lunar Eclipses in One Year

Eclipse Combinations*	Number of Years	Percent	Examples (Years)**
NNN	74	45.4%	..., 2002, 2027, 2031, 2049, 2060, ...
NNP	21	12.9%	..., 1958, 2013, 2147, 2168, 2186, ...
NNT	0	0.0%	—
NPP	33	20.2%	..., 1871, 2075, 2140, 2151, 2169, ...
NPT	6	3.7%	[1525, 1936, 1963, 2001, 2048, 2066]
NTT	1	0.6%	[2466]
PPT	6	3.7%	[1610, 1833, 1898, 2028, 2113, 2178]
PPP	0	0.0%	—
PTT	18	11.0%	..., 1852, 2094, 2159, 2224, 2243, ...
TTT	4	2.5%	[1544, 1917, 1982, 2485]

* N = Penumbral, P = Partial, and T = Total.
** For years bounded by a square bracket, there are no other examples beyond those years.

When four eclipses occur in one calendar year, there are three combinations of eclipse types N and P (no total eclipses occur). This happens for 120 years in the *Canon*. Table 3–9 lists the frequency of each eclipse combination along with five examples nearest the present when each combination occurs. The table makes no distinction in the order of eclipses in the combinations.

Table 3–9. Four Lunar Eclipses in One Year

Eclipse Combinations*	Number of Years	Percent	Examples (Years)
NNNN	94	78.3%	..., 1944, 2020, 2038, 2056, 2085, ...
NNNP	23	19.2%	..., 1991, 2009, 2150, 2197, 2215, ...
NNPP	3	2.5%	[1684, 2205, 2411]

* N = Penumbral, P = Partial.

The maximum number of five lunar eclipses in one calendar year is quite rare. Over the 1000-year span of the *Canon*, only seven years contain five lunar eclipses. They occur in two combinations of eclipse types where three or four eclipses are of type N. The first eclipse of such a quintet always occurs in the first half of January, while the last eclipse falls in the latter half of December. Table 3–10 lists all seven years containing five eclipses along with their eclipse combinations and frequencies. Once again, no distinction is made here in the order of eclipses.

Table 3–10. Five Lunar Eclipses in One Year

Eclipse Combinations*	Number of Years	Percent	Examples (Years)**
NNNNP	5	71.4%	[1676, 1879, 2132, 2262, 2400]
NNNPP	2	28.6%	[1694, 1749]

* N = Penumbral, P = Partial.
** For years surrounded by square brackets, there are no other examples outside this range.

3.5 Extremes in Eclipse Magnitude: Penumbral Lunar Eclipses

The penumbral eclipse magnitude is defined as the fraction of the Moon's diameter immersed in Earth's penumbral shadow. It is a unitless number that can be expressed numerically by

$$Mp = xp/dm \tag{3-1}$$

where *Mp* is the penumbral eclipse magnitude, *xp* is the distance measured from the edge of the penumbral shadow to the edge of the Moon deepest in the penumbra, and *dm* is the apparent diameter of the Moon.

The penumbral eclipse magnitude reaches its maximum value at the instant of greatest eclipse (when the Moon passes closest to the shadow axis). A search through the 2,424 eclipses in the *Canon* reveals some interesting cases involving extreme values of the penumbral eclipse magnitude.

Six penumbral eclipses have a maximum magnitude less than 0.006 (Table 3–11). These events are all the first or last members in a Saros series[3]. The smallest magnitude is the penumbral eclipse of 2027 Jul 18 with a magnitude of 0.0015.

Table 3–11. Penumbral Lunar Eclipses with Magnitude ≤ 0.006

Date (Dynamical Time)	Saros	Gamma	Penumbral Eclipse Magnitude	Penumbral Eclipse Duration
1550 Apr 01	134	1.5507	0.0022	13.1m
1752 Apr 28	98	−1.5699	0.0060	23.6m
2027 Jul 18	110	−1.5759	0.0015	12.1m
2096 Jun 06	151	−1.5724	0.0048	21.3m
2107 May 07	152	1.5589	0.0059	22.3m
2411 Jul 06	165	−1.5405	0.0028	14.2m

The parameter gamma is the distance of the Moon's center from the shadow axis at greatest eclipse measured in units of Earth's equatorial radius. Negative values are south of the shadow axis.

---

[3] The Saros is a period of 223 synodic months (~ 18 years, 11 days, and 8 hours). Eclipses separated by this interval belong to the same Saros series and share similar geometry and characteristics. The system of numbering Saros series was introduced by van den Bergh (1955).

Table 3-12 lists the eight penumbral eclipses having a maximum magnitude greater than 1.05. The greatest penumbral eclipse occurred on 1988 Mar 03 with a maximum magnitude of 1.0908. The penumbral magnitudes of these eclipses are all greater than 1.0, so they are classified as *total* penumbral eclipses because the Moon is completely immersed within the penumbral shadow.

Table 3-12. Total Penumbral Lunar Eclipses with Magnitude ≥ 1.05

Date (Dynamical Time)	Saros	Gamma	Penumbral Eclipse Magnitude	Penumbral Eclipse Duration
1607 Mar 13	126	1.0028	1.0510	281.7m
1988 Mar 03	113	0.9886	1.0908	293.8m
2070 Apr 25	142	1.0044	1.0516	287.0m
2139 Feb 13	145	-1.0083	1.0574	290.9m
2222 Aug 23	151	-1.0043	1.0526	289.5m
2429 Dec 11	132	-0.9905	1.0853	290.2m
2447 Dec 22	132	-1.0002	1.0673	287.8m
2466 Jan 01	132	-1.0071	1.0540	285.7m

3.6 Extremes in Eclipse Magnitude: Partial Lunar Eclipses

The umbral eclipse magnitude is defined as the fraction of the Moon's diameter immersed in Earth's umbral shadow. It is a unitless number that can be expressed numerically by

$$Mu = xu/dm \qquad (3-2)$$

where *Mu* is the umbral eclipse magnitude, *xu* is the distance measured from the edge of the umbral shadow to the edge of the Moon deepest in the umbra, and *dm* is the apparent diameter of the Moon.

The umbral eclipse magnitude reaches its maximum value at the instant of greatest eclipse. A search through the 2,424 eclipses in the *Canon* reveals interesting cases involving extreme values of the umbral eclipse magnitude in partial and total lunar eclipses.

Four partial eclipses have a maximum magnitude less than or equal to 0.005 (Table 3-13). The partial eclipse with the smallest magnitude (0.0001) occurred on 1553 Jul 25.

Table 3-13. Partial Lunar Eclipses with Magnitude ≤ 0.005

Date (Dynamical Time)	Saros	Gamma	Umbral Eclipse Magnitude	Partial Eclipse Duration
1553 Jul 25	131	-1.0254	0.0001	2.2m
1890 Nov 26	114	-0.9994	0.0018	9.9m
2157 Feb 24	145	-0.9868	0.0006	6.0m
2421 Jun 16	156	1.0225	0.0011	7.5m

Six partial eclipses have a maximum magnitude greater than or equal to 0.99 (Table 3–14). The partial eclipse with the largest magnitude (0.9994) occurs on 2413 Nov 08.

Table 3–14. Partial Lunar Eclipses with Magnitude ≥ 0.99

Date (Dynamical Time)	Saros	Gamma	Umbral Eclipse Magnitude	Partial Eclipse Duration
1540 Sep 16	110	–0.4584	0.9948	202.4m
1856 Oct 13	134	0.4810	0.9960	186.2m
1899 Dec 17	133	–0.4552	0.9922	202.0m
2196 Jul 10	142	0.4577	0.9960	205.8m
2413 Nov 08	152	0.4733	0.9994	189.5m
2460 May 05	148	0.4549	0.9950	206.0m

3.7 Extremes in Eclipse Magnitude: Total Lunar Eclipses

Six total eclipses have a maximum magnitude less than or equal to 1.004 (Table 3–15). The smallest magnitude was the total eclipse of 1529 Oct 17 with a value of 1.0002. The total eclipse of 2015 Apr 04 has a magnitude of 1.0008. Because the Moon's passage though the umbral shadow is so shallow, these events all have short total phases of less than 9 minutes.

Table 3–15. Total Lunar Eclipses with Magnitude ≤ 1.004

Date (Dynamical Time)	Saros	Gamma	Umbral Eclipse Magnitude	Total Eclipse Duration
1529 Oct 17	109	0.4775	1.0002	2.2m
2015 Apr 04	132	0.4460	1.0008	4.7m
2144 Apr 18	124	–0.4787	1.0026	7.6m
2155 Sep 11	130	–0.4752	1.0003	2.6m
2366 May 25	146	0.4817	1.0007	4.1m
2419 Jul 07	136	–0.4754	1.0031	8.5m

Eight total eclipses have a maximum magnitude greater than or equal to 1.85. Their total phase durations all exceed 99 minutes. The gamma values are close to 0.0 indicating that the Moon passes centrally through the middle of the umbral shadow. These eclipses take place when the Moon is near perigee—the time when the Moon's diameter is at maximum. The total eclipse with the largest magnitude (1.8721) occurred on 1631 May 15

Table 3–16. Total Lunar Eclipses with Magnitude ≥ 1.85

Date (Dynamical Time)	Saros	Gamma	Umbral Eclipse Magnitude	Total Eclipse Duration
1631 May 15	115	0.0051	1.8721	99.8m
1754 Apr 07	118	−0.0140	1.8507	99.4m
1765 Aug 30	124	−0.0004	1.8629	101.4m
1953 Jul 26	128	−0.0071	1.8629	100.7m
2264 Nov 04	140	−0.0039	1.8684	98.6m
2340 Apr 13	137	0.0074	1.8575	99.9m
2492 Aug 08	146	−0.0196	1.8505	99.4m

3.8 Greatest Duration: Penumbral Lunar Eclipses

Seven penumbral eclipses each have durations of 288 minutes or more. Since the penumbral eclipse magnitude of each of these events is greater than 1.0, they are all classified as *total* penumbral eclipses. Each eclipse in Table 3–17 occurs near lunar apogee. The Moon then exhibits a small angular diameter while traveling relatively slowly, thereby extending the length of the eclipse.

Table 3–17. Penumbral Lunar Eclipses with a Duration ≥ 288 minutes

Date (Dynamical Time)	Saros	Gamma	Penumbral Eclipse Magnitude	Penumbral Eclipse Duration
1901 May 03	110	−1.0101	1.0431	288.3m
1988 Mar 03	113	0.9886	1.0908	293.8m
2099 Sep 29	148	1.0175	1.0341	288.4m
2121 Feb 02	145	−1.0235	1.0309	288.5m
2139 Feb 13	145	−1.0083	1.0574	290.9m
2222 Aug 23	151	−1.0043	1.0526	289.5m
2429 Dec 11	132	−0.9905	1.0853	290.2m

3.9 Greatest Duration: Partial Lunar Eclipses

Eight partial eclipses have durations of 206 minutes or more. These eclipses occur with the Moon near apogee so its slow trajectory through the umbra tends to prolong the partial phase.

Table 3–18. Partial Lunar Eclipses with a Duration ≥ 206 minutes

Date (Dynamical Time)	Saros	Gamma	Umbral Eclipse Magnitude	Partial Eclipse Duration
1511 Apr 13	104	−0.4585	0.9828	207.5m
1598 Feb 21	107	0.4537	0.9851	206.6m
1892 May 11	129	−0.4735	0.9555	206.3m
2021 Nov 19	126	−0.4552	0.9742	208.4m
2039 Nov 30	126	−0.4721	0.9426	206.0m
2231 Aug 13	132	−0.4786	0.9439	206.9m
2460 May 05	148	0.4549	0.9950	206.0m
2489 Oct 09	154	0.4679	0.9575	207.5m

3.10 Greatest Duration: Total Lunar Eclipses

Fourteen total eclipses have durations greater than or equal to 105 minutes. The most recent one was 2000 Jul 16 while the next is 2123 Jun 09. These eclipses all occur with the Moon near apogee. The Moon then has a small angular diameter coupled with a relatively slow orbital motion. Such conditions prolong the Moon's passage through the umbra to produce long total lunar eclipses.

Table 3–19. Total Lunar Eclipses with a Duration ≥ 105 minutes

Date (Dynamical Time)	Saros	Gamma	Umbral Eclipse Magnitude	Total Eclipse Duration
1584 May 24	114	−0.0065	1.8146	106.1m
1707 Apr 17	117	−0.0018	1.8178	105.7m
1718 Sep 09	123	−0.0636	1.7016	105.0m
1736 Sep 20	123	−0.0042	1.8087	106.0m
1754 Oct 01	123	0.0478	1.7268	105.2m
1859 Aug 13	126	0.0038	1.8148	106.5m
1982 Jul 06	129	−0.0579	1.7180	105.7m
2000 Jul 16	129	0.0302	1.7684	106.4m
2123 Jun 09	132	0.0406	1.7488	106.1m
2141 Jun 19	132	−0.0446	1.7415	106.1m
2246 May 01	135	−0.0575	1.7137	105.2m
2264 May 12	135	0.0121	1.7979	106.2m
2351 Mar 14	138	0.0206	1.7744	105.1m
2369 Mar 24	138	−0.0135	1.7885	105.4m

3.11 Total Penumbral Lunar Eclipses

During most penumbral eclipses, only part of the Moon passes through Earth's penumbral shadow. It is also possible to have a penumbral eclipse in which the entire Moon passes within Earth's penumbral shadow while not entering the umbra. The geocentric apparent diameter of the Moon ranges from a minimum of 1763.0 arc-seconds (apogee) to a maximum of 2011.8 arc-seconds (perigee). The penumbral annulus formed by the zone between the outer edges of the penumbra and umbra also undergoes extremes ranging from 1887.7 arc-seconds (aphelion) to 1951.9 arc-seconds (perihelion). From these values it is apparent that the Moon cannot fit entirely within the penumbral annulus when it is near perigee (Meeus, 1997). Because of this restrictive geometry, total penumbral eclipses are rare and account for just 3.7 % or 33 of the 883 penumbral eclipses in the *Canon*. Table 3–20 lists the dates of all 33 total penumbral eclipses.

The frequency of total penumbral eclipse varies with time. If the 1000-year period covered by the *Canon* is divided into 100-year intervals, the number of total penumbral eclipses per century ranges from 0 to a maximum of 9 (Table 3–4). The number of total penumbral eclipse appears to be directly correlated with the number of total eclipses as well as the number of tetrads per century, and inversely correlated with the overall number of all lunar eclipses per century. When a century has a relatively large number of lunar eclipses, it has fewer total lunar eclipses and few or no total penumbral lunar eclipses nor tetrads.

Table 3–20. Total Penumbral Lunar Eclipses: 1501 to 2500

1502 Apr 22	1900 Jun 13	1981 Jan 20	2099 Sep 29	2447 Dec 22
1513 Sep 15	1901 May 03	1988 Mar 03	2103 Jan 23	2458 May 28
1542 Aug 25	1908 Dec 07	1999 Jan 31	2121 Feb 02	2466 Jan 01
1607 Mar 13	1926 Dec 19	2006 Mar 14	2128 Mar 16	2484 Jan 13
1637 Jul 07	1944 Dec 29	2053 Aug 29	2139 Feb 13	2498 Sep 30
1665 Jul 27	1948 Oct 18	2070 Apr 25	2222 Aug 23	
1806 Jun 30	1963 Jan 09	2082 Aug 08	2429 Dec 11	

3.12 Lunar Eclipse Duos

A duo is a pair of eclipses separated by one lunation or synodic month. Of the 2,424 eclipses in the *Canon*, 634 eclipses (26.2%) belong to a duo. One eclipse of a duo always passes north of Earth's shadow axis while the other eclipse passes to the south. In most cases, both eclipses in a duo are penumbral eclipses; there are 11 instances (3.5% of duos) where one eclipse is penumbral and the other is partial. In each of these pairs, the eclipse magnitudes are small. The dates of the lunar eclipse duos of two types are listed in Table 3–21.

Table 3–21. Lunar Eclipse Duos of Two Types*

1553 Jun–Jul — NP	2013 Apr–May — PN
1608 Jul–Aug — PN	2147 Aug–Sep — PN
1694 Jun–Jul — NP	2288 Jul–Aug — PN
1749 Jun–Jul — PN	2411 Jun–Jul — PN
1835 May–Jun — NP	2429 Jun–Jul — PN
1958 Apr–May — NP	

* N = Penumbral and P = Partial

3.13 Lunar Eclipses Duos in One Calendar Month

There are 10 instances where both members of an eclipse duo occur in one calendar month. In all cases, both eclipses are penumbral. The year and month of each duo appears in Table 3–22.

Table 3–22. Two Lunar Eclipses in One Calendar Month

1694 Dec	2172 Oct
1705 Nov	2208 May
1716 Oct	2284 Apr
1817 May	2295 Mar
1904 Mar	2382 Jan

3.14 January–March Lunar Eclipse Duos

The mean length of one synodic month is 29.5306 days (in year 2000). Because this is longer than the month of February, it is possible to have one member of an eclipse duo in January followed by the second in March. There are three instances of these rare January/March duos: 1915, 2306, and 2371. In all cases, both eclipses in the duos are penumbral.

3.15 Total Lunar Eclipse Multiplets

A total lunar eclipse is usually preceded or succeeded by at least one other total lunar eclipse. Of the 685 total eclipses in the *Canon*, 370 of them (54.0%) are part of a doublet. Another 195 eclipses (28.5%) belong to a triplet. Finally, 108 total eclipses (15.8%) are part of a quadruplet known as a tetrad. In comparison, only 12 total eclipses (1.8%) occur as solitary singlets.

A key feature of total lunar eclipse muliplets is that the individual members are separated by six lunations. A summary of the muliplet statistics appears in Table 3–23.

Table 3–23. Total Lunar Eclipse Muliplets

Total Eclipse Multiplet	Number of Eclipses Per Multiplet	Number of Multiplets	Number of Total Eclipses	Percent of Total Eclipses	Recent Examples
All Total Eclipses	—	—	685	100.0 %	
Singlet	1	12	12	1.8 %	1997 Sep 16; 2021 May 26
Doublet	2	185	370	54.0 %	1978; 1996; 2022; 2040
Triplet	3	65	195	28.5 %	2007–2008; 2010–2011
Tetrad	4	27	108	15.8 %	2003–2004; 2014–2015

3.16 Lunar Eclipse Tetrads

When four consecutive lunar eclipses are all total, the group is termed a tetrad. 15.8% (108 out of 685) of all total eclipses are members of a tetrad. They occur because of the eccentricity of Earth's orbit in conjunction with the timing of eclipse seasons (Section 3.18). During the 1000 years of the *Canon*, the first eclipse of every tetrad occurs between January and June. In later millennia, the first eclipse date occurs later in the year because of precession.

Italian astronomer Giovanni Schiaparelli first pointed out that the frequency of tetrads is variable over time. He noticed that tetrads were relatively plentiful during one 300-year interval, while none occurred during the next 300 years. For example, there are no tetrads from 1582 to 1908, but 17 tetrads occur during the following 2 ½ centuries from 1909 to 2156. The 565-year period of the tetrad "seasons" is tied to the slowly decreasing eccentricity of Earth's orbit. Consequently, the tetrad period is gradually decreasing (Hughes, 2004). The absolute number of tertrads also decreases with decreasing eccentricity. In the distant future when Earth's eccentricity is 0, tetrads will no longer occur.

The umbral magnitudes of the total eclipses making up a tetrad are all relatively small. For the 300-year period 1901 to 2200, the largest umbral magnitude of a tetrad eclipse is 1.4251 on 1949 Apr 13. Table 3–24 lists the date of the first total eclipse in each of the 27 tetrads in the *Canon*.

Table 3–24. Date of First Total Eclipse in Lunar Eclipse Tetrads: 1501 to 2500

1504 Mar 01	1927 Jun 15	2043 Mar 25	2137 Mar 07
1515 Jan 30	1949 Apr 13	2050 May 06	2155 Mar 19
1522 Mar 12	1967 Apr 24	2061 Apr 04	2448 Jun 17
1533 Feb 09	1985 May 04	2072 Mar 04	2466 Jun 28
1562 Jan 20	2003 May 16	2090 Mar 15	2477 May 28
1580 Jan 31	2014 Apr 15	2101 Feb 14	2495 Jun 08
1909 Jun 04	2032 Apr 25	2119 Feb 25	

3.18 Eclipse Seasons

The ·~5.1° inclination of the lunar orbit around Earth means that the Moon's orbit crosses the ecliptic at two points or nodes. If Full Moon takes place within approximately 17° of a node,[4] then a lunar eclipse will be visible from a portion of Earth.

The Sun makes one complete circuit of the ecliptic in 365.24 days, so its average angular velocity is 0.99° per day. At this rate, it takes 34.5 days for the Sun and, at the opposite node, Earth's umbral and penumbral shadows to cross the 34° wide eclipse zone centered on each node. Because the Moon's orbit with respect to the Sun has a mean duration of 29.53 days, there will always be one and possibly two lunar eclipses during each 34.5-day interval when the Sun (and Earth's shadows) pass through the nodal eclipse zones. These time periods are called eclipse seasons.

---

[4] The exact angular distance from the node depends of the distances of the Sun and Moon from Earth, which determine their angular diameters as well as the diameters of Earth's shadows.

The mid-point of each eclipse season is separated by 173.3 days because this is the mean time for the Sun to travel from one node to the next. The period is a little less that half a calendar year because the lunar nodes regress westward by 19.3° per year.

3.19 Quincena

The mean time interval between New Moon and Full Moon is 14.77 days. This is less than half the duration of an eclipse season. As a consequence, the same Sun–node alignment geometry responsible for producing a lunar eclipse always results in a complementary solar eclipse within a fortnight. The solar eclipse may either precede or succeed the lunar eclipse. In either case, the pair of eclipses is referred to here as a quincena[5]. The QSE (Quincena Solar Eclipse parameter) identifies the type of the solar eclipse and whether it precedes or succeeds a particular lunar eclipse.

There are four basic types of solar eclipses:
1. partial solar eclipse (p) — The Moon's penumbral shadow traverses Earth; the umbral/antumbral shadow misses Earth
2. annular solar eclipse (a) — The Moon's antumbral shadow traverses Earth; the Moon is too far to completely cover the Sun
3. total solar eclipse (t) — The Moon's umbral shadow traverses Earth; the Moon is close enough to completely cover the Sun
4. hybrid solar eclipse (h) — The Moon's umbral and antumbral shadows traverse different parts of Earth; the eclipse appears either total or annular along different sections of its path; hybrid eclipses are also known as annular-total eclipses

The QSE is a two character string consisting of one or more of the above solar eclipse types. The first character in the QSE identifies the type of solar eclipse preceding a lunar eclipse. The second character identifies the type of solar eclipse succeeding a lunar eclipse. In most instances, one of the two characters is "–" indicating no solar eclipse occurs. For example, a QSE of "–p" means that no solar eclipse precedes the lunar eclipse, but the lunar eclipse is followed by a partial solar eclipse 15 days later.

On rare occasions, a double quincena occurs in which a lunar eclipse is both preceded and succeeded by a solar eclipse. In every case in the *Canon*, the lunar eclipse is always total (see the last three entries in Table 3–27).

---

[5] Quincena is a Spanish word meaning *a period of fifteen days*. This also happens to be the time, rounded to the nearest day, between New Moon and Full Moon, or Full Moon and New Moon. So *quincena* is a convenient and appropriate term for describing a pair of eclipses (one solar and one lunar) separated by this period.

3.20 Quincena Combinations with Penumbral Lunar Eclipses

A penumbral lunar eclipse can be preceded or succeeded by a total solar eclipse (36.2%), an annular solar eclipse (57.9%), or a hybrid solar eclipse (4.9%). There are no instances of a quincena involving a partial solar and a penumbral lunar eclipse, nor are there any double quincenas with a penumbral lunar eclipse in the *Canon*. A list of quincena solar eclipse combinations with penumbral lunar eclipses appears in Table 3–25. Five examples nearest the present when each quincena combination occurs are given in the last column.

Table 3–25. Quincena Combinations with Penumbral Lunar Eclipses

Solar Eclipse Combinations	QSE	Number	Percent	Examples (Years)
total –	t–	158	17.9%	...,, 1998, 2009, 2012, 2016, 2027,...
– total	–t	162	18.3%	..., 2006, 2009, 2020, 2024, 2027,...
annular –	a–	262	29.7%	..., 2002, 2009, 2013, 2016, 2020,...
– annular	–a	258	29.2%	..., 2002, 2017, 2020, 2031, 2035,...
hybrid –	h–	21	2.4%	..., 1987, 2005, 2023, 2172, 2190,...
– hybrid	–h	22	2.5%	..., 1908, 2013, 2031, 2049, 2067,...

3.21 Quincena Combinations with Partial Lunar Eclipses

A partial lunar eclipse can be preceded or succeeded by a total solar eclipse (40.9%), an annular solar eclipse (50.6%), or a hybrid solar eclipse (8.4%). In rare instances, a partial lunar eclipse can be followed by a partial solar eclipse (0.1%). Double quincenas do not occur with partial lunar eclipses in the *Canon*. A list of quincena solar eclipse combinations with partial lunar eclipses appears in Table 3–26. Several examples nearest the present when each quincena combination occurs are given in the last column.

Table 3–26. Quincena Combinations with Partial Lunar Eclipses

Solar Eclipse Combinations	QSE	Number	Percent	Examples (Years)
total –	t–	179	20.9%	..., 2008, 2019, 2026, 2037, 2041,...
– total	–t	171	20.0%	..., 1999, 2010, 2017, 2021, 2028,...
annular –	a–	231	27.0%	..., 2005, 2012, 2023, 2030, 2034,...
– annular	–a	202	23.6%	..., 2006, 2009, 2013, 2024, 2028,...
hybrid –	h–	18	2.1%	..., 1827, 1845, 2164, 2182, 2323,...
– hybrid	–h	54	6.3%	..., 1912, 1930, 2209, 2350, 2368,...
– partial	–p	1	0.1%	[2086]*

*only one example appears in the entire *Canon*.

3.22 Quincena Combinations with Total Lunar Eclipses

A total lunar eclipse can be preceded or succeeded by a total solar eclipse (7.2%), an annular solar eclipse (10.4%), a hybrid solar eclipse (1.0%), or a partial solar eclipse (40.3%). Double quincenas (a lunar eclipse is both preceded and succeeded by a solar eclipse) occur with a frequency of 41.1% and usually consist of two partial solar eclipses (40.7%). In rare instances, a double quincena consists of a total and a partial solar eclipse (0.4%). A complete list of all quincena solar eclipse combinations with total lunar eclipses appears in Table 3–27. Several examples nearest the present when each quincena combination occurs are given in the last column.

Table 3–27 Quincena Combinations with Total Lunar Eclipses

Solar Eclipse Combinations	QSE	Number	Percent	Examples (Years)*
– total	–t	23	3.4%	…, 1985,2003,2043,2061,2072,…
total –	t–	26	3.8%	…, 1968,2015,2033,2044, 2073,…
– annular	–a	37	5.4%	…, 2003,2014,2021,2032, 2042,…
annular –	a–	34	5.0%	…, 1990,2008,2026,2044,2102,…
– hybrid	–h	6	0.9%	[1544,1627,1645,1768,1909,2050]
hybrid –	h–	1	0.1%	[1986]
– partial	–p	131	19.1%	…,2007,2010,2014,2018, 2025,…
partial –	p–	145	21.2%	…,2004,2011,2015,2019, 2022,…
total–partial	tp	1	0.1%	[1928]
partial–total	pt	2	0.3%	[2195,2459]
partial–partial	pp	279	40.7%	…, 2000,2011,2018,2029, 2036,…

* For years bounded by a square bracket, there are no other examples beyond that year.

Section 4: Explanation of Lunar Eclipse Catalog in Appendix A

4.1 Introduction

Earth experiences 2,424 eclipses of the Moon during the 1000-year period from 1501 to 2500. The catalog in *Appendix A* consists of a series of tables that summarize the principal characteristics of each lunar eclipse over this time interval. The tables complement the eclipse maps and diagrams in *Appendix B.*

Each line in the tables corresponds to a single lunar eclipse and provides concise parameters to characterize the eclipse. The calendar date and Dynamical Time of the instant of greatest eclipse (when the Moon passes closest to the axis of Earth's shadows) are given along with the adopted value of Delta T (ΔT). The lunation number and the Saros series are listed along with the eclipse type (N=Penumbral, P=Partial, or T=Total). Gamma is the distance from the Moon's center to the axis of Earth's shadow cones at greatest eclipse, while the penumbral and umbral eclipse magnitudes are defined as the fraction of the Moon's diameter immersed in each shadow at that instant. The duration of the penumbral, partial, and total eclipse phases are given in minutes. Finally, the geographic latitude and longitude are given for the location where the Moon lies in the zenith at greatest eclipse. A more detailed description of each field in the catalog appears in the following sections.

4.2 Cat Num (Catalog Number)

The catalog number is the sequential number assigned to each eclipse from 1 to 2,424.

4.3 Canon Plate

Appendix B consists of 200 plates with 12 lunar eclipse diagrams per plate. The canon plate identifies the plate number where each eclipse appears.

4.4 Calendar Date

The Julian calendar is used prior to 1582 Oct 15. All eclipse dates from 1582 Oct 15 onwards use the modern Gregorian calendar currently found throughout most of the world. Because of the Gregorian Calendar Reform, the day following 1582 Oct 04 (Julian calendar) is 1582 Oct 15 (Gregorian calendar).

4.5 TD of Greatest Eclipse (Terrestrial Dynamical Time of Greatest Eclipse)

The instant of greatest eclipse occurs when the distance between the center of the Moon and the axis of Earth's umbral shadow cone reaches a minimum. Because of Earth's flattening, the instant of greatest eclipse differs slightly from the instant of greatest magnitude. In practice, Earth's atmosphere diffuses the edges of the penumbral and umbral shadows such that the difference between greatest eclipse and greatest magnitude cannot be distinguished observationally.

Lunar eclipses occur when the Moon is near one of the nodes of its orbit moving at an angle of $\sim 5°$ to the ecliptic. Unless the eclipse is perfectly central, the instant of greatest eclipse does not coincide with that of apparent ecliptic conjunction with Earth's shadow (i.e., Full Moon), nor with the time of conjunction in Right Ascension.

Greatest eclipse is given in Terrestrial Dynamical Time or TD (Sect. 2.5), which is a time system based on International Atomic Time. As such, TD is the modern equivalent to its predecessor Ephemeris Time and is used in theories of planetary motion in the Solar System. To determine the geographic visibility of an eclipse, TD is converted to Universal Time (UT1) using the parameter Delta T (Sect. 2.6).

4.6 ΔT (Delta T)

ΔT (Delta T) is the arithmetic difference, in seconds, between Terrestrial Dynamical Time (TD) and Universal Time (UT1). For more information on ΔT, see Section 2.6.

4.7 Luna Num (Lunation Number)

The lunation number is the number of synodic months, or lunations, since New Moon on 2000 Jan 06. It can be converted to the Brown Lunation Number[6] by adding 953.

4.8 Saros Num (Saros Series Number)

Each lunar eclipse belongs to a Saros series using a numbering system first introduced by van den Bergh (1955). Eclipses with an odd Saros number take place at the descending node of the Moon's orbit, while those with an even Saros number take place at the ascending node. This relationship is reversed for *solar* eclipses.

The Saros is a period of 223 synodic months ($\sim$ 18 years, 11 days, and 8 hours). Eclipses separated by this interval belong to the same Saros series and share similar geometry and characteristics.

4.9 Ecl Type (Lunar Eclipse Type)

The first character in this 2-character parameter gives the lunar eclipse type. The three basic types of lunar eclipses are:

1. Penumbral Lunar Eclipse (N) — The Moon passes partially or completely into Earth's penumbral shadow
2. Partial Lunar Eclipse (P) — The Moon passes partly into Earth's umbral shadow
3. Total Lunar Eclipse (T) — The Moon passes completely into Earth's umbral shadow

---

[6] The *Brown Lunation Number* defines lunation 1 as beginning at the first New Moon of 1923, the year when Ernest W. Brown's lunar theory was introduced in the major national astronomical almanacs.

The second character of the lunar eclipse type is a qualifier defined as follows.

1. m = Middle eclipse of Saros series
2. + = Central total eclipse (Moon's center passes north of shadow axis)
3. – = Central total eclipse (Moon's center passes south of shadow axis)
4. * = Total penumbral eclipse
5. b = Saros series begins (first penumbral eclipse in a Saros series)
6. e = Saros series ends (last penumbral eclipse in a Saros series)

Qualifiers 1 through 3 are used exclusively with total lunar eclipses while qualifiers 4 through 6 are only used with penumbral eclipses.

4.10 QSE (Quincena Solar Eclipse Parameter)

A solar eclipse always occurs within 15 days of a lunar eclipse. The Quincena Solar Eclipse parameter (QSE) identifies the type of the solar eclipse and whether it precedes or succeeds a particular lunar eclipse. There are four basic types of solar eclipses:

1. Partial Solar Eclipse (p) — The Moon's penumbral shadow traverses Earth; the umbral/antumbral shadow completely misses Earth
2. Annular Solar Eclipse (a) — The Moon's penumbral and antumbral shadows traverse Earth; the Moon is too far from Earth to completely cover the Sun
3. Total Solar Eclipse (t) — The Moon's penumbral and umbral shadow traverse Earth; the Moon is close enough to Earth to completely cover the Sun
4. Hybrid Solar Eclipse (h) — The Moon's penumbral , umbral and antumbral shadows traverse different parts of Earth; the eclipse appears either total or annular along different sections of its path; hybrid eclipses are also known as annular-total eclipses

The QSE is a two character string consisting of one or more of the above solar eclipse types. The first character in the QSE identifies a solar eclipse preceding a lunar eclipse, while the second character identifies a solar eclipse succeeding a lunar eclipse. In most instances, one of the two characters is "–" indicating no solar eclipse occurs. On rare occasions, a double quincena occurs in which a lunar eclipse is both preceded and succeeded by solar eclipses. See Section 3.20 for more information on the Quincena.

4.11 Gamma

Gamma is the minimum distance from the center of the Moon to the axis of Earth's umbral shadow cone in units of Earth's equatorial radius. This distance is positive or negative, depending on whether the Moon passes north or south, respectively, of the shadow cone axis.

4.12 Pen Mag (Penumbral Eclipse Magnitude)

The eclipse magnitude is defined as the fraction of the Moon's diameter immersed in Earth's shadows. Because there are two shadows— penumbral and umbral—there are two corresponding eclipse magnitudes. The eclipse magnitudes are given at the instant of greatest eclipse when the Moon passes closest to the axis of the two shadow cones.

The penumbral eclipse magnitude of penumbral eclipses in the *Canon* ranges from 0.0015 to 1.0908. For most penumbral eclipses the penumbral magnitude is less than 1, meaning only a fraction of the Moon's disk enters the penumbra. When the penumbral magnitude is greater than or equal to 1, the Moon's entire disk is immersed in the penumbra and the event is termed a total penumbral eclipse. Penumbral eclipses are subtle events (Sect. 1.3). They cannot be detected visually (with or without optical aid) unless the eclipse magnitude is greater than ~0.6. The umbral eclipse magnitude of a penumbral eclipse is always negative. It is a measure of the distance of the Moon's limb to the edge of the umbral shadow in units of the Moon's diameter.

4.13 Um Mag (Umbral Eclipse Magnitude)

The umbral magnitude is defined as the fraction of the Moon's diameter immersed in Earth's umbral shadow. During a partial lunar eclipse, some portion of the Moon's disk enters the umbral shadow. The umbral magnitude for partial eclipses in the *Canon* ranges from 0.0001 to 0.9994 (Sect. 3.6). Of course, the Moon also passes through the penumbra during a partial eclipse, so the penumbral magnitude is usually greater than 1.

In the case of a total lunar eclipse, the Moon's entire disk passes through Earth's umbral shadow, so the umbral magnitude is always equal to or greater than 1.0. During totality, the Moon can take on a range of colors from bright orange, to deep red, dark brown, or even very dark gray (Sect. 1.5). The only light reaching the Moon at this time is heavily filtered and attenuated by Earth's atmosphere. The umbral magnitude for total eclipses in the *Canon* ranges from 1.0002 to 1.8721 (Sect. 3.7).

4.14 Phase Durations (Pen, Par & Total)

The duration of a penumbral eclipse "Pen" is the time between first and last external tangencies of the Moon with the penumbral shadow (= P4 – P1). Similarly, the duration of a partial eclipse "Par" is the time between first and last external tangencies of the Moon with the umbral shadow (= U4 – U1). Finally, the duration of a total eclipse "Total" is the time between first and last internal tangencies of the Moon with the umbral shadow (= U3 – U2). The position of the Moon at each contact is illustrated in Figure 2–1. The duration given for each eclipse phase is rounded to the nearest minute.

4.15 Greatest in Zenith Lat Long (Latitude & Longitude)

The latitude and longitude correspond to the geographic location where the Moon appears in the zenith at greatest eclipse.

4.16 EclipseWise.com and Lunar Eclipse Catalog

The maps and catalog in the *Thousand Year Canon* form the basis of a new website on solar and lunar eclipse predictions: *www.EclipseWise.com*. A plain file containing the lunar eclipse catalog in *Appendix A* can be downloaded at: *www.EclipseWise.com/lunar/LEpubs/TYCLEcatalog.txt*. This catalog is for private use only. It may not be distributed, published, posted or used in any other fashion without written permission from the author.

Section 5: Explanation of Lunar Eclipse Maps in Appendix B

5.1 Introduction

Earth experiences 2,424 eclipses of the Moon during the 1000-year period from 1501 to 2500. An individual diagram and visibility map for every lunar eclipse over this interval is presented in *Appendix B*. The Moon's path through Earth's penumbral and umbral shadows illustrates the eclipse geometry and the accompanying map shows the geographic region of visibility during each phase of every eclipse.

The figure for each eclipse consists of two diagrams. The top one depicts the Moon's path through Earth's penumbral and umbral shadows with Celestial North directed up. The second diagram is a map showing the global visibility of each eclipse phase. All salient features in these diagrams are identified in figure 5–1, which serves as a key.

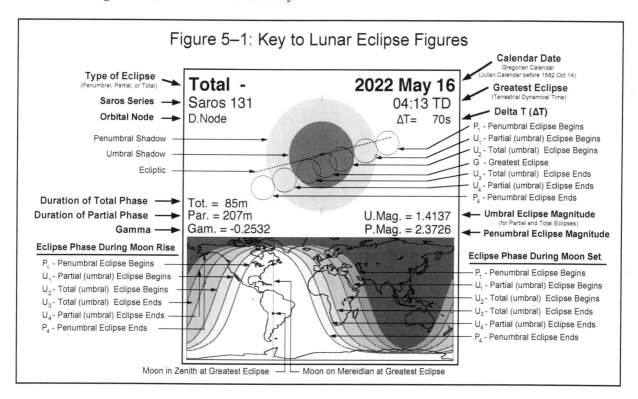

In the top diagram, the Moon's orbital motion with respect to the shadows is from west to east (right to left). Each phase of the eclipse is defined by the instant when the Moon's limb is externally or internally tangent to the penumbra or umbra. The six primary contacts of the Moon with the penumbral and umbral shadows are defined as follows.

P1 — Instant of first exterior tangency of the Moon with the Penumbra
(Penumbral Eclipse Begins)
U1 — Instant of first exterior tangency of the Moon with the Umbra
(Partial Umbral Eclipse Begins)
U2 — Instant of first interior tangency of the Moon with the Umbra
(Total Umbral Eclipse Begins)

    U3 — Instant of last interior tangency of the Moon with the Umbra
      (Total Umbral Eclipse Ends)
    U4 — Instant of last exterior tangency of the Moon with the Umbra
      (Partial Umbral Eclipse Ends)
    P4 — Instant of last exterior tangency of the Moon with the Penumbra
      (Penumbral Eclipse Ends)

Penumbral lunar eclipses have two primary contacts: P1 and P4, but neither is observable.

In addition to the penumbral contacts, partial lunar eclipses have two more contacts as the Moon's limb enters and exits the umbral shadow: U1 and U4, respectively. These two contacts mark the instants when the partial phase of the eclipse begins and ends.

Total lunar eclipses undergo all six contacts. The two additional umbral contacts are the instants when the Moon's entire disk is first and last internally tangent to the umbra: U2 and U3, respectively. They mark the times when the total phase of the eclipse begins and ends.

The Moon passes closest to the shadow axis at the instant of greatest eclipse. This corresponds to the maximum phase of the eclipse and the Moon's position at this instant is also depicted in the path diagrams.

The bottom diagram in each figure is an equidistant cylindrical projection map of Earth showing the geographic region of visibility at each phase of the eclipse. This is accomplished using a series of curves showing where Moonrise and Moonset occur at each eclipse contact. The map is shaded to indicate eclipse visibility. The entire eclipse is visible from the zone with no shading. Conversely, none of the eclipse can be seen from the zone with the darkest shading.

At the instant of greatest eclipse, the Moon is deepest in Earth's shadow. A vertical line running through the middle of the clear zone (complete eclipse visibility) indicates the meridian or line of longitude that the Moon is crossing. An observer positioned on this line would then see the Moon at its highest point in the sky due south or due north, depending on the observer's latitude and the Moon's declination. The geographic location where the Moon appears in the zenith at greatest eclipse is shown by a black dot on the meridian. All salient features of the eclipse figures are identified in Figure 5–1, which serves as the key to the figures in *Appendix B*.

Data relevant to the eclipse appear in the corners of each figure. To the top left are the eclipse type (penumbral, partial or total), the Saros series of the eclipse, and the node of the Moon's orbit where the eclipse occurs. To the top right are the Gregorian calendar date (Julian calendar dates are used prior to 1582 Oct 15), the time of greatest eclipse (Terrestrial Dynamical Time), and the value of ΔT (Delta T). The lower left corner lists the duration of the major phases of the eclipse in minutes. Depending on the eclipse type, the duration of the penumbral, partial or total phases are given. Beneath the eclipse durations is the quantity gamma, the minimum distance of the Moon's center from the axis of Earth's shadow cones at the instant of greatest eclipse. The umbral and penumbral eclipse magnitudes are given to the lower right.

A detailed explanation of the data in the lunar eclipse figures appears in the following sections.

5.2 Lunar Eclipse Type

The three basic types of lunar eclipses are:

1. Penumbral Lunar Eclipse — The Moon passes partially or completely into Earth's penumbral shadow
2. Partial Lunar Eclipse — The Moon passes partly into Earth's umbral shadow
3. Total Lunar Eclipse — The Moon passes completely into Earth's umbral shadow

On rare occasions, a penumbral eclipse can occur in which the Moon's entire disk is enveloped within the penumbra. These total penumbral eclipses are indicated by "(T)" after the eclipse type (e.g., Penumbral (T)).

Regarding total (umbral) lunar eclipses, most are non-central where the Moon's disk misses the central axis of the umbral shadow cone. If a total eclipse is central, it is indicated by a "+" or "–" after the eclipse type, depending on whether the Moon's center passes north or south of the shadow axis (e.g., Total +).

5.3 Saros Series Number

Each lunar eclipse belongs to a Saros series using a numbering system first introduced by van den Bergh (1955). Eclipses with an odd Saros number take place at the descending node of the Moon's orbit, while those with an even Saros number take place at the ascending node. This relationship is reversed for *solar* eclipses.

The Saros is a period of 223 synodic months (~ 18 years, 11 days, and 8 hours). Eclipses separated by this interval belong to the same Saros series and share similar geometry and characteristics.

5.4 Node

A lunar eclipse is only possible when Full Moon occurs near one of the Moon's two orbital nodes. The ascending node (A. Node) is the point where the Moon travels from south to north through Earth's orbital plane. Similarly, the descending node (D. Node) is the point where the Moon travels from north to south through Earth's orbital plane.

5.5 Calendar Date

The Julian calendar is used prior to 1582 Oct 15. All eclipse dates from 1582 Oct 15 onwards use the modern Gregorian calendar currently found throughout most of the world. Because of the Gregorian Calendar Reform, the day following 1582 Oct 04 (Julian calendar) is 1582 Oct 15 (Gregorian calendar).

5.6 Greatest Eclipse

The instant of greatest eclipse occurs when the distance between the center of the Moon and the axis of Earth's umbral shadow cone reaches a minimum. Because of Earth's flattening, the instant of greatest eclipse differs slightly from the instant of greatest magnitude. In practice, Earth's atmosphere diffuses the edges of the penumbral and umbral shadows such that the difference between greatest eclipse and greatest magnitude cannot be distinguished observationally.

Greatest eclipse is given in Terrestrial Dynamical Time or TD (Sect. 2.5), which is a time system based on International Atomic Time. As such, TD is the modern equivalent to its predecessor Ephemeris Time and is used in theories of planetary motion in the Solar System. To determine the geographic visibility of an eclipse, TD is converted to Universal Time (UT1) using the parameter Delta T (Sect. 2.6).

5.7 ΔT (Delta T)

ΔT (Delta T) is the arithmetic difference, in seconds, between Terrestrial Dynamical Time (TD) and Universal Time (UT1). For more information on ΔT, see Section 2.6.

5.8 Duration of Eclipse Phases

The duration of a penumbral eclipse "Pen." is the time between first and last external tangencies of the Moon with the penumbral shadow (P4 – P1). Similarly, the duration of a partial eclipse "Par." is the time between first and last external tangencies of the Moon with the umbral shadow (U4 – U1). Finally, the duration of a total eclipse "Tot." is the time between first and last internal tangencies of the Moon with the umbral shadow (U3 – U2). The position of the Moon at each contact is illustrated in Figure 2–1.

The duration given for each eclipse phase is rounded to the nearest minute.

5.9 Gamma

The quantity gamma is the minimum distance from the center of the Moon to the axis of Earth's umbral shadow cone in units of Earth's equatorial radius. This distance is positive or negative, depending on whether the Moon passes north or south, respectively, of the shadow cone axis.

5.10 Eclipse Magnitude

The eclipse magnitude is defined as the fraction of the Moon's diameter immersed in Earth's shadows. Since there are two shadows — penumbral and umbral — there are two corresponding eclipse magnitudes. *U.Mag* is the umbral eclipse magnitude while *P.Mag* is the penumbral eclipse magnitude. The eclipse magnitudes appearing in the figures are given at the instant of greatest eclipse when the Moon passes closest to the axis of the shadow cones. Section 4.12 has more information on eclipse magnitude.

References

Astronomical Almanac for 2008, Washington: US Government Printing Office; London: HM Stationery Office (2006).

Astronomical Almanac for 2011, Washington: US Government Printing Office; London: HM Stationery Office (2010).

Bretagnon, P., and Francou G., "Planetary theories in rectangular and spherical variables: VSOP87 solution," *Astron. Astrophys.,* **202**(309) (1988).

Chapront-Touzé, M., and Chapront, J., "The Lunar Ephemeris ELP 2000," *Astron. Astrophys.,* vol. 124, no. 1, pp. 50–62 (1983).

Chapront, J., Chapront-Touzé, M., and Francou, G., "A new determination of lunar orbital parameters, precession constant and tidal acceleration from LLR measurements," *Astron. Astrophys.,* vol. 387, pp. 700–709 (2002).

Chauvenet, W.A., *Manual of Spherical and Practical Astronomy,* Vol.1, edition of 1891, (Dover reprint, New York, 1960).

Danjon, A., "Les éclipses de Lune par la pénombre en 1951," *L'Astronomie,* 65, 51–53 (1951).

Dickey, J.O., Bender, P.L., Faller, J.E., Newhall, X.X., Ricklefs, R.L., Ries,, J.G., Shelus, P.J., Veillet, C., Whipple, A.L., Wiant, J.R., Williams, J.G., and Yoder, C.F., "Lunar Laser Ranging: a Continuing Legacy of the Apollo Program," *Science,* 265, pp. 482–490 (1994).

Espenak, F., *Fifty Year Canon of Solar Eclipses: 1986–2035,* Sky Publishing Corp., Cambridge, Massuchusetts (1987).

Espenak, F., *Fifty Year Canon of Lunar Eclipses: 1986–2035,* Sky Publishing Corp., Cambridge, Massuchusetts (1989).

Espenak, F., *Thousand Year Canon of Solar Eclipses: 1501 to 2500,* Astropixels Publishing, Portal, Arizona (2014).

Espenak, F., and Meeus, J., *Five Millennium Canon of Solar Eclipses: –1999 to +3000 (2000 BCE to 3000 CE),* NASA Tech. Pub. 2006-214141, NASA Goddard Space Flight Center, Greenbelt, Maryland (2006).

Espenak, F., and Meeus, J., *Five Millennium Canon of Lunar Eclipses: –1999 to +3000 (2000 BCE to 3000 CE),* NASA Tech. Pub. 2006-214172, NASA Goddard Space Flight Center, Greenbelt, Maryland (2009a).

Espenak, F., and Meeus, J., *Five Millennium Catalog of Lunar Eclipses: –1999 to +3000 (2000 BCE to 3000 CE),* NASA Tech. Pub. 2006-214173, NASA Goddard Space Flight Center, Greenbelt, Maryland (2009b).

49

Espenak, F., *Thousand Year Catalog of Solar Eclipses: 1501 to 2500*, Astropixels Publishing, Portal, Arizona (2014).

Espenak, F., and Meeus, J., *Five Millennium Catalog of Solar Eclipses: −1999 to +3000 (2000 BCE to 3000 CE)*, NASA Tech. Pub. 2006–214174, NASA Goddard Space Flight Center, Greenbelt, Maryland (2009c).

Explanatory Supplement to the Ephemeris, H.M. Almanac Office, London (1974).

Hughes, T., *"Addendum"* In: J. Meeus, *Mathematical Astronomy Morsels III*, Willmann-Bell, pp. 137–140, (2004).

Keen, R. A., "Volcanic Aerosols and Lunar Eclipses", *Science*, vol. 222, p. 1011-1013, Dec. 2, 1983.

Lahire, P., *Tabulae Astronomicae* (Paris 1707).

Link, F., *Eclipse Phenomena in Astronomy*, Springer-Verlag, New York (1969).

Liu, Bao-Lin and Fiala, A. D., *Canon of Lunar Eclipses 1500 B.C.-A.D. 3000*, Willmann-Bell, p215 (1992).

Meeus, J. and Mucke, H., *Canon of Lunar Eclipse: -2002 to +2526*, Astronomisches Buro, Wein (1979).

Meeus, J., *Mathematical Astronomy Morsels*, Willmann-Bell, pp. 108–110, (1997).

——, *Mathematical Astronomy Morsels III*, Willmann-Bell, pp. 123-140, (2004).

Morrison, L., and Stephenson, F.R., "Historical Values of the Earth's Clock Error DT and the Calculation of Eclipses," *J. Hist. Astron.*, Vol. 35 Part 3, August 2004, No. 120, pp, 327–336 (2004).

Newcomb, S., "Tables of the Motion of the Earth on its Axis Around the Sun," *Astron. Papers Amer. Eph.*, Vol. 6, Part I (1895).

Stephenson, F.R., *Historical Eclipses and Earth's Rotation*, Cambridge University Press, Cambridge (1997).

van den Bergh, *Periodicity and Variation of Solar (and Lunar) Eclipses*, Tjeenk Willink, and Haarlem, Netherlands (1955).

van der Sluys, M. , *http://hemel.waarnemen.com/Computing/deltat.html* (2010).

von Oppolzer, T.R., *Canon der Finsternisse*, Wien, (1887); Gingerich, O., (Translator) *Canon of Eclipses*, Dover Publications, New York (1962).

Appendix A

Lunar Eclipse Catalog: 1501 to 2500

Key to Lunar Eclipse Catalog

Cat Num — sequential Catalog Number assigned to each eclipse from 1 to 2,424

Canon Plate — plate number assigned to each eclipse diagram and map

Calendar Date — Gregorian date of Greatest Eclipse (Julian date prior to 1582 Oct 04)

TD of Greatest Eclipse — Terrestrial Dynamical Time of Greatest Eclipse

ΔT — arithmetic difference between Terrestrial Dynamical Time Universal Time (seconds)

Luna Num — number of synodic months, or lunations, since New Moon on 2000 Jan 06

Saros Num — Saros Series Number of eclipse

Ecl Type — Lunar Eclipse Type

      N = Penumbral Lunar Eclipse
      P = Partial Lunar Eclipse
      T = Total Lunar Eclipse
      m = Middle eclipse of Saros series
      + = Central total eclipse (Moon's center passes north of shadow axis)
      – = Central total eclipse (Moon's center passes south of shadow axis)
      * = Total penumbral eclipse
      b = Saros series begins (first penumbral eclipse in a Saros series)
      e = Saros series ends (last penumbral eclipse in a Saros series)

QSE — Quincena Solar Eclipse Parameter

      p = Partial Solar Eclipse
      a = Annular Solar Eclipse
      t = Total Solar Eclipse
      h = Hybrid Solar Eclipse

Gamma — minimum distance from center of Moon to axis of Earth's umbral shadow cone

Pen Mag — Penumbral Magnitude; fraction of the Moon's diameter immersed in penumbra

Um Mag — Umbral Magnitude; fraction of the Moon's diameter immersed in umbra

Phase Durations
      Pen — duration from contact P1 to P4 (minutes)
      Par — duration from contact U1 to U4 (minutes)
      Total — duration from contact U2 to U3 (minutes)

Greatest in Zenith
Lat & Long — latitude and longitude where Moon appears in zenith at greatest eclipse

Cat Num	Canon Plate	Calendar Date	TD of Greatest Eclipse	ΔT s	Luna Num	Saros Num	Ecl Type	QSE	Gamma	Pen Mag	Um Mag	Pen m	Par m	Total m	Lat	Long
0001	001	1501 May 03	05:13:24	194	-6168	113	T-	pp	-0.2065	2.4787	1.4796	337.9	217.0	91.9	18S	79W
0002	001	1501 Oct 26	08:54:56	193	-6162	118	T+	p-	0.2000	2.4944	1.4878	333.9	213.9	90.8	16N	137W
0003	001	1502 Apr 22	12:22:41	193	-6156	123	Nx	t-	-1.0034	1.0445	-0.0104	281.4	-	-	16S	174E
0004	001	1502 Oct 15	23:10:38	192	-6150	128	P	a-	0.8760	1.2335	0.2675	264.2	108.8	-	13N	9E
0005	001	1503 Mar 12	20:51:37	192	-6145	095	N	-t	1.1652	0.7604	-0.3198	252.0	-	-	1N	50E
0006	001	1503 Sep 06	05:48:24	191	-6139	100	N	-a	-1.0620	0.8995	-0.0810	240.7	-	-	4S	87W
0007	001	1504 Mar 01	00:44:45	191	-6133	105	T	-p	0.4057	2.1319	1.0957	339.8	205.8	47.6	4N	8W
0008	001	1504 Aug 25	16:30:39	190	-6127	110	T	-a	-0.3517	2.2287	1.1967	344.6	212.3	66.6	8S	113E
0009	001	1505 Feb 18	11:45:01	190	-6121	115	T	p-	-0.3241	2.2559	1.2707	321.3	203.7	72.4	8N	172W
0010	001	1505 Aug 14	20:05:57	189	-6115	120	T	t-	0.4064	2.1487	1.0766	360.7	214.4	44.7	11S	60E
0011	001	1506 Feb 08	03:14:05	189	-6109	125	P	a-	-0.9932	1.0177	0.0532	244.7	49.8	-	11N	44W
0012	001	1506 Aug 03	20:24:27	188	-6103	130	N	t-	1.1457	0.7897	-0.2775	255.5	-	-	14S	55E
0013	002	1506 Dec 30	06:22:24	188	-6098	097	N	-a	1.0490	0.9434	-0.0768	252.5	-	-	23N	93W
0014	002	1507 Jun 24	14:33:58	188	-6092	102	P	-h	-0.8306	1.3283	0.3395	285.6	127.0	-	24S	143E
0015	002	1507 Dec 19	13:12:59	187	-6086	107	T	-a	0.3872	2.1869	1.1090	355.0	211.7	51.6	24N	163E
0016	002	1508 Jun 13	05:14:01	187	-6080	112	T-	pp	-0.0503	2.7390	1.7919	319.8	212.6	99.4	24S	78W
0017	002	1508 Dec 07	13:26:11	186	-6074	117	T	p-	-0.2962	2.3680	1.2617	372.8	224.7	77.4	23N	158W
0018	002	1509 Jun 02	22:29:16	186	-6068	122	P	a-	0.6867	1.5701	0.6253	285.5	158.0	-	22S	23E
0019	002	1509 Nov 26	13:18:01	185	-6062	127	P	h-	-0.9626	1.1329	0.0514	292.0	54.5	-	22N	159E
0020	002	1510 Apr 24	03:27:15	185	-6057	094	N	-h	-1.1769	0.7071	-0.3099	229.1	-	-	17S	52W
0021	002	1510 May 23	13:38:06	185	-6056	132	N	h-	1.4702	0.1523	-0.8316	108.2	-	-	21S	156E
0022	002	1510 Oct 17	07:21:58	184	-6051	099	N	-a	1.1638	0.7176	-0.2723	219.0	-	-	14N	114W
0023	002	1511 Apr 13	08:29:05	184	-6045	104	P	-t	-0.4585	2.0511	0.9828	354.9	207.5	-	13S	127W
0024	002	1511 Oct 06	22:42:05	183	-6039	109	T	-a	0.4533	2.0062	1.0458	304.8	189.1	31.4	9N	17E
0025	003	1512 Apr 01	08:40:56	183	-6033	114	T	pp	0.2779	2.3882	1.3087	369.2	225.9	82.9	8S	129W
0026	003	1512 Sep 25	14:37:18	182	-6027	119	T-	p-	-0.2435	2.3992	1.4231	322.2	208.1	85.6	4N	139E
0027	003	1513 Mar 21	11:22:50	182	-6021	124	P	h-	0.9923	1.0591	0.0158	276.6	29.8	-	3S	169W
0028	003	1513 Sep 15	02:30:21	181	-6015	129	Nx	t-	-1.0061	1.0244	-0.0003	266.9	-	-	0S	39W
0029	003	1514 Feb 09	10:45:13	181	-6010	096	N	-a	-1.0259	0.9637	-0.0126	243.1	-	-	10N	157W
0030	003	1514 Aug 05	15:39:53	181	-6004	101	N	-t	1.0845	0.9056	-0.1689	272.7	-	-	13S	127E
0031	003	1515 Jan 30	02:35:55	180	-5998	106	T	-p	-0.3447	2.2095	1.2411	312.0	198.6	67.8	15N	35W
0032	003	1515 Jul 25	16:29:55	180	-5992	111	T	pp	0.3252	2.2894	1.2336	359.3	220.1	73.5	17S	115E
0033	003	1516 Jan 19	17:02:12	179	-5986	116	T	p-	0.3438	2.2296	1.2247	326.5	204.2	67.6	19N	109E
0034	003	1516 Jul 13	22:58:22	179	-5980	121	T	a-	-0.4501	2.0334	1.0308	328.8	199.7	27.3	21S	18E
0035	003	1517 Jan 08	01:41:56	178	-5974	126	N	t-	1.0863	0.8971	-0.1668	260.9	-	-	22N	22W
0036	003	1517 Jun 04	05:34:11	178	-5969	093	N	-a	1.3316	0.3854	-0.5566	160.1	-	-	22S	83W
0037	004	1517 Jul 03	12:28:22	178	-5968	131	N	a-	-1.1694	0.6892	-0.2649	210.9	-	-	23S	175E
0038	004	1517 Nov 28	07:44:08	177	-5963	098	N	-t	-1.2510	0.6151	-0.4888	232.9	-	-	22N	117W
0039	004	1518 May 24	22:40:53	177	-5957	103	P	-a	0.6180	1.7003	0.7474	295.1	170.6	-	22S	20E
0040	004	1518 Nov 17	08:59:10	177	-5951	108	P	-t	-0.5379	1.9040	0.8386	339.6	191.9	-	21N	137W
0041	004	1519 May 14	12:25:25	176	-5945	113	T-	pp	-0.1349	2.6107	1.6101	341.0	220.4	98.3	21S	173E
0042	004	1519 Nov 06	17:22:25	176	-5939	118	T+	p-	0.1846	2.5223	1.5162	333.3	214.0	92.1	19N	96E
0043	004	1520 May 02	19:14:14	175	-5933	123	P	t-	-0.9344	1.1712	0.1162	294.7	81.5	-	19S	71E
0044	004	1520 Oct 26	07:43:00	175	-5927	128	P	a-	0.0550	1.2729	0.3053	267.0	115.5	-	16N	119W
0045	004	1521 Mar 23	04:07:01	174	-5922	095	N	-t	1.2110	0.6739	-0.4013	238.6	-	-	4S	60W
0046	004	1521 Sep 16	13:41:13	174	-5916	100	N	-a	-1.1087	0.8167	-0.1694	232.2	-	-	0N	154E
0047	004	1521 Oct 15	23:41:23	174	-5915	138	N	a-	1.5291	0.0387	-0.9343	53.2	-	-	14N	1E
0048	004	1522 Mar 12	08:32:35	173	-5910	105	T	-t	0.4404	2.0649	1.0351	335.8	201.8	29.3	0N	125W
0049	005	1522 Sep 05	23:50:38	173	-5904	110	T	-a	-0.4089	2.1270	1.0888	343.2	207.4	46.4	3S	2E
0050	005	1523 Mar 01	20:01:59	173	-5898	115	T	p-	-0.2962	2.3044	1.3244	321.3	205.3	77.7	4N	63E
0051	005	1523 Aug 26	02:57:00	172	-5892	120	T	t-	0.3396	2.2734	1.1970	365.5	221.0	68.9	7S	44W
0052	005	1524 Feb 19	11:45:13	172	-5886	125	P	a-	-0.9720	1.0555	0.0934	248.1	65.7	-	7N	173W
0053	005	1524 Aug 14	03:11:09	171	-5880	130	N	t-	1.0729	0.9238	-0.1443	272.2	-	-	10S	47W
0054	005	1525 Jan 09	14:56:49	171	-5875	097	N	-a	1.0577	0.9284	-0.0937	251.7	-	-	21N	140E
0055	005	1525 Jul 04	21:43:22	170	-5869	102	P	-h	-0.9030	1.1941	0.2081	273.9	101.0	-	23S	36E
0056	005	1525 Dec 29	21:26:18	170	-5863	107	T	-a	0.3944	2.1747	1.0947	355.7	211.4	48.4	23N	41E
0057	005	1526 Jun 24	12:39:42	169	-5857	112	T-	pp	-0.1248	2.6017	1.6560	318.3	211.0	96.4	23S	172E
0058	005	1526 Dec 18	21:27:47	169	-5851	117	T	p-	-0.2888	2.3819	1.2753	373.2	224.9	79.0	23N	39E
0059	005	1527 Jun 14	05:54:50	169	-5845	122	P	a-	0.6135	1.7050	0.7592	293.1	170.6	-	23S	88W
0060	005	1527 Dec 07	21:30:03	168	-5839	127	P	h-	-0.9541	1.1477	0.0678	292.7	62.3	-	23N	37E

Cat Num	Canon Plate	Calendar Date	TD of Greatest Eclipse	ΔT s	Luna Num	Saros Num	Ecl Type	QSE	Gamma	Pen Mag	Um Mag	Phase ---- Durations ---- Pen m	Par m	Total m	Greatest in Zenith Lat	Long
0061	006	1528 May 04	10:37:12	168	-5834	094	N	-h	-1.2477	0.5778	-0.4405	210.5	–	–	20S	160W
0062	006	1528 Jun 02	20:49:33	168	-5833	132	N	h-	1.4027	0.2774	-0.7089	144.9	–	–	22S	48E
0063	006	1528 Oct 27	15:48:34	167	-5828	099	N	-a	1.1787	0.6902	-0.2997	214.9	–	–	17N	119E
0064	006	1529 Apr 23	15:20:26	167	-5822	104	P	-t	-0.5277	1.9238	0.8564	350.0	198.6	–	16S	130E
0065	006	1529 Oct 17	07:09:31	166	-5816	109	T	-a	0.4775	1.9631	1.0002	303.4	186.4	2.2	13N	111W
0066	006	1530 Apr 12	15:36:21	166	-5810	114	T+	pp	0.2151	2.5012	1.4259	370.6	229.6	92.9	12S	126E
0067	006	1530 Oct 06	22:49:12	166	-5804	119	T-	p-	-0.2127	2.4583	1.4771	324.4	209.9	89.0	9N	15E
0068	006	1531 Apr 01	18:47:56	165	-5798	124	P	h-	0.9400	1.1518	0.1148	284.3	79.0	–	7S	79E
0069	006	1531 Sep 26	10:13:21	165	-5792	129	P	t-	-0.9697	1.0946	0.0633	275.1	58.4	–	4N	155W
0070	006	1532 Feb 20	19:11:55	164	-5787	096	N	-a	-1.0452	0.9260	-0.0460	238.6	–	–	6N	76E
0071	006	1532 Aug 15	22:22:06	164	-5781	101	N	-t	1.1560	0.7762	-0.3015	256.1	–	–	10S	25E
0072	006	1533 Feb 09	11:13:51	164	-5775	106	T	-p	-0.3602	2.1804	1.2135	311.4	197.6	64.5	11N	164W
0073	007	1533 Aug 04	23:15:58	163	-5769	111	T	-t	0.3999	2.1521	1.0967	354.3	212.8	49.4	14S	13E
0074	007	1534 Jan 30	01:34:31	163	-5763	116	T	p-	0.3341	2.2477	1.2420	327.9	205.5	70.0	15N	19W
0075	007	1534 Jul 25	06:07:00	162	-5757	121	T	a-	-0.3755	2.1694	1.1687	332.0	206.5	61.1	18S	90W
0076	007	1535 Jan 19	09:56:16	162	-5751	126	N	t-	1.0801	0.9091	-0.1561	263.1	–	–	19N	145W
0077	007	1535 Jun 15	13:01:27	161	-5746	093	N	-a	1.4024	0.2551	-0.6860	131.8	–	–	22S	166E
0078	007	1535 Jul 14	19:54:00	161	-5745	131	N	a-	-1.0957	0.8238	-0.1292	227.0	–	–	21S	64E
0079	007	1535 Dec 09	15:45:19	161	-5740	098	N	-t	-1.2588	0.6007	-0.5033	230.3	–	–	22N	124E
0080	007	1536 Jun 04	06:06:31	161	-5734	103	P	-a	0.6920	1.5651	0.6110	288.6	158.0	–	23S	91W
0081	007	1536 Nov 27	17:14:00	160	-5728	108	P	-t	-0.5457	1.8890	0.8250	337.9	190.3	–	22N	100E
0082	007	1537 May 24	19:33:11	160	-5722	113	T-	pp	-0.0608	2.7477	1.7450	343.4	222.7	102.1	22S	67E
0083	007	1537 Nov 17	01:55:49	159	-5716	118	T+	p-	0.1739	2.5415	1.5364	332.6	213.8	92.9	21N	31W
0084	007	1538 May 14	01:57:58	159	-5710	123	P	t-	-0.8595	1.3090	0.2535	307.6	118.3	–	21S	30W
0085	008	1538 Nov 06	16:22:00	159	-5704	128	P	a-	0.8393	1.3023	0.3334	269.0	120.1	–	20N	111E
0086	008	1539 Apr 03	11:13:11	158	-5699	095	N	-t	1.2644	0.5733	-0.4966	221.5	–	–	8S	167W
0087	008	1539 Sep 27	21:41:55	158	-5693	100	N	-a	-1.1485	0.7465	-0.2453	224.5	–	–	4N	33E
0088	008	1539 Oct 27	08:10:56	158	-5692	138	N	a-	1.5127	0.0710	-0.9062	72.0	–	–	17N	127W
0089	008	1540 Mar 22	16:11:06	157	-5687	105	P	-t	0.4838	1.9821	0.9587	331.1	196.4	–	4S	119E
0090	008	1540 Sep 16	07:18:54	157	-5681	110	P	-a	-0.4584	2.0394	0.9948	341.7	202.4	–	1N	111W
0091	008	1541 Mar 12	04:11:18	157	-5675	115	T-	p-	-0.2612	2.3660	1.3911	321.4	207.2	83.3	1S	60W
0092	008	1541 Sep 05	09:54:44	156	-5669	120	T	pp	0.2784	2.3878	1.3071	369.4	225.8	82.7	3S	149W
0093	008	1542 Mar 01	20:09:58	156	-5663	125	P	a-	-0.9456	1.1026	0.1430	252.2	80.7	–	3N	60E
0094	008	1542 Aug 25	10:04:50	155	-5657	130	Nx	t-	1.0046	1.0495	-0.0196	285.9	–	–	7S	151W
0095	008	1543 Jan 20	23:27:43	155	-5652	097	N	-a	1.0685	0.9093	-0.1142	250.4	–	–	19N	13E
0096	008	1543 Jul 16	04:55:01	155	-5646	102	P	-h	-0.9742	1.0624	0.0785	261.1	63.0	–	21S	71W
0097	009	1544 Jan 10	05:37:49	154	-5640	107	T	-h	0.4024	2.1606	1.0793	356.1	211.0	44.6	21N	81W
0098	009	1544 Jul 04	20:06:55	154	-5634	112	T-	-p	-0.1982	2.4666	1.5216	316.2	208.4	90.9	22S	60E
0099	009	1544 Dec 29	05:29:08	153	-5628	117	T	p-	-0.2809	2.3960	1.2900	373.5	225.5	80.7	22N	80W
0100	009	1545 Jun 24	13:21:00	153	-5622	122	P	a-	0.5409	1.8389	0.8915	299.7	181.0	–	22S	161E
0101	009	1545 Dec 18	05:44:59	153	-5616	127	P	h-	-0.9471	1.1595	0.0818	293.0	68.2	–	22N	85W
0102	009	1546 May 15	17:40:50	152	-5611	094	N	-h	-1.3224	0.4417	-0.5782	187.2	–	–	22S	94E
0103	009	1546 Jun 14	03:57:37	152	-5610	132	N	h-	1.3330	0.4067	-0.5825	174.0	–	–	22S	59W
0104	009	1546 Nov 08	00:21:31	152	-5605	099	N	-a	1.1891	0.6710	-0.3188	211.8	–	–	20N	9W
0105	009	1547 May 04	22:04:30	152	-5599	104	P	-t	-0.6022	1.7867	0.7199	343.8	186.8	–	19S	28E
0106	009	1547 Oct 28	15:43:38	151	-5593	109	P	-a	0.4960	1.9304	0.9652	302.3	184.2	–	17N	121E
0107	009	1548 Apr 22	22:24:49	151	-5587	114	T+	pp	0.1463	2.6254	1.5543	371.5	232.4	100.3	15S	24E
0108	009	1548 Oct 17	07:08:28	150	-5581	119	T-	p-	-0.1886	2.5050	1.5188	326.2	211.2	91.4	13N	110W
0109	010	1549 Apr 12	02:06:53	150	-5575	124	P	h-	0.8818	1.2555	0.2247	292.1	108.5	–	11S	31W
0110	010	1549 Oct 06	18:02:24	150	-5569	129	P	t-	-0.9388	1.1543	0.1168	282.0	78.9	–	8N	87E
0111	010	1550 Mar 03	03:31:33	149	-5564	096	N	-a	-1.0707	0.8771	-0.0906	232.8	–	–	2N	50W
0112	010	1550 Apr 01	12:54:38	149	-5563	134	Nb	a-	1.5507	0.0022	-0.9770	13.1	–	–	7S	168E
0113	010	1550 Aug 27	05:11:26	149	-5558	101	N	-t	1.2211	0.6583	-0.4225	238.8	–	–	6S	78W
0114	010	1551 Feb 20	19:43:10	149	-5552	106	T	-p	-0.3827	2.1382	1.1729	310.4	196.1	58.9	7N	68E
0115	010	1551 Aug 16	06:09:50	148	-5546	111	P	-t	0.4689	2.0256	0.9703	348.8	204.6	–	10S	92W
0116	010	1552 Feb 10	09:58:44	148	-5540	116	T	p-	0.3184	2.2769	1.2707	329.6	207.2	73.5	12N	145W
0117	010	1552 Aug 04	13:22:36	147	-5534	121	T	a-	-0.3055	2.2970	1.2977	334.2	211.3	77.5	15S	161E
0118	010	1553 Jan 29	18:03:49	147	-5528	126	N	t-	1.0691	0.9295	-0.1363	266.3	–	–	16N	94E
0119	010	1553 Jun 25	20:29:07	147	-5523	093	N	-a	1.4727	0.1259	-0.8148	93.6	–	–	21S	54E
0120	010	1553 Jul 25	03:24:10	147	-5522	131	P	a-	-1.0254	0.9527	0.0001	240.3	2.2	–	18S	49W

Cat Num	Canon Plate	Calendar Date	TD of Greatest Eclipse	ΔT s	Luna Num	Saros Num	Ecl Type	QSE	Gamma	Pen Mag	Um Mag	Pen m	Par m	Total m	Lat	Long
0121	011	1553 Dec 19	23:49:18	146	-5517	098	N	-t	-1.2644	0.5901	-0.5131	228.2	–	–	22N	4E
0122	011	1554 Jun 15	13:27:57	146	-5511	103	P	-a	0.7688	1.4251	0.4692	280.8	141.8	–	23S	159E
0123	011	1554 Dec 09	01:34:25	146	-5505	108	P	-t	-0.5496	1.8808	0.8189	336.4	189.3	–	23N	24W
0124	011	1555 Jun 05	02:34:52	145	-5499	113	T+	pp	0.0172	2.8291	1.8238	345.1	223.8	103.1	23S	38W
0125	011	1555 Nov 28	10:34:49	145	-5493	118	T+	p-	0.1671	2.5533	1.5495	331.8	213.6	93.3	23N	160W
0126	011	1556 May 24	08:36:03	145	-5487	123	P	t-	-0.7803	1.4546	0.3983	319.7	145.4	–	23S	129W
0127	011	1556 Nov 17	01:06:52	144	-5481	128	P	a-	0.8287	1.3223	0.3523	270.3	123.0	–	22N	19W
0128	011	1557 Apr 13	18:14:10	144	-5476	095	N	-t	1.3222	0.4646	-0.6002	200.8	–	–	11S	87E
0129	011	1557 May 13	09:23:01	144	-5475	133	No	t-	-1.5371	0.0735	-0.9975	83.9	–	–	22S	142W
0130	011	1557 Oct 08	05:47:56	144	-5470	100	N	-a	-1.1834	0.6855	-0.3121	217.3	–	–	8N	89W
0131	011	1557 Nov 06	16:44:58	143	-5469	138	N	a-	1.5004	0.0955	-0.8857	83.5	–	–	20N	105E
0132	011	1558 Apr 02	23:45:09	143	-5464	105	P	-t	0.5316	1.8911	0.8741	325.7	189.9	–	8S	5E
0133	012	1558 Sep 27	14:53:06	143	-5458	110	P	-a	-0.5022	1.9622	0.9113	340.2	197.2	–	5N	135E
0134	012	1559 Mar 23	12:13:17	142	-5452	115	T-	p-	-0.2197	2.4396	1.4697	321.6	209.0	88.5	5S	178E
0135	012	1559 Sep 16	17:00:59	142	-5446	120	T+	pp	0.2244	2.4890	1.4040	372.3	229.3	91.3	1N	103E
0136	012	1560 Mar 12	04:26:25	142	-5440	125	P	a-	-0.9127	1.1617	0.2045	257.2	95.8	–	1S	65W
0137	012	1560 Sep 04	17:08:48	141	-5434	130	P	t-	0.9441	1.1611	0.0910	296.6	72.8	–	3S	102E
0138	012	1561 Jan 31	07:51:02	141	-5429	097	N	-a	1.0850	0.8796	-0.1449	247.9	–	–	15N	113W
0139	012	1561 Jul 26	12:13:48	141	-5423	102	N	-a	-1.0403	0.9403	-0.0419	247.9	–	–	18S	179E
0140	012	1562 Jan 20	13:43:39	140	-5417	107	T	-t	0.4147	2.1385	1.0565	356.2	210.1	38.0	18N	158E
0141	012	1562 Jul 16	03:36:18	140	-5411	112	T-	-p	-0.2701	2.3346	1.3897	313.5	204.7	82.5	20S	52W
0142	012	1563 Jan 09	13:28:26	140	-5405	117	T-	p-	-0.2713	2.4130	1.3084	373.6	226.2	82.6	20N	161E
0143	012	1563 Jul 05	20:46:25	139	-5399	122	T	a-	0.4679	1.9740	1.0244	305.7	189.8	23.4	21S	50E
0144	012	1563 Dec 29	13:59:50	139	-5393	127	P	h-	-0.9393	1.1722	0.0975	293.2	74.1	–	22N	152E
0145	013	1564 May 26	00:37:04	139	-5388	094	N	-h	-1.4019	0.2969	-0.7251	156.1	–	–	24S	9W
0146	013	1564 Jun 24	11:03:06	139	-5387	132	N	h-	1.2617	0.5393	-0.4534	198.7	–	–	22S	165W
0147	013	1564 Nov 18	09:01:31	138	-5382	099	N	-a	1.1947	0.6605	-0.3288	209.9	–	–	23N	138W
0148	013	1564 Dec 17	21:16:35	138	-5381	137	N	a-	-1.5589	0.0066	-1.0110	23.0	–	–	22N	42E
0149	013	1565 May 15	04:41:15	138	-5376	104	P	-t	-0.6820	1.6401	0.5737	335.8	171.1	–	22S	71W
0150	013	1565 Nov 08	00:23:47	138	-5370	109	P	-a	0.5096	1.9065	0.9391	301.6	182.5	–	20N	9W
0151	013	1566 May 04	05:06:55	137	-5364	114	T+	pp	0.0717	2.7602	1.6931	371.7	234.2	104.7	18S	77W
0152	013	1566 Oct 28	15:34:04	137	-5358	119	T-	p-	-0.1704	2.5408	1.5497	327.9	212.3	92.9	16N	123E
0153	013	1567 Apr 23	09:18:47	137	-5352	124	P	h-	0.8169	1.3716	0.3469	299.9	131.9	–	15S	140W
0154	013	1567 Oct 18	01:59:01	136	-5346	129	P	t-	-0.9150	1.2012	0.1576	287.5	91.4	–	12N	33W
0155	013	1568 Mar 13	11:44:26	136	-5341	096	N	-a	-1.1022	0.8172	-0.1461	225.6	–	–	2S	174W
0156	013	1568 Apr 11	20:39:01	136	-5340	134	N	a-	1.4971	0.0979	-0.8760	85.4	–	–	11S	51E
0157	014	1568 Sep 06	12:08:32	136	-5335	101	N	-t	1.2796	0.5525	-0.5316	221.3	–	–	1S	177E
0158	014	1569 Mar 03	04:06:07	135	-5329	106	T	-a	-0.4104	2.0866	1.1229	309.0	193.9	50.5	3N	59W
0159	014	1569 Aug 26	13:12:19	135	-5323	111	P	-t	0.5313	1.9111	0.8557	343.0	195.7	–	6S	162E
0160	014	1570 Feb 20	18:16:29	135	-5317	116	T	p-	0.2981	2.3142	1.3078	331.5	209.2	77.5	7N	90E
0161	014	1570 Aug 15	20:44:32	134	-5311	121	T-	p-	-0.2401	2.4165	1.4182	335.5	214.6	87.6	11S	50E
0162	014	1571 Feb 10	02:04:37	134	-5305	126	N	t-	1.0536	0.9581	-0.1079	270.3	–	–	12N	27W
0163	014	1571 Aug 05	10:59:41	134	-5299	131	P	a-	-0.9592	1.0742	0.1214	251.4	75.3	–	15S	163W
0164	014	1571 Dec 31	07:51:30	134	-5294	098	N	-L	-1.2712	0.5760	-0.5248	225.6	–	–	21N	115W
0165	014	1572 Jun 25	20:49:38	133	-5288	103	P	-a	0.8446	1.2873	0.3289	272.0	121.5	–	22S	49E
0166	014	1572 Dec 19	09:56:06	133	-5282	108	P	-h	-0.5525	1.8741	0.8149	334.9	188.5	–	23N	148W
0167	014	1573 Jun 15	09:33:59	133	-5276	113	T+	pp	0.0963	2.6854	1.6770	346.0	223.5	101.2	23S	143W
0168	014	1573 Dec 08	19:16:15	132	-5270	118	T+	p-	0.1620	2.5617	1.5597	330.9	213.3	93.5	24N	71E
0169	015	1574 Jun 04	15:09:12	132	-5264	123	P	t-	-0.6978	1.6067	0.5492	330.9	167.1	–	24S	133E
0170	015	1574 Nov 28	09:55:42	132	-5258	128	P	a-	0.8213	1.3362	0.3655	271.2	125.0	–	24N	150W
0171	015	1575 Apr 25	01:06:07	131	-5253	095	N	-t	1.3873	0.3426	-0.7172	173.8	–	–	15S	16W
0172	015	1575 May 24	15:51:34	131	-5252	133	N	t-	-1.4543	0.2241	-0.8445	144.4	–	–	24S	122E
0173	015	1575 Oct 19	14:02:17	131	-5247	100	N	-a	-1.2107	0.6381	-0.3650	211.5	–	–	12N	147E
0174	015	1575 Nov 18	01:25:10	131	-5246	138	N	a-	1.4937	0.1097	-0.8751	89.6	–	–	23N	24W
0175	015	1576 Apr 13	07:11:15	131	-5241	105	P	-t	0.5866	1.7872	0.7764	319.3	181.4	–	12S	108W
0176	015	1576 Oct 07	22:35:10	131	-5235	110	P	-a	-0.5385	1.8988	0.8417	339.0	192.4	–	9N	18E
0177	015	1577 Apr 02	20:08:12	130	-5229	115	T-	p-	-0.1720	2.5248	1.5598	321.8	210.7	93.1	9S	59E
0178	015	1577 Sep 27	00:16:05	130	-5223	120	T+	pp	0.1782	2.5760	1.4868	374.5	231.6	96.7	5N	7W
0179	015	1578 Mar 23	12:35:21	130	-5217	125	P	a-	-0.8739	1.2318	0.2770	262.8	110.4	–	6S	172E
0180	015	1578 Sep 16	00:21:26	129	-5211	130	P	t-	0.8898	1.2613	0.1901	305.3	103.5	–	2N	7W

Cat Num	Canon Plate	Calendar Date	TD of Greatest Eclipse	ΔT s	Luna Num	Saros Num	Ecl Type	QSE	Gamma	Pen Mag	Um Mag	Pen m	Par m	Total m	Lat	Long
0181	016	1579 Feb 11	16:08:35	129	-5206	097	N	-a	1.1054	0.8425	-0.1826	244.3	–	–	12N	122E
0182	016	1579 Aug 06	19:37:40	129	-5200	102	N	-a	-1.1029	0.8249	-0.1563	234.2	–	–	15S	68W
0183	016	1580 Jan 31	21:43:38	129	-5194	107	T	-t	0.4311	2.1084	1.0264	355.9	208.8	26.3	15N	39E
0184	016	1580 Jul 26	11:09:57	128	-5188	112	T	-p	-0.3387	2.2090	1.2636	310.4	200.0	70.8	17S	166W
0185	016	1581 Jan 19	21:24:55	128	-5182	117	T-	p-	-0.2590	2.4346	1.3319	373.8	227.0	84.9	18N	43E
0186	016	1581 Jul 16	04:13:14	128	-5176	122	T	p-	0.3965	2.1064	1.1540	310.8	196.9	56.5	19S	62W
0187	016	1582 Jan 08	22:14:13	127	-5170	127	P	a-	-0.9305	1.1866	0.1155	293.6	80.2	–	20N	30E
0188	016	1582 Jun 06	07:29:31	127	-5165	094	N	-t	-1.4831	0.1492	-0.8753	112.6	–	–	25S	112W
0189	016	1582 Jul 05	18:07:58	127	-5164	132	N	t-	1.1904	0.6722	-0.3246	219.9	–	–	20S	89E
0190	016	1582 Dec 09	17:45:07	127	-5159	099	N	-a	1.1978	0.6544	-0.3340	208.5	–	–	24N	93E
0191	016	1583 Jan 08	05:55:01	127	-5158	137	N	a-	-1.5514	0.0186	-0.9958	38.5	–	–	21N	87W
0192	016	1583 Jun 05	11:12:21	127	-5153	104	P	-t	-0.7656	1.4867	0.4204	326.0	150.3	–	23S	168W
0193	017	1583 Nov 29	09:08:52	126	-5147	109	P	-a	0.5191	1.8901	0.9208	301.1	181.3	–	22N	140W
0194	017	1584 May 24	11:45:09	126	-5141	114	T-	pp	-0.0065	2.8780	1.8146	371.0	234.5	106.1	21S	177W
0195	017	1584 Nov 18	00:04:26	126	-5135	119	T-	p-	-0.1567	2.5682	1.5726	329.5	213.1	94.0	19N	4W
0196	017	1585 May 13	16:27:06	126	-5129	124	P	h-	0.7478	1.4955	0.4764	307.2	151.1	–	18S	113E
0197	017	1585 Nov 07	10:01:46	125	-5123	129	P	t-	-0.8966	1.2379	0.1885	291.9	99.8	–	16N	154W
0198	017	1586 Apr 03	19:49:06	125	-5118	096	N	-a	-1.1406	0.7446	-0.2145	216.5	–	–	7S	64E
0199	017	1586 May 03	04:16:35	125	-5117	134	N	a-	1.4374	0.2050	-0.7639	122.0	–	–	14S	64W
0200	017	1586 Sep 27	19:14:31	125	-5112	101	N	-t	1.3307	0.4605	-0.6269	203.9	–	–	3N	69E
0201	017	1587 Mar 24	12:19:46	125	-5106	106	T	-a	-0.4456	2.0212	1.0591	307.2	190.9	35.8	2S	177E
0202	017	1587 Sep 16	20:25:04	124	-5100	111	P	-t	0.5857	1.8114	0.7555	337.4	186.6	–	2S	53E
0203	017	1588 Mar 13	02:23:34	124	-5094	116	T+	p-	0.2699	2.3661	1.3596	333.6	211.6	82.5	3N	33W
0204	017	1588 Sep 05	04:15:58	124	-5088	121	T-	p-	-0.1819	2.5231	1.5254	336.1	216.6	93.8	7S	64W
0205	018	1589 Mar 02	09:56:49	123	-5082	126	N	t-	1.0320	0.9977	-0.0682	275.3	–	–	8N	145W
0206	018	1589 Aug 25	18:40:23	123	-5076	131	P	a-	-0.8970	1.1887	0.2352	260.8	102.9	–	12S	81E
0207	018	1590 Jan 20	15:53:19	123	-5071	098	N	-t	-1.2784	0.5625	-0.5369	222.7	–	–	19N	125E
0208	018	1590 Jul 17	04:09:54	123	-5065	103	P	-a	0.9206	1.1494	0.1879	261.8	94.0	–	20S	61W
0209	018	1591 Jan 09	18:19:20	123	-5059	108	P	-h	-0.5552	1.8675	0.8116	333.4	187.7	–	22N	88E
0210	018	1591 Jul 06	16:29:28	122	-5053	113	T+	pp	0.1776	2.5382	1.5261	346.0	221.6	95.7	23S	114E
0211	018	1591 Dec 30	04:00:34	122	-5047	118	T+	p-	0.1588	2.5665	1.5667	329.9	212.9	93.7	23N	59W
0212	018	1592 Jun 24	21:40:10	122	-5041	123	P	t-	-0.6136	1.7620	0.7028	340.8	184.6	–	24S	36E
0213	018	1592 Dec 18	18:46:57	122	-5035	128	P	a-	0.8161	1.3460	0.3749	271.8	126.4	–	24N	78E
0214	018	1593 May 15	07:55:14	121	-5030	095	N	-t	1.4548	0.2164	-0.8387	139.3	–	–	18S	119W
0215	018	1593 Jun 13	22:19:49	121	-5029	133	N	t-	-1.3705	0.3769	-0.6895	184.3	–	–	25S	25E
0216	018	1593 Nov 08	22:22:02	121	-5024	100	N	-a	-1.2329	0.6001	-0.4084	206.7	–	–	16N	22E
0217	019	1593 Dec 08	10:08:27	121	-5023	138	N	a-	1.4900	0.1180	-0.8701	93.1	–	–	24N	154W
0218	019	1594 May 04	14:32:41	121	-5018	105	P	-t	0.6462	1.6748	0.6700	312.0	171.1	–	15S	142E
0219	019	1594 Oct 29	06:23:43	121	-5012	110	P	-a	-0.5687	1.8463	0.7834	338.0	188.0	–	13N	99W
0220	019	1595 Apr 24	03:56:43	120	-5006	115	T-	p-	-0.1185	2.6206	1.6602	321.8	212.1	96.7	13S	59W
0221	019	1595 Oct 18	07:40:05	120	-5000	120	T+	pp	0.1391	2.6497	1.5567	376.1	233.1	100.2	10N	118W
0222	019	1596 Apr 12	20:35:29	120	-4994	125	P	a-	-0.8279	1.3151	0.3623	269.0	124.8	–	10S	51E
0223	019	1596 Oct 06	07:45:08	120	-4988	130	P	t-	0.8436	1.3465	0.2742	311.9	122.6	–	6N	119W
0224	019	1597 Mar 04	00:16:53	120	-4983	097	N	-a	1.1329	0.7922	-0.2333	238.8	–	–	7N	0W
0225	019	1597 Aug 27	03:08:44	119	-4977	102	N	-a	-1.1604	0.7190	-0.2615	220.4	–	–	11S	46W
0226	019	1597 Sep 25	13:40:49	119	-4976	140	N	a-	1.5117	0.0924	-0.9236	86.8	–	–	2N	152E
0227	019	1598 Feb 21	05:35:26	119	-4971	107	P	-t	0.4537	2.0666	0.9851	355.0	206.6	–	11N	80W
0228	019	1598 Aug 16	18:47:57	119	-4965	112	T	-a	-0.4040	2.0898	1.1433	306.9	194.6	54.2	14S	80E
0229	020	1599 Feb 10	05:14:34	119	-4959	117	T-	p-	-0.2410	2.4660	1.3662	373.9	228.1	88.0	14N	74W
0230	020	1599 Aug 06	11:42:05	118	-4953	122	T	p-	0.3273	2.2352	1.2793	315.2	202.6	73.1	17S	174W
0231	020	1600 Jan 30	06:25:27	118	-4947	127	P	a-	-0.9183	1.2067	0.1399	294.3	87.8	–	17N	93W
0232	020	1600 Jul 26	01:13:16	117	-4941	132	N	t-	1.1201	0.8035	-0.1979	238.3	–	–	18S	17W
0233	020	1600 Dec 20	02:31:53	117	-4936	099	N	-a	1.1990	0.6515	-0.3355	207.7	–	–	25N	38W
0234	020	1601 Jan 18	14:32:21	117	-4935	137	N	a-	-1.5426	0.0330	-0.9777	51.0	–	–	19N	145E
0235	020	1601 Jun 15	17:39:33	117	-4930	104	P	-t	-0.8517	1.3288	0.2622	314.2	121.7	–	24S	96E
0236	020	1601 Dec 09	17:58:32	116	-4924	109	P	-a	0.5249	1.8800	0.9093	300.9	180.6	–	23N	89E
0237	020	1602 Jun 04	18:18:11	116	-4918	114	T-	pp	-0.0895	2.7240	1.6640	369.3	233.2	104.0	23S	85E
0238	020	1602 Nov 29	08:40:25	115	-4912	119	T-	p-	-0.1482	2.5859	1.5861	330.9	213.7	94.6	21N	132W
0239	020	1603 May 24	23:30:54	115	-4906	124	P	a-	0.6737	1.6287	0.6150	314.0	167.4	–	20S	7E
0240	020	1603 Nov 18	18:10:29	114	-4900	129	P	t-	-0.8838	1.2640	0.2093	295.4	105.2	–	18N	84E

Cat Num	Canon Plate	Calendar Date	TD of Greatest Eclipse	ΔT s	Luna Num	Saros Num	Ecl Type	QSE	Gamma	Pen Mag	Um Mag	Pen m	Par m	Total m	Lat	Long
0241	021	1604 Apr 14	03:47:04	114	-4895	096	N	-a	-1.1848	0.6614	-0.2937	205.3	–	–	11S	57W
0242	021	1604 May 13	11:49:46	114	-4894	134	N	a-	1.3733	0.3201	-0.6441	150.3	–	–	17S	178W
0243	021	1604 Oct 08	02:29:41	113	-4889	101	N	-t	1.3742	0.3822	-0.7083	187.2	–	–	7N	40W
0244	021	1605 Apr 03	20:27:01	113	-4883	106	P	-a	-0.4858	1.9467	0.9861	304.9	187.0	–	6S	54E
0245	021	1605 Sep 27	03:46:01	112	-4877	111	P	-t	0.6341	1.7229	0.6667	331.9	177.5	–	2N	58W
0246	021	1606 Mar 24	10:23:17	111	-4871	116	T+	p-	0.2363	2.4276	1.4211	335.9	214.1	87.5	1S	154W
0247	021	1606 Sep 16	11:55:20	111	-4865	121	T-	p-	-0.1296	2.6188	1.6215	336.1	217.7	97.5	3S	180W
0248	021	1607 Mar 13	17:38:52	110	-4859	126	Nx	t-	1.0028	1.0510	-0.0145	281.7	–	–	4N	98E
0249	021	1607 Sep 06	02:28:41	110	-4853	131	P	a-	-0.8408	1.2923	0.3377	268.4	121.3	–	8S	37W
0250	021	1608 Jan 31	23:50:20	109	-4848	098	N	-t	-1.2895	0.5406	-0.5557	218.4	–	–	16N	6E
0251	021	1608 Jul 27	11:33:01	109	-4842	103	P	-a	0.9936	1.0172	0.0521	250.8	50.5	–	18S	172W
0252	021	1608 Aug 25	19:20:07	109	-4841	141	Nb	a-	-1.5414	0.0062	-0.9470	21.2	–	–	12S	71E
0253	022	1609 Jan 20	02:39:40	108	-4836	108	P	-h	-0.5607	1.8553	0.8034	331.5	186.5	–	20N	37W
0254	022	1609 Jul 16	23:25:48	108	-4830	113	T+	-p	0.2570	2.3946	1.3783	345.1	218.3	86.3	21S	10E
0255	022	1610 Jan 09	12:44:35	107	-4824	118	T+	p-	0.1550	2.5721	1.5751	329.0	212.7	93.9	22N	171E
0256	022	1610 Jul 06	04:08:02	106	-4818	123	P	t-	-0.5274	1.9212	0.8600	349.5	199.1	–	23S	61W
0257	022	1610 Dec 30	03:39:53	106	-4812	128	P	a-	0.8125	1.3526	0.3816	272.2	127.4	–	24N	54W
0258	022	1611 May 26	14:38:03	105	-4807	095	Ne	-t	1.5270	0.0817	-0.9689	86.3	–	–	20S	140E
0259	022	1611 Jun 25	04:45:07	105	-4806	133	N	t-	-1.2837	0.5352	-0.5295	216.1	–	–	25S	71W
0260	022	1611 Nov 20	06:48:14	105	-4801	100	N	-a	-1.2493	0.5725	-0.4410	203.2	–	–	19N	105W
0261	022	1611 Dec 19	18:54:20	104	-4800	138	N	a-	1.4893	0.1208	-0.8700	94.4	–	–	25N	76E
0262	022	1612 May 14	21:48:16	104	-4795	105	P	-t	0.7111	1.5528	0.5535	303.5	157.9	–	18S	33E
0263	022	1612 Nov 08	14:19:55	103	-4789	110	P	-h	-0.5915	1.8071	0.7388	337.4	184.5	–	16N	142E
0264	022	1613 May 04	11:39:02	103	-4783	115	T-	pp	-0.0593	2.7271	1.7709	321.5	212.9	99.0	16S	175W
0265	023	1613 Oct 28	15:11:39	102	-4777	120	T+	pp	0.1064	2.7115	1.6149	377.3	234.1	102.3	13N	128E
0266	023	1614 Apr 24	04:28:47	101	-4771	125	P	a-	-0.7766	1.4083	0.4573	275.5	138.4	–	14S	68W
0267	023	1614 Oct 17	15:18:15	101	-4765	130	P	t-	0.8044	1.4191	0.3458	316.9	135.9	–	10N	127E
0268	023	1615 Mar 15	08:16:13	100	-4760	097	N	-a	1.1667	0.7302	-0.2955	231.5	–	–	3N	121W
0269	023	1615 Apr 13	19:38:27	100	-4759	135	Nb	a-	-1.5327	0.0400	-0.9486	55.8	–	–	10S	65E
0270	023	1615 Sep 07	10:47:19	100	-4754	102	N	-a	-1.2123	0.6236	-0.3567	206.6	–	–	7S	161W
0271	023	1615 Oct 06	21:30:13	99	-4753	140	N	a-	1.4676	0.1731	-0.8428	117.6	–	–	6N	34E
0272	023	1616 Mar 03	13:19:27	99	-4748	107	P	-t	0.4820	2.0142	0.9336	353.6	203.4	–	7N	164E
0273	023	1616 Aug 27	02:31:49	98	-4742	112	T	-a	-0.4643	1.9799	1.0319	303.2	188.6	26.4	10S	37W
0274	023	1617 Feb 20	12:58:53	98	-4736	117	T-	pp	-0.2186	2.5056	1.4090	374.0	229.3	91.4	11N	169E
0275	023	1617 Aug 16	19:15:09	97	-4730	122	T+	p-	0.2621	2.3567	1.3970	318.9	207.0	83.7	13S	72E
0276	023	1618 Feb 09	14:33:23	96	-4724	127	P	a-	-0.9028	1.2327	0.1708	295.5	96.3	–	14N	145E
0277	024	1618 Aug 06	08:19:42	96	-4718	132	N	t-	1.0514	0.9321	-0.0742	254.5	–	–	16S	124W
0278	024	1618 Dec 31	11:19:57	95	-4713	099	N	-a	1.1997	0.6493	-0.3360	206.9	–	–	24N	168W
0279	024	1619 Jan 29	23:07:06	95	-4712	137	N	a-	-1.5311	0.0519	-0.9546	63.6	–	–	16N	17E
0280	024	1619 Jun 27	00:04:47	94	-4707	104	P	-t	-0.9390	1.1691	0.1018	300.3	77.7	–	24S	0W
0281	024	1619 Dec 21	02:49:27	94	-4701	109	P	-a	0.5298	1.8716	0.8998	300.8	180.0	–	24N	42W
0282	024	1620 Jun 15	00:50:48	93	-4695	114	T-	pp	-0.1735	2.5684	1.5114	366.6	230.2	97.9	24S	12W
0283	024	1620 Dec 09	17:19:12	92	-4689	119	T-	p-	-0.1423	2.5987	1.5951	332.2	214.3	95.1	23N	99E
0284	024	1621 Jun 04	06:32:44	92	-4683	124	P	a-	0.5970	1.7669	0.7582	320.0	100.9		22S	98W
0285	024	1621 Nov 29	02:23:00	91	-4677	129	P	t-	-0.8746	1.2832	0.2237	298.1	108.8	–	21N	38W
0286	024	1622 Apr 25	11:37:46	90	-4672	096	N	-a	-1.2353	0.5670	-0.3845	191.5	–	–	14S	175W
0287	024	1622 May 24	19:18:15	90	-4671	134	N	a-	1.3047	0.4440	-0.5161	174.4	–	–	20S	70E
0288	024	1622 Oct 19	09:54:36	90	-4666	101	N	-t	1.4097	0.3185	-0.7749	172.0	–	–	11N	152W
0289	025	1623 Apr 15	04:23:32	89	-4660	106	P	-a	-0.5346	1.8566	0.8973	301.7	181.5	–	10S	66W
0290	025	1623 Oct 08	11:18:41	88	-4654	111	P	-t	0.6735	1.6509	0.5942	326.9	169.1	–	6N	173W
0291	025	1624 Apr 03	18:12:07	88	-4648	116	T+	pp	0.1945	2.5044	1.4977	338.2	216.8	92.5	5S	88E
0292	025	1624 Sep 26	19:44:23	87	-4642	121	T-	pp	-0.0846	2.7014	1.7042	335.7	218.1	99.5	2N	62E
0293	025	1625 Mar 24	01:11:27	86	-4636	126	P	t-	0.9666	1.1171	0.0523	289.1	55.0	–	1S	16W
0294	025	1625 Sep 16	10:24:15	85	-4630	131	P	a-	-0.7904	1.3855	0.4294	274.7	134.8	–	3S	157W
0295	025	1626 Feb 11	07:43:54	85	-4625	098	N	-t	-1.3035	0.5129	-0.5797	212.8	–	–	13N	112W
0296	025	1626 Aug 07	18:56:22	84	-4619	103	N	-a	1.0655	0.8875	-0.0819	238.3	–	–	15S	77E
0297	025	1626 Sep 06	03:05:57	84	-4618	141	N	a-	-1.4898	0.1029	-0.8544	85.7	–	–	8S	46W
0298	025	1627 Jan 31	10:59:16	83	-4613	108	P	-h	-0.5675	1.8405	0.7933	329.5	185.2	–	17N	161W
0299	025	1627 Jul 28	06:21:39	83	-4607	113	T	-h	0.3356	2.2527	1.2318	343.4	213.5	71.4	19S	94W
0300	025	1628 Jan 20	21:27:25	82	-4601	118	T+	p-	0.1499	2.5797	1.5861	328.0	212.5	94.2	20N	41E

Cat Num	Canon Plate	Calendar Date	TD of Greatest Eclipse	ΔT s	Luna Num	Saros Num	Ecl Type	QSE	Gamma	Pen Mag	Um Mag	Pen m	Par m	Total m	Lat	Long
0301	026	1628 Jul 16	10:36:56	81	-4595	123	T	t-	-0.4425	2.0782	1.0146	356.9	210.5	19.9	22S	158W
0302	026	1629 Jan 09	12:32:46	80	-4589	128	P	a-	0.8093	1.3581	0.3876	272.5	128.2	–	23N	174E
0303	026	1629 Jul 05	11:11:36	80	-4583	133	N	t-	-1.1970	0.6937	-0.3696	241.8	–	–	24S	167W
0304	026	1629 Nov 30	15:17:32	79	-4578	100	N	-a	-1.2625	0.5506	-0.4676	200.5	–	–	21N	129E
0305	026	1629 Dec 30	03:40:30	79	-4577	138	N	a-	1.4894	0.1218	-0.8713	95.1	–	–	25N	54W
0306	026	1630 May 26	05:01:21	78	-4572	105	P	-h	0.7788	1.4259	0.4318	293.8	141.7	–	20S	76W
0307	026	1630 Nov 19	22:20:55	78	-4566	110	P	-h	-0.6100	1.7757	0.7024	337.1	181.4	–	19N	22E
0308	026	1631 May 15	19:15:40	77	-4560	115	T+	pp	0.0051	2.8246	1.8721	320.8	213.0	99.8	19S	70E
0309	026	1631 Nov 08	22:51:37	76	-4554	120	T+	pp	0.0806	2.7604	1.6607	378.2	234.7	103.5	17N	13E
0310	026	1632 May 04	12:15:03	75	-4548	125	P	a-	-0.7196	1.5121	0.5625	282.2	151.2	–	17S	175E
0311	026	1632 Oct 27	23:00:30	75	-4542	130	P	t-	0.7719	1.4790	0.4051	320.6	145.4	–	14N	11E
0312	026	1633 Mar 25	16:05:28	74	-4537	097	N	-a	1.2080	0.6545	-0.3714	221.5	–	–	1S	121E
0313	027	1633 Apr 24	03:17:43	74	-4536	135	N	a-	-1.4853	0.1272	-0.8618	98.9	–	–	14S	50W
0314	027	1633 Sep 17	18:34:53	73	-4531	102	N	-a	-1.2576	0.5406	-0.4397	193.4	–	–	3S	81E
0315	027	1633 Oct 17	05:29:16	73	-4530	140	N	a-	1.4307	0.2409	-0.7749	137.4	–	–	11N	86W
0316	027	1634 Mar 14	20:53:00	73	-4525	107	P	-t	0.5184	1.9469	0.8675	351.2	198.9	–	3N	50E
0317	027	1634 Sep 07	10:21:49	72	-4519	112	P	-a	-0.5196	1.8795	0.9294	299.4	182.2	–	7S	155W
0318	027	1635 Mar 03	20:34:49	71	-4513	117	T-	pp	-0.1890	2.5579	1.4653	374.2	230.7	95.3	7N	55E
0319	027	1635 Aug 28	02:53:00	70	-4507	122	T+	p-	0.2013	2.4705	1.5063	322.0	210.3	90.8	10S	43W
0320	027	1636 Feb 20	22:34:48	70	-4501	127	P	a-	-0.8810	1.2699	0.2135	297.4	106.7	–	10N	25E
0321	027	1636 Aug 16	15:29:54	69	-4495	132	P	t-	0.9862	1.0545	0.0426	268.5	47.8	–	13S	128E
0322	027	1637 Jan 10	20:08:48	68	-4490	099	N	-a	1.2008	0.6463	-0.3368	206.0	–	–	23N	61E
0323	027	1637 Feb 09	07:38:42	68	-4489	137	N	a-	-1.5165	0.0764	-0.9254	76.8	–	–	13N	111W
0324	027	1637 Jul 07	06:28:08	67	-4484	104	Nx	-t	-1.0271	1.0080	-0.0604	284.0	–	–	24S	96W
0325	028	1637 Dec 31	11:42:24	67	-4478	109	P	-a	0.5331	1.8660	0.8934	300.8	179.7	–	24N	174W
0326	028	1638 Jun 26	07:21:46	66	-4472	114	T-	pp	-0.2595	2.4091	1.3549	362.7	225.3	86.8	24S	110W
0327	028	1638 Dec 21	02:00:38	65	-4466	119	T-	pp	-0.1394	2.6057	1.5988	333.4	214.9	95.4	23N	30W
0328	028	1639 Jun 15	13:32:41	65	-4460	124	P	a-	0.5177	1.9102	0.9059	325.1	192.1	–	23S	157E
0329	028	1639 Dec 10	10:39:49	64	-4454	129	P	t-	-0.8696	1.2945	0.2308	300.2	110.7	–	22N	161W
0330	028	1640 May 05	19:23:34	63	-4449	096	N	-a	-1.2900	0.4649	-0.4833	174.9	–	–	18S	68E
0331	028	1640 Jun 04	02:45:05	63	-4448	134	N	a-	1.2341	0.5718	-0.3848	194.8	–	–	21S	42W
0332	028	1640 Oct 29	17:27:10	62	-4443	101	N	-t	1.4391	0.2658	-0.8300	157.9	–	–	15N	94E
0333	028	1641 Apr 25	12:14:35	62	-4437	106	P	-a	-0.5876	1.7589	0.8004	297.9	174.6	–	14S	176E
0334	028	1641 Oct 18	19:00:24	61	-4431	111	P	-t	0.7062	1.5909	0.5340	322.3	161.4	–	11N	71E
0335	028	1642 Apr 15	01:52:18	60	-4425	116	T+	pp	0.1463	2.5930	1.5860	340.5	219.3	97.0	10S	28W
0336	028	1642 Oct 08	03:42:19	59	-4419	121	T-	pp	-0.0462	2.7718	1.7746	335.1	218.0	100.3	6N	58W
0337	029	1643 Apr 04	08:33:33	59	-4413	126	P	t-	0.9222	1.1981	0.1341	297.4	87.2	–	5S	127W
0338	029	1643 Sep 27	18:28:13	58	-4407	131	P	a-	-0.7469	1.4663	0.5085	279.7	144.8	–	1N	81E
0339	029	1644 Feb 22	15:29:25	57	-4402	098	N	-t	-1.3241	0.4731	-0.6152	204.6	–	–	9N	131E
0340	029	1644 Aug 18	02:25:16	57	-4396	103	N	-a	1.1320	0.7680	-0.2061	225.3	–	–	12S	36W
0341	029	1644 Sep 16	10:59:46	57	-4395	141	N	a-	-1.4449	0.1874	-0.7741	115.1	–	–	4S	166W
0342	029	1645 Feb 10	19:13:46	56	-4390	108	P	-h	-0.5789	1.8169	0.7749	326.9	183.1	–	13N	75E
0343	029	1645 Aug 07	13:19:25	55	-4384	113	T	-h	0.4115	2.1160	1.0900	340.9	207.2	46.7	16S	162E
0344	029	1646 Jan 31	06:07:04	55	-4378	118	T+	p-	0.1417	2.5929	1.6030	327.1	212.4	94.7	17N	88W
0345	029	1646 Jul 27	17:06:35	54	-4372	123	T	t-	-0.3586	2.2334	1.1670	362.9	219.4	64.2	19S	105E
0346	029	1647 Jan 20	21:23:09	53	-4366	128	P	a-	0.8040	1.3674	0.3978	273.1	129.7	–	21N	43E
0347	029	1647 Jul 16	17:39:13	52	-4360	133	N	t-	-1.1101	0.8526	-0.2097	263.4	–	–	22S	97E
0348	029	1647 Dec 11	23:51:13	52	-4355	100	N	-a	-1.2717	0.5358	-0.4864	198.8	–	–	22N	1E
0349	030	1648 Jan 10	12:26:14	52	-4354	138	N	a-	1.4898	0.1219	-0.8730	95.4	–	–	23N	176E
0350	030	1648 Jun 05	12:11:38	51	-4349	105	P	-h	0.8497	1.2936	0.3042	282.9	120.8	–	22S	177E
0351	030	1648 Nov 30	06:26:41	50	-4343	110	P	-h	-0.6238	1.7525	0.6748	337.0	179.1	–	21N	99W
0352	030	1649 May 26	02:48:35	50	-4337	115	T+	pp	0.0732	2.6981	1.7489	319.7	212.2	98.6	21S	43W
0353	030	1649 Nov 19	06:38:53	49	-4331	120	T+	pp	0.0608	2.7979	1.6956	378.7	235.0	104.1	20N	130E
0354	030	1650 May 15	19:54:18	48	-4325	125	P	a-	-0.6571	1.6265	0.6778	288.9	163.1	–	20S	60E
0355	030	1650 Nov 08	06:52:24	48	-4319	130	P	t-	0.7465	1.5257	0.4515	323.2	152.0	–	17N	107W
0356	030	1651 Apr 05	23:45:28	47	-4314	097	N	-a	1.2558	0.5669	-0.4591	208.6	–	–	5S	5E
0357	030	1651 May 05	10:48:38	47	-4313	135	N	a-	-1.4322	0.2250	-0.7646	130.9	–	–	18S	163W
0358	030	1651 Sep 29	02:31:08	46	-4308	102	N	-a	-1.2966	0.4691	-0.5115	180.9	–	–	1N	39W
0359	030	1651 Oct 28	13:37:35	46	-4307	140	N	a-	1.4004	0.2964	-0.7191	151.2	–	–	14N	151E
0360	030	1652 Mar 25	04:17:29	46	-4302	107	P	-t	0.5617	1.8668	0.7888	348.0	192.7	–	2S	62W

Cat Num	Canon Plate	Calendar Date	TD of Greatest Eclipse	ΔT s	Luna Num	Saros Num	Ecl Type	QSE	Gamma	Pen Mag	Um Mag	Pen m	Par m	Total m	Lat	Long
0361	031	1652 Sep 17	18:19:28	45	-4296	112	P	-a	-0.5687	1.7906	0.8381	295.7	175.7	–	2S	84E
0362	031	1653 Mar 14	04:04:30	44	-4290	117	T-	pp	-0.1538	2.6204	1.5320	374.2	232.1	98.9	2N	59W
0363	031	1653 Sep 07	10:35:25	43	-4284	122	T+	pp	0.1448	2.5766	1.6076	324.5	212.6	95.4	6S	159W
0364	031	1654 Mar 03	06:31:28	43	-4278	127	P	a-	-0.8545	1.3156	0.2650	299.9	117.6	–	6N	95W
0365	031	1654 Aug 27	22:43:59	42	-4272	132	P	t-	0.9246	1.1704	0.1526	280.6	89.3	–	9S	19E
0366	031	1655 Jan 22	04:54:44	42	-4267	099	N	-a	1.2045	0.6380	-0.3424	204.4	–	–	21N	70W
0367	031	1655 Feb 20	16:03:52	41	-4266	137	N	a-	-1.4963	0.1110	-0.8858	91.9	–	–	9N	122E
0368	031	1655 Jul 18	12:53:09	41	-4261	104	N	-t	-1.1132	0.8507	-0.2191	265.4	–	–	22S	169E
0369	031	1656 Jan 11	20:33:33	40	-4255	109	P	-a	0.5380	1.8572	0.8844	300.7	179.2	–	22N	54E
0370	031	1656 Jul 06	13:55:39	40	-4249	114	T	-t	-0.3437	2.2535	1.2015	357.8	218.6	69.0	23S	152E
0371	031	1656 Dec 31	10:41:02	39	-4243	119	T-	pp	-0.1360	2.6133	1.6037	334.6	215.4	95.7	23N	159W
0372	031	1657 Jun 25	20:33:50	38	-4237	124	T	a-	0.4381	2.0544	1.0539	329.2	201.0	35.9	23S	52E
0373	032	1657 Dec 20	18:57:59	38	-4231	129	P	t-	-0.8662	1.3026	0.2353	302.0	112.0	–	23N	75E
0374	032	1658 May 17	03:01:52	37	-4226	096	N	-a	-1.3511	0.3514	-0.5940	153.5	–	–	21S	47W
0375	032	1658 Jun 15	01:07:59	37	-4225	134	N	a-	1.1594	0.7073	-0.2463	213.2	–	–	22S	152W
0376	032	1658 Nov 10	01:09:23	36	-4220	101	N	-t	1.4610	0.2268	-0.8712	146.3	–	–	18N	21W
0377	032	1658 Dec 09	20:10:46	36	-4219	139	N	t-	-1.5785	0.0140	-1.0897	37.2	–	–	22N	56E
0378	032	1659 May 06	19:56:12	36	-4214	106	P	-a	-0.6484	1.6470	0.6890	292.9	165.3	–	17S	60E
0379	032	1659 Oct 30	02:52:51	35	-4208	111	P	-t	0.7310	1.5455	0.4885	318.5	155.1	–	14N	47W
0380	032	1660 Apr 25	09:22:00	35	-4202	116	T+	pp	0.0901	2.6965	1.6889	342.6	221.5	100.5	13S	141W
0381	032	1660 Oct 18	11:50:07	34	-4196	121	T-	pp	-0.0151	2.8288	1.8315	334.3	217.5	100.5	10N	179E
0382	032	1661 Apr 14	15:46:18	33	-4190	126	P	t-	0.8709	1.2919	0.2286	306.3	112.5	–	9S	124E
0383	032	1661 Oct 08	02:39:02	33	-4184	131	P	a-	-0.7089	1.5369	0.5771	283.8	152.4	–	5N	43W
0384	032	1662 Mar 04	23:10:07	32	-4179	098	N	-t	-1.3487	0.4255	-0.6580	194.4	–	–	5N	15E
0385	033	1662 Aug 29	09:57:00	32	-4173	103	N	-a	1.1951	0.6547	-0.3246	211.2	–	–	8S	149W
0386	033	1662 Sep 27	18:59:21	31	-4172	141	N	a-	-1.4053	0.2625	-0.7036	135.6	–	–	1N	73E
0387	033	1663 Feb 22	03:23:34	31	-4167	108	P	-h	-0.5950	1.7845	0.7481	323.9	180.2	–	10N	47W
0388	033	1663 Aug 18	20:20:08	30	-4161	113	P	-h	0.4840	1.9858	0.9543	337.7	199.4	–	13S	56E
0389	033	1664 Feb 11	14:43:15	30	-4155	118	T+	p-	0.1304	2.6116	1.6258	326.2	212.4	95.4	14N	143E
0390	033	1664 Aug 06	23:40:03	29	-4149	123	T	pp	-0.2780	2.3829	1.3135	367.7	226.1	83.5	17S	6E
0391	033	1665 Jan 31	06:10:20	29	-4143	128	P	a-	0.7964	1.3807	0.4124	274.0	131.8	–	18N	89W
0392	033	1665 Jul 27	00:11:35	28	-4137	133	Nx	t-	-1.0261	1.0063	-0.0554	281.1	–	–	20S	1W
0393	033	1665 Dec 22	08:25:41	28	-4132	100	N	-a	-1.2796	0.5231	-0.5027	197.4	–	–	22N	126W
0394	033	1666 Jan 20	21:09:12	28	-4131	138	N	a-	1.4887	0.1246	-0.8717	96.6	–	–	21N	46E
0395	033	1666 Jun 16	19:20:40	27	-4126	105	P	-h	0.9222	1.1585	0.1732	270.6	92.6	–	23S	70E
0396	033	1666 Dec 11	14:35:35	26	-4120	110	P	-h	-0.6344	1.7351	0.6536	337.2	177.3	–	23N	140E
0397	034	1667 Jun 06	10:18:29	26	-4114	115	T+	pp	0.1438	2.5671	1.6206	317.9	210.4	95.2	23S	155W
0398	034	1667 Nov 30	14:31:25	25	-4108	120	T+	pp	0.0456	2.8269	1.7227	379.1	235.1	104.5	22N	140E
0399	034	1668 May 26	03:28:46	25	-4102	125	P	a-	-0.5909	1.7477	0.7993	295.3	173.9	–	22S	53W
0400	034	1668 Nov 18	14:52:17	24	-4096	130	P	h-	0.7274	1.5606	0.4865	324.7	156.6	–	20N	133E
0401	034	1669 Apr 16	07:15:33	24	-4091	097	N	-h	1.3108	0.4661	-0.5602	191.6	–	–	9S	108W
0402	034	1669 May 15	18:11:55	24	-4090	135	N	h-	-1.3734	0.3333	-0.6574	158.2	–	–	20S	86E
0403	034	1669 Oct 09	10:35:59	23	-4085	102	N	-a	-1.3293	0.4094	-0.5717	169.6	–	–	5N	161W
0404	034	1669 Nov 07	21:54:05	23	-4084	140	N	a-	1.3761	0.3406	-0.6744	160.9	–	–	18N	27E
0405	034	1670 Apr 05	11:31:32	23	-4079	107	P	-t	0.6128	1.7721	0.6956	343.5	184.2	–	6S	172W
0406	034	1670 Sep 29	02:24:54	22	-4073	112	P	-a	-0.6114	1.7136	0.7584	292.3	169.4	–	2N	38W
0407	034	1671 Mar 25	11:23:34	22	-4067	117	T-	pp	-0.1096	2.6992	1.6154	374.1	233.4	102.3	2S	169W
0408	034	1671 Sep 18	18:25:15	21	-4061	122	T+	pp	0.0951	2.6705	1.6963	326.5	214.2	98.1	2S	82E
0409	035	1672 Mar 13	14:20:47	21	-4055	127	P	a-	-0.8211	1.3738	0.3293	303.1	129.5	–	2N	147E
0410	035	1672 Sep 07	06:03:26	20	-4049	132	P	t-	0.8682	1.2770	0.2531	291.1	113.8	–	5S	92W
0411	035	1673 Feb 01	13:38:12	20	-4044	099	N	-a	1.2108	0.6249	-0.3524	202.1	–	–	18N	160E
0412	035	1673 Mar 03	00:23:59	20	-4043	137	N	a-	-1.4715	0.1538	-0.8379	107.3	–	–	5N	4W
0413	035	1673 Jul 28	19:20:13	20	-4038	104	N	-t	-1.1971	0.6976	-0.3739	244.3	–	–	20S	72E
0414	035	1674 Jan 22	05:23:56	19	-4032	109	P	-a	0.5433	1.8473	0.8746	300.5	178.7	–	20N	78W
0415	035	1674 Jul 17	20:30:09	19	-4026	114	T	-t	-0.4280	2.0980	1.0478	351.7	210.0	35.3	21S	54E
0416	035	1675 Jan 11	19:21:43	18	-4020	119	T-	pp	-0.1334	2.6192	1.6073	335.8	216.0	96.0	22N	72E
0417	035	1675 Jul 07	03:36:10	18	-4014	124	T	a-	0.3583	2.1991	1.2020	332.4	207.9	66.2	22S	53W
0418	035	1676 Jan 01	03:16:17	17	-4008	129	P	t-	-0.8635	1.3091	0.2389	303.5	113.1	–	22N	48W
0419	035	1676 May 27	10:37:27	17	-4003	096	N	-a	-1.4146	0.2337	-0.7095	126.4	–	–	23S	160W
0420	035	1676 Jun 25	17:32:05	17	-4002	134	N	a-	1.0850	0.8426	-0.1086	228.9	–	–	22S	97E

59

Cat Num	Canon Plate	Calendar Date	TD of Greatest Eclipse	ΔT s	Luna Num	Saros Num	Ecl Type	QSE	Gamma	Pen Mag	Um Mag	Pen m	Par m	Total m	Lat	Long
0421	036	1676 Nov 20	08:58:23	17	-3997	101	N	-t	1.4778	0.1967	-0.9027	136.6	–	–	21N	138W
0422	036	1676 Dec 20	04:11:42	17	-3996	139	N	t-	-1.5711	0.0284	-1.0768	52.9	–	–	22N	63W
0423	036	1677 May 17	03:32:57	16	-3991	106	P	-a	-0.7127	1.5290	0.5711	286.9	153.7	–	20S	54W
0424	036	1677 Nov 09	10:52:39	16	-3985	111	P	-t	0.7504	1.5097	0.4530	315.3	149.8	–	18N	167W
0425	036	1678 May 06	16:44:20	15	-3979	116	T+	pp	0.0285	2.8099	1.8015	344.4	223.0	102.5	17S	108E
0426	036	1678 Oct 29	20:06:20	15	-3973	121	T+	pp	0.0093	2.8395	1.8422	333.3	216.9	100.2	14N	54E
0427	036	1679 Apr 25	22:48:28	15	-3967	126	P	t-	0.8116	1.4005	0.3378	315.7	134.9	–	13S	18E
0428	036	1679 Oct 19	10:58:53	14	-3961	131	P	a-	-0.6784	1.5939	0.6321	287.0	158.0	–	9N	168W
0429	036	1680 Mar 15	06:41:50	14	-3956	098	N	-t	-1.3805	0.3646	-0.7138	180.4	–	–	1N	99W
0430	036	1680 Apr 13	23:18:01	14	-3955	136	Nb	t-	1.5495	0.0561	-1.0254	73.6	–	–	8S	11E
0431	036	1680 Sep 08	17:35:17	14	-3950	103	N	-a	1.2521	0.5528	-0.4319	196.9	–	–	4S	95E
0432	036	1680 Oct 08	03:06:26	14	-3949	141	N	a-	-1.3720	0.3258	-0.6449	150.6	–	–	5N	49W
0433	037	1681 Mar 04	11:26:32	13	-3944	108	P	-h	-0.6173	1.7406	0.7102	320.2	176.2	–	6N	169W
0434	037	1681 Aug 29	03:25:57	13	-3938	113	P	-h	0.5511	1.8655	0.8282	334.1	190.6	–	9S	51W
0435	037	1682 Feb 21	23:13:11	13	-3932	118	T+	p-	0.1133	2.6408	1.6594	325.4	212.5	96.4	10N	15E
0436	037	1682 Aug 18	06:17:11	12	-3926	123	T-	pp	-0.2006	2.5267	1.4538	371.3	230.8	95.0	13S	93W
0437	037	1683 Feb 11	14:52:34	12	-3920	128	P	a-	0.7848	1.4011	0.4345	275.3	134.9	–	15N	141E
0438	037	1683 Aug 07	06:48:53	12	-3914	133	P	t-	-0.9453	1.1546	0.0931	295.8	73.7	–	17S	101W
0439	037	1684 Jan 02	17:00:33	12	-3909	100	N	-a	-1.2865	0.5119	-0.5168	196.2	–	–	22N	106E
0440	037	1684 Feb 01	05:47:51	11	-3908	138	N	a-	1.4850	0.1319	-0.8653	99.6	–	–	19N	83W
0441	037	1684 Jun 27	02:30:11	11	-3903	105	P	-h	0.9949	1.0233	0.0417	257.0	46.1	–	22S	37W
0442	037	1684 Dec 21	22:47:24	11	-3897	110	P	-h	-0.6415	1.7235	0.6390	337.5	176.1	–	23N	18E
0443	037	1685 Jun 16	17:45:42	11	-3891	115	T+	-p	0.2172	2.4315	1.4870	315.6	207.5	89.0	23S	94E
0444	037	1685 Dec 10	22:29:22	10	-3885	120	T+	pp	0.0346	2.8475	1.7422	379.2	235.1	104.7	23N	21E
0445	038	1686 Jun 06	10:58:28	10	-3879	125	P	a-	-0.5211	1.8759	0.9272	301.4	183.5	–	23S	165W
0446	038	1686 Nov 29	22:59:47	10	-3873	130	P	h-	0.7135	1.5859	0.5125	325.5	159.7	–	22N	12E
0447	038	1687 Apr 27	14:36:01	10	-3868	097	N	-h	1.3727	0.3529	-0.6739	169.1	–	–	13S	141E
0448	038	1687 May 27	01:28:11	10	-3867	135	N	h-	-1.3096	0.4512	-0.5410	182.7	–	–	23S	23W
0449	038	1687 Oct 20	18:50:04	10	-3862	102	N	-a	-1.3555	0.3617	-0.6199	159.7	–	–	9N	74E
0450	038	1687 Nov 19	06:18:47	10	-3861	140	N	a-	1.3576	0.3742	-0.6401	167.6	–	–	21N	99W
0451	038	1688 Apr 15	18:37:20	9	-3856	107	P	-t	0.6704	1.6657	0.5909	337.8	173.0	–	10S	81E
0452	038	1688 Oct 09	10:37:18	9	-3850	112	P	-a	-0.6485	1.6469	0.6888	289.1	163.2	–	6N	162W
0453	038	1689 Apr 04	18:36:37	9	-3844	117	T-	pp	-0.0599	2.7880	1.7088	373.7	234.2	104.7	6S	82E
0454	038	1689 Sep 29	02:21:14	9	-3838	122	T+	pp	0.0510	2.7541	1.7746	328.3	215.2	99.5	3N	38W
0455	038	1690 Mar 24	22:03:02	9	-3832	127	P	a-	-0.7809	1.4443	0.4062	306.8	141.8	–	3S	30E
0456	038	1690 Sep 18	13:28:35	9	-3826	132	P	t-	0.8170	1.3742	0.3440	300.1	131.2	–	1S	156E
0457	039	1691 Feb 12	22:16:34	8	-3821	099	N	-a	1.2219	0.6028	-0.3711	198.5	–	–	15N	30E
0458	039	1691 Mar 14	08:36:41	8	-3820	137	N	a-	-1.4403	0.2084	-0.7779	123.9	–	–	1N	127W
0459	039	1691 Aug 09	01:52:20	8	-3815	104	N	-t	-1.2766	0.5527	-0.5209	220.7	–	–	17S	26W
0460	039	1692 Feb 02	14:08:39	8	-3809	109	P	-a	0.5536	1.8282	0.8560	299.9	177.5	–	17N	152E
0461	039	1692 Jul 28	03:10:54	8	-3803	114	P	-t	-0.5080	1.9505	0.9017	344.8	199.6	–	19S	46W
0462	039	1693 Jan 22	03:58:34	8	-3797	119	T-	pp	-0.1279	2.6302	1.6166	337.0	216.7	96.6	19N	57W
0463	039	1693 Jul 17	10:41:01	8	-3791	124	T	p-	0.2794	2.3425	1.3482	334.6	213.0	82.4	21S	159W
0464	039	1694 Jan 11	11:33:04	8	-3785	129	P	t-	-0.8599	1.3167	0.2444	305.1	114.6	–	21N	171W
0465	039	1694 Jun 07	18:08:12	8	-3780	096	N	-a	-1.4824	0.1085	-0.8330	87.0	–	–	24S	88E
0466	039	1694 Jul 07	00:55:24	8	-3779	134	P	a-	1.0090	0.9813	0.0317	242.9	39.0	–	22S	13W
0467	039	1694 Dec 01	16:54:28	8	-3774	101	N	-t	1.4890	0.1766	-0.9237	129.5	–	–	23N	104E
0468	039	1694 Dec 31	12:13:57	8	-3773	139	N	t-	-1.5646	0.0405	-1.0653	63.1	–	–	22N	177E
0469	040	1695 May 28	11:01:57	8	-3768	106	P	-a	-0.7831	1.4003	0.4417	279.4	138.2	–	22S	166W
0470	040	1695 Nov 20	19:02:05	8	-3762	111	P	-t	0.7629	1.4864	0.4303	312.7	146.1	–	21N	71E
0471	040	1696 May 16	23:58:19	8	-3756	116	T-	pp	-0.0392	2.7910	1.7813	345.7	223.6	102.7	20S	1W
0472	040	1696 Nov 09	04:30:20	8	-3750	121	T+	pp	0.0281	2.8050	1.8078	332.4	216.3	99.8	17N	71W
0473	040	1697 May 06	05:42:53	8	-3744	126	P	t-	0.7461	1.5203	0.4581	325.0	154.6	–	16S	87W
0474	040	1697 Oct 29	19:25:59	8	-3738	131	P	a-	-0.6537	1.6403	0.6764	289.4	162.2	–	13N	65E
0475	040	1698 Mar 26	14:06:35	8	-3733	098	N	-t	-1.4183	0.2925	-0.7805	162.1	–	–	4S	149E
0476	040	1698 Apr 25	06:11:32	8	-3732	136	N	t-	1.4877	0.1675	-0.9101	125.8	–	–	12S	93W
0477	040	1698 Sep 20	01:18:38	8	-3727	103	N	-a	1.3044	0.4599	-0.5307	181.9	–	–	0N	22W
0478	040	1698 Oct 19	11:20:31	8	-3726	141	N	a-	-1.3448	0.3783	-0.5973	162.0	–	–	9N	173W
0479	040	1699 Mar 15	19:23:52	8	-3721	108	P	-h	-0.6453	1.6862	0.6620	315.8	171.0	–	1N	71E
0480	040	1699 Sep 09	10:37:09	8	-3715	113	P	-h	0.6130	1.7550	0.7117	330.1	180.8	–	5S	160W

Cat Num	Canon Plate	Calendar Date	TD of Greatest Eclipse	ΔT s	Luna Num	Saros Num	Ecl Type	QSE	Gamma	Pen Mag	Um Mag	Pen m	Par m	Total m	Lat	Long
0481	041	1700 Mar 05	07:37:27	8	-3709	118	T+	p-	0.0909	2.6794	1.7026	324.6	212.7	97.5	6N	111W
0482	041	1700 Aug 29	13:01:24	8	-3703	123	T-	pp	-0.1291	2.6596	1.5833	373.9	233.7	101.7	9S	165E
0483	041	1701 Feb 22	23:29:56	8	-3697	128	P	a-	0.7695	1.4283	0.4634	277.1	138.8	-	11N	11E
0484	041	1701 Aug 18	13:32:17	8	-3691	133	P	t-	-0.8684	1.2956	0.2341	307.9	114.3	-	14S	158E
0485	041	1702 Jan 14	01:33:36	8	-3686	100	N	-a	-1.2943	0.4989	-0.5323	194.5	-	-	20N	21W
0486	041	1702 Feb 12	14:21:25	8	-3685	138	N	a-	1.4779	0.1451	-0.8527	104.6	-	-	15N	149E
0487	041	1702 Jul 09	09:41:33	8	-3680	105	N	-h	1.0665	0.8904	-0.0882	242.2	-	-	21S	144W
0488	041	1703 Jan 03	06:58:06	8	-3674	110	P	-h	-0.6493	1.7103	0.6236	337.7	174.7	-	22N	103W
0489	041	1703 Jun 29	01:12:46	8	-3668	115	T	-p	0.2910	2.2954	1.3522	312.5	203.5	79.5	23S	18W
0490	041	1703 Dec 23	06:29:53	8	-3662	120	T+	pp	0.0258	2.8639	1.7582	379.2	235.1	104.7	23N	98W
0491	041	1704 Jun 17	18:25:45	8	-3656	125	T	a-	-0.4495	2.0078	1.0583	307.0	191.7	35.7	24S	84E
0492	041	1704 Dec 11	07:11:29	9	-3650	130	P	a-	0.7023	1.6057	0.5336	325.8	162.0	-	24N	110W
0493	042	1705 May 08	21:47:47	9	-3645	097	N`	-h	1.4405	0.2290	-0.7987	138.2	-	-	16S	33E
0494	042	1705 Jun 07	08:39:02	9	-3644	135	N	h-	-1.2420	0.5763	-0.4180	204.8	-	-	24S	130W
0495	042	1705 Nov 01	03:12:45	9	-3639	102	N	-a	-1.3754	0.3254	-0.6567	151.7	-	-	13N	52W
0496	042	1705 Nov 30	14:50:03	9	-3638	140	N	a-	1.3440	0.3987	-0.6145	172.1	-	-	23N	134E
0497	042	1706 Apr 28	01:31:44	9	-3633	107	P	-t	0.7365	1.5436	0.4703	330.3	157.6	-	13S	23W
0498	042	1706 Oct 21	18:58:21	9	-3627	112	P	-a	-0.6785	1.5934	0.6324	286.5	157.8	-	10N	72E
0499	042	1707 Apr 17	01:39:36	9	-3621	117	T-	pp	-0.0018	2.8922	1.8178	372.8	234.5	105.7	10S	25W
0500	042	1707 Oct 11	10:24:59	9	-3615	122	T+	pp	0.0139	2.8248	1.8399	329.8	215.8	100.1	7N	159W
0501	042	1708 Apr 05	05:37:45	9	-3609	127	P	a-	-0.7338	1.5276	0.4959	311.0	154.0	-	7S	84W
0502	042	1708 Sep 29	21:01:04	9	-3603	132	P	t-	0.7725	1.4590	0.4224	307.6	144.2	-	3N	42E
0503	042	1709 Feb 24	06:50:39	9	-3598	099	N	-a	1.2369	0.5734	-0.3968	193.8	-	-	11N	99W
0504	042	1709 Mar 25	16:43:31	9	-3597	137	N	a-	-1.4038	0.2726	-0.7082	140.3	-	-	3S	110E
0505	043	1709 Aug 20	08:27:56	9	-3592	104	N	-t	-1.3530	0.4138	-0.6621	193.6	-	-	14S	126W
0506	043	1709 Sep 19	00:30:44	9	-3591	142	Nb	t-	1.5440	0.0643	-1.0135	78.3	-	-	0S	10W
0507	043	1710 Feb 13	22:50:15	9	-3586	109	P	-a	0.5663	1.8044	0.8330	299.2	176.0	-	14N	21E
0508	043	1710 Aug 09	09:55:48	9	-3580	114	P	-t	-0.5854	1.8080	0.7602	337.2	187.4	-	16S	147W
0509	043	1711 Feb 03	12:31:29	9	-3574	119	T-	pp	-0.1197	2.6457	1.6309	338.2	217.5	97.3	17N	176E
0510	043	1711 Jul 29	17:50:24	9	-3568	124	T+	p-	0.2033	2.4810	1.4889	335.8	216.5	92.2	19S	94E
0511	043	1712 Jan 23	19:47:09	9	-3562	129	P	t-	-0.8545	1.3274	0.2535	306.8	116.8	-	19N	66E
0512	043	1712 Jul 18	08:21:47	9	-3556	134	P	a-	0.9351	1.1162	0.1677	254.8	87.9	-	20S	124W
0513	043	1712 Dec 13	00:53:52	9	-3551	101	N	-t	1.4978	0.1604	-0.9401	123.5	-	-	25N	15W
0514	043	1713 Jan 11	20:14:53	9	-3550	139	N	t-	-1.5570	0.0545	-1.0512	73.1	-	-	20N	58E
0515	043	1713 Jun 08	18:28:14	9	-3545	106	P	-a	-0.8551	1.2686	0.3090	270.7	118.2	-	24S	83E
0516	043	1713 Dec 02	03:17:08	9	-3539	111	P	-h	0.7716	1.4699	0.4150	310.6	143.4	-	23N	52W
0517	044	1714 May 29	07:05:02	9	-3533	116	T-	pp	-0.1120	2.6582	1.6468	346.2	223.1	100.3	22S	107W
0518	044	1714 Nov 21	13:01:43	9	-3527	121	T+	pp	0.0414	2.7803	1.7836	331.5	215.7	99.4	20N	161E
0519	044	1715 May 18	12:28:52	9	-3521	126	P	t-	0.6740	1.6526	0.5905	334.2	172.2	-	19S	172E
0520	044	1715 Nov 11	04:00:14	9	-3515	131	P	a-	-0.6348	1.6760	0.7102	291.2	165.1	-	17N	64W
0521	044	1716 Apr 06	21:22:31	10	-3510	098	N	-t	-1.4634	0.2069	-0.8605	136.9	-	-	8S	40E
0522	044	1716 May 06	12:57:42	10	-3509	136	N	t-	1.4193	0.2912	-0.7828	163.8	-	-	15S	165E
0523	044	1716 Oct 01	09:10:09	10	-3504	103	N	-a	1.3494	0.3803	-0.6162	167.4	-	-	5N	141W
0524	044	1716 Oct 30	19:42:20	10	-3503	141	N	a-	-1.3239	0.4189	-0.5613	170.3	-	-	13N	61E
0525	044	1717 Mar 27	03:13:40	10	-3498	108	P	-h	-0.6800	1.6193	0.6014	310.5	164.2	-	3S	47W
0526	044	1717 Sep 20	17:54:24	10	-3492	113	P	-h	0.6690	1.6554	0.6060	326.1	170.2	-	0S	90E
0527	044	1718 Mar 16	15:54:35	10	-3486	118	T+	p-	0.0622	2.7297	1.7576	323.9	212.9	98.5	2N	124E
0528	044	1718 Sep 09	19:52:28	10	-3480	123	T-	pp	-0.0636	2.7818	1.7016	375.6	235.3	105.0	5S	61E
0529	045	1719 Mar 06	07:59:12	10	-3474	128	P	a-	0.7478	1.4671	0.5043	279.6	144.0	-	7N	117W
0530	045	1719 Aug 29	20:24:03	10	-3468	133	P	t-	-0.7975	1.4259	0.3640	317.6	139.5	-	10S	54E
0531	045	1720 Jan 25	10:04:08	10	-3463	100	N	-a	-1.3033	0.4833	-0.5498	192.4	-	-	18N	148W
0532	045	1720 Feb 23	22:48:33	10	-3462	138	N	a-	1.4667	0.1659	-0.8322	112.0	-	-	11N	22E
0533	045	1720 Jul 19	16:55:33	10	-3457	105	N	-a	1.1367	0.7604	-0.2158	226.0	-	-	20S	107E
0534	045	1720 Aug 18	02:31:48	10	-3456	143	N	a-	-1.4937	0.1214	-0.8866	99.3	-	-	15S	37W
0535	045	1721 Jan 13	15:08:18	10	-3451	110	P	-t	-0.6569	1.6973	0.6090	337.7	173.4	-	21N	135E
0536	045	1721 Jul 09	08:39:47	10	-3445	115	T	-p	0.3651	2.1591	1.2167	308.8	198.2	65.3	22S	129W
0537	045	1722 Jan 02	14:32:52	10	-3439	120	T+	pp	0.0187	2.8767	1.7714	379.0	235.1	104.8	23N	143E
0538	045	1722 Jun 29	01:49:15	10	-3433	125	T	p-	-0.3750	2.1452	1.1941	312.0	198.8	62.7	24S	27W
0539	045	1722 Dec 22	15:28:30	10	-3427	130	P	a-	0.6948	1.6186	0.5484	325.6	163.4	-	24N	128E
0540	045	1723 May 20	04:51:54	10	-3422	097	Ne	-t	1.5130	0.0964	-0.9324	91.1	-	-	19S	73W

Cat Num	Canon Plate	Calendar Date	TD of Greatest Eclipse	ΔT s	Luna Num	Saros Num	Ecl Type	QSE	Gamma	Pen Mag	Um Mag	Pen m	Par m	Total m	Lat	Long
0541	046	1723 Jun 18	15:45:34	10	-3421	135	N	t-	-1.1716	0.7067	-0.2902	224.8	–	–	25S	124E
0542	046	1723 Nov 12	11:42:34	10	-3416	102	N	-a	-1.3902	0.2983	-0.6840	145.3	–	–	16N	179W
0543	046	1723 Dec 11	23:25:50	10	-3415	140	N	a-	1.3334	0.4173	-0.5944	175.2	–	–	24N	7E
0544	046	1724 May 08	08:19:43	10	-3410	107	P	-t	0.8072	1.4132	0.3412	321.1	137.1	–	16S	126W
0545	046	1724 Nov 01	03:26:08	10	-3404	112	P	-a	-0.7028	1.5503	0.5864	284.4	153.1	–	14N	55W
0546	046	1725 Apr 27	08:37:09	10	-3398	117	T+	pp	0.0614	2.7804	1.7107	371.4	233.8	104.8	14S	130W
0547	046	1725 Oct 21	18:34:40	10	-3392	122	T-	pp	-0.0177	2.8206	1.8302	331.1	216.2	100.1	11N	78E
0548	046	1726 Apr 16	13:06:30	10	-3386	127	P	a-	-0.6806	1.6220	0.5966	315.3	165.7	–	11S	163E
0549	046	1726 Oct 11	04:40:32	10	-3380	132	P	t-	0.7342	1.5326	0.4897	314.0	154.1	–	8N	74W
0550	046	1727 Mar 07	15:16:36	10	-3375	099	N	-a	1.2592	0.5306	-0.4358	186.8	–	–	6N	134E
0551	046	1727 Apr 06	00:41:51	10	-3374	137	N	a-	-1.3596	0.3509	-0.6246	157.5	–	–	7S	10W
0552	046	1727 Aug 31	15:12:02	10	-3369	104	N	-t	-1.4223	0.2879	-0.7905	163.4	–	–	10S	133E
0553	047	1727 Sep 30	07:40:10	10	-3368	142	N	t-	1.4949	0.1567	-0.9258	121.6	–	–	4N	118W
0554	047	1728 Feb 25	07:24:24	10	-3363	109	P	-a	0.5855	1.7687	0.7984	297.9	173.6	–	10N	107W
0555	047	1728 Aug 19	16:48:39	10	-3357	114	P	-t	-0.6570	1.6763	0.6292	329.1	173.9	–	13S	109E
0556	047	1729 Feb 13	20:57:43	10	-3351	119	T-	pp	-0.1065	2.6705	1.6548	339.5	218.4	98.2	13N	49E
0557	047	1729 Aug 09	01:05:16	10	-3345	124	T+	pp	0.1306	2.6136	1.6232	336.2	218.4	98.0	16S	15W
0558	047	1730 Feb 03	03:55:44	10	-3339	129	P	t-	-0.8452	1.3449	0.2702	309.0	120.6	–	16N	56W
0559	047	1730 Jul 29	15:49:45	10	-3333	134	P	a-	0.8619	1.2503	0.3022	265.2	115.5	–	18S	124E
0560	047	1730 Dec 24	08:58:03	11	-3328	101	N	-t	1.5033	0.1501	-0.9498	119.4	–	–	25N	134W
0561	047	1731 Jan 23	04:14:11	11	-3327	139	N	t-	-1.5478	0.0710	-1.0338	83.3	–	–	18N	61W
0562	047	1731 Jun 20	01:49:42	11	-3322	106	P	-a	-0.9308	1.1306	0.1693	260.3	89.4	–	24S	27W
0563	047	1731 Dec 13	11:38:05	11	-3316	111	P	-h	0.7765	1.4601	0.4069	308.9	141.8	–	24N	176W
0564	047	1732 Jun 08	14:06:11	11	-3310	116	T-	-p	-0.1887	2.5185	1.5049	346.0	221.3	94.6	23S	148E
0565	048	1732 Dec 01	21:39:42	11	-3304	121	T+	pp	0.0502	2.7638	1.7678	330.5	215.1	99.0	22N	33E
0566	048	1733 May 28	19:08:09	11	-3298	126	P	t-	0.5967	1.7945	0.7324	342.9	187.6	–	21S	72E
0567	048	1733 Nov 21	12:40:54	11	-3292	131	P	a-	-0.6211	1.7020	0.7343	292.6	167.2	–	19N	166E
0568	048	1734 Apr 18	04:32:25	11	-3287	098	N	-t	-1.5137	0.1118	-0.9500	101.2	–	–	12S	69W
0569	048	1734 May 17	19:38:12	11	-3286	136	N	t-	1.3453	0.4252	-0.6453	195.1	–	–	18S	65E
0570	048	1734 Oct 12	17:08:03	11	-3281	103	N	-a	1.3884	0.3118	-0.6907	153.2	–	–	9N	99E
0571	048	1734 Nov 11	04:10:31	11	-3280	141	N	a-	-1.3089	0.4488	-0.5360	176.3	–	–	16N	66W
0572	048	1735 Apr 07	10:56:50	11	-3275	108	P	-h	-0.7210	1.5409	0.5293	304.3	155.3	–	7S	164W
0573	048	1735 Oct 02	01:19:12	11	-3269	113	P	-h	0.7178	1.5689	0.5134	322.2	159.5	–	4N	23W
0574	048	1736 Mar 27	00:05:53	11	-3263	118	T+	pp	0.0283	2.7897	1.8222	323.1	213.0	99.2	3S	0W
0575	048	1736 Sep 20	02:51:00	11	-3257	123	T-	pp	-0.0042	2.8925	1.8087	376.5	235.8	106.0	1S	44W
0576	048	1737 Mar 16	16:22:12	11	-3251	128	P	a-	0.7211	1.5151	0.5542	282.6	149.9	–	2N	117E
0577	049	1737 Sep 09	03:24:12	11	-3245	133	P	t-	-0.7326	1.5453	0.4829	325.4	157.4	–	6S	52W
0578	049	1738 Feb 04	18:29:00	11	-3240	100	N	-a	-1.3165	0.4598	-0.5746	188.7	–	–	15N	86E
0579	049	1738 Mar 06	07:07:16	11	-3239	138	N	a-	1.4493	0.1979	-0.8003	122.3	–	–	7N	103W
0580	049	1738 Jul 31	00:13:24	11	-3234	105	N	-a	1.2043	0.6353	-0.3391	208.5	–	–	17S	2W
0581	049	1738 Aug 29	09:51:17	11	-3233	143	N	a-	-1.4269	0.2433	-0.7636	138.6	–	–	11S	147W
0582	049	1739 Jan 24	23:14:13	11	-3228	110	P	-t	-0.6674	1.6783	0.5892	337.3	171.5	–	19N	15E
0583	049	1739 Jul 20	16:09:12	11	-3222	115	T	-a	0.4373	2.0265	1.0842	304.6	191.7	42.3	20S	119E
0584	049	1740 Jan 13	22:33:32	11	-3216	120	T+	pp	0.0096	2.8928	1.7887	378.7	235.0	104.9	21N	24E
0585	049	1740 Jul 09	09:13:15	11	-3210	125	T	p-	-0.3014	2.2813	1.3281	316.2	204.5	78.0	23S	137W
0586	049	1741 Jan 01	23:47:05	12	-3204	130	P	a-	0.6880	1.6297	0.5621	325.2	164.6	–	24N	4E
0587	049	1741 Jun 28	22:47:45	12	-3198	135	N	t-	-1.0982	0.8429	-0.1571	243.2	–	–	24S	19E
0588	049	1741 Nov 22	20:19:32	12	-3193	102	N	-a	-1.3999	0.2805	-0.7019	140.9	–	–	19N	52E
0589	050	1741 Dec 22	08:05:40	12	-3192	140	N	a-	1.3257	0.4305	-0.5792	177.2	–	–	25N	122W
0590	050	1742 May 19	14:58:37	12	-3187	107	P	-t	0.8846	1.2706	0.1998	309.7	107.3	–	19S	135E
0591	050	1742 Nov 12	12:01:43	12	-3181	112	P	-a	-0.7209	1.5184	0.5517	282.8	149.4	–	17N	176E
0592	050	1743 May 08	15:26:07	12	-3175	117	T+	pp	0.1323	2.6480	1.5830	369.1	231.9	101.1	17S	128E
0593	050	1743 Nov 02	02:52:31	12	-3169	122	T-	pp	-0.0421	2.7786	1.7829	332.4	216.4	99.7	15N	47W
0594	050	1744 Apr 26	20:29:07	12	-3163	127	P	a-	-0.6212	1.7278	0.7086	319.7	176.8	–	14S	52E
0595	050	1744 Oct 21	12:26:27	12	-3157	132	P	t-	0.7017	1.5953	0.5462	319.5	161.7	–	12N	169E
0596	050	1745 Mar 17	23:37:14	12	-3152	099	N	-a	1.2862	0.4790	-0.4835	178.0	–	–	2N	8E
0597	050	1745 Apr 16	08:34:52	12	-3151	137	N	a-	-1.3106	0.4383	-0.5320	174.0	–	–	11S	129W
0598	050	1745 Sep 10	22:02:30	12	-3146	104	N	-t	-1.4863	0.1718	-0.9093	127.6	–	–	6S	29E
0599	050	1745 Oct 10	14:56:54	12	-3145	142	N	t-	1.4515	0.2387	-0.8484	149.3	–	–	8N	132E
0600	050	1746 Mar 07	15:52:17	12	-3140	109	P	-a	0.6096	1.7239	0.7548	296.1	170.3	–	6N	125E

Cat Num	Canon Plate	Calendar Date	TD of Greatest Eclipse	ΔT s	Luna Num	Saros Num	Ecl Type	QSE	Gamma	Pen Mag	Um Mag	Phase Durations Pen m	Phase Durations Par m	Phase Durations Total m	Greatest in Zenith Lat	Greatest in Zenith Long
0601	051	1746 Aug 30	23:48:16	12	-3134	114	P	-t	-0.7237	1.5537	0.5070	320.6	158.7	-	9S	3E
0602	051	1747 Feb 25	05:17:42	12	-3128	119	T-	pp	-0.0887	2.7033	1.6871	340.8	219.4	99.3	9N	76W
0603	051	1747 Aug 20	08:26:59	12	-3122	124	T+	pp	0.0627	2.7375	1.7483	335.9	219.2	100.8	13S	126W
0604	051	1748 Feb 14	11:58:05	12	-3116	129	P	t-	-0.8312	1.3706	0.2956	311.8	126.0	-	12N	176W
0605	051	1748 Aug 08	23:23:27	13	-3110	134	P	a-	0.7930	1.3769	0.4287	273.9	134.9	-	15S	10E
0606	051	1749 Jan 03	17:03:07	13	-3105	101	N	-t	1.5086	0.1397	-0.9589	115.1	-	-	24N	106E
0607	051	1749 Feb 02	12:09:39	13	-3104	139	N	t-	-1.5352	0.0932	-1.0099	95.2	-	-	15N	179W
0608	051	1749 Jun 30	09:09:16	13	-3099	106	P	-a	-1.0074	0.9913	0.0277	248.3	37.0	-	24S	136W
0609	051	1749 Jul 29	16:30:59	13	-3098	144	Nb	a-	1.5084	0.0643	-0.8841	67.8	-	-	17S	113E
0610	051	1749 Dec 23	20:02:10	13	-3093	111	P	-h	0.7796	1.4532	0.4024	307.4	140.7	-	24N	60E
0611	051	1750 Jun 19	21:03:02	13	-3087	116	T-	-p	-0.2684	2.3736	1.3574	344.8	217.8	84.6	24S	45E
0612	051	1750 Dec 13	06:21:46	13	-3081	121	T+	pp	0.0561	2.7524	1.7576	329.6	214.6	98.7	23N	97W
0613	052	1751 Jun 09	01:41:58	13	-3075	126	P	t-	0.5151	1.9445	0.8819	350.8	200.9	-	22S	26W
0614	052	1751 Dec 02	21:26:52	13	-3069	131	P	a-	-0.6116	1.7201	0.7511	293.5	168.6	-	21N	36E
0615	052	1752 Apr 28	11:35:08	13	-3064	098	Ne	-t	-1.5699	0.0060	-1.0504	23.6	-	-	16S	175W
0616	052	1752 May 28	02:13:58	13	-3063	136	N	t-	1.2667	0.5677	-0.4996	221.9	-	-	20S	34W
0617	052	1752 Oct 23	01:12:54	13	-3058	103	N	-a	1.4212	0.2546	-0.7538	139.7	-	-	13N	22W
0618	052	1752 Nov 21	12:43:58	13	-3057	141	N	a-	-1.2984	0.4701	-0.5189	180.6	-	-	19N	166E
0619	052	1753 Apr 17	18:33:18	13	-3052	108	P	-h	-0.7684	1.4508	0.4455	297.1	143.9	-	11S	81E
0620	052	1753 Oct 12	08:51:29	13	-3046	113	P	-h	0.7598	1.4950	0.4334	318.6	148.8	-	8N	136W
0621	052	1754 Apr 07	08:08:01	13	-3040	118	T-	pp	-0.0140	2.8136	1.8507	322.1	212.9	99.4	7S	121W
0622	052	1754 Oct 01	09:58:28	13	-3034	123	T+	pp	0.0478	2.8144	1.7268	376.9	235.5	105.2	3N	152W
0623	052	1755 Mar 28	00:36:25	14	-3028	128	P	a-	0.6872	1.5764	0.6175	286.3	156.8	-	2S	7W
0624	052	1755 Sep 20	10:34:08	14	-3022	133	P	t-	-0.6746	1.6520	0.5890	331.4	170.5	-	2S	160W
0625	053	1756 Feb 16	02:47:51	14	-3017	100	N	-a	-1.3339	0.4282	-0.6071	183.2	-	-	11N	39W
0626	053	1756 Mar 16	15:17:48	14	-3016	138	N	a-	1.4259	0.2407	-0.7575	134.7	-	-	3N	133E
0627	053	1756 Aug 10	07:36:46	14	-3011	105	N	-a	1.2682	0.5174	-0.4557	189.7	-	-	14S	113W
0628	053	1756 Sep 08	17:19:29	14	-3010	143	N	a-	-1.3659	0.3549	-0.6513	165.1	-	-	7S	100E
0629	053	1757 Feb 04	07:16:53	14	-3005	110	P	-t	-0.6801	1.6551	0.5659	336.6	169.0	-	16N	106W
0630	053	1757 Jul 30	23:39:48	14	-2999	115	P	-a	0.5087	1.8957	0.9529	299.7	183.9	-	18S	6E
0631	053	1758 Jan 24	06:34:14	14	-2993	120	T+	pp	0.0004	2.9089	1.8067	378.2	234.9	104.9	19N	95W
0632	053	1758 Jul 20	16:36:43	14	-2987	125	T-	p-	-0.2280	2.4175	1.4615	319.9	209.0	88.3	21S	112E
0633	053	1759 Jan 13	08:06:35	14	-2981	130	P	a-	0.6812	1.6404	0.5762	324.8	165.9	-	22N	119W
0634	053	1759 Jul 10	05:48:57	14	-2975	135	N	t-	-1.0247	0.9797	-0.0240	259.6	-	-	23S	86W
0635	053	1759 Dec 04	05:01:58	14	-2970	102	N	-a	-1.4059	0.2694	-0.7128	137.9	-	-	21N	77W
0636	053	1760 Jan 02	16:47:25	14	-2969	140	N	a-	1.3192	0.4411	-0.5661	178.6	-	-	24N	109E
0637	054	1760 May 29	21:33:40	14	-2964	107	P	-t	0.9647	1.1232	0.0532	296.1	56.6	-	21S	36E
0638	054	1760 Nov 22	20:41:36	14	-2958	112	P	-a	-0.7356	1.4928	0.5236	281.6	146.2	-	20N	47E
0639	054	1761 May 18	22:11:58	15	-2952	117	T+	pp	0.2063	2.5100	1.4493	366.0	228.5	94.1	20S	26E
0640	054	1761 Nov 12	11:15:47	15	-2946	122	T-	-p	-0.0614	2.7457	1.7450	333.6	216.6	99.3	18N	173W
0641	054	1762 May 08	03:45:36	15	-2940	127	P	a-	-0.5558	1.8449	0.8317	323.9	186.9	-	18S	58W
0642	054	1762 Nov 01	20:19:49	15	-2934	132	P	t-	0.6759	1.6455	0.5905	323.9	167.4	-	15N	51E
0643	054	1763 Mar 29	07:49:15	15	-2929	099	N	-a	1.3205	0.4142	-0.5445	166.3	-	-	2S	115W
0644	054	1763 Apr 27	16:20:36	15	-2928	137	N	a-	-1.2552	0.5375	-0.4280	190.2	-	-	15S	114E
0645	054	1763 Sep 22	05:03:02	15	-2923	104	N	-t	-1.5421	0.0708	-1.0129	82.7	-	-	2S	77W
0646	054	1763 Oct 21	22:22:43	15	-2922	142	N	t-	1.4153	0.3072	-0.7841	168.7	-	-	12N	20E
0647	054	1764 Mar 18	00:11:05	15	-2917	109	P	-a	0.6410	1.6656	0.6977	293.6	165.5	-	1N	0W
0648	054	1764 Sep 10	06:58:28	15	-2911	114	P	-t	-0.7824	1.4459	0.3993	312.3	142.8	-	5S	105W
0649	055	1765 Mar 07	13:28:56	15	-2905	119	T-	pp	-0.0643	2.7483	1.7317	342.1	220.5	100.5	5N	161E
0650	055	1765 Aug 30	15:55:31	15	-2899	124	T-	pp	-0.0004	2.8513	1.8629	335.0	218.9	101.4	9S	121E
0651	055	1766 Feb 24	19:52:50	15	-2893	129	P	t-	-0.8116	1.4065	0.3317	315.3	133.0	-	9N	65E
0652	055	1766 Aug 20	07:01:42	15	-2887	134	P	a-	0.7273	1.4978	0.5489	281.4	149.7	-	12S	105W
0653	055	1767 Jan 15	01:08:12	15	-2882	101	N	-t	1.5141	0.1284	-0.9679	110.3	-	-	23N	14W
0654	055	1767 Feb 13	19:59:00	15	-2881	139	N	t-	-1.5175	0.1245	-0.9762	109.7	-	-	12N	63E
0655	055	1767 Jul 11	16:27:13	15	-2876	106	N	-a	-1.0846	0.8512	-0.1155	234.3	-	-	23S	115E
0656	055	1767 Aug 10	00:02:52	15	-2875	144	N	a-	1.4447	0.1827	-0.7689	113.3	-	-	14S	0E
0657	055	1768 Jan 04	04:29:31	15	-2870	111	P	-h	0.7811	1.4491	0.4011	306.0	140.1	-	24N	66W
0658	055	1768 Jun 30	03:56:19	16	-2864	116	T	-h	-0.3500	2.2256	1.2062	342.7	212.5	68.0	24S	58W
0659	055	1768 Dec 23	15:07:13	16	-2858	121	T+	pp	0.0597	2.7449	1.7518	328.7	214.1	98.4	24N	133E
0660	055	1769 Jun 19	08:11:39	16	-2852	126	T	t-	0.4302	2.1005	1.0372	357.8	212.0	31.5	23S	123W

Cat Num	Canon Plate	Calendar Date	TD of Greatest Eclipse	ΔT s	Luna Num	Saros Num	Ecl Type	QSE	Gamma	Pen Mag	Um Mag	Phase ---- Durations ---- Pen m	Par m	Total m	Greatest in Zenith Lat	Long
0661	056	1769 Dec 13	06:17:03	16	-2846	131	P	a-	-0.6059	1.7312	0.7611	294.1	169.4	-	23N	96W
0662	056	1770 Jun 08	08:45:13	16	-2840	136	N	t-	1.1836	0.7186	-0.3457	245.5	-	-	22S	132W
0663	056	1770 Nov 03	09:24:28	16	-2835	103	N	-a	1.4478	0.2086	-0.8056	127.6	-	-	17N	145W
0664	056	1770 Dec 02	21:22:32	16	-2834	141	N	a-	-1.2927	0.4825	-0.5104	183.3	-	-	21N	37E
0665	056	1771 Apr 29	02:04:09	16	-2829	108	P	-h	-0.8212	1.3509	0.3516	288.6	129.3	-	15S	32W
0666	056	1771 Oct 23	16:30:23	16	-2823	113	P	-h	0.7955	1.4323	0.3649	315.4	138.3	-	12N	108E
0667	056	1772 Apr 17	16:04:45	16	-2817	118	T-	pp	-0.0611	2.7249	1.7663	321.0	212.3	98.6	11S	119E
0668	056	1772 Oct 11	17:14:40	16	-2811	123	T+	pp	0.0928	2.7337	1.6426	377.0	234.7	103.3	8N	98E
0669	056	1773 Apr 07	08:43:30	16	-2805	128	P	a-	0.6477	1.6479	0.6908	290.3	164.1	-	6S	130W
0670	056	1773 Sep 30	17:53:06	16	-2799	133	P	t-	-0.6232	1.7466	0.6829	336.1	180.3	-	3N	89E
0671	056	1774 Feb 26	10:58:52	16	-2794	100	N	-a	-1.3568	0.3865	-0.6493	175.3	-	-	7N	162W
0672	056	1774 Mar 27	23:19:03	16	-2793	138	N	a-	1.3960	0.2955	-0.7026	148.9	-	-	2S	12E
0673	057	1774 Aug 21	15:06:38	16	-2788	105	N	-a	1.3272	0.4090	-0.5634	169.9	-	-	11S	134E
0674	057	1774 Sep 20	00:57:05	16	-2787	143	N	a-	-1.3119	0.4539	-0.5520	184.3	-	-	2S	15W
0675	057	1775 Feb 15	15:10:58	16	-2782	110	P	-t	-0.6990	1.6202	0.5314	334.9	165.0	-	12N	136E
0676	057	1775 Aug 11	07:15:46	16	-2776	115	P	-a	0.5755	1.7738	0.8298	294.5	175.3	-	15S	108W
0677	057	1776 Feb 04	14:29:50	16	-2770	120	T-	pp	-0.0128	2.8846	1.7851	377.5	234.7	104.9	16N	146E
0678	057	1776 Jul 31	00:02:02	16	-2764	125	T-	pp	-0.1566	2.5500	1.5907	322.8	212.2	94.9	18S	1E
0679	057	1777 Jan 23	16:24:08	16	-2758	130	P	a-	0.6724	1.6547	0.5944	324.4	167.5	-	20N	117E
0680	057	1777 Jul 20	12:48:46	17	-2752	135	P	t-	-0.9509	1.1173	0.1093	274.4	75.8	-	21S	169E
0681	057	1777 Dec 14	13:48:59	17	-2747	102	N	-a	-1.4088	0.2638	-0.7178	136.3	-	-	22N	152E
0682	057	1778 Jan 13	01:29:24	17	-2746	140	N	a-	1.3125	0.4519	-0.5522	180.0	-	-	23N	20W
0683	057	1778 Jun 10	04:01:09	17	-2741	107	N	-t	1.0502	0.9661	-0.1033	279.4	-	-	22S	60W
0684	057	1778 Dec 04	05:27:52	17	-2735	112	P	-a	-0.7448	1.4769	0.5055	281.0	144.2	-	22N	84W
0685	058	1779 May 30	04:52:10	17	-2729	117	T	pp	0.2853	2.3630	1.3065	361.8	223.5	82.1	22S	74W
0686	058	1779 Nov 23	19:44:46	17	-2723	122	T-	-p	-0.0752	2.7227	1.7172	334.9	216.8	98.9	20N	61E
0687	058	1780 May 18	10:58:17	17	-2717	127	P	a-	-0.4863	1.9696	0.9620	327.6	195.8	-	20S	166W
0688	058	1780 Nov 12	04:19:51	17	-2711	132	P	t-	0.6566	1.6839	0.6232	327.5	171.5	-	18N	69W
0689	058	1781 Apr 08	15:55:08	17	-2706	099	N	-a	1.3602	0.3396	-0.6154	151.4	-	-	6S	122E
0690	058	1781 May 08	00:01:07	17	-2705	137	N	a-	-1.1949	0.6458	-0.3151	205.6	-	-	18S	2W
0691	058	1781 Nov 01	05:56:09	17	-2699	142	N	t-	1.3851	0.3647	-0.7307	183.1	-	-	16N	94W
0692	058	1782 Mar 29	08:23:07	17	-2694	109	P	-a	0.6779	1.5974	0.6307	290.4	159.4	-	3S	124W
0693	058	1782 Sep 21	14:17:33	17	-2688	114	P	-a	-0.8348	1.3498	0.3032	304.2	125.9	-	1S	144E
0694	058	1783 Mar 18	21:31:30	17	-2682	119	T-	pp	-0.0333	2.8053	1.7886	343.4	221.5	101.5	1N	39E
0695	058	1783 Sep 10	23:33:06	17	-2676	124	T-	pp	-0.0569	2.7474	1.7595	333.7	217.9	100.4	5S	6E
0696	058	1784 Mar 07	03:39:42	17	-2670	129	P	t-	-0.7859	1.4535	0.3792	319.5	141.5	-	4N	52W
0697	059	1784 Aug 30	14:45:57	17	-2664	134	P	a-	0.6662	1.6104	0.6602	287.5	161.1	-	8S	138E
0698	059	1785 Jan 25	09:10:58	17	-2659	101	N	-t	1.5218	0.1128	-0.9807	103.3	-	-	20N	134W
0699	059	1785 Feb 24	03:42:20	17	-2658	139	N	t-	-1.4947	0.1648	-0.9330	125.6	-	-	8N	53W
0700	059	1785 Jul 21	23:45:47	17	-2653	106	N	-a	-1.1606	0.7134	-0.2567	218.3	-	-	21S	5E
0701	059	1785 Aug 20	07:38:37	17	-2652	144	N	a-	1.3843	0.2954	-0.6597	142.9	-	-	11S	114W
0702	059	1786 Jan 14	12:55:56	17	-2647	111	P	-h	0.7838	1.4421	0.3978	304.3	139.2	-	22N	169E
0703	059	1786 Jul 11	10:47:19	17	-2641	116	T	-t	-0.4324	2.0762	1.0531	339.4	205.2	36.3	22S	160W
0704	059	1787 Jan 03	23:53:37	16	-2635	121	T+	pp	0.0632	2.7375	1.7465	327.8	213.7	98.2	23N	3E
0705	059	1787 Jun 30	14:39:31	16	-2629	126	T	t-	0.3441	2.2592	1.1947	363.6	220.8	68.6	23S	141E
0706	059	1787 Dec 24	15:08:29	16	-2623	131	P	a-	-0.6011	1.7404	0.7696	294.6	170.1	-	23N	133E
0707	059	1788 Jun 18	15:15:24	16	-2617	136	N	t-	1.0986	0.8734	-0.1883	265.9	-	-	22S	131E
0708	059	1788 Nov 13	17:42:35	16	-2612	103	N	-a	1.4690	0.1726	-0.8471	116.9	-	-	20N	90E
0709	060	1788 Dec 13	06:04:27	16	-2611	141	N	a-	-1.2899	0.4894	-0.5069	185.0	-	-	22N	92W
0710	060	1789 May 09	09:28:39	16	-2606	108	P	-h	-0.8800	1.2401	0.2465	278.8	109.6	-	18S	143W
0711	060	1789 Nov 03	00:17:05	16	-2600	113	P	-h	0.8243	1.3824	0.3094	312.8	128.7	-	16N	8W
0712	060	1790 Apr 28	23:53:38	16	-2594	118	T-	pp	-0.1156	2.6230	1.6685	319.5	211.1	96.6	15S	1E
0713	060	1790 Oct 23	00:40:41	16	-2588	123	T+	pp	0.1296	2.6678	1.5734	376.8	233.6	100.9	12N	14W
0714	060	1791 Apr 18	16:41:28	16	-2582	128	P	a-	0.6008	1.7331	0.7776	294.8	171.8	-	10S	110E
0715	060	1791 Oct 12	01:23:20	16	-2576	133	P	t-	-0.5802	1.8258	0.7614	339.5	187.4	-	7N	24W
0716	060	1792 Mar 08	19:02:21	16	-2571	100	N	-a	-1.3849	0.3352	-0.7010	164.6	-	-	3N	77E
0717	060	1792 Apr 07	07:12:02	16	-2570	138	N	a-	1.3603	0.3612	-0.6370	164.2	-	-	6S	107W
0718	060	1792 Aug 31	22:42:41	16	-2565	105	N	-a	1.3817	0.3087	-0.6633	148.6	-	-	7S	19E
0719	060	1792 Sep 30	08:43:06	16	-2564	143	N	a-	-1.2636	0.5423	-0.4634	199.1	-	-	2N	133W
0720	060	1793 Feb 25	22:59:33	16	-2559	110	P	-t	-0.7219	1.5777	0.4899	332.6	159.7	-	8N	18E

Cat Num	Canon Plate	Calendar Date	TD of Greatest Eclipse	ΔT s	Luna Num	Saros Num	Ecl Type	QSE	Gamma	Pen Mag	Um Mag	Phase ---- Durations ----			Greatest in Zenith	
												Pen m	Par m	Total m	Lat	Long
0721	061	1793 Aug 21	14:55:22	15	-2553	115	P	-a	0.6392	1.6576	0.7120	288.9	165.5	–	11S	137E
0722	061	1794 Feb 14	22:21:16	15	-2547	120	T-	pp	-0.0300	2.8514	1.7553	376.6	234.5	104.8	13N	28E
0723	061	1794 Aug 11	07:29:21	15	-2541	125	T-	pp	-0.0874	2.6790	1.7157	325.1	214.3	98.8	15S	111W
0724	061	1795 Feb 04	00:39:45	15	-2535	130	P	a-	0.6610	1.6732	0.6175	324.2	169.7	–	17N	6W
0725	061	1795 Jul 31	19:50:34	15	-2529	135	P	t-	-0.8791	1.2513	0.2386	287.4	110.4	–	19S	64E
0726	061	1795 Dec 25	22:37:34	15	-2524	102	N	-a	-1.4110	0.2592	-0.7214	134.9	–	–	22N	21E
0727	061	1796 Jan 24	10:09:21	15	-2523	140	N	a-	1.3036	0.4664	-0.5341	182.1	–	–	20N	149W
0728	061	1796 Jun 20	10:28:08	15	-2518	107	N	-t	1.1355	0.8095	-0.2597	260.0	–	–	22S	157W
0729	061	1796 Dec 14	14:16:42	15	-2512	112	P	-a	-0.7519	1.4649	0.4915	280.6	142.6	–	23N	145E
0730	061	1797 Jun 09	11:30:23	14	-2506	117	T	-t	0.3666	2.2120	1.1593	356.5	216.5	62.2	23S	173W
0731	061	1797 Dec 04	04:17:57	14	-2500	122	T-	-p	-0.0850	2.7070	1.6971	336.1	217.1	98.6	22N	67W
0732	061	1798 May 29	18:07:26	14	-2494	127	T	a-	-0.4130	2.1014	1.0990	330.8	203.4	48.0	22S	87E
0733	062	1798 Nov 23	12:25:23	14	-2488	132	P	t-	0.6422	1.7128	0.6472	330.5	174.5	–	21N	170E
0734	062	1799 Apr 19	23:52:15	14	-2483	099	N	-a	1.4072	0.2515	-0.7001	131.2	–	–	10S	2E
0735	062	1799 May 19	07:35:59	14	-2482	137	N	a-	-1.1294	0.7639	-0.1929	220.4	–	–	21S	115W
0736	062	1799 Nov 12	13:38:18	13	-2476	142	N	t-	1.3618	0.4091	-0.6897	193.4	–	–	19N	151E
0737	062	1800 Apr 09	16:26:01	13	-2471	109	P	-a	0.7221	1.5157	0.5500	286.1	151.1	–	7S	114E
0738	062	1800 Oct 02	21:46:41	13	-2465	114	P	-t	-0.8798	1.2673	0.2206	296.6	108.4	–	3N	31E
0739	062	1801 Mar 30	05:24:05	13	-2459	119	T+	pp	0.0052	2.8569	1.8400	344.6	222.3	102.1	4S	80W
0740	062	1801 Sep 22	07:18:55	13	-2453	124	T-	pp	-0.1074	2.6548	1.6670	332.2	216.4	98.2	1S	111W
0741	062	1802 Mar 19	11:15:28	13	-2447	129	P	t-	-0.7518	1.5156	0.4423	324.5	151.7	–	0N	167W
0742	062	1802 Sep 11	22:36:46	13	-2441	134	P	a-	0.6106	1.7134	0.7615	292.6	170.0	–	4S	20E
0743	062	1803 Feb 06	17:10:44	12	-2436	101	N	-t	1.5322	0.0919	-0.9979	93.2	–	–	17N	107E
0744	062	1803 Mar 08	11:17:37	12	-2435	139	N	t-	-1.4654	0.2169	-0.8775	143.3	–	–	4N	167W
0745	063	1803 Aug 03	07:05:10	12	-2430	106	N	-a	-1.2349	0.5791	-0.3952	200.1	–	–	19S	104W
0746	063	1803 Sep 01	15:19:08	12	-2429	144	N	a-	1.3282	0.4004	-0.5588	165.2	–	–	7S	130E
0747	063	1804 Jan 26	21:21:21	12	-2424	111	P	-h	0.7882	1.4320	0.3918	302.4	137.9	–	20N	43E
0748	063	1804 Jul 22	17:38:00	12	-2418	116	P	-t	-0.5141	1.9284	0.9012	335.1	195.8	–	21S	97E
0749	063	1805 Jan 15	08:40:57	12	-2412	121	T+	pp	0.0663	2.7305	1.7420	326.8	213.3	98.1	21N	128W
0750	063	1805 Jul 11	21:04:52	12	-2406	126	T+	pp	0.2561	2.4214	1.3553	368.3	227.6	87.6	22S	45E
0751	063	1806 Jan 05	00:02:03	12	-2400	131	P	a-	-0.5982	1.7459	0.7748	295.0	170.6	–	22N	1E
0752	063	1806 Jun 30	21:44:38	12	-2394	136	Nx	t-	1.0116	1.0319	-0.0276	283.6	–	–	22S	35E
0753	063	1806 Nov 26	02:05:37	12	-2389	103	N	-a	1.4854	0.1451	-0.8797	107.9	–	–	22N	35W
0754	063	1806 Dec 25	14:48:03	12	-2388	141	N	a-	-1.2892	0.4923	-0.5071	186.1	–	–	22N	138E
0755	063	1807 May 21	16:49:32	12	-2383	108	P	-h	-0.9424	1.1229	0.1346	267.5	82.0	–	21S	107E
0756	063	1807 Nov 15	08:09:58	12	-2377	113	P	-h	0.8473	1.3426	0.2646	310.8	120.1	–	19N	126W
0757	064	1808 May 10	07:38:16	12	-2371	118	T-	-p	-0.1736	2.5145	1.5637	317.6	209.3	92.8	18S	116W
0758	064	1808 Nov 03	08:13:38	12	-2365	123	T+	pp	0.1607	2.6122	1.5148	376.4	232.4	98.1	15N	127W
0759	064	1809 Apr 30	00:33:02	12	-2359	128	P	a-	0.5490	1.8275	0.8732	299.4	179.4	–	14S	9W
0760	064	1809 Oct 23	09:02:46	12	-2353	133	P	t-	-0.5441	1.8924	0.8275	341.9	192.6	–	11N	139W
0761	064	1810 Mar 21	02:54:47	12	-2348	100	N	-a	-1.4210	0.2690	-0.7673	148.8	–	–	1S	42W
0762	064	1810 Apr 19	14:54:07	12	-2347	138	N	a-	1.3166	0.4414	-0.5570	180.7	–	–	10S	137E
0763	064	1810 Sep 13	06:27:09	12	-2342	105	N	-a	1.4299	0.2203	-0.7519	126.2	–	–	3S	98W
0764	064	1810 Oct 12	16:39:21	12	-2341	143	N	a-	-1.2230	0.6167	-0.3809	210.1	–	–	0N	107E
0765	064	1811 Mar 10	06:37:39	12	-2336	110	P	-t	-0.7527	1.5205	0.4341	329.1	151.9	–	4N	97W
0766	064	1811 Sep 02	22:41:51	12	-2330	115	P	-a	0.6972	1.5523	0.6045	283.4	155.1	–	7S	19E
0767	064	1812 Feb 27	06:04:51	12	-2324	120	T-	pp	-0.0538	2.8057	1.7136	375.6	234.1	104.3	9N	88W
0768	064	1812 Aug 22	15:01:21	12	-2318	125	T-	pp	-0.0229	2.7997	1.8320	326.8	215.4	100.4	12S	135E
0769	065	1813 Feb 15	08:50:46	12	-2312	130	P	a-	0.6454	1.6993	0.6488	324.3	172.6	–	13N	129W
0770	065	1813 Aug 12	02:52:49	12	-2306	135	P	t-	-0.8086	1.3833	0.3655	299.1	134.6	–	16S	42W
0771	065	1814 Jan 06	07:28:19	12	-2301	102	N	-a	-1.4119	0.2568	-0.7223	134.1	–	–	21N	111W
0772	065	1814 Feb 04	18:47:01	12	-2300	140	N	a-	1.2927	0.4843	-0.5122	184.6	–	–	17N	82E
0773	065	1814 Jul 02	16:51:30	12	-2295	107	N	-t	1.2225	0.6498	-0.4195	236.8	–	–	22S	108E
0774	065	1814 Dec 26	23:08:27	12	-2289	112	P	-a	-0.7564	1.4573	0.4826	280.4	141.6	–	23N	13E
0775	065	1815 Jun 21	18:06:32	12	-2283	117	T	-t	0.4498	2.0575	1.0082	350.0	207.4	14.8	23S	89E
0776	065	1815 Dec 16	12:55:05	12	-2277	122	T-	-p	-0.0906	2.6988	1.6850	337.3	217.4	98.4	23N	165E
0777	065	1816 Jun 10	01:14:25	12	-2271	127	T	a-	-0.3369	2.2387	1.2410	333.3	209.5	71.3	23S	19W
0778	065	1816 Dec 04	20:35:14	12	-2265	132	P	t-	0.6320	1.7338	0.6636	332.9	176.7	–	23N	49E
0779	065	1817 May 01	07:44:03	12	-2260	099	N	-a	1.4587	0.1555	-0.7929	104.0	–	–	14S	116W
0780	065	1817 May 30	15:07:29	12	-2259	137	N	a-	-1.0608	0.8881	-0.0652	233.9	–	–	23S	132E

Cat Num	Canon Plate	Calendar Date	TD of Greatest Eclipse	ΔT s	Luna Num	Saros Num	Ecl Type	QSE	Gamma	Pen Mag	Um Mag	Pen m	Par m	Total m	Lat	Long
0781	066	1817 Nov 23	21:26:56	12	-2253	142	N	t-	1.3436	0.4441	-0.6576	201.2	–	–	22N	35E
0782	066	1818 Apr 21	00:20:29	12	-2248	109	P	-a	0.7729	1.4222	0.4573	280.8	140.0	–	11S	5W
0783	066	1818 Oct 14	05:25:27	12	-2242	114	P	-t	-0.9175	1.1981	0.1512	289.8	90.4	–	7N	84W
0784	066	1819 Apr 10	13:07:52	12	-2236	119	T+	pp	0.0502	2.7745	1.7574	345.5	222.7	101.8	8S	163E
0785	066	1819 Oct 03	15:13:28	12	-2230	124	T-	pp	-0.1510	2.5747	1.5868	330.2	214.6	95.3	4N	129E
0786	066	1820 Mar 29	18:42:42	12	-2224	129	P	t-	-0.7112	1.5895	0.5171	330.1	162.4	–	4S	80E
0787	066	1820 Sep 22	06:35:09	11	-2218	134	P	a-	0.5612	1.8049	0.8511	296.8	176.8	–	0N	101W
0788	066	1821 Feb 17	01:05:20	11	-2213	101	N	-t	1.5470	0.0627	-1.0228	76.9	–	–	13N	12W
0789	066	1821 Mar 18	18:44:56	11	-2212	139	N	t-	-1.4293	0.2812	-0.8094	161.9	–	–	0S	80E
0790	066	1821 Aug 13	14:26:44	11	-2207	106	N	-a	-1.3067	0.4499	-0.5291	179.3	–	–	16S	145E
0791	066	1821 Sep 11	23:04:54	11	-2206	144	N	a-	1.2767	0.4972	-0.4665	182.9	–	–	3S	12E
0792	066	1822 Feb 06	05:43:26	11	-2201	111	P	-a	0.7961	1.4151	0.3797	300.0	135.6	–	16N	82W
0793	067	1822 Aug 03	00:30:07	11	-2195	116	P	-t	-0.5938	1.7846	0.7526	329.9	184.2	–	18S	6W
0794	067	1823 Jan 26	17:24:53	11	-2189	121	T+	pp	0.0729	2.7169	1.7315	325.8	212.9	97.8	19N	102E
0795	067	1823 Jul 23	03:32:23	10	-2183	126	T+	pp	0.1699	2.5805	1.5124	371.7	232.3	98.6	20S	52W
0796	067	1824 Jan 16	08:54:08	10	-2177	131	P	a-	-0.5938	1.7538	0.7829	295.4	171.3	–	21N	131W
0797	067	1824 Jul 11	04:14:59	10	-2171	136	P	t-	0.9245	1.1907	0.1330	298.8	87.6	–	21S	63W
0798	067	1824 Dec 06	10:32:40	10	-2166	103	N	-a	1.4981	0.1241	-0.9053	100.3	–	–	24N	160W
0799	067	1825 Jan 04	23:31:52	10	-2165	141	N	a-	-1.2890	0.4937	-0.5081	186.9	–	–	21N	8E
0800	067	1825 Jun 01	00:06:18	10	-2160	108	P	-h	-1.0090	0.9983	0.0149	254.5	27.6	–	23S	2W
0801	067	1825 Nov 25	16:09:25	9	-2154	113	P	-h	0.8643	1.3138	0.2312	309.5	113.1	–	22N	114E
0802	067	1826 May 21	15:15:25	9	-2148	118	T-	-p	-0.2384	2.3941	1.4465	315.1	206.4	86.5	20S	130E
0803	067	1826 Nov 14	15:56:14	9	-2142	123	T+	pp	0.1840	2.5707	1.4709	376.0	231.2	95.6	18N	117E
0804	067	1827 May 11	08:16:56	9	-2136	128	P	a-	0.4910	1.9335	0.9801	304.1	186.8	–	17S	125W
0805	068	1827 Nov 03	16:51:55	8	-2130	133	P	h-	-0.5151	1.9456	0.8805	343.4	196.3	–	15N	103E
0806	068	1828 Mar 31	10:38:44	8	-2125	100	N	-h	-1.4631	0.1919	-0.8445	126.9	–	–	6S	159W
0807	068	1828 Apr 29	22:28:39	8	-2124	138	N	h-	1.2675	0.5318	-0.4671	197.3	–	–	13S	22E
0808	068	1828 Sep 23	14:19:41	8	-2119	105	N	-a	1.4724	0.1425	-0.8300	102.0	–	–	2N	143E
0809	068	1828 Oct 23	00:44:42	8	-2118	143	N	a-	-1.1889	0.6793	-0.3263	218.5	–	–	10N	15W
0810	068	1829 Mar 20	14:08:13	8	-2113	110	P	-t	-0.7892	1.4527	0.3681	324.5	141.5	–	1S	150E
0811	068	1829 Sep 13	06:33:27	8	-2107	115	P	-a	0.7510	1.4550	0.5047	277.8	143.9	–	3S	100W
0812	068	1830 Mar 09	13:42:57	7	-2101	120	T-	pp	-0.0824	2.7510	1.6633	374.3	233.5	103.3	4N	157E
0813	068	1830 Sep 02	22:37:55	7	-2095	125	T+	pp	0.0371	2.7760	1.8034	328.0	215.7	100.2	8S	20E
0814	068	1831 Feb 26	16:56:21	7	-2089	130	P	a-	0.6246	1.7346	0.6897	324.8	176.2	–	9N	109E
0815	068	1831 Aug 23	09:59:56	7	-2083	135	P	t-	-0.7429	1.5067	0.4833	309.2	152.5	–	12S	149W
0816	068	1832 Jan 17	16:18:14	7	-2078	102	N	-a	-1.4136	0.2527	-0.7244	132.9	–	–	19N	118E
0817	069	1832 Feb 16	03:20:41	7	-2077	140	N	a-	1.2784	0.5083	-0.4838	188.1	–	–	14N	46W
0818	069	1832 Jul 12	23:15:58	6	-2072	107	N	-t	1.3082	0.4929	-0.5769	209.4	–	–	21S	12E
0819	069	1832 Aug 11	14:14:53	6	-2071	145	Nb	t-	-1.5397	0.0662	-0.9999	79.2	–	–	17S	148E
0820	069	1833 Jan 06	07:59:45	6	-2066	112	P	-a	-0.7612	1.4492	0.4734	280.3	140.6	–	22N	118W
0821	069	1833 Jul 02	00:43:22	6	-2060	117	P	-t	0.5329	1.9036	0.8572	342.4	196.2	–	23S	10W
0822	069	1833 Dec 26	21:32:54	6	-2054	122	T-	-p	-0.0951	2.6920	1.6749	338.5	217.8	98.3	23N	37E
0823	069	1834 Jun 21	08:19:45	6	-2048	127	T-	p-	-0.2584	2.3806	1.3871	335.1	214.2	85.6	24S	125W
0824	069	1834 Dec 16	04:48:06	6	-2042	132	P	t-	0.6249	1.7487	0.6746	334.9	178.2	–	24N	73W
0825	069	1835 May 12	15:28:44	6	-2037	099	Ne	-a	1.5160	0.0491	-0.8968	58.9	–	–	17S	127E
0826	069	1835 Jun 10	22:35:53	6	-2036	137	P	a-	-0.9889	1.0184	0.0681	246.5	56.9	–	24S	21E
0827	069	1835 Dec 05	05:20:18	6	-2030	142	N	t-	1.3291	0.4717	-0.6322	207.0	–	–	23N	83W
0828	069	1836 May 01	08:06:48	5	-2025	109	P	-a	0.8299	1.3174	0.3528	274.1	125.2	–	14S	122W
0829	070	1836 Oct 24	13:14:43	5	-2019	114	P	-t	-0.9473	1.1436	0.0966	283.9	72.6	–	11N	158E
0830	070	1837 Apr 20	20:40:45	5	-2013	119	T+	pp	0.1033	2.6772	1.6598	346.1	222.6	100.2	12S	50E
0831	070	1837 Oct 13	23:17:06	5	-2007	124	T-	-p	-0.1878	2.5074	1.5192	328.7	212.7	92.0	8N	7E
0832	070	1838 Apr 10	01:58:48	5	-2001	129	P	t-	-0.6622	1.6788	0.6076	336.1	173.9	–	8S	30W
0833	070	1838 Oct 03	14:41:27	5	-1995	134	P	a-	0.5183	1.8849	0.9288	300.1	182.1	–	4N	137E
0834	070	1839 Feb 28	08:53:42	5	-1990	101	Ne	-t	1.5671	0.0234	-1.0574	47.0	–	–	9N	130W
0835	070	1839 Mar 30	02:03:03	5	-1989	139	N	t-	-1.3854	0.3596	-0.7268	181.5	–	–	5S	30W
0836	070	1839 Aug 24	21:52:13	5	-1984	106	N	-a	-1.3743	0.3283	-0.6558	155.6	–	–	12S	33E
0837	070	1839 Sep 23	06:57:38	5	-1983	144	N	a-	1.2312	0.5831	-0.3854	197.1	–	–	1N	107W
0838	070	1840 Feb 17	14:02:35	5	-1978	111	P	-a	0.8074	1.3918	0.3616	297.1	132.3	–	13N	153E
0839	070	1840 Aug 13	07:23:08	5	-1972	116	P	-t	-0.6716	1.6443	0.6074	323.6	170.1	–	15S	109W
0840	070	1841 Feb 06	02:07:13	5	-1966	121	T+	pp	0.0812	2.6999	1.7178	324.8	212.5	97.5	16N	28W

Thousand Year Canon of Lunar Eclipses: 1501 to 2500

Cat Num	Canon Plate	Calendar Date	TD of Greatest Eclipse	ΔT s	Luna Num	Saros Num	Ecl Type	QSE	Gamma	Pen Mag	Um Mag	Pen m	Par m	Total m	Lat	Long
0841	071	1841 Aug 02	10:00:51	5	-1960	126	T+	pp	0.0847	2.7381	1.6678	373.9	235.1	104.6	18S	149W
0842	071	1842 Jan 26	17:44:27	5	-1954	131	P	a-	-0.5884	1.7634	0.7930	296.0	172.2	-	18N	97E
0843	071	1842 Jul 22	10:47:38	6	-1948	136	P	t-	0.8384	1.3480	0.2917	311.7	126.5	-	20S	161W
0844	071	1842 Dec 17	19:02:29	6	-1943	103	N	-a	1.5079	0.1082	-0.9253	94.2	-	-	25N	74E
0845	071	1843 Jan 16	08:14:23	6	-1942	141	N	a-	-1.2886	0.4956	-0.5083	187.7	-	-	20N	121W
0846	071	1843 Jun 12	07:22:16	6	-1937	108	N	-h	-1.0768	0.8717	-0.1073	240.0	-	-	24S	111W
0847	071	1843 Jul 11	16:49:52	6	-1936	146	Nb	h-	1.5469	0.0226	-0.9830	43.3	-	-	21S	108E
0848	071	1843 Dec 07	00:11:30	6	-1931	113	P	-t	0.8785	1.2897	0.2031	308.4	106.6	-	23N	5W
0849	071	1844 May 31	22:50:43	6	-1925	118	T	-p	-0.3050	2.2706	1.3255	312.1	202.5	77.1	22S	17E
0850	071	1844 Nov 24	23:44:52	6	-1919	123	T+	pp	0.2026	2.5375	1.4358	375.5	230.2	93.3	21N	1E
0851	071	1845 May 21	15:54:30	6	-1913	128	T	a-	0.4281	2.0488	1.0957	308.7	193.7	45.3	20S	121W
0852	071	1845 Nov 14	00:49:42	6	-1907	133	P	h-	-0.4925	1.9871	0.9221	344.3	198.9	-	18N	16W
0853	072	1846 Apr 11	18:11:34	6	-1902	100	N	-h	-1.5132	0.0999	-0.9365	92.6	-	-	10S	87E
0854	072	1846 May 11	05:53:43	6	-1901	138	N	h-	1.2112	0.6355	-0.3643	214.2	-	-	17S	89W
0855	072	1846 Oct 04	22:21:37	6	-1896	105	N	-a	1.5078	0.0780	-0.8952	75.7	-	-	6N	21E
0856	072	1846 Nov 03	08:59:23	6	-1895	143	N	a-	-1.1619	0.7287	-0.2766	224.6	-	-	14N	139W
0857	072	1847 Mar 31	21:27:02	6	-1890	110	P	-t	-0.8346	1.3684	0.2857	318.3	126.4	-	5S	39E
0858	072	1847 Sep 24	14:33:44	7	-1884	115	P	-a	0.7974	1.3714	0.4181	272.6	132.8	-	1N	139E
0859	072	1848 Mar 19	21:12:12	7	-1878	120	T-	pp	-0.1185	2.6823	1.5993	372.6	232.4	101.4	0N	44E
0860	072	1848 Sep 13	06:19:24	7	-1872	125	T+	pp	0.0922	2.6776	1.6998	328.9	215.4	98.6	4S	96W
0861	072	1849 Mar 09	00:55:48	7	-1866	130	P	a-	0.5980	1.7804	0.7414	325.7	180.6	-	5N	11W
0862	072	1849 Sep 02	17:10:17	7	-1860	135	P	t-	-0.6807	1.6238	0.5945	318.0	166.6	-	8S	103E
0863	072	1850 Jan 28	01:06:05	7	-1855	102	N	-a	-1.4176	0.2443	-0.7305	130.5	-	-	17N	13W
0864	072	1850 Feb 26	11:48:12	7	-1854	140	N	a-	1.2587	0.5420	-0.4453	192.9	-	-	10N	173W
0865	073	1850 Jul 24	05:40:15	7	-1849	107	N	-t	1.3933	0.3371	-0.7336	175.8	-	-	19S	84W
0866	073	1850 Aug 22	20:55:01	7	-1848	145	N	t-	-1.4680	0.1997	-0.8703	136.2	-	-	13S	47E
0867	073	1851 Jan 17	16:50:46	7	-1843	112	P	-a	-0.7660	1.4406	0.4642	280.1	139.6	-	20N	110E
0868	073	1851 Jul 13	07:21:41	7	-1837	117	P	-t	0.6155	1.7508	0.7069	333.7	182.3	-	21S	109W
0869	073	1852 Jan 07	06:10:43	7	-1831	122	T-	-p	-0.0991	2.6863	1.6663	339.7	218.3	98.3	22N	91W
0870	073	1852 Jul 01	15:26:12	7	-1825	127	T-	p-	-0.1799	2.5227	1.5330	336.0	217.4	94.6	23S	129E
0871	073	1852 Dec 26	13:03:06	7	-1819	132	P	t-	0.6203	1.7588	0.6815	336.6	179.4	-	24N	164E
0872	073	1853 Jun 21	06:01:48	7	-1813	137	P	a-	-0.9146	1.1535	0.2056	257.9	96.8	-	24S	90W
0873	073	1853 Dec 15	13:18:42	7	-1807	142	N	t-	1.3187	0.4917	-0.6138	211.0	-	-	24N	159E
0874	073	1854 May 12	15:46:09	7	-1802	109	P	-a	0.8919	1.2035	0.2390	266.0	105.0	-	17S	123E
0875	073	1854 Nov 04	21:12:49	7	-1796	114	P	-h	-0.9707	1.1005	0.0538	279.0	54.3	-	15N	38E
0876	073	1855 May 02	04:05:23	7	-1790	119	T+	-p	0.1625	2.5690	1.5509	346.2	221.5	96.5	15S	62W
0877	074	1855 Oct 25	07:29:40	7	-1784	124	T-	-p	-0.2177	2.4528	1.4643	327.0	210.8	88.7	12N	116W
0878	074	1856 Apr 20	09:06:46	7	-1778	129	P	t-	-0.6068	1.7799	0.7098	342.4	185.1	-	12S	137W
0879	074	1856 Oct 13	22:54:33	7	-1772	134	P	a-	0.4810	1.9545	0.9960	302.8	186.2	-	9N	13E
0880	074	1857 Apr 09	09:13:17	7	-1766	139	N	t-	-1.3347	0.4504	-0.6317	201.0	-	-	9S	138W
0881	074	1857 Sep 04	05:22:16	7	-1761	106	N	-a	-1.4376	0.2150	-0.7746	127.8	-	-	8S	80W
0882	074	1857 Oct 03	14:56:56	7	-1760	144	N	a-	1.1914	0.6586	-0.3149	208.5	-	-	5N	132E
0883	074	1858 Feb 27	22:14:20	7	-1755	111	P	-a	0.8253	1.3561	0.3316	293.1	126.9	-	9N	30E
0884	074	1858 Aug 24	14:20:47	7	-1749	116	P	-t	-0.7446	1.5131	0.4708	316.8	153.5	-	12S	146E
0885	074	1859 Feb 17	10:43:28	7	-1743	121	T+	pp	0.0950	2.6727	1.6944	323.7	211.9	96.9	12N	157W
0886	074	1859 Aug 13	16:34:25	7	-1737	126	T+	pp	0.0038	2.8877	1.8148	375.0	236.0	106.5	15S	113E
0887	074	1860 Feb 07	02:29:45	8	-1731	131	P	a-	-0.5791	1.7801	0.8106	296.9	173.7	-	15N	34W
0888	074	1860 Aug 01	17:25:02	8	-1725	136	P	t-	0.7551	1.5003	0.4450	322.3	152.3	-	17S	100E
0889	075	1860 Dec 28	03:33:55	8	-1720	103	N	-a	1.5160	0.0951	-0.9419	88.7	-	-	25N	53W
0890	075	1861 Jan 26	16:54:01	8	-1719	141	N	a-	-1.2865	0.5002	-0.5051	189.1	-	-	17N	109E
0891	075	1861 Jun 22	14:35:15	8	-1714	108	N	-a	-1.1477	0.7397	-0.2355	223.3	-	-	25S	142E
0892	075	1861 Jul 21	23:50:37	8	-1713	146	N	a-	1.4660	0.1696	-0.8333	116.7	-	-	19S	3E
0893	075	1861 Dec 17	08:18:43	8	-1708	113	P	-t	0.8881	1.2738	0.1840	307.9	102.0	-	24N	125W
0894	075	1862 Jun 12	06:21:03	8	-1702	118	T	-p	-0.3763	2.1387	1.1957	308.3	197.2	62.4	24S	95W
0895	075	1862 Dec 06	07:40:21	7	-1696	123	T+	pp	0.2157	2.5142	1.4113	375.1	229.4	91.5	23N	117W
0896	075	1863 Jun 01	23:26:14	7	-1690	128	T	p-	0.3606	2.1729	1.2195	313.0	200.0	66.1	22S	8E
0897	075	1863 Nov 25	08:56:11	7	-1684	133	P	a-	-0.4761	2.0170	0.9525	344.5	200.5	-	20N	137W
0898	075	1864 May 21	13:12:02	6	-1678	138	N	h-	1.1503	0.7480	-0.2531	230.7	-	-	19S	161E
0899	075	1864 Oct 15	06:30:45	6	-1673	105	N	-a	1.5380	0.0230	-0.9511	41.2	-	-	10N	102W
0900	075	1864 Nov 13	17:21:25	6	-1672	143	N	a-	-1.1403	0.7683	-0.2367	229.0	-	-	17N	96E

Cat Num	Canon Plate	Calendar Date	TD of Greatest Eclipse	ΔT s	Luna Num	Saros Num	Ecl Type	QSE	Gamma	Pen Mag	Um Mag	Pen m	Par m	Total m	Lat	Long
0901	076	1865 Apr 11	04:38:10	6	-1667	110	P	-t	-0.8857	1.2736	0.1930	310.5	105.4	–	9S	69W
0902	076	1865 Oct 04	22:40:00	5	-1661	115	P	-a	0.8386	1.2973	0.3408	267.7	121.3	–	5N	17E
0903	076	1866 Mar 31	04:33:35	5	-1655	120	T-	pp	-0.1614	2.6011	1.5232	370.5	230.7	98.2	4S	67W
0904	076	1866 Sep 24	14:07:14	4	-1649	125	T+	-p	0.1412	2.5904	1.6071	329.5	214.6	96.0	1N	146E
0905	076	1867 Mar 20	08:49:01	4	-1643	130	P	a-	0.5657	1.8366	0.8038	326.9	185.5	–	1N	130W
0906	076	1867 Sep 14	00:26:27	3	-1637	135	P	t-	-0.6240	1.7309	0.6956	325.6	177.8	–	4S	7W
0907	076	1868 Feb 08	09:49:39	3	-1632	102	N	-a	-1.4252	0.2288	-0.7433	126.3	–	–	14N	144W
0908	076	1868 Mar 08	20:09:49	3	-1631	140	N	a-	1.2340	0.5850	-0.3974	198.9	–	–	6N	61E
0909	076	1868 Aug 03	12:09:12	2	-1626	107	N	-t	1.4741	0.1895	-0.8824	133.6	–	–	16S	179E
0910	076	1868 Sep 02	03:41:28	2	-1625	145	N	t-	-1.4013	0.3242	-0.7498	172.0	–	–	9S	55W
0911	076	1869 Jan 28	01:38:27	2	-1620	112	P	-a	-0.7733	1.4273	0.4507	279.6	138.0	–	17N	21W
0912	076	1869 Jul 23	14:02:45	1	-1614	117	P	-t	0.6962	1.6017	0.5600	323.9	165.8	–	19S	151E
0913	077	1870 Jan 17	14:46:33	1	-1608	122	T-	-p	-0.1037	2.6789	1.6566	340.8	218.7	98.2	21N	141E
0914	077	1870 Jul 12	22:34:23	0	-1602	127	T-	pp	-0.1023	2.6636	1.6769	336.1	219.2	99.7	22S	23E
0915	077	1871 Jan 06	21:16:40	-0	-1596	132	P	t-	0.6154	1.7690	0.6893	338.1	180.6	–	23N	42E
0916	077	1871 Jul 02	13:27:48	-1	-1590	137	P	a-	-0.8401	1.2893	0.3432	268.0	122.4	–	24S	159E
0917	077	1871 Dec 26	21:19:32	-1	-1584	142	N	t-	1.3106	0.5068	-0.5995	214.0	–	–	25N	40E
0918	077	1872 May 22	23:18:24	-1	-1579	109	P	-a	0.9593	1.0802	0.1152	256.2	74.4	–	20S	10E
0919	077	1872 Nov 15	05:19:37	-2	-1573	114	P	-h	0.9876	1.0692	0.0230	275.1	35.5	–	18N	83W
0920	077	1873 May 12	11:20:26	-2	-1567	119	T+	-p	0.2284	2.4485	1.4295	345.6	219.3	89.9	18S	171W
0921	077	1873 Nov 04	15:51:03	-2	-1561	124	T-	-p	-0.2408	2.4104	1.4217	325.5	209.1	85.7	15N	118E
0922	077	1874 May 01	16:03:17	-3	-1555	129	P	t-	-0.5426	1.8971	0.8282	348.8	196.2	–	16S	118E
0923	077	1874 Oct 25	07:16:22	-3	-1549	134	T	a-	0.4510	2.0108	1.0497	304.9	189.2	32.7	12N	113W
0924	077	1875 Apr 20	16:15:21	-3	-1543	139	N	t-	-1.2770	0.5541	-0.5237	220.3	–	–	13S	115E
0925	078	1875 Sep 15	12:57:29	-4	-1538	106	N	-a	-1.4955	0.1117	-0.8837	93.3	–	–	4S	165E
0926	078	1875 Oct 14	23:02:54	-4	-1537	144	N	a-	1.1578	0.7229	-0.2557	217.8	–	–	9N	10E
0927	078	1876 Mar 10	06:21:31	-4	-1532	111	P	-a	0.8475	1.3124	0.2938	288.5	119.7	–	5N	92W
0928	078	1876 Sep 03	21:22:33	-4	-1526	116	P	-t	-0.8130	1.3904	0.3425	309.3	133.9	–	8S	39E
0929	078	1877 Feb 27	19:15:37	-4	-1520	121	T+	-p	0.1125	2.6386	1.6644	322.6	211.4	96.2	8N	74E
0930	078	1877 Aug 23	23:11:35	-4	-1514	126	T-	pp	-0.0738	2.7606	1.6850	375.1	235.4	104.9	11S	13E
0931	078	1878 Feb 17	11:11:05	-5	-1508	131	P	a-	-0.5667	1.8021	0.8339	298.0	175.6	–	11N	164W
0932	078	1878 Aug 13	00:08:22	-5	-1502	136	P	t-	0.6757	1.6458	0.5912	330.9	171.1	–	14S	1W
0933	078	1879 Jan 08	12:04:11	-5	-1497	103	N	-a	1.5243	0.0812	-0.9587	82.4	–	–	24N	179W
0934	078	1879 Feb 07	01:28:33	-5	-1496	141	N	a-	-1.2810	0.5109	-0.4955	191.4	–	–	14N	19W
0935	078	1879 Jul 03	21:50:28	-5	-1491	108	N	-a	-1.2173	0.6103	-0.3617	204.7	–	–	24S	34E
0936	078	1879 Aug 02	06:57:43	-5	-1490	146	N	a-	1.3889	0.3098	-0.6908	155.1	–	–	17S	103W
0937	079	1879 Dec 28	16:26:22	-5	-1485	113	P	-t	0.8970	1.2587	0.1664	307.3	97.4	–	24N	114E
0938	079	1880 Jun 22	13:50:27	-5	-1479	118	T	-a	-0.4484	2.0057	1.0641	303.8	190.6	37.2	24S	153E
0939	079	1880 Dec 16	15:39:03	-5	-1473	123	T+	pp	0.2263	2.4949	1.3915	374.5	228.6	89.9	24N	124E
0940	079	1881 Jun 12	06:53:44	-5	-1467	128	T	p-	0.2899	2.3030	1.3488	316.9	205.3	79.9	23S	104W
0941	079	1881 Dec 05	17:08:33	-5	-1461	133	P	a-	-0.4640	2.0386	0.9751	344.3	201.5	–	22N	101E
0942	079	1882 Jun 01	20:21:58	-5	-1455	138	N	t-	1.0833	0.8717	-0.1311	246.8	–	–	21S	54E
0943	079	1882 Nov 25	01:51:01	-6	-1449	143	N	a-	-1.1243	0.7972	-0.2071	231.9	–	–	20N	31W
0944	079	1883 Apr 22	11:38:29	-6	-1444	110	P	-t	-0.9449	1.1640	0.0854	300.6	71.3	–	13S	175W
0945	079	1883 Oct 16	06:54:15	-6	-1438	115	P	-a	0.8732	1.2355	0.2757	263.4	110.1	–	10N	107W
0946	079	1884 Apr 10	11:46:34	-6	-1432	120	T-	pp	-0.2116	2.5065	1.4337	367.8	228.2	92.9	8S	176W
0947	079	1884 Oct 04	22:01:55	-6	-1426	125	T+	-p	0.1839	2.5151	1.5260	330.0	213.5	92.6	5N	27E
0948	079	1885 Mar 30	16:34:07	-6	-1420	130	P	a-	0.5258	1.9066	0.8802	328.5	191.0	–	4S	113E
0949	080	1885 Sep 24	07:48:12	-6	-1414	135	P	t-	-0.5726	1.8284	0.7867	332.1	186.7	–	0N	119W
0950	080	1886 Feb 18	18:29:00	-6	-1409	102	N	-a	-1.4366	0.2064	-0.7626	120.0	–	–	10N	86E
0951	080	1886 Mar 20	04:24:17	-6	-1408	140	N	a-	1.2030	0.6393	-0.3381	206.2	–	–	1N	64W
0952	080	1886 Aug 14	18:42:03	-6	-1403	107	Ne	-t	1.5512	0.0489	-1.0246	68.7	–	–	13S	80E
0953	080	1886 Sep 13	10:34:43	-6	-1402	145	N	t-	-1.3399	0.4390	-0.6392	198.4	–	–	5S	159W
0954	080	1887 Feb 08	10:22:03	-6	-1397	112	P	-a	-0.7837	1.4082	0.4318	278.8	135.6	–	14N	152W
0955	080	1887 Aug 03	20:48:53	-6	-1391	117	P	-t	0.7732	1.4595	0.4194	313.4	146.3	–	17S	49E
0956	080	1888 Jan 28	23:20:01	-6	-1385	122	T-	-p	-0.1095	2.6692	1.6452	341.9	219.1	98.1	18N	13E
0957	080	1888 Jul 23	05:44:47	-6	-1379	127	T-	pp	-0.0256	2.8030	1.8189	335.4	219.6	101.8	20S	85W
0958	080	1889 Jan 17	05:29:39	-6	-1373	132	P	t-	0.6106	1.7787	0.6972	339.6	181.7	–	21N	80W
0959	080	1889 Jul 12	20:53:52	-6	-1367	137	P	a-	-0.7655	1.4257	0.4807	276.9	141.7	–	23S	48E
0960	080	1890 Jan 06	05:21:26	-6	-1361	142	N	t-	1.3030	0.5209	-0.5854	216.7	–	–	24N	79W

Cat Num	Canon Plate	Calendar Date	TD of Greatest Eclipse	ΔT s	Luna Num	Saros Num	Ecl Type	QSE	Gamma	Pen Mag	Um Mag	Phase Durations Pen m	Par m	Total m	Greatest in Zenith Lat	Long
0961	081	1890 Jun 03	06:44:43	-6	-1356	109	N	-a	1.0309	0.9492	-0.0168	244.2	–	–	21S	101W
0962	081	1890 Jul 02	14:08:36	-6	-1355	147	N	a-	-1.4872	0.1025	-0.8445	85.3	–	–	25S	149E
0963	081	1890 Nov 26	13:33:48	-6	-1350	114	P	-h	-0.9994	1.0471	0.0018	272.0	9.9	–	20N	154E
0964	081	1891 May 23	18:29:11	-6	-1344	119	T	-a	0.2988	2.3199	1.2996	344.2	215.7	79.1	20S	82E
0965	081	1891 Nov 16	00:18:46	-6	-1338	124	T-	-p	-0.2592	2.3766	1.3880	324.1	207.7	83.1	18N	8W
0966	081	1892 May 11	22:53:20	-6	-1332	129	P	t-	-0.4735	2.0236	0.9555	354.8	206.3	–	19S	16E
0967	081	1892 Nov 04	15:44:52	-6	-1326	134	T	p-	0.4268	2.0565	1.0930	306.6	191.5	44.1	16N	119E
0968	081	1893 Apr 30	23:08:57	-6	-1320	139	N	t-	-1.2120	0.6713	-0.4022	239.2	–	–	16S	12E
0969	081	1893 Sep 25	20:39:02	-6	-1315	106	Ne	-a	-1.5476	0.0192	-0.9822	39.2	–	–	0S	49E
0970	081	1893 Oct 25	07:16:14	-6	-1314	144	N	a-	1.1306	0.7753	-0.2084	225.1	–	–	13N	114W
0971	081	1894 Mar 21	14:20:28	-6	-1309	111	P	-h	0.8771	1.2550	0.2425	282.7	109.3	–	0N	147E
0972	081	1894 Sep 15	04:31:25	-6	-1303	116	P	-t	-0.8749	1.2798	0.2261	301.8	111.0	–	4S	69W
0973	082	1895 Mar 11	03:39:10	-6	-1297	121	T+	-p	0.1376	2.5904	1.6204	321.3	210.5	94.8	4N	52W
0974	082	1895 Sep 04	05:56:52	-6	-1291	126	T-	pp	-0.1449	2.6318	1.5530	374.5	233.5	100.5	7S	89W
0975	082	1896 Feb 28	19:45:40	-6	-1285	131	P	a-	-0.5489	1.8342	0.8673	299.6	178.2	–	7N	66E
0976	082	1896 Aug 23	06:57:19	-6	-1279	136	P	t-	0.5998	1.7849	0.7306	337.9	185.4	–	11S	104W
0977	082	1897 Jan 18	20:33:09	-6	-1274	103	N	-a	1.5333	0.0660	-0.9762	74.6	–	–	22N	55E
0978	082	1897 Feb 17	09:57:43	-6	-1273	141	N	a-	-1.2717	0.5282	-0.4789	194.9	–	–	11N	146W
0979	082	1897 Jul 14	05:05:20	-5	-1268	108	N	-a	-1.2880	0.4793	-0.4901	183.0	–	–	23S	75W
0980	082	1897 Aug 12	14:08:37	-5	-1267	146	N	a-	1.3136	0.4473	-0.5517	183.2	–	–	14S	148E
0981	082	1898 Jan 08	00:34:46	-5	-1262	113	P	-t	0.9046	1.2456	0.1516	306.8	93.3	–	23N	7W
0982	082	1898 Jul 03	21:17:19	-5	-1256	118	P	-a	-0.5228	1.8689	0.9280	298.5	182.3	–	23S	42E
0983	082	1898 Dec 27	23:41:52	-4	-1250	123	T+	pp	0.2339	2.4809	1.3777	373.9	228.0	88.8	24N	5E
0984	082	1899 Jun 23	14:17:52	-3	-1244	128	T+	p-	0.2169	2.4376	1.4820	320.3	209.6	89.5	23S	146E
0985	083	1899 Dec 17	01:25:45	-3	-1238	133	P	a-	-0.4552	2.0540	0.9922	343.8	202.0	–	23N	22W
0986	083	1900 Jun 13	03:27:37	-2	-1232	138	Nx	t-	1.0134	1.0010	-0.0040	262.0	–	–	22S	52W
0987	083	1900 Dec 06	10:26:29	-1	-1226	143	N	a-	-1.1126	0.8183	-0.1851	233.8	–	–	21N	159W
0988	083	1901 May 03	18:30:37	-1	-1221	110	Nx	-t	-1.0101	1.0431	-0.0334	288.3	–	–	17S	81E
0989	083	1901 Oct 27	15:15:17	-0	-1215	115	P	-a	0.9022	1.1841	0.2209	259.7	99.4	–	14N	127E
0990	083	1902 Apr 22	18:52:40	0	-1209	120	T-	pp	-0.2680	2.4003	1.3327	364.4	224.6	84.6	12S	76E
0991	083	1902 Oct 17	06:03:26	1	-1203	125	T+	-p	0.2201	2.4514	1.4566	330.5	212.3	88.8	9N	95W
0992	083	1903 Apr 12	00:12:59	2	-1197	130	P	a-	0.4798	1.9877	0.9677	330.2	196.6	–	8S	3W
0993	083	1903 Oct 06	15:17:33	2	-1191	135	P	t-	-0.5280	1.9133	0.8654	337.6	193.7	–	4N	128E
0994	083	1904 Mar 02	03:02:32	3	-1186	102	N	-a	-1.4529	0.1749	-0.7909	110.6	–	–	6N	43W
0995	083	1904 Mar 31	12:32:29	3	-1185	140	N	a-	1.1666	0.7036	-0.2688	214.2	–	–	3S	173E
0996	083	1904 Sep 24	17:34:45	3	-1179	145	N	t-	-1.2838	0.5440	-0.5384	219.1	–	–	1S	95E
0997	084	1905 Feb 19	19:00:02	4	-1174	112	P	-a	-0.7984	1.3809	0.4050	277.3	132.1	–	11N	78E
0998	084	1905 Aug 15	03:40:59	5	-1168	117	P	-t	0.8457	1.3259	0.2871	302.4	123.1	–	14S	54W
0999	084	1906 Feb 09	07:46:58	5	-1162	122	T-	-p	-0.1199	2.6507	1.6254	342.9	219.5	97.8	15N	113W
1000	084	1906 Aug 04	13:00:10	6	-1156	127	T+	pp	0.0477	2.7615	1.7794	334.1	218.7	101.2	17S	166E
1001	084	1907 Jan 29	13:37:59	6	-1150	132	P	t-	0.6028	1.7936	0.7110	341.2	183.5	–	19N	159E
1002	084	1907 Jul 25	04:22:27	7	-1144	137	P	a-	-0.6925	1.5595	0.6149	284.6	156.8	–	21S	64W
1003	084	1908 Jan 18	13:21:37	8	-1138	142	N	t-	1.2940	0.5370	-0.5685	219.6	–	–	22N	162E
1004	084	1908 Jun 14	14:06:32	8	-1133	109	N	-a	1.1054	0.8135	0.1541	230.0			22S	149E
1005	084	1908 Jul 13	21:33:55	8	-1132	147	N	a-	-1.4186	0.2292	-0.7195	126.3	–	–	23S	38E
1006	084	1908 Dec 07	21:55:10	9	-1127	114	Nx	-h	-1.0060	1.0344	-0.0096	269.8	–	–	22N	29E
1007	084	1909 Jun 04	01:28:51	10	-1121	119	T	-h	0.3755	2.1800	1.1580	341.7	210.3	60.4	22S	23W
1008	084	1909 Nov 27	08:54:41	10	-1115	124	T-	-p	-0.2713	2.3544	1.3660	323.0	206.5	81.2	21N	137W
1009	085	1910 May 24	05:34:15	11	-1109	129	T	t-	-0.3976	2.1625	1.0950	360.4	215.4	49.5	21S	85W
1010	085	1910 Nov 17	00:20:52	12	-1103	134	T	p-	0.4089	2.0904	1.1246	307.9	193.0	50.6	19N	9W
1011	085	1911 May 13	05:56:23	12	-1097	139	N	t-	-1.1414	0.7988	-0.2706	257.0	–	–	19S	90W
1012	085	1911 Nov 06	15:36:44	13	-1091	144	N	a-	1.1101	0.8155	-0.1733	230.7	–	–	17N	121E
1013	085	1912 Apr 01	22:14:16	13	-1086	111	P	-h	0.9116	1.1885	0.1821	275.9	95.2	–	4S	28E
1014	085	1912 Sep 26	11:44:50	14	-1080	116	P	-t	-0.9320	1.1779	0.1184	294.0	81.8	–	0N	178W
1015	085	1913 Mar 22	11:57:49	15	-1074	121	T+	-p	0.1671	2.5340	1.5683	319.8	209.4	92.8	0S	178W
1016	085	1913 Sep 15	12:48:19	15	-1068	126	T-	pp	-0.2109	2.5123	1.4304	373.1	230.6	93.5	3S	167E
1017	085	1914 Mar 12	04:13:08	16	-1062	131	P	a-	-0.5254	1.8764	0.9111	301.6	181.5	–	3N	61W
1018	085	1914 Sep 04	13:54:56	17	-1056	136	P	t-	0.5301	1.9127	0.8584	343.2	196.0	–	7S	151E
1019	085	1915 Jan 31	04:57:45	17	-1051	103	N	-a	1.5450	0.0453	-0.9987	62.1	–	–	19N	70W
1020	085	1915 Mar 01	18:19:31	17	-1050	141	N	a-	-1.2573	0.5549	-0.4527	199.8	–	–	7N	88E

Cat Num	Canon Plate	Calendar Date	TD of Greatest Eclipse	ΔT s	Luna Num	Saros Num	Ecl Type	QSE	Gamma	Pen Mag	Um Mag	Durations Pen m	Par m	Total m	Greatest in Zenith Lat	Long
1021	086	1915 Jul 26	12:24:40	18	-1045	108	N	-a	-1.3554	0.3546	-0.6128	158.8	–	–	21S	176E
1022	086	1915 Aug 24	21:27:16	18	-1044	146	N	a-	1.2436	0.5750	-0.4225	204.5	–	–	10S	38E
1023	086	1916 Jan 20	08:39:41	18	-1039	113	P	-t	0.9146	1.2278	0.1327	305.8	87.7	–	21N	127W
1024	086	1916 Jul 15	04:46:08	19	-1033	118	P	-a	-0.5957	1.7351	0.7944	292.5	172.5	–	22S	70W
1025	086	1917 Jan 08	07:44:48	19	-1027	123	T+	pp	0.2415	2.4663	1.3642	373.2	227.4	87.6	23N	114W
1026	086	1917 Jul 04	21:39:04	20	-1021	128	T+	pp	0.1419	2.5762	1.6185	323.0	212.8	96.0	23S	36E
1027	086	1917 Dec 28	09:46:31	20	-1015	133	T	a-	-0.4484	2.0652	1.0056	343.1	202.4	12.0	23N	146W
1028	086	1918 Jun 24	10:28:03	20	-1009	138	P	t-	0.9398	1.1375	0.1297	276.4	82.4	–	23S	157W
1029	086	1918 Dec 17	19:06:00	21	-1003	143	N	a-	-1.1036	0.8340	-0.1679	235.0	–	–	22N	73E
1030	086	1919 May 15	01:14:00	21	-998	110	N	-t	-1.0820	0.9103	-0.1644	273.2	–	–	20S	20W
1031	086	1919 Nov 07	23:44:28	21	-992	115	P	-a	0.9246	1.1446	0.1780	256.8	89.8	–	17N	0W
1032	086	1920 May 03	01:51:08	21	-986	120	T	-p	-0.3312	2.2818	1.2194	360.2	219.7	71.5	16S	29W
1033	087	1920 Oct 27	14:11:38	22	-980	125	T+	-p	0.2502	2.3992	1.3987	331.0	211.2	85.0	13N	143E
1034	087	1921 Apr 22	07:44:39	22	-974	130	T	a-	0.4269	2.0815	1.0678	332.0	202.1	40.1	12S	116W
1035	087	1921 Oct 16	22:53:59	22	-968	135	P	t-	-0.4902	1.9858	0.9317	342.2	199.1	–	9N	13E
1036	087	1922 Mar 13	11:28:46	23	-963	102	N	-a	-1.4753	0.1321	-0.8302	96.4	–	–	2N	170W
1037	087	1922 Apr 11	20:32:13	23	-962	140	N	a-	1.1229	0.7812	-0.1863	223.3	–	–	7S	53E
1038	087	1922 Oct 06	00:43:51	23	-956	145	N	t-	-1.2349	0.6358	-0.4508	235.3	–	–	4N	13W
1039	087	1923 Mar 03	03:32:09	23	-951	112	P	-a	-0.8176	1.3453	0.3701	275.3	127.2	–	6N	50W
1040	087	1923 Aug 26	10:39:51	23	-945	117	P	-t	0.9133	1.2013	0.1634	290.9	94.3	–	10S	160W
1041	087	1924 Feb 20	16:08:55	24	-939	122	T-	-p	-0.1338	2.6257	1.5995	343.7	219.7	97.1	11N	121E
1042	087	1924 Aug 14	20:20:30	24	-933	127	T+	pp	0.1175	2.6326	1.6519	332.1	216.9	98.2	14S	56E
1043	087	1925 Feb 08	21:42:22	24	-927	132	P	t-	0.5921	1.8134	0.7304	343.0	185.7	–	15N	38E
1044	087	1925 Aug 04	11:52:57	24	-921	137	P	a-	-0.6208	1.6909	0.7463	291.3	168.9	–	18S	177W
1045	088	1926 Jan 28	21:20:25	24	-915	142	N	t-	1.2837	0.5551	-0.5488	222.7	–	–	19N	43E
1046	088	1926 Jun 25	21:25:07	24	-910	109	N	-a	1.1815	0.6750	-0.2948	213.2	–	–	22S	40E
1047	088	1926 Jul 25	05:00:12	24	-909	147	N	a-	-1.3512	0.3542	-0.5970	155.6	–	–	21S	73W
1048	088	1926 Dec 19	06:20:08	24	-904	114	Nx	-a	-1.0102	1.0257	-0.0163	268.0	–	–	22N	96W
1049	088	1927 Jun 15	08:24:41	24	-898	119	T	-t	0.4543	2.0366	1.0123	338.2	202.8	17.7	23S	126W
1050	088	1927 Dec 08	17:35:10	24	-892	124	T	-p	-0.2796	2.3389	1.3510	321.9	205.6	79.8	22N	94E
1051	088	1928 Jun 03	12:09:57	24	-886	129	T	tp	-0.3175	2.3092	1.2421	365.3	223.0	75.3	23S	177E
1052	088	1928 Nov 27	09:01:47	24	-880	134	T	p-	0.3953	2.1166	1.1486	308.9	194.2	54.8	22N	139W
1053	088	1929 May 23	12:37:44	24	-874	139	N	t-	-1.0651	0.9367	-0.1287	273.8	–	–	21S	169E
1054	088	1929 Nov 17	00:03:12	24	-868	144	N	a-	1.0947	0.8461	-0.1474	235.1	–	–	20N	5W
1055	088	1930 Apr 13	05:58:54	24	-863	111	P	-h	0.9545	1.1067	0.1065	267.4	73.4	–	8S	89W
1056	088	1930 Oct 07	19:07:10	24	-857	116	P	-t	-0.9812	1.0907	0.0253	286.7	38.4	–	5N	71E
1057	089	1931 Apr 02	20:07:55	24	-851	121	T+	-p	0.2043	2.4637	1.5021	318.0	207.9	89.6	5S	59E
1058	089	1931 Sep 26	19:48:29	24	-845	126	T-	pp	-0.2698	2.4059	1.3208	371.3	226.9	84.2	1N	61E
1059	089	1932 Mar 22	12:32:39	24	-839	131	P	a-	-0.4956	1.9303	0.9666	303.9	185.4	–	1S	173E
1060	089	1932 Sep 14	21:01:00	24	-833	136	P	t-	0.4664	2.0296	0.9752	347.3	204.0	–	3S	44E
1061	089	1933 Feb 10	13:17:35	24	-828	103	N	-a	1.5600	0.0184	-1.0268	39.8	–	–	16N	165E
1062	089	1933 Mar 12	02:33:02	24	-827	141	N	a-	-1.2369	0.5924	-0.4153	206.3	–	–	2N	36W
1063	089	1933 Aug 05	19:46:07	24	-822	108	N	-a	-1.4216	0.2324	-0.7336	129.6	–	–	18S	66E
1064	089	1933 Sep 04	04:52:19	24	-821	146	N	a-	1.1776	0.6956	-0.3012	221.5	–	–	6S	74W
1065	089	1934 Jan 30	16:42:43	24	-816	113	P	-t	0.9258	1.2073	0.1120	304.4	80.9	–	18N	113E
1066	089	1934 Jul 26	12:15:38	24	-810	118	P	-a	-0.6681	1.6025	0.6612	285.8	160.8	–	20S	178E
1067	089	1935 Jan 19	15:47:35	24	-804	123	T+	pp	0.2498	2.4502	1.3499	372.2	226.7	86.3	21N	126E
1068	089	1935 Jul 16	05:00:05	24	-798	128	T+	pp	0.0672	2.7146	1.7542	325.1	214.8	99.6	21S	73W
1069	090	1936 Jan 08	18:09:58	24	-792	133	T	a-	-0.4429	2.0740	1.0173	342.2	202.5	20.8	22N	89E
1070	090	1936 Jul 04	17:25:23	24	-786	138	P	t-	0.8642	1.2778	0.2668	289.6	116.3	–	22S	100E
1071	090	1936 Dec 28	03:49:08	24	-780	143	N	a-	-1.0971	0.8451	-0.1550	235.6	–	–	22N	57W
1072	090	1937 May 25	07:51:34	24	-775	110	N	-t	-1.1582	0.7697	-0.3033	254.8	–	–	22S	119W
1073	090	1937 Nov 18	08:19:25	24	-769	115	P	-a	0.9421	1.1141	0.1443	254.6	81.3	–	20N	129W
1074	090	1938 May 14	08:44:00	24	-763	120	T	-t	-0.3994	2.1540	1.0966	355.0	213.1	49.4	19S	132W
1075	090	1938 Nov 07	22:26:42	24	-757	125	T	-p	0.2739	2.3585	1.3525	331.6	210.2	81.4	17N	19E
1076	090	1939 May 03	15:11:43	24	-751	130	T	a-	0.3693	2.1842	1.1765	333.6	207.1	62.4	15S	131E
1077	090	1939 Oct 28	06:36:43	24	-745	135	P	t-	-0.4581	2.0477	0.9876	346.2	203.4	–	12N	103W
1078	090	1940 Mar 23	19:48:17	24	-740	102	N	-a	-1.5034	0.0789	-0.8802	74.7	–	–	3S	64E
1079	090	1940 Apr 22	04:26:26	25	-739	140	N	a-	1.0741	0.8684	-0.0945	232.6	–	–	11S	67W
1080	090	1940 Oct 16	08:01:18	25	-733	145	N	t-	-1.1925	0.7157	-0.3749	248.0	–	–	8N	124W

Cat Num	Canon Plate	Calendar Date	TD of Greatest Eclipse	ΔT s	Luna Num	Saros Num	Ecl Type	QSE	Gamma	Pen Mag	Um Mag	Phase Durations			Greatest in Zenith	
												Pen m	Par m	Total m	Lat	Long
1081	091	1941 Mar 13	11:55:47	25	-728	112	P	-a	-0.8437	1.2971	0.3226	272.3	119.8	-	2N	177W
1082	091	1941 Sep 05	17:47:14	25	-722	117	P	-t	0.9747	1.0884	0.0511	279.4	53.4	-	6S	93E
1083	091	1942 Mar 03	00:21:54	25	-716	122	T-	-p	-0.1545	2.5879	1.5612	344.4	219.7	95.9	7N	2W
1084	091	1942 Aug 26	03:48:25	26	-710	127	T+	pp	0.1818	2.5142	1.5344	329.6	214.2	93.4	10S	57W
1085	091	1943 Feb 20	05:38:23	26	-704	132	P	t-	0.5752	1.8444	0.7616	345.2	189.0	-	12N	81W
1086	091	1943 Aug 15	19:28:46	26	-698	137	P	a-	-0.5533	1.8152	0.8697	296.8	178.4	-	15S	69E
1087	091	1944 Feb 09	05:14:57	26	-692	142	N	t-	1.2698	0.5793	-0.5223	226.7	-	-	16N	75W
1088	091	1944 Jul 06	04:40:01	27	-687	109	N	-a	1.2597	0.5328	-0.4398	192.8	-	-	21S	69W
1089	091	1944 Aug 04	12:26:52	27	-686	147	N	a-	-1.2843	0.4785	-0.4758	179.2	-	-	18S	175E
1090	091	1944 Dec 29	14:49:35	27	-681	114	Nx	-a	-1.0115	0.0220	-0.0176	266.7	-	-	22N	138E
1091	091	1945 Jun 25	15:14:22	27	-675	119	P	-t	0.5370	1.8862	0.8593	333.4	192.7	-	23S	132E
1092	091	1945 Dec 19	02:20:47	27	-669	124	T	-p	-0.2845	2.3293	1.3424	321.0	204.9	78.9	23N	36W
1093	092	1946 Jun 14	18:39:17	28	-663	129	T-	pp	-0.2324	2.4654	1.3983	369.3	229.1	91.1	23S	80E
1094	092	1946 Dec 08	17:48:28	28	-657	134	T	p-	0.3864	2.1337	1.1639	309.6	194.9	57.3	23N	91E
1095	092	1947 Jun 03	19:15:43	28	-651	139	P	t-	-0.9850	1.0819	0.0202	289.0	34.7	-	23S	70E
1096	092	1947 Nov 28	08:34:28	28	-645	144	N	a-	1.0838	0.8684	-0.1297	238.4	-	-	22N	132W
1097	092	1948 Apr 23	13:39:19	28	-640	111	P	-a	1.0016	1.0172	0.0230	257.7	34.4	-	12S	155E
1098	092	1948 Oct 18	02:35:41	29	-634	116	Nx	-t	-1.0245	1.0141	-0.0571	279.8	-	-	9N	42W
1099	092	1949 Apr 13	04:11:25	29	-628	121	T+	-p	0.2474	2.3825	1.4251	315.9	205.7	84.9	9S	62W
1100	092	1949 Oct 07	02:56:55	29	-622	126	T	-p	-0.3219	2.3118	1.2236	369.3	222.9	72.8	5N	47W
1101	092	1950 Apr 02	20:44:34	29	-616	131	T	a-	-0.4599	1.9951	1.0329	306.6	189.6	26.9	5S	50E
1102	092	1950 Sep 26	04:17:11	29	-610	136	T	t-	0.4101	2.1331	1.0783	350.1	209.8	44.3	1N	66W
1103	092	1951 Mar 23	10:37:32	30	-604	141	N	a-	-1.2099	0.6419	-0.3660	214.4	-	-	2S	158W
1104	092	1951 Aug 17	03:14:41	30	-599	108	N	-a	-1.4828	0.1196	-0.8455	93.7	-	-	15S	47W
1105	093	1951 Sep 15	12:27:05	30	-598	146	N	a-	1.1187	0.8035	-0.1927	234.7	-	-	2S	172E
1106	093	1952 Feb 11	00:39:48	30	-593	113	P	-t	0.9416	1.1782	0.0832	302.0	70.1	-	15N	6W
1107	093	1952 Aug 05	19:47:55	30	-587	118	P	-a	-0.7383	1.4742	0.5318	278.5	147.2	-	18S	65E
1108	093	1953 Jan 29	23:47:49	30	-581	123	T+	-p	0.2606	2.4291	1.3314	371.1	225.8	84.5	18N	7E
1109	093	1953 Jul 26	12:21:10	30	-575	128	T-	pp	-0.0071	2.8265	1.8629	326.6	215.7	100.7	19S	176E
1110	093	1954 Jan 19	02:32:21	31	-569	133	T	a-	-0.4357	2.0852	1.0322	341.3	202.9	28.2	20N	35W
1111	093	1954 Jul 16	00:20:51	31	-563	138	P	t-	0.7877	1.4202	0.4054	301.7	140.9	-	21S	4W
1112	093	1955 Jan 08	12:33:20	31	-557	143	N	a-	-1.0907	0.8555	-0.1421	236.1	-	-	21N	173E
1113	093	1955 Jun 05	14:23:23	31	-552	110	N	-t	-1.2384	0.6218	-0.4498	232.4	-	-	24S	144E
1114	093	1955 Nov 29	16:59:59	31	-546	115	P	-a	0.9551	1.0917	0.1190	253.1	74.2	-	22N	102E
1115	093	1956 May 24	15:31:52	32	-540	120	P	-t	-0.4726	2.0174	0.9647	348.6	204.5	-	21S	126E
1116	093	1956 Nov 18	06:48:16	32	-534	125	T	-p	0.2917	2.3285	1.3172	332.3	209.5	78.4	20N	106W
1117	094	1957 May 13	22:31:28	32	-528	130	T	a-	0.3046	2.3001	1.2982	335.1	211.6	77.6	18S	21E
1118	094	1957 Nov 07	14:27:30	32	-522	135	T	t-	-0.4332	2.0963	1.0305	349.5	206.6	27.9	16N	139E
1119	094	1958 Apr 04	04:00:13	32	-517	102	Ne	-a	-1.5380	0.0136	-0.9421	31.2	-	-	7S	60W
1120	094	1958 May 03	12:13:30	32	-516	140	P	a-	1.0188	0.9676	0.0092	242.3	21.1	-	15S	176E
1121	094	1958 Oct 27	15:27:51	33	-510	145	N	t-	-1.1571	0.7825	-0.3118	258.0	-	-	12N	124E
1122	094	1959 Mar 24	20:11:57	33	-505	112	P	-a	-0.8757	1.2379	0.2643	268.3	109.6	-	2S	58E
1123	094	1959 Sep 17	01:03:36	33	-499	117	N	-t	1.0296	0.9874	-0.0495	268.1	-	-	2S	17W
1124	094	1960 Mar 13	08:28:21	33	-493	122	T-	-p	-0.1799	2.5415	1.5145	344.9	219.4	94.0	3N	125W
1125	094	1960 Sep 05	11:21:51	33	-487	127	T+	-p	0.2422	2.4031	1.4239	326.8	210.9	86.7	6S	171W
1126	094	1961 Mar 02	13:28:40	34	-481	132	P	t-	0.5541	1.8828	0.8006	347.7	192.9	-	8N	161E
1127	094	1961 Aug 26	03:08:51	34	-475	137	P	a-	-0.4895	1.9330	0.9863	301.5	186.0	-	11S	46W
1128	094	1962 Feb 19	13:03:43	34	-469	142	N	t-	1.2511	0.6120	-0.4865	232.0	-	-	12N	168E
1129	095	1962 Jul 17	11:54:48	34	-464	109	N	-a	1.3371	0.3925	-0.5835	168.3	-	-	20S	177W
1130	095	1962 Aug 15	19:57:31	34	-463	147	N	a-	-1.2210	0.5963	-0.3615	198.3	-	-	15S	62E
1131	095	1963 Jan 09	23:19:42	35	-458	114	Nx	-a	-1.0128	1.0180	-0.0184	265.4	-	-	21N	12E
1132	095	1963 Jul 06	22:02:59	35	-452	119	P	-t	0.6197	1.7360	0.7060	327.3	179.9	-	22S	31E
1133	095	1963 Dec 30	11:07:25	35	-446	124	T	-p	-0.2889	2.3206	1.3350	320.1	204.3	78.1	23N	166W
1134	095	1964 Jun 25	01:06:50	35	-440	129	T-	pp	-0.1461	2.6238	1.5565	372.2	233.3	100.8	24S	16W
1135	095	1964 Dec 19	02:37:54	36	-434	134	T	p-	0.3801	2.1461	1.1748	310.2	195.5	58.9	24N	40W
1136	095	1965 Jun 14	01:49:26	36	-428	139	P	t-	-0.9006	1.2351	0.1767	302.8	100.3	-	24S	27W
1137	095	1965 Dec 08	17:10:31	36	-422	144	N	a-	1.0775	0.8820	-0.1200	240.8	-	-	24N	100E
1138	095	1966 May 04	21:12:07	37	-417	111	N	-a	1.0554	0.9158	-0.0727	246.0	-	-	15S	42E
1139	095	1966 Oct 29	10:12:54	37	-411	116	N	-t	-1.0600	0.9517	-0.1249	273.8	-	-	12N	157W
1140	095	1967 Apr 24	12:07:04	38	-405	121	T	-p	0.2972	2.2892	1.3356	313.4	202.8	77.9	12S	178E

Cat Num	Canon Plate	Calendar Date	TD of Greatest Eclipse	ΔT s	Luna Num	Saros Num	Ecl Type	QSE	Gamma	Pen Mag	Um Mag	Pen m	Par m	Total m	Lat	Long
1141	096	1967 Oct 18	10:15:48	38	-399	126	T	-t	-0.3653	2.2337	1.1426	367.2	218.9	59.8	9N	157W
1142	096	1968 Apr 13	04:48:01	39	-393	131	T	p-	-0.4173	2.0725	1.1116	309.6	194.2	48.5	9S	72W
1143	096	1968 Oct 06	11:42:35	39	-387	136	T	t-	0.3605	2.2242	1.1691	352.1	214.0	63.0	6N	179W
1144	096	1969 Apr 02	18:33:05	39	-381	141	N	a-	-1.1765	0.7034	-0.3046	223.8	-	-	6S	82E
1145	096	1969 Aug 27	10:48:17	40	-376	108	Ne	-a	-1.5407	0.0134	-0.9514	31.5	-	-	11S	161W
1146	096	1969 Sep 25	20:10:18	40	-375	146	N	a-	1.0656	0.9008	-0.0952	245.2	-	-	2N	55E
1147	096	1970 Feb 21	08:30:44	40	-370	113	P	-t	0.9620	1.1403	0.0464	298.6	52.7	-	11N	124W
1148	096	1970 Aug 17	03:24:06	41	-364	118	P	-a	-0.8053	1.3521	0.4080	270.7	131.4	-	14S	49W
1149	096	1971 Feb 10	07:45:21	41	-358	123	T	-p	0.2741	2.4026	1.3082	369.6	224.7	82.2	15N	112W
1150	096	1971 Aug 06	19:43:52	42	-352	128	T-	pp	-0.0794	2.6958	1.7283	327.4	215.5	99.4	17S	66E
1151	096	1972 Jan 30	10:54:05	42	-346	133	T	a-	-0.4273	2.0987	1.0497	340.4	203.4	34.8	17N	160W
1152	096	1972 Jul 26	07:16:21	43	-340	138	P	t-	0.7117	1.5618	0.5427	312.5	160.2	-	19S	108W
1153	097	1973 Jan 18	21:17:57	43	-334	143	N	a-	-1.0845	0.8656	-0.1292	236.6	-	-	19N	43E
1154	097	1973 Jun 15	20:50:41	44	-329	110	N	-t	-1.3217	0.4685	-0.6020	204.7	-	-	25S	48E
1155	097	1973 Jul 15	11:39:17	44	-328	148	Nb	t-	1.5178	0.1047	-0.9580	99.1	-	-	20S	174W
1156	097	1973 Dec 10	01:45:06	44	-323	115	P	-a	0.9644	1.0760	0.1007	252.1	68.5	-	24N	28W
1157	097	1974 Jun 04	22:16:44	45	-317	120	P	-t	-0.5489	1.8752	0.8270	341.2	193.6	-	23S	26E
1158	097	1974 Nov 29	15:14:07	45	-311	125	T	-p	0.3054	2.3058	1.2896	333.2	209.0	75.8	22N	129E
1159	097	1975 May 25	05:48:47	46	-305	130	T+	p-	-0.2367	2.4218	1.4253	336.0	215.2	88.3	21S	88W
1160	097	1975 Nov 18	22:24:13	46	-299	135	T	p-	-0.4134	2.1352	1.0642	352.2	209.0	40.2	19N	20E
1161	097	1976 May 13	19:55:08	47	-293	140	P	a-	0.9586	1.0761	0.1217	251.9	75.4	-	18S	61E
1162	097	1976 Nov 06	23:02:00	47	-287	145	N	t-	-1.1276	0.8383	-0.2593	265.9	-	-	15N	11E
1163	097	1977 Apr 04	04:19:03	48	-282	112	P	-a	-0.9148	1.1657	0.1929	263.0	94.8	-	7S	64W
1164	097	1977 Sep 27	08:30:08	48	-276	117	N	-t	1.0768	0.9008	-0.1360	257.6	-	-	3N	130W
1165	098	1978 Mar 24	16:23:11	49	-270	122	T-	-p	-0.2140	2.4790	1.4518	345.0	218.6	90.7	2S	116E
1166	098	1978 Sep 16	19:05:01	49	-264	127	T	-p	0.2951	2.3060	1.3268	323.9	207.2	78.6	2S	73E
1167	098	1979 Mar 13	21:08:52	50	-258	132	P	t-	0.5254	1.9350	0.8538	350.7	197.7	-	3N	46E
1168	098	1979 Sep 06	10:55:02	50	-252	137	T	a-	-0.4305	2.0421	1.0936	305.3	191.9	44.4	7S	164W
1169	098	1980 Mar 01	20:46:04	51	-246	142	N	t-	1.2270	0.6545	-0.4404	238.6	-	-	8N	52E
1170	098	1980 Jul 27	19:08:58	51	-241	109	N	-a	1.4139	0.2535	-0.7263	137.6	-	-	18S	74E
1171	098	1980 Aug 26	03:31:21	51	-240	147	N	a-	-1.1608	0.7089	-0.2531	214.4	-	-	12S	52W
1172	098	1981 Jan 20	07:50:48	51	-235	114	Nx	-a	-1.0142	1.0136	-0.0192	263.9	-	-	19N	115W
1173	098	1981 Jul 17	04:47:40	52	-229	119	P	-t	0.7045	1.5822	0.5486	319.7	163.2	-	21S	70W
1174	098	1982 Jan 09	19:56:43	52	-223	124	T	-p	-0.2916	2.3147	1.3310	319.2	203.9	77.7	22N	63E
1175	098	1982 Jul 06	07:31:47	53	-217	129	T-	pp	-0.0579	2.7860	1.7180	374.0	235.6	105.7	23S	112W
1176	098	1982 Dec 30	11:29:37	53	-211	134	T	p-	0.3758	2.1545	1.1822	310.7	195.9	60.0	24N	172W
1177	099	1983 Jun 25	08:23:11	53	-205	139	P	t-	-0.8152	1.3901	0.3348	314.8	134.6	-	24S	125W
1178	099	1983 Dec 20	01:49:57	54	-199	144	N	a-	1.0747	0.8890	-0.1167	242.3	-	-	24N	28W
1179	099	1984 May 15	04:41:03	54	-194	111	N	-a	1.1131	0.8071	-0.1759	232.6	-	-	18S	71W
1180	099	1984 Jun 13	14:26:38	54	-193	149	Nb	a-	-1.5240	0.0647	-0.9414	73.0	-	-	25S	143E
1181	099	1984 Nov 08	17:56:09	54	-188	116	N	-t	-1.0900	0.8993	-0.1825	268.5	-	-	16N	88E
1182	099	1985 May 04	19:57:19	55	-182	121	T	-p	0.3520	2.1870	1.2369	310.3	199.0	67.7	16S	60E
1183	099	1985 Oct 28	17:43:17	55	-176	126	T	-t	-0.4022	2.1673	1.0736	365.1	215.0	43.9	13N	91E
1184	099	1986 Apr 24	12:43:30	55	-170	131	T	p-	-0.3683	2.1620	1.2022	312.7	198.8	63.6	13S	169E
1185	099	1986 Oct 17	19:18:54	55	-164	136	T	h-	0.3189	2.3008	1.2455	353.3	216.8	73.7	10N	67E
1186	099	1987 Apr 14	02:19:48	55	-158	141	N	h-	-1.1364	0.7770	-0.2312	234.2	-	-	10S	35W
1187	099	1987 Oct 07	04:02:29	56	-152	146	N	a-	1.0189	0.9864	-0.0095	253.6	-	-	6N	64W
1188	099	1988 Mar 03	16:13:42	56	-147	113	Nx	-t	0.9886	1.0908	-0.0016	293.8	-	-	7N	120E
1189	100	1988 Aug 27	11:05:29	56	-141	118	P	-a	-0.8682	1.2380	0.2916	262.6	113.0	-	11S	165W
1190	100	1989 Feb 20	15:36:18	56	-135	123	T	-p	0.2935	2.3651	1.2747	367.8	223.1	78.5	11N	130E
1191	100	1989 Aug 17	03:09:07	57	-129	128	T-	-p	-0.1491	2.5703	1.5984	327.6	214.3	95.8	14S	46W
1192	100	1990 Feb 09	19:12:02	57	-123	133	T	a-	-0.4148	2.1191	1.0750	339.7	204.3	42.3	14N	76E
1193	100	1990 Aug 06	14:13:15	57	-117	138	P	t-	0.6374	1.7005	0.6766	322.1	175.5	-	16S	148E
1194	100	1991 Jan 30	05:59:37	58	-111	143	N	a-	-1.0752	0.8808	-0.1106	237.6	-	-	17N	87W
1195	100	1991 Jun 27	03:15:42	58	-106	110	N	-t	-1.4064	0.3127	-0.7571	169.6	-	-	25S	48W
1196	100	1991 Jul 26	18:08:48	58	-105	148	N	t-	1.4370	0.2542	-0.8109	152.8	-	-	18S	89E
1197	100	1991 Dec 21	10:34:00	58	-100	115	P	-a	0.9709	1.0651	0.0876	251.6	64.1	-	24N	159W
1198	100	1992 Jun 15	04:57:57	59	-94	120	P	-t	-0.6289	1.7264	0.6822	332.3	179.8	-	24S	74W
1199	100	1992 Dec 09	23:45:05	59	-88	125	T	-p	0.3144	2.2915	1.2709	334.2	208.8	73.9	23N	2E
1200	100	1993 Jun 04	13:01:26	59	-82	130	T+	p-	0.1638	2.5532	1.5617	336.4	217.9	95.8	22S	164E

THOUSAND YEAR CANON OF LUNAR ECLIPSES: 1501 TO 2500

Cat Num	Canon Plate	Calendar Date	TD of Greatest Eclipse	ΔT s	Luna Num	Saros Num	Ecl Type	QSE	Gamma	Pen Mag	Um Mag	Pen m	Par m	Total m	Lat	Long
1201	101	1993 Nov 29	06:27:06	60	-76	135	T	p-	-0.3994	2.1633	1.0876	354.5	210.8	46.7	21N	99W
1202	101	1994 May 25	03:31:20	60	-70	140	P	a-	0.8933	1.1941	0.2432	261.3	104.6	-	20S	53W
1203	101	1994 Nov 18	06:44:54	61	-64	145	N	t-	-1.1048	0.8816	-0.2189	271.7	-	-	18N	105W
1204	101	1995 Apr 15	12:19:04	61	-59	112	P	-a	-0.9594	1.0836	0.1114	256.4	73.0	-	11S	175E
1205	101	1995 Oct 08	16:05:12	61	-53	117	N	-t	1.1179	0.8253	-0.2115	247.7	-	-	7N	116E
1206	101	1996 Apr 04	00:10:47	62	-47	122	T-	-p	-0.2534	2.4068	1.3795	344.8	217.2	85.8	6S	2W
1207	101	1996 Sep 27	02:55:24	62	-41	127	T	-p	0.3426	2.2188	1.2395	321.0	203.3	69.2	2N	46W
1208	101	1997 Mar 24	04:40:28	62	-35	132	P	t-	0.4899	1.9994	0.9195	354.0	203.1	-	1S	68W
1209	101	1997 Sep 16	18:47:42	63	-29	137	T	p-	-0.3768	2.1417	1.1909	308.3	196.5	61.5	3S	77E
1210	101	1998 Mar 13	04:21:09	63	-23	142	N	t-	1.1964	0.7086	-0.3824	246.4	-	-	4N	62W
1211	101	1998 Aug 08	02:25:55	63	-18	109	N	-a	1.4876	0.1206	-0.8637	96.5	-	-	15S	35W
1212	101	1998 Sep 06	11:11:11	63	-17	147	N	a-	-1.1058	0.8122	-0.1544	227.9	-	-	7S	168W
1213	102	1999 Jan 31	16:18:34	63	-12	114	Nx	-a	-1.0190	1.0027	-0.0258	261.8	-	-	16N	119E
1214	102	1999 Jul 28	11:34:46	64	-6	119	P	-t	0.7863	1.4342	0.3966	311.0	142.6	-	18S	172W
1215	102	2000 Jan 21	04:44:35	64	0	124	T	-p	-0.2957	2.3060	1.3246	318.3	203.3	77.0	20N	68W
1216	102	2000 Jul 16	13:56:39	64	6	129	T+	pp	0.0302	2.8375	1.7684	374.5	236.0	106.4	21S	153E
1217	102	2001 Jan 09	20:21:40	64	12	134	T	p-	0.3720	2.1618	1.1889	311.2	196.3	61.0	22N	57E
1218	102	2001 Jul 05	14:56:23	64	18	139	P	t-	-0.7287	1.5476	0.4947	325.2	159.3	-	23S	137E
1219	102	2001 Dec 30	10:30:22	64	24	144	N	a-	1.0732	0.8933	-0.1155	243.6	-	-	24N	157W
1220	102	2002 May 26	12:04:27	64	29	111	N	-a	1.1759	0.6893	-0.2888	216.6	-	-	20S	179E
1221	102	2002 Jun 24	21:28:12	64	30	149	N	a-	-1.4440	0.2095	-0.7925	129.1	-	-	25S	39E
1222	102	2002 Nov 20	01:47:41	64	35	116	N	-t	-1.1127	0.8600	-0.2264	264.4	-	-	19N	30W
1223	102	2003 May 16	03:41:13	64	41	121	T	-a	0.4123	2.0747	1.1276	306.6	193.9	51.4	19S	56W
1224	102	2003 Nov 09	01:19:38	64	47	126	T	-t	-0.4319	2.1139	1.0178	363.3	211.4	22.0	16N	24W
1225	103	2004 May 04	20:31:17	65	53	131	T	p-	-0.3132	2.2627	1.3035	315.8	203.2	75.5	17S	51E
1226	103	2004 Oct 28	03:05:11	65	59	136	T	p-	0.2846	2.3637	1.3081	353.9	218.7	80.5	13N	50W
1227	103	2005 Apr 24	09:55:54	65	65	141	N	h-	-1.0885	0.8651	-0.1435	245.7	-	-	14S	150W
1228	103	2005 Oct 17	12:04:27	65	71	146	P	a-	0.9796	1.0586	0.0626	259.9	56.0	-	10N	175E
1229	103	2006 Mar 14	23:48:35	65	76	113	Nx	-t	1.0211	1.0301	-0.0603	287.5	-	-	3N	6E
1230	103	2006 Sep 07	18:52:25	65	82	118	P	-a	-0.9262	1.1330	0.1838	254.5	91.1	-	7S	77E
1231	103	2007 Mar 03	23:21:59	65	88	123	T	-p	0.3175	2.3188	1.2328	365.5	221.1	73.4	7N	13E
1232	103	2007 Aug 28	10:38:27	65	94	128	T-	-p	-0.2146	2.4526	1.4758	327.4	212.2	90.0	10S	159W
1233	103	2008 Feb 21	03:27:09	66	100	133	T	a-	-0.3992	2.1451	1.1062	339.1	205.5	49.8	10N	48W
1234	103	2008 Aug 16	21:11:12	66	106	138	P	t-	0.5646	1.8366	0.8076	330.6	188.2	-	13S	43E
1235	103	2009 Feb 09	14:39:21	66	112	143	N	a-	-1.0640	0.8995	-0.0882	238.9	-	-	14N	144E
1236	103	2009 Jul 07	09:39:44	66	117	110	N	-t	-1.4916	0.1562	-0.9132	121.5	-	-	24S	143W
1237	104	2009 Aug 06	00:40:16	66	118	148	N	t-	1.3572	0.4020	-0.6660	189.9	-	-	16S	9W
1238	104	2009 Dec 31	19:23:46	66	123	115	P	-a	0.9766	1.0556	0.0764	251.1	60.0	-	24N	70E
1239	104	2010 Jun 26	11:39:34	66	129	120	P	-t	-0.7091	1.5773	0.5368	322.2	162.9	-	24S	174W
1240	104	2010 Dec 21	08:18:04	66	135	125	T	-p	0.3214	2.2807	1.2561	335.2	208.7	72.3	24N	125W
1241	104	2011 Jun 15	20:13:43	67	141	130	T+	pp	0.0897	2.6868	1.6999	336.2	219.3	100.2	23S	57E
1242	104	2011 Dec 10	14:32:57	67	147	135	T	p-	-0.3882	2.1860	1.1061	356.5	212.3	51.1	23N	140E
1243	104	2012 Jun 04	11:04:20	67	153	140	P	a-	0.8248	1.3183	0.3704	270.1	126.6	-	22S	166W
1244	104	2012 Nov 28	14:34:07	67	159	145	N	t-	-1.0869	0.9155	-0.1873	276.1	-	-	20N	130E
1245	104	2013 Apr 25	20:08:37	67	164	112	P	-a	-1.0121	0.9867	0.0148	247.8	27.0	-	14S	57E
1246	104	2013 May 25	04:11:07	67	165	150	Nb	a-	1.5351	0.0157	-0.9335	33.6	-	-	19S	63W
1247	104	2013 Oct 18	23:51:25	67	170	117	N	-h	1.1508	0.7649	-0.2718	239.2	-	-	11N	2W
1248	104	2014 Apr 15	07:46:48	67	176	122	T	-a	-0.3017	2.3182	1.2907	344.0	214.7	77.8	10S	116W
1249	105	2014 Oct 08	10:55:44	67	182	127	T	-p	0.3827	2.1456	1.1659	318.2	199.5	58.8	6N	167W
1250	105	2015 Apr 04	12:01:24	68	188	132	T	t-	0.4460	2.0792	1.0008	357.6	209.0	4.7	5S	179W
1251	105	2015 Sep 28	02:48:17	68	194	137	T	p-	-0.3296	2.2296	1.2764	310.8	199.9	71.9	2N	44W
1252	105	2016 Mar 23	11:48:22	68	200	142	N	t-	1.1592	0.7748	-0.3118	255.4	-	-	0S	175W
1253	105	2016 Sep 16	18:55:27	68	206	147	N	a-	-1.0549	0.9080	-0.0635	239.4	-	-	3S	75E
1254	105	2017 Feb 11	00:45:03	68	211	114	N	-a	-1.0255	0.9884	-0.0354	259.2	-	-	13N	8W
1255	105	2017 Aug 07	18:21:38	69	217	119	P	-t	0.8669	1.2886	0.2465	301.0	115.3	-	15S	86E
1256	105	2018 Jan 31	13:31:00	69	223	124	T	-p	-0.3014	2.2941	1.3155	317.3	202.8	76.1	17N	161E
1257	105	2018 Jul 27	20:22:54	69	229	129	T+	pp	0.1168	2.6792	1.6087	373.9	234.6	103.0	19S	56E
1258	105	2019 Jan 21	05:13:27	69	235	134	T	p-	0.3684	2.1684	1.1953	311.6	196.8	62.0	20N	75W
1259	105	2019 Jul 16	21:31:55	69	241	139	P	t-	-0.6430	1.7037	0.6531	333.8	178.0	-	22S	39E
1260	105	2020 Jan 10	19:11:11	69	247	144	N	a-	1.0727	0.8956	-0.1160	244.7	-	-	23N	74E

Cat Num	Canon Plate	Calendar Date	TD of Greatest Eclipse	ΔT s	Luna Num	Saros Num	Ecl Type	QSE	Gamma	Pen Mag	Um Mag	Pen m	Par m	Total m	Lat	Long
1261	106	2020 Jun 05	19:26:14	70	252	111	N	-a	1.2406	0.5683	-0.4053	198.3	–	–	21S	69E
1262	106	2020 Jul 05	04:31:12	70	253	149	N	a-	-1.3639	0.3546	-0.6436	165.1	–	–	24S	66W
1263	106	2020 Nov 30	09:44:02	70	258	116	N	-t	-1.1309	0.8285	-0.2619	261.1	–	–	21N	148W
1264	106	2021 May 26	11:19:53	70	264	121	T	-a	0.4774	1.9540	1.0095	302.1	187.4	14.5	21S	170W
1265	106	2021 Nov 19	09:04:06	70	270	126	P	-t	-0.4552	2.0720	0.9742	361.6	208.4	–	19N	139W
1266	106	2022 May 16	04:12:42	70	276	131	T-	p-	-0.2532	2.3726	1.4137	318.8	207.3	84.9	19S	64W
1267	106	2022 Nov 08	11:00:22	71	282	136	T+	p-	0.2570	2.4143	1.3589	354.0	219.9	85.0	17N	169W
1268	106	2023 May 05	17:24:04	71	288	141	N	h-	-1.0350	0.9637	-0.0456	257.6	–	–	17S	98E
1269	106	2023 Oct 28	20:15:17	71	294	146	P	a-	0.9472	1.1181	0.1221	264.7	77.4	–	14N	52E
1270	106	2024 Mar 25	07:14:00	71	299	113	N	-t	1.0610	0.9557	-0.1324	279.2	–	–	1S	106W
1271	106	2024 Sep 18	02:45:26	71	305	118	P	-a	-0.9792	1.0373	0.0849	246.4	62.8	–	3S	42W
1272	106	2025 Mar 14	06:59:56	72	311	123	T	-p	0.3485	2.2595	1.1784	362.7	218.3	65.4	3N	102W
1273	107	2025 Sep 07	18:12:58	72	317	128	T	-p	-0.2752	2.3440	1.3619	326.8	209.4	82.1	6S	87E
1274	107	2026 Mar 03	11:34:52	72	323	133	T	a-	-0.3765	2.1839	1.1507	338.7	207.2	58.3	6N	171W
1275	107	2026 Aug 28	04:14:04	72	329	138	P	t-	0.4964	1.9645	0.9299	337.9	198.1	–	9S	63W
1276	107	2027 Feb 20	23:14:05	73	335	143	N	a-	-1.0480	0.9267	-0.0568	241.1	–	–	10N	15E
1277	107	2027 Jul 18	16:04:11	73	340	110	Ne	-t	-1.5759	0.0015	-1.0679	12.1	–	–	22S	121E
1278	107	2027 Aug 17	07:14:58	73	341	148	N	t-	1.2797	0.5457	-0.5253	218.7	–	–	12S	108W
1279	107	2028 Jan 12	04:14:13	73	346	115	P	-a	0.9818	1.0468	0.0662	250.8	56.0	–	23N	61W
1280	107	2028 Jul 06	18:20:57	73	352	120	P	-t	-0.7904	1.4266	0.3892	310.7	141.5	–	23S	86E
1281	107	2028 Dec 31	16:53:15	73	358	125	T	-p	0.3258	2.2742	1.2463	336.3	208.9	71.3	23N	108E
1282	107	2029 Jun 26	03:23:22	74	364	130	T+	pp	0.0124	2.8266	1.8436	335.2	219.6	101.9	23S	50W
1283	107	2029 Dec 20	22:43:12	74	370	135	T	p-	-0.3811	2.2008	1.1174	358.1	213.3	53.7	23N	19E
1284	107	2030 Jun 15	18:34:33	74	376	140	P	a-	0.7535	1.4480	0.5025	278.3	144.4	–	23S	82E
1285	108	2030 Dec 09	22:28:51	74	382	145	N	t-	-1.0732	0.9416	-0.1628	279.3	–	–	22N	21E
1286	108	2031 May 07	03:52:01	75	387	112	N	-a	-1.0695	0.8815	-0.0904	237.4	–	–	18S	59W
1287	108	2031 Jun 05	11:45:17	75	388	150	N	a-	1.4732	0.1292	-0.8199	95.6	–	–	21S	176W
1288	108	2031 Oct 30	07:46:44	75	393	117	N	-h	1.1774	0.7161	-0.3204	231.8	–	–	15N	121W
1289	108	2032 Apr 25	15:14:51	75	399	122	T	-a	-0.3558	2.2192	1.1913	342.5	211.2	65.5	14S	131E
1290	108	2032 Oct 18	19:03:40	75	405	127	T	-p	0.4169	2.0830	1.1028	315.5	196.0	47.1	10N	71E
1291	108	2033 Apr 14	19:13:51	76	411	132	T	t-	0.3954	2.1711	1.0944	361.3	215.0	49.2	9S	72E
1292	108	2033 Oct 08	10:56:23	76	417	137	T	p-	-0.2889	2.3057	1.3497	312.7	202.4	78.8	6N	167W
1293	108	2034 Apr 03	19:07:00	76	423	142	N	t-	1.1144	0.8546	-0.2274	265.5	–	–	5S	75E
1294	108	2034 Sep 28	02:47:37	76	429	147	P	a-	-1.0110	0.9911	0.0145	248.8	26.7	–	1N	44W
1295	108	2035 Feb 22	09:06:11	76	434	114	N	-a	-1.0367	0.9652	-0.0535	255.8	–	–	9N	133W
1296	108	2035 Aug 19	01:12:15	77	440	119	P	-t	0.9434	1.1507	0.1037	289.9	76.5	–	12S	17W
1297	109	2036 Feb 11	22:13:06	77	446	124	T	-p	-0.3110	2.2751	1.2995	316.2	202.0	74.5	14N	31E
1298	109	2036 Aug 07	02:52:32	77	452	129	T+	pp	0.2004	2.5266	1.4544	372.2	231.4	95.3	16S	41W
1299	109	2037 Jan 31	14:01:38	78	458	134	T	p-	0.3619	2.1803	1.2074	312.2	197.5	63.7	18N	153E
1300	109	2037 Jul 27	04:09:53	78	464	139	P	t-	-0.5582	1.8584	0.8095	340.9	192.4	–	20S	60W
1301	109	2038 Jan 21	03:49:52	78	470	144	N	a-	1.0711	0.8996	-0.1140	245.9	–	–	21N	54W
1302	109	2038 Jun 17	02:45:02	78	475	111	N	-a	1.3083	0.4422	-0.5274	176.4	–	–	22S	41W
1303	109	2038 Jul 16	11:35:56	78	476	149	N	a-	-1.2838	0.4999	-0.4952	192.5	–	–	23S	172W
1304	109	2038 Dec 11	17:45:00	79	481	116	N	-t	-1.1449	0.8046	-0.2892	258.5	–	–	22N	93E
1305	109	2039 Jun 06	18:54:25	79	487	121	P	-a	0.5460	1.8272	0.8846	296.8	179.3	–	22S	77E
1306	109	2039 Nov 30	16:56:28	79	493	126	P	-t	-0.4721	2.0418	0.9426	360.2	206.0	–	21N	103E
1307	109	2040 May 26	11:46:22	79	499	131	T-	p-	-0.1872	2.4938	1.5348	321.5	210.8	92.3	21S	177W
1308	109	2040 Nov 18	19:04:41	80	505	136	T+	p-	0.2361	2.4525	1.3974	353.7	220.5	87.8	20N	70E
1309	110	2041 May 16	00:43:02	80	511	141	P	t-	-0.9747	1.0748	0.0645	269.8	58.5	–	20S	12W
1310	110	2041 Nov 08	04:35:04	80	517	146	P	a-	0.9212	1.1657	0.1696	268.1	90.4	–	18N	73W
1311	110	2042 Apr 05	14:30:12	80	522	113	N	-t	1.1080	0.8681	-0.2175	268.5	–	–	5S	144E
1312	110	2042 Sep 29	10:45:47	81	528	118	N	-a	-1.0262	0.9529	-0.0030	238.6	–	–	2N	163W
1313	110	2043 Mar 25	14:32:04	81	534	123	T	-t	0.3849	2.1900	1.1142	359.4	214.6	53.4	2S	144E
1314	110	2043 Sep 19	01:51:50	81	540	128	N	-a	-0.3316	2.2433	1.2556	325.8	206.1	71.7	2S	29W
1315	110	2044 Mar 13	19:38:33	82	546	133	T	a-	-0.3496	2.2303	1.2031	338.5	209.1	66.4	2N	68E
1316	110	2044 Sep 07	11:20:44	82	552	138	T	t-	0.4318	2.0860	1.0456	344.1	206.2	33.9	5S	171W
1317	110	2045 Mar 03	07:43:25	82	558	143	N	a-	-1.0274	0.9624	-0.0168	244.0	–	–	6N	113W
1318	110	2045 Aug 27	13:54:49	82	564	148	N	t-	1.2061	0.6826	-0.3918	241.8	–	–	9S	151E
1319	110	2046 Jan 22	13:02:37	83	569	115	P	-a	0.9886	1.0348	0.0533	250.1	50.4	–	21N	168E
1320	110	2046 Jul 18	01:06:06	83	575	120	P	-t	-0.8692	1.2807	0.2461	298.2	114.6	–	22S	14W

Cat Num	Canon Plate	Calendar Date	TD of Greatest Eclipse	ΔT s	Luna Num	Saros Num	Ecl Type	QSE	Gamma	Pen Mag	Um Mag	Phase Durations Pen m	Phase Durations Par m	Phase Durations Total m	Greatest in Zenith Lat	Greatest in Zenith Long
1321	111	2047 Jan 12	01:26:14	83	581	125	T	-p	0.3317	2.2649	1.2341	337.3	208.9	70.0	22N	19W
1322	111	2047 Jul 07	10:35:45	84	587	130	T-	pp	-0.0636	2.7310	1.7513	333.6	218.6	100.8	23S	157W
1323	111	2048 Jan 01	06:53:55	84	593	135	T	p-	-0.3746	2.2141	1.1280	359.5	214.3	55.9	23N	102W
1324	111	2048 Jun 26	02:02:28	84	599	140	P	a-	0.6797	1.5825	0.6388	285.8	159.2	-	23S	30W
1325	111	2048 Dec 20	06:27:48	84	605	145	N	t-	-1.0624	0.9617	-0.1436	281.7	-	-	22N	97W
1326	111	2049 May 17	11:26:38	85	610	112	N	-a	-1.1337	0.7638	-0.2085	224.3	-	-	21S	172W
1327	111	2049 Jun 15	19:14:12	85	611	150	N	a-	1.4069	0.2511	-0.6985	132.0	-	-	22S	72E
1328	111	2049 Nov 09	15:52:11	85	616	117	N	-h	1.1965	0.6809	-0.3553	226.1	-	-	18N	118E
1329	111	2050 May 06	22:32:02	85	622	122	T	-h	-0.4181	2.1052	1.0767	340.1	206.0	43.2	17S	21E
1330	111	2050 Oct 30	03:21:47	86	628	127	T	-p	0.4435	2.0345	1.0538	313.2	192.9	34.5	14N	54W
1331	111	2051 Apr 26	02:16:28	86	634	132	T	p-	0.3371	2.2773	1.2022	364.9	220.9	69.6	13S	34W
1332	111	2051 Oct 19	19:11:50	86	640	137	T-	p-	-0.2542	2.3708	1.4118	314.3	204.3	83.6	10N	69E
1333	112	2052 Apr 14	02:18:06	87	646	142	N	t-	1.0629	0.9466	-0.1305	276.1	-	-	9S	34W
1334	112	2052 Oct 08	10:45:58	87	652	147	P	a-	-0.9727	1.0642	0.0821	256.7	63.3	-	5N	164W
1335	112	2053 Mar 04	17:22:09	87	657	114	N	-a	-1.0531	0.9323	-0.0807	251.2	-	-	5N	102E
1336	112	2053 Aug 29	08:05:50	88	663	119	Nx	-t	1.0165	1.0192	-0.0330	277.8	-	-	8S	121W
1337	112	2054 Feb 22	06:51:27	88	669	124	T	-p	-0.3242	2.2491	1.2769	314.9	200.9	72.1	10N	99W
1338	112	2054 Aug 18	09:26:30	88	675	129	T	pp	0.2806	2.3805	1.3062	369.6	226.6	83.0	13S	140W
1339	112	2055 Feb 11	22:46:17	88	681	134	T	p-	0.3526	2.1970	1.2246	313.0	198.5	66.0	14N	22E
1340	112	2055 Aug 07	10:53:18	89	687	139	P	t-	-0.4769	2.0069	0.9594	346.4	203.4	-	17S	161W
1341	112	2056 Feb 01	12:26:06	89	693	144	N	a-	1.0682	0.9056	-0.1096	247.3	-	-	18N	177E
1342	112	2056 Jun 27	10:03:09	89	698	111	N	-a	1.3770	0.3143	-0.6519	150.0	-	-	22S	150W
1343	112	2056 Jul 26	18:43:25	89	699	149	N	a-	-1.2048	0.6435	-0.3489	214.5	-	-	20S	81E
1344	112	2056 Dec 22	01:48:56	90	704	116	N	-t	-1.1560	0.7857	-0.3109	256.5	-	-	22N	27W
1345	113	2057 Jun 17	02:26:20	90	710	121	P	-a	0.6168	1.6967	0.7555	290.7	169.3	-	23S	36W
1346	113	2057 Dec 11	00:53:38	90	716	126	P	-t	-0.4853	2.0178	0.9181	358.9	204.0	-	23N	15W
1347	113	2058 Jun 06	19:15:48	91	722	131	T-	pp	-0.1181	2.6210	1.6612	323.7	213.4	97.3	23S	71E
1348	113	2058 Nov 30	03:16:18	91	728	136	T+	p-	0.2208	2.4803	1.4260	353.1	220.7	89.7	22N	52W
1349	113	2059 May 27	07:55:34	91	734	141	P	t-	-0.9098	1.1946	0.1830	281.8	97.2	-	22S	119W
1350	113	2059 Nov 19	13:01:36	92	740	146	P	a-	0.9004	1.2038	0.2080	270.6	99.3	-	20N	161E
1351	113	2060 Apr 15	21:37:05	92	745	113	N	-t	1.1622	0.7675	-0.3155	255.0	-	-	9S	37E
1352	113	2060 Oct 09	18:53:33	92	751	118	N	-a	-1.0671	0.8797	-0.0799	231.4	-	-	6N	74E
1353	113	2060 Nov 08	04:04:13	93	752	156	N	a-	1.5332	0.0268	-0.9374	43.8	-	-	18N	65W
1354	113	2061 Apr 04	21:54:05	93	757	123	T	-t	0.4300	2.1044	1.0341	355.1	209.7	29.9	6S	33E
1355	113	2061 Sep 29	09:38:13	93	763	128	T	-a	-0.3810	2.1556	1.1621	324.9	202.4	59.0	2N	146W
1356	113	2062 Mar 25	03:33:50	94	769	133	T	p-	-0.3150	2.2905	1.2695	338.4	211.4	74.7	2S	52W
1357	114	2062 Sep 18	18:34:02	94	775	138	T	p-	0.3736	2.1959	1.1496	349.3	212.5	59.5	1S	80E
1358	114	2063 Mar 14	16:05:49	94	781	143	P	a-	-1.0008	1.0089	0.0343	247.9	40.7	-	1N	121E
1359	114	2063 Sep 07	20:41:11	95	787	148	N	t-	1.1375	0.8102	-0.2677	260.5	-	-	5S	49E
1360	114	2064 Feb 02	21:48:57	95	792	115	P	-a	0.9969	1.0197	0.0377	249.1	42.6	-	18N	37E
1361	114	2064 Jul 28	07:52:48	95	798	120	P	-t	-0.9473	1.1361	0.1038	284.4	75.7	-	20S	116W
1362	114	2065 Jan 22	09:58:59	96	804	125	T	-p	0.3371	2.2561	1.2231	338.3	209.0	68.8	20N	146W
1363	114	2065 Jul 17	17:48:40	96	810	130	T-	pp	-0.1402	2.5890	1.6121	331.2	216.3	97.0	21S	95E
1364	114	2066 Jan 11	15:04:47	96	816	135	T	p-	-0.3687	2.2259	1.1370	360.8	215.2	57.9	21N	136E
1365	114	2066 Jul 07	09:30:29	97	822	140	P	a-	0.6056	1.7179	0.7753	292.4	171.3	-	22S	141W
1366	114	2066 Dec 31	14:30:09	97	828	145	N'	t-	-1.0540	0.9773	-0.1281	283.4	-	-	22N	143E
1367	114	2067 May 28	18:56:07	97	833	112	N	-a	-1.2013	0.6403	-0.3329	208.6	-	-	23S	76E
1368	114	2067 Jun 27	02:41:06	98	834	150	N	a-	1.3394	0.3755	-0.5752	159.9	-	-	22S	39W
1369	115	2067 Nov 21	00:04:42	98	839	117	N	-h	1.2107	0.6544	-0.3811	221.6	-	-	21N	4W
1370	115	2068 May 17	05:42:17	98	845	122	P	-t	-0.4852	1.9826	0.9532	336.8	199.0	-	20S	86W
1371	115	2068 Nov 09	11:47:00	99	851	127	T	-p	0.4645	1.9962	1.0149	311.3	190.2	18.4	18N	180E
1372	115	2069 May 06	09:09:57	99	857	132	T+	pp	0.2717	2.3965	1.3230	368.2	226.2	84.3	17S	138W
1373	115	2069 Oct 30	03:35:06	99	863	137	T-	p-	-0.2263	2.4235	1.4616	315.5	205.6	86.8	14N	57W
1374	115	2070 Apr 25	09:21:25	100	869	142	Nx	t-	1.0044	1.0516	-0.0208	287.0	-	-	12S	140W
1375	115	2070 Oct 19	18:51:12	100	875	147	P	a-	-0.9406	1.1258	0.1383	263.3	81.7	-	9N	74E
1376	115	2071 Mar 16	01:31:09	100	880	114	N	-a	-1.0757	0.8879	-0.1194	245.2	-	-	1N	21W
1377	115	2071 Sep 09	15:05:40	101	886	119	N	-t	1.0835	0.8989	-0.1586	265.2	-	-	4S	133E
1378	115	2072 Mar 04	15:23:07	101	892	124	T	-p	-0.3431	2.2126	1.2441	313.3	199.4	68.5	6N	132E
1379	115	2072 Aug 28	16:05:42	102	898	129	T	-t	0.3563	2.2428	1.1662	366.1	220.3	64.2	9S	119E
1380	115	2073 Feb 22	07:24:53	102	904	134	T	p-	0.3389	2.2218	1.2503	313.9	199.8	69.2	10N	107W

Cat Num	Canon Plate	Calendar Date	TD of Greatest Eclipse	ΔT s	Luna Num	Saros Num	Ecl Type	QSE	Gamma	Pen Mag	Um Mag	Pen m	Par m	Total m	Lat	Long
1381	116	2073 Aug 17	17:42:41	102	910	139	T	t-	-0.3998	2.1479	1.1013	350.6	211.6	50.1	13S	96E
1382	116	2074 Feb 11	20:55:58	103	916	144	N	a-	1.0612	0.9192	-0.0972	249.6	–	–	15N	50E
1383	116	2074 Jul 08	17:21:37	103	921	111	N	-a	1.4457	0.1870	-0.7765	116.7	–	–	21S	101E
1384	116	2074 Aug 07	01:56:04	103	922	149	N	a-	-1.1291	0.7814	-0.2091	232.3	–	–	17S	27W
1385	116	2075 Jan 02	09:55:03	104	927	116	N	-t	-1.1643	0.7714	-0.3271	255.0	–	–	22N	147W
1386	116	2075 Jun 28	09:55:36	104	933	121	P	-a	0.6897	1.5624	0.6220	283.5	157.0	–	23S	148W
1387	116	2075 Dec 22	08:55:55	104	939	126	P	-t	-0.4945	2.0008	0.9012	357.8	202.6	–	23N	134W
1388	116	2076 Jun 17	02:39:47	105	945	131	T-	pp	-0.0452	2.7555	1.7943	325.5	215.1	100.2	23S	39W
1389	116	2076 Dec 10	11:34:51	105	951	136	T+	p-	0.2102	2.4990	1.4460	352.3	220.6	90.8	23N	175W
1390	116	2077 Jun 06	14:59:52	106	957	141	P	t-	-0.8388	1.3258	0.3123	293.7	125.1	–	24S	135E
1391	116	2077 Nov 29	21:35:53	106	963	146	P	a-	0.8855	1.2309	0.2356	272.1	105.0	–	23N	33E
1392	116	2078 Apr 27	04:35:45	106	968	113	N	-t	1.2223	0.6558	-0.4245	238.3	–	–	13S	69W
1393	117	2078 Oct 21	03:08:04	107	974	118	N	-a	-1.1022	0.8172	-0.1461	224.9	–	–	10N	50W
1394	117	2078 Nov 19	12:40:02	107	975	156	N	a-	1.5148	0.0616	-0.9046	66.1	–	–	21N	166E
1395	117	2079 Apr 16	05:10:45	107	980	123	P	-t	0.4800	2.0100	0.9451	350.2	203.4	–	10S	77W
1396	117	2079 Oct 10	17:30:30	108	986	128	T	-a	-0.4246	2.0786	1.0791	323.9	198.7	42.4	7N	95E
1397	117	2080 Apr 04	11:23:38	108	992	133	T	p-	-0.2751	2.3607	1.3460	338.4	213.6	82.1	6S	170W
1398	117	2080 Sep 29	01:52:42	108	998	138	T	p-	0.3203	2.2967	1.2443	353.8	217.4	73.8	3N	30W
1399	117	2081 Mar 25	00:22:01	109	1004	143	P	a-	-0.9688	1.0653	0.0953	252.5	67.1	–	3S	4W
1400	117	2081 Sep 18	03:35:25	109	1010	148	N	t-	1.0748	0.9271	-0.1544	275.8	–	–	1S	55W
1401	117	2082 Feb 13	06:29:20	110	1015	115	P	-a	1.0101	0.9956	0.0134	247.3	25.6	–	14N	93W
1402	117	2082 Aug 08	14:46:42	110	1021	120	Nx	-t	-1.0204	1.0012	-0.0293	269.8	–	–	17S	141E
1403	117	2083 Feb 02	18:26:46	111	1027	125	T	-p	0.3464	2.2400	1.2052	339.0	208.8	66.5	17N	87E
1404	117	2083 Jul 29	01:05:34	111	1033	130	T-	pp	-0.2143	2.4520	1.4773	328.1	212.9	90.4	19S	14W
1405	118	2084 Jan 22	23:13:00	111	1039	135	T	p-	-0.3610	2.2407	1.1513	362.1	216.3	60.5	19N	15E
1406	118	2084 Jul 17	16:58:51	112	1045	140	P	a-	0.5313	1.8540	0.9119	298.2	181.4	–	20S	107E
1407	118	2085 Jan 10	22:32:29	112	1051	145	N	t-	-1.0453	0.9927	-0.1119	285.0	–	–	21N	24E
1408	118	2085 Jun 08	02:17:36	113	1056	112	N	-a	-1.2746	0.5065	-0.4682	188.6	–	–	24S	34W
1409	118	2085 Jul 07	10:04:39	113	1057	150	N	a-	1.2695	0.5047	-0.4477	183.5	–	–	21S	150W
1410	118	2085 Dec 01	08:25:35	113	1062	117	N	-a	1.2190	0.6387	-0.3957	218.5	–	–	23N	129W
1411	118	2086 May 28	12:43:47	114	1068	122	P	-t	-0.5585	1.8486	0.8180	332.1	189.5	–	22S	169E
1412	118	2086 Nov 20	20:19:42	114	1074	127	P	-p	0.4800	1.9679	0.9865	309.6	188.2	–	20N	52E
1413	118	2087 May 17	15:55:20	115	1080	132	T+	pp	0.1999	2.5276	1.4555	371.1	230.7	95.1	19S	121E
1414	118	2087 Nov 10	12:05:33	115	1086	137	T-	p-	-0.2043	2.4654	1.5006	316.6	206.6	88.9	17N	175E
1415	118	2088 May 05	16:16:50	115	1092	142	P	t-	0.9388	1.1696	0.1020	298.0	77.1	–	16S	116E
1416	118	2088 Oct 30	03:03:20	116	1098	147	P	a-	-0.9147	1.1761	0.1831	268.6	93.7	–	13N	49W
1417	119	2089 Mar 26	09:34:13	116	1103	114	N	-a	-1.1039	0.8332	-0.1681	237.9	–	–	4S	142W
1418	119	2089 Sep 19	22:11:16	117	1109	119	N	-t	1.1448	0.7893	-0.2737	252.3	–	–	0N	26E
1419	119	2090 Mar 15	23:48:31	117	1115	124	T	-p	-0.3675	2.1659	1.2012	311.4	197.5	63.0	1N	5E
1420	119	2090 Sep 08	22:52:29	118	1121	129	T	-t	0.4257	2.1167	1.0377	362.1	213.1	31.8	5S	17E
1421	119	2091 Mar 05	15:58:22	118	1127	134	T	p-	0.3212	2.2537	1.2832	315.1	201.3	72.9	6N	124E
1422	119	2091 Aug 29	00:38:25	119	1133	139	T	t-	-0.3270	2.2810	1.2351	353.5	217.5	72.9	10S	9W
1423	119	2092 Feb 23	05:21:00	119	1139	144	N	a-	1.0509	0.9383	-0.0788	252.4	–	–	11N	76W
1424	119	2092 Jul 19	00:41:57	120	1144	111	Ne	-a	1.5132	0.0621	-0.8992	67.8	–	–	19S	9W
1425	119	2092 Aug 17	09:14:00	120	1145	149	N	a-	-1.0569	0.9131	-0.0757	246.8	–	–	14S	137W
1426	119	2093 Jan 12	18:00:02	120	1150	116	N	-t	-1.1734	0.7553	-0.3443	253.2	–	–	20N	93E
1427	119	2093 Jul 08	17:24:18	120	1156	121	P	-a	0.7632	1.4275	0.4872	275.4	141.9	–	22S	101E
1428	119	2094 Jan 01	17:00:06	121	1162	126	P	-t	-0.5025	1.9858	0.8871	356.6	201.2	–	22N	106E
1429	120	2094 Jun 28	10:01:57	121	1168	131	T+	pp	0.0288	2.7865	1.8234	326.6	215.7	100.6	23S	149W
1430	120	2094 Dec 21	19:56:32	122	1174	136	T+	p-	0.2016	2.5138	1.4627	351.3	220.5	91.6	24N	61E
1431	120	2095 Jun 17	22:00:11	122	1180	141	P	t-	-0.7653	1.4617	0.4459	304.8	147.0	–	24S	31E
1432	120	2095 Dec 11	06:15:02	123	1186	146	P	a-	0.8743	1.2510	0.2565	273.0	109.0	–	24N	95W
1433	120	2096 May 07	11:24:44	123	1191	113	N	-t	1.2897	0.5309	-0.5469	217.0	–	–	16S	171W
1434	120	2096 Jun 06	02:43:40	123	1192	151	Nb	t-	-1.5724	0.0048	-1.0583	21.3	–	–	24S	41W
1435	120	2096 Oct 31	11:30:24	124	1197	118	N	-a	-1.1308	0.7666	-0.2005	219.4	–	–	13N	176W
1436	120	2096 Nov 29	21:22:20	124	1198	156	N	a-	1.5018	0.0863	-0.8815	78.1	–	–	23N	37E
1437	120	2097 Apr 26	12:18:17	124	1203	123	P	-t	0.5377	1.9013	0.8420	344.1	195.2	–	13S	176E
1438	120	2097 Oct 21	01:30:55	125	1209	128	T	-a	-0.4608	2.0152	1.0097	323.1	195.3	15.2	11N	26W
1439	120	2098 Apr 15	19:04:48	125	1215	133	T-	p-	-0.2272	2.4454	1.4370	338.4	215.8	89.0	10S	74E
1440	120	2098 Oct 10	09:19:58	126	1221	138	T	pp	0.2749	2.3831	1.3246	357.5	221.0	82.7	7N	143W

Cat Num	Canon Plate	Calendar Date	TD of Greatest Eclipse	ΔT s	Luna Num	Saros Num	Ecl Type	QSE	Gamma	Pen Mag	Um Mag	Pen m	Par m	Total m	Lat	Long
1441	121	2099 Apr 05	08:30:56	126	1227	143	P	a-	-0.9304	1.1334	0.1680	257.8	88.1	–	7S	127W
1442	121	2099 Sep 29	10:36:38	127	1233	148	Nx	t-	1.0175	1.0341	-0.0511	288.4	–	–	3N	162W
1443	121	2100 Feb 24	15:05:12	127	1238	115	N	-a	1.0267	0.9650	-0.0169	244.7	–	–	10N	138E
1444	121	2100 Aug 19	21:44:59	128	1244	120	N	-t	-1.0906	0.8716	-0.1575	254.3	–	–	13S	36E
1445	121	2101 Feb 14	02:50:00	128	1250	125	T	-a	0.3584	2.2184	1.1825	339.5	208.4	63.4	13N	38W
1446	121	2101 Aug 09	08:25:34	129	1256	130	T	-p	-0.2864	2.3189	1.3458	324.5	208.4	80.7	16S	124W
1447	121	2102 Feb 03	07:18:21	129	1262	135	T	p-	-0.3514	2.2585	1.1686	363.3	217.5	63.6	16N	106W
1448	121	2102 Jul 30	00:29:10	130	1268	140	T	a-	0.4586	1.9874	1.0451	303.1	189.5	31.3	18S	5W
1449	121	2103 Jan 23	06:34:00	130	1274	145	Nx	t-	-1.0358	1.0096	-0.0936	286.6	–	–	19N	95W
1450	121	2103 Jun 20	09:36:11	131	1279	112	N	-a	-1.3493	0.3704	-0.6062	163.9	–	–	25S	143W
1451	121	2103 Jul 19	17:28:42	131	1280	150	N	a-	1.2003	0.6329	-0.3219	203.5	–	–	20S	100E
1452	121	2103 Dec 13	16:51:38	131	1285	117	N	-a	1.2240	0.6287	-0.4042	216.3	–	–	24N	106E
1453	122	2104 Jun 08	19:38:40	132	1291	122	P	-t	-0.6362	1.7069	0.6746	326.0	176.9	–	23S	66E
1454	122	2104 Dec 02	04:58:11	132	1297	127	P	-a	0.4911	1.9476	0.9661	308.3	186.5	–	22N	77W
1455	122	2105 May 28	22:34:06	133	1303	132	T+	pp	0.1227	2.6687	1.5977	373.2	234.0	102.4	21S	21E
1456	122	2105 Nov 21	20:42:00	133	1309	137	T-	p-	-0.1875	2.4976	1.5301	317.4	207.3	90.4	20N	47E
1457	122	2106 May 17	23:06:43	134	1315	142	P	t-	0.8678	1.2975	0.2345	308.5	114.5	–	19S	13E
1458	122	2106 Nov 11	11:22:14	134	1321	147	P	a-	-0.8948	1.2153	0.2171	272.9	101.7	–	16N	174W
1459	122	2107 Apr 07	17:30:10	135	1326	114	N	-a	-1.1383	0.7671	-0.2283	228.8	–	–	8S	98E
1460	122	2107 May 07	04:30:26	135	1327	152	Nb	a-	1.5589	0.0059	-1.0103	22.3	–	–	15S	68W
1461	122	2107 Oct 02	05:23:18	135	1332	119	N	-t	1.1998	0.6911	-0.3774	239.2	–	–	4N	83W
1462	122	2108 Mar 27	08:06:28	136	1338	124	T	-p	-0.3982	2.1076	1.1466	309.1	194.9	54.7	3S	120W
1463	122	2108 Sep 20	05:47:10	136	1344	129	P	-t	0.4884	2.0030	0.9213	357.7	205.1	–	1S	88W
1464	122	2109 Mar 17	00:22:28	137	1350	134	T	p-	0.2962	2.2989	1.3296	316.5	203.3	77.5	2N	3W
1465	123	2109 Sep 09	07:43:03	137	1356	139	T-	p-	-0.2608	2.4024	1.3568	355.3	221.6	85.6	6S	116W
1466	123	2110 Mar 06	13:37:21	138	1362	144	N	a-	1.0346	0.9686	-0.0490	256.5	–	–	7N	159E
1467	123	2110 Aug 29	16:38:48	138	1368	149	P	a-	-0.9893	1.0366	0.0488	258.6	49.8	–	10S	111E
1468	123	2111 Jan 25	02:03:06	139	1373	116	N	-t	-1.1834	0.7371	-0.3630	250.8	–	–	18N	27W
1469	123	2111 Jul 21	00:53:17	139	1379	121	P	-a	0.8362	1.2938	0.3530	266.4	123.2	–	20S	11W
1470	123	2112 Jan 14	01:06:36	140	1385	126	P	-t	-0.5087	1.9735	0.8764	355.4	200.1	–	21N	14W
1471	123	2112 Jul 09	17:19:51	141	1391	131	T+	pp	0.1055	2.6470	1.6814	327.0	215.2	98.4	22S	102E
1472	123	2113 Jan 02	04:22:59	141	1397	136	T+	p-	0.1964	2.5221	1.4735	350.2	220.2	92.1	23N	64W
1473	123	2113 Jun 29	04:55:26	142	1403	141	P	t-	-0.6888	1.6035	0.5850	315.2	165.2	–	24S	72W
1474	123	2113 Dec 22	14:58:42	142	1409	146	P	a-	0.8666	1.2644	0.2712	273.3	111.5	–	24N	135E
1475	123	2114 May 19	18:07:34	143	1414	113	N	-t	1.3612	0.3984	-0.6770	190.2	–	–	19S	88E
1476	123	2114 Jun 18	09:17:06	143	1415	151	N	t-	-1.4945	0.1479	-0.9157	117.4	–	–	25S	139W
1477	124	2114 Nov 12	19:59:34	143	1420	118	N	-a	-1.1534	0.7271	-0.2439	214.9	–	–	17N	57E
1478	124	2114 Dec 12	06:09:25	143	1421	156	N	a-	1.4932	0.1026	-0.8666	85.1	–	–	25N	94W
1479	124	2115 May 08	19:21:24	144	1426	123	P	-t	0.5996	1.7849	0.7311	337.0	185.0	–	17S	70E
1480	124	2115 Nov 02	09:36:34	144	1432	128	P	-a	-0.4919	1.9611	0.9498	322.5	192.0	–	14N	147W
1481	124	2116 Apr 27	02:41:18	145	1438	133	T-	p-	-0.1746	2.5388	1.5364	338.2	217.7	94.6	14S	40W
1482	124	2116 Oct 21	16:53:39	146	1444	138	T+	pp	0.2353	2.4587	1.3943	360.6	223.9	88.8	11N	103E
1483	124	2117 Apr 16	16:32:00	146	1450	143	P	a-	-0.8852	1.2140	0.2530	263.7	106.7	–	11S	112E
1484	124	2117 Oct 10	17:47:12	147	1456	148	P	t-	0.9676	1.1274	0.0387	298.6	48.5	–	8N	90E
1485	124	2118 Mar 07	23:33:05	147	1461	115	N	-a	1.0496	0.9229	-0.0587	240.9	–	–	6N	11E
1486	124	2118 Aug 31	04:51:46	148	1467	120	N	-t	-1.1543	0.7541	-0.2739	238.5	–	–	10S	72W
1487	124	2119 Feb 25	11:05:13	148	1473	125	T	-a	0.3765	2.1857	1.1490	339.6	207.4	58.1	10N	162W
1488	124	2119 Aug 20	15:51:55	149	1479	130	T	-p	-0.3538	2.1946	1.2227	320.4	203.2	67.3	13S	124E
1489	125	2120 Feb 14	15:17:20	149	1485	135	T	p-	-0.3371	2.2848	1.1950	364.7	219.2	67.9	13N	135E
1490	125	2120 Aug 09	08:01:32	150	1491	140	T	a-	0.3875	2.1182	1.1751	307.2	196.0	59.3	15S	118W
1491	125	2121 Feb 02	14:32:39	151	1497	145	Nx	t-	-1.0235	1.0309	-0.0700	288.5	–	–	16N	145E
1492	125	2121 Jun 30	16:49:53	151	1502	112	N	-a	-1.4273	0.2287	-0.7505	131.0	–	–	25S	109E
1493	125	2121 Jul 30	00:52:43	151	1503	150	N	a-	1.1312	0.7611	-0.1968	220.9	–	–	17S	11W
1494	125	2121 Dec 24	01:22:13	152	1508	117	N	-a	1.2261	0.6238	-0.4071	214.9	–	–	25N	20W
1495	125	2122 Jun 20	02:27:47	152	1514	122	P	-t	-0.7177	1.5584	0.5240	318.4	160.2	–	24S	36W
1496	125	2122 Dec 13	13:42:41	153	1520	127	P	-a	0.4980	1.9348	0.9536	307.2	185.4	–	24N	153E
1497	125	2123 Jun 09	05:06:28	153	1526	132	T+	pp	0.0406	2.8189	1.7488	374.4	235.8	106.1	23S	76W
1498	125	2123 Dec 03	05:24:09	154	1532	137	T-	p-	-0.1755	2.5208	1.5507	318.1	207.8	91.4	22N	83W
1499	125	2124 May 28	05:50:59	155	1538	142	P	t-	0.7913	1.4357	0.3770	318.5	141.9	–	21S	88W
1500	125	2124 Nov 21	19:47:21	155	1544	147	P	a-	-0.8809	1.2434	0.2401	276.2	106.9	–	19N	60E

Cat Num	Canon Plate	Calendar Date	TD of Greatest Eclipse	ΔT s	Luna Num	Saros Num	Ecl Type	QSE	Gamma	Pen Mag	Um Mag	Phase Durations Pen m	Par m	Total m	Greatest in Zenith Lat	Long
1501	126	2125 Apr 18	01:18:47	156	1549	114	N	-a	-1.1792	0.6890	-0.3004	217.6	–	–	12S	19W
1502	126	2125 May 17	11:46:31	156	1550	152	N	a-	1.4924	0.1249	-0.8854	101.0	–	–	18S	177W
1503	126	2125 Oct 12	12:43:05	156	1555	119	N	-t	1.2476	0.6062	-0.4679	226.7	–	–	9N	166E
1504	126	2126 Apr 07	16:17:55	157	1561	124	T	-a	-0.4346	2.0389	1.0817	306.4	191.5	41.6	7S	117E
1505	126	2126 Oct 01	12:49:48	158	1567	129	P	-t	0.5447	1.9011	0.8169	353.2	196.7	–	4N	165E
1506	126	2127 Mar 28	08:40:17	158	1573	134	T+	p-	0.2664	2.3531	1.3849	318.1	205.5	82.3	3S	128W
1507	126	2127 Sep 20	14:56:04	159	1579	139	T-	p-	-0.2007	2.5127	1.4672	356.3	224.2	93.5	1S	135E
1508	126	2128 Mar 16	21:46:08	159	1585	144	Nx	a-	1.0128	1.0086	-0.0093	261.4	–	–	2N	37E
1509	126	2128 Sep 09	00:10:30	160	1591	149	P	a-	-0.9266	1.1513	0.1642	268.3	89.7	–	6S	2W
1510	126	2129 Feb 04	10:02:24	160	1596	116	N	-t	-1.1959	0.7140	-0.3858	247.7	–	–	15N	147W
1511	126	2129 Jul 31	08:24:30	161	1602	121	P	-a	0.9070	1.1644	0.2224	256.6	99.7	–	17S	124W
1512	126	2130 Jan 24	09:10:19	162	1608	126	P	-t	-0.5173	1.9565	0.8619	353.8	198.7	–	19N	134W
1513	127	2130 Jul 21	00:38:56	162	1614	131	T+	-p	0.1803	2.5113	1.5426	326.7	213.4	93.6	20S	7W
1514	127	2131 Jan 13	12:49:59	163	1620	136	T+	p-	0.1915	2.5296	1.4842	349.0	219.9	92.5	22N	170E
1515	127	2131 Jul 10	11:47:56	164	1626	141	P	t-	-0.6108	1.7484	0.7265	324.6	180.5	–	23S	175W
1516	127	2132 Jan 02	23:44:22	164	1632	146	P	a-	0.8604	1.2750	0.2835	273.5	113.6	–	24N	5E
1517	127	2132 May 30	00:42:51	165	1637	113	N	-t	1.4381	0.2563	-0.8169	154.5	–	–	21S	10W
1518	127	2132 Jun 28	15:45:35	165	1638	151	N	-t	-1.4128	0.2982	-0.7662	164.8	–	–	24S	125E
1519	127	2132 Nov 23	04:35:11	165	1643	118	N	-a	-1.1708	0.6969	-0.2776	211.5	–	–	19N	71W
1520	127	2132 Dec 22	14:59:50	165	1644	156	N	a-	1.4874	0.1139	-0.8564	89.6	–	–	25N	135E
1521	127	2133 May 19	02:16:19	166	1649	123	P	-t	0.6688	1.6553	0.6067	328.5	171.6	–	19S	34W
1522	127	2133 Nov 12	17:50:08	167	1655	128	P	-a	-0.5157	1.9203	0.9033	322.3	189.3	–	17N	89E
1523	127	2134 May 08	10:10:41	167	1661	133	T-	pp	-0.1152	2.6447	1.6482	337.7	219.0	98.8	17S	153W
1524	127	2134 Nov 02	00:34:20	168	1667	138	T+	pp	0.2022	2.5222	1.4522	363.2	226.0	93.0	15N	12W
1525	128	2135 Apr 28	00:26:35	169	1673	143	P	a-	-0.8344	1.3052	0.3484	270.0	123.3	–	15S	7W
1526	128	2135 Oct 22	01:06:04	169	1679	148	P	t-	0.9243	1.2086	0.1164	306.7	83.1	–	12N	20W
1527	128	2136 Mar 18	07:53:56	170	1684	115	N	-a	1.0778	0.8708	-0.1103	235.7	–	–	2N	115W
1528	128	2136 Apr 16	17:08:42	170	1685	153	Nb	a-	-1.5241	0.0398	-0.9171	53.5	–	–	12S	103E
1529	128	2136 Sep 10	12:05:08	170	1690	120	N	-t	-1.2134	0.6453	-0.3820	222.3	–	–	6S	179E
1530	128	2137 Mar 07	19:13:43	171	1696	125	T	-a	0.3993	2.1441	1.1069	339.4	205.9	50.0	5N	75E
1531	128	2137 Aug 30	23:24:05	172	1702	130	T	-p	-0.4171	2.0782	1.1069	316.0	197.2	48.3	9S	10E
1532	128	2138 Feb 24	23:09:56	172	1708	135	T	p-	-0.3178	2.3198	1.2306	366.2	221.1	73.1	9N	16E
1533	128	2138 Aug 20	15:38:45	173	1714	140	T	p-	0.3204	2.2421	1.2977	310.5	200.9	74.3	12S	127E
1534	128	2139 Feb 13	22:28:16	174	1720	145	Nx	t-	-1.0083	1.0574	-0.0406	290.9	–	–	12N	27E
1535	128	2139 Jul 12	00:01:47	174	1725	112	Ne	-a	-1.5055	0.0866	-0.8956	82.0	–	–	23S	2E
1536	128	2139 Aug 10	08:18:09	174	1726	150	N	a-	1.0638	0.8866	-0.0748	236.1	–	–	15S	123W
1537	129	2140 Jan 04	09:55:17	175	1731	117	N	-a	1.2271	0.6209	-0.4075	213.7	–	–	24N	147W
1538	129	2140 Jun 30	09:13:17	175	1737	122	P	-t	-0.8013	1.4064	0.3695	309.0	138.2	–	24S	136W
1539	129	2140 Dec 23	22:29:48	176	1743	127	P	-a	0.5028	1.9255	0.9450	306.3	184.6	–	24N	23E
1540	129	2141 Jun 19	11:34:51	177	1749	132	T-	pp	-0.0446	2.8112	1.7415	374.5	235.9	106.1	23S	173W
1541	129	2141 Dec 13	14:10:16	177	1755	137	T-	p-	-0.1671	2.5374	1.5652	318.8	208.2	92.0	23N	147E
1542	129	2142 Jun 08	12:32:42	178	1761	142	P	t-	0.7119	1.5794	0.5247	327.4	163.2	–	22S	172E
1543	129	2142 Dec 03	04:16:11	179	1767	147	P	a-	-0.8705	1.2648	0.2569	279.0	110.6	–	21N	66W
1544	129	2143 Apr 29	09:01:21	179	1772	114	N	-a	-1.2257	0.6009	-0.3829	204.2	–	–	16S	135W
1545	129	2143 May 28	18:59:25	179	1773	152	N	a-	1.4220	0.2513	-0.7536	140.9	–	–	20S	75W
1546	129	2143 Oct 23	20:10:37	180	1778	119	N	-t	1.2886	0.5337	-0.5457	214.9	–	–	13N	54E
1547	129	2144 Apr 18	00:20:29	181	1784	124	T	-a	-0.4787	1.9563	1.0026	303.0	187.0	7.6	11S	5W
1548	129	2144 Oct 11	20:02:14	181	1790	129	P	-t	0.5930	1.8136	0.7268	348.8	188.4	–	8N	57E
1549	130	2145 Apr 07	16:48:09	182	1796	134	T+	p-	0.2285	2.4221	1.4550	319.9	207.9	87.3	7S	109E
1550	130	2145 Sep 30	22:19:51	183	1802	139	T-	pp	-0.1486	2.6083	1.5628	356.6	225.7	98.2	3N	23E
1551	130	2146 Mar 28	05:44:28	183	1808	144	P	a-	0.9833	1.0630	0.0449	267.7	48.6	–	2S	84W
1552	130	2146 Sep 20	07:51:28	184	1814	149	P	a-	-0.8707	1.2537	0.2669	276.0	112.3	–	2S	118W
1553	130	2147 Feb 15	17:57:14	185	1819	116	N	-t	-1.2115	0.6849	-0.4138	243.4	–	–	12N	95E
1554	130	2147 Aug 11	15:57:02	185	1825	121	P	-a	0.9765	1.0378	0.0941	245.9	66.0	–	14S	123E
1555	130	2147 Sep 09	23:11:35	185	1826	159	Nb	a-	-1.5372	0.0124	-0.9379	29.8	–	–	7S	13E
1556	130	2148 Feb 04	17:13:45	186	1831	126	P	-t	-0.5265	1.9380	0.8465	352.1	197.2	–	16N	106E
1557	130	2148 Jul 31	07:56:37	187	1837	131	T+	-p	0.2554	2.3755	1.4030	325.8	210.4	85.3	18S	117W
1558	130	2149 Jan 23	21:17:23	187	1843	136	T+	p-	0.1859	2.5379	1.4962	347.8	219.6	93.0	19N	44E
1559	130	2149 Jul 20	18:38:11	188	1849	141	P	t-	-0.5315	1.8957	0.8701	333.2	193.3	–	21S	83E
1560	130	2150 Jan 13	08:31:36	189	1855	146	P	a-	0.8552	1.2834	0.2941	273.4	115.3	–	22N	125W

Cat Num	Canon Plate	Calendar Date	TD of Greatest Eclipse	ΔT s	Luna Num	Saros Num	Ecl Type	QSE	Gamma	Pen Mag	Um Mag	Phase Durations Pen m	Phase Durations Par m	Phase Durations Total m	Greatest in Zenith Lat	Greatest in Zenith Long
1561	131	2150 Jun 10	07:14:49	189	1860	113	Ne	-t	1.5172	0.1101	-0.9612	102.5	-	-	22S	108W
1562	131	2150 Jul 09	22:13:22	189	1861	151	N	t-	-1.3301	0.4506	-0.6150	200.0	-	-	23S	29E
1563	131	2150 Dec 04	13:14:46	190	1866	118	N	-a	-1.1849	0.6727	-0.3050	208.8	-	-	21N	160E
1564	131	2151 Jan 02	23:51:26	190	1867	156	N	a-	1.4829	0.1225	-0.8484	92.9	-	-	24N	4E
1565	131	2151 May 30	09:09:10	191	1872	123	P	-t	0.7403	1.5216	0.4780	318.7	155.1	-	21S	137W
1566	131	2151 Nov 24	02:08:13	191	1878	128	P	-a	-0.5351	1.8875	0.8651	322.3	187.0	-	20N	35W
1567	131	2152 May 18	17:35:13	192	1884	133	T-	pp	-0.0511	2.7597	1.7688	336.8	219.7	101.2	20S	96E
1568	131	2152 Nov 12	08:21:47	193	1890	138	T+	pp	0.1753	2.5743	1.4989	365.5	227.5	95.8	18N	129W
1569	131	2153 May 08	08:14:39	194	1896	143	P	a-	-0.7781	1.4065	0.4536	276.4	138.3	-	18S	124W
1570	131	2153 Nov 01	08:34:03	194	1902	148	P	t-	0.8882	1.2763	0.1811	313.1	102.7	-	15N	132W
1571	131	2154 Mar 29	16:05:08	195	1907	115	N	-a	1.1136	0.8050	-0.1756	228.7	-	-	3S	121E
1572	131	2154 Apr 28	01:04:31	195	1908	153	N	a-	-1.4784	0.1230	-0.8326	93.3	-	-	15S	17W
1573	132	2154 Sep 21	19:29:08	196	1913	120	N	-t	-1.2647	0.5511	-0.4758	206.6	-	-	2S	67E
1574	132	2154 Oct 21	09:26:05	196	1914	158	Nb	t-	1.5560	0.0350	-1.0284	56.6	-	-	12N	145W
1575	132	2155 Mar 19	03:12:45	196	1919	125	T	-a	0.4293	2.0891	1.0517	338.6	203.4	35.5	1N	45W
1576	132	2155 Sep 11	07:03:11	197	1925	130	T	-a	-0.4752	1.9715	1.0003	311.5	190.7	2.6	5S	106W
1577	132	2156 Mar 07	06:54:14	198	1931	135	T	p-	-0.2922	2.3663	1.2783	367.8	223.5	79.0	5N	100W
1578	132	2156 Aug 30	23:20:37	198	1937	140	T+	p-	0.2569	2.3595	1.4132	313.1	204.6	83.9	8S	11E
1579	132	2157 Feb 24	06:16:35	199	1943	145	P	t-	-0.9868	1.0950	0.0006	294.3	6.0	-	9N	90W
1580	132	2157 Aug 20	15:46:35	200	1949	150	P	a-	0.9993	1.0071	0.0416	249.3	45.1	-	11S	125E
1581	132	2158 Jan 14	18:29:53	200	1954	117	N	-a	1.2275	0.6184	-0.4068	212.6	-	-	22N	86E
1582	132	2158 Jul 11	15:55:51	201	1960	122	P	-t	-0.8860	1.2525	0.2126	297.8	107.6	-	23S	124E
1583	132	2159 Jan 04	07:19:20	202	1966	127	P	-a	0.5062	1.9188	0.9394	305.5	184.0	-	23N	108W
1584	132	2159 Jun 30	18:00:09	203	1972	132	T-	pp	-0.1323	2.6503	1.5809	373.5	234.1	102.0	23S	92E
1585	133	2159 Dec 24	23:00:09	203	1978	137	T-	p-	-0.1619	2.5478	1.5737	319.3	208.5	92.4	23N	16E
1586	133	2160 Jun 18	19:10:10	204	1984	142	P	t-	0.6280	1.7313	0.6804	335.3	180.8	-	23S	74E
1587	133	2160 Dec 13	12:50:19	205	1990	147	P	a-	-0.8651	1.2768	0.2647	280.9	112.4	-	22N	167E
1588	133	2161 May 09	16:38:02	205	1995	114	N	-a	-1.2777	0.5027	-0.4757	187.8	-	-	19S	110E
1589	133	2161 Jun 08	02:08:54	206	1996	152	N	a-	1.3476	0.3853	-0.6145	171.6	-	-	22S	32W
1590	133	2161 Nov 03	03:45:48	206	2001	119	N	-t	1.3227	0.4736	-0.6107	204.2	-	-	16N	60W
1591	133	2162 Apr 29	08:17:08	207	2007	124	P	-a	-0.5280	1.8642	0.9137	299.0	181.3	-	15S	124W
1592	133	2162 Oct 23	03:23:58	208	2013	129	P	-t	0.6341	1.7395	0.6504	344.7	180.3	-	12N	54W
1593	133	2163 Apr 19	00:49:33	208	2019	134	T+	p-	0.1858	2.5001	1.5338	321.6	210.2	91.8	11S	12W
1594	133	2163 Oct 12	05:51:53	209	2025	139	T-	pp	-0.1026	2.6927	1.6471	356.4	226.3	100.9	7N	90W
1595	133	2164 Apr 07	13:34:34	210	2031	144	P	h-	0.9480	1.1278	0.1095	274.7	75.5	-	6S	158E
1596	133	2164 Sep 30	15:40:32	211	2037	149	P	a-	-0.8210	1.3450	0.3582	282.1	128.0	-	2N	123E
1597	134	2165 Feb 26	01:44:01	211	2042	116	N	-t	-1.2329	0.6447	-0.4524	237.2	-	-	8N	22W
1598	134	2165 Aug 21	23:34:20	212	2048	121	N	-a	1.0418	0.9193	-0.0268	234.6	-	-	11S	8E
1599	134	2165 Sep 20	07:05:17	212	2049	159	N	a-	-1.4859	0.1075	-0.8446	86.9	-	-	2S	107W
1600	134	2166 Feb 15	01:11:40	213	2054	126	P	-t	-0.5403	1.9109	0.8232	349.9	195.0	-	12N	14W
1601	134	2166 Aug 11	15:17:07	214	2060	131	T	-a	0.3274	2.2456	1.2688	324.2	206.3	73.3	15S	133E
1602	134	2167 Feb 04	05:41:32	214	2066	136	T+	p-	0.1772	2.5517	1.5143	346.5	219.5	93.8	16N	81W
1603	134	2167 Aug 01	01:28:59	215	2072	141	T	t-	-0.4536	2.0407	1.0108	340.6	203.7	16.7	18S	20W
1604	134	2168 Jan 24	17:17:30	216	2078	146	P	a-	0.8487	1.2940	0.3074	273.5	117.4	-	20N	105E
1605	134	2168 Jul 20	04:38:50	217	2084	151	N	t-	-1.2455	0.6066	-0.4606	229.0	-	-	22S	67W
1606	134	2168 Dec 14	21:59:25	217	2089	118	N	-a	-1.1945	0.6565	-0.3242	207.0	-	-	22N	30E
1607	134	2169 Jan 13	08:43:52	217	2090	156	N	a-	1.4795	0.1288	-0.8423	95.2	-	-	23N	128W
1608	134	2169 Jun 09	15:57:06	218	2095	123	P	-t	0.8159	1.3806	0.3416	307.3	133.5	-	22S	122E
1609	135	2169 Dec 04	10:31:58	219	2101	128	P	-a	-0.5488	1.8648	0.8375	322.6	185.4	-	22N	159W
1610	135	2170 May 30	00:55:17	220	2107	133	T+	pp	0.0174	2.8188	1.8330	335.4	219.4	101.7	22S	13W
1611	135	2170 Nov 23	16:16:21	220	2113	138	T+	pp	0.1554	2.6134	1.5331	367.3	228.7	97.7	21N	113E
1612	135	2171 May 19	15:56:55	221	2119	143	P	a-	-0.7167	1.5175	0.5681	282.8	151.9	-	21S	121E
1613	135	2171 Nov 12	16:10:02	222	2125	148	P	t-	0.8584	1.3323	0.2344	318.1	115.9	-	18N	114E
1614	135	2172 Apr 09	00:08:53	223	2130	115	N	-a	1.1549	0.7290	-0.2512	219.9	-	-	7S	0W
1615	135	2172 May 08	08:53:16	223	2131	153	N	a-	-1.4275	0.2158	-0.7387	122.7	-	-	19S	134W
1616	135	2172 Oct 02	03:01:43	223	2136	120	N	-h	-1.3098	0.4682	-0.5584	191.3	-	-	3N	47W
1617	135	2172 Oct 31	17:09:14	223	2137	158	N	h-	1.5198	0.1017	-0.9622	95.6	-	-	16N	99E
1618	135	2173 Mar 29	11:02:23	224	2142	125	P	-a	0.4662	2.0214	0.9839	337.2	199.9	-	3S	163W
1619	135	2173 Sep 21	14:50:18	225	2148	130	P	-a	-0.5273	1.8761	0.9046	307.0	184.0	-	1S	137E
1620	135	2174 Mar 18	14:30:50	226	2154	135	T-	pp	-0.2605	2.4236	1.3371	369.5	226.0	85.2	1N	145E

Cat Num	Canon Plate	Calendar Date	TD of Greatest Eclipse	ΔT s	Luna Num	Saros Num	Ecl Type	QSE	Gamma	Pen Mag	Um Mag	Pen m	Par m	Total m	Lat	Long
1621	136	2174 Sep 11	07:08:03	226	2160	140	T+	p-	0.1982	2.4683	1.5197	315.1	207.3	90.3	4S	107W
1622	136	2175 Mar 07	13:59:52	227	2166	145	P	t-	-0.9608	1.1406	0.0503	298.2	54.8	–	4N	153E
1623	136	2175 Aug 31	23:19:03	228	2172	150	P	a-	0.9385	1.1208	0.1507	260.7	84.8	–	8S	11E
1624	136	2176 Jan 26	03:03:40	229	2177	117	N	-a	1.2293	0.6133	-0.4082	211.0	–	–	20N	42W
1625	136	2176 Jul 21	22:36:53	230	2183	122	P	-t	-0.9708	1.0986	0.0553	284.7	56.3	–	21S	24E
1626	136	2177 Jan 14	16:08:55	230	2189	127	P	-a	0.5099	1.9112	0.9334	304.7	183.3	–	22N	121E
1627	136	2177 Jul 11	00:25:22	231	2195	132	T-	pp	-0.2199	2.4896	1.4199	371.3	230.4	93.0	22S	4W
1628	136	2178 Jan 04	07:50:14	232	2201	137	T-	p-	-0.1570	2.5574	1.5820	319.9	208.8	92.8	23N	115W
1629	136	2178 Jun 30	01:48:39	233	2207	142	P	t-	0.5439	1.8841	0.8365	341.9	194.6	–	23S	25W
1630	136	2178 Dec 24	21:26:20	234	2213	147	P	a-	-0.8615	1.2853	0.2694	282.6	113.6	–	23N	39E
1631	136	2179 May 21	00:09:09	234	2218	114	N	-a	-1.3347	0.3956	-0.5778	167.6	–	–	21S	2W
1632	136	2179 Jun 19	09:16:10	234	2219	152	N	a-	1.2702	0.5251	-0.4702	196.8	–	–	22S	138W
1633	137	2179 Nov 14	11:28:05	235	2224	119	N	-t	1.3505	0.4249	-0.6641	194.8	–	–	19N	175W
1634	137	2180 May 09	16:05:58	236	2230	124	P	-a	-0.5840	1.7599	0.8123	294.2	173.9	–	18S	119E
1635	137	2180 Nov 02	10:55:47	237	2236	129	P	-t	0.6669	1.6802	0.5891	341.1	173.2	–	16N	167W
1636	137	2181 Apr 29	08:40:08	237	2242	134	T+	pp	0.1345	2.5938	1.6281	323.4	212.4	95.9	15S	130W
1637	137	2181 Oct 22	13:35:21	238	2248	139	T-	pp	-0.0652	2.7613	1.7157	355.8	226.4	102.2	11N	153E
1638	137	2182 Apr 18	21:14:15	239	2254	144	P	h-	0.9050	1.2069	0.1884	282.6	98.3	–	10S	42E
1639	137	2182 Oct 11	23:38:06	240	2260	149	P	a-	-0.7776	1.4246	0.4376	286.9	139.4	–	7N	3E
1640	137	2183 Mar 09	09:24:15	241	2265	116	N	-t	-1.2593	0.5953	-0.4997	229.1	–	–	3N	138W
1641	137	2183 Sep 02	07:15:21	241	2271	121	N	-a	1.1037	0.8072	-0.1418	222.7	–	–	7S	108W
1642	137	2183 Oct 01	15:05:27	242	2272	159	N	a-	-1.4397	0.1934	-0.7609	115.6	–	–	2N	133E
1643	137	2184 Feb 26	09:05:35	242	2277	126	P	-t	-0.5579	1.8762	0.7930	347.2	192.0	–	8N	132W
1644	137	2184 Aug 21	22:38:35	243	2283	131	T	-a	0.3977	2.1190	1.1374	322.1	201.0	54.8	11S	22E
1645	138	2185 Feb 14	14:03:41	244	2289	136	T+	p-	0.1660	2.5697	1.5372	345.2	219.4	94.8	13N	154E
1646	138	2185 Aug 11	08:20:59	245	2295	141	T	t-	-0.3774	2.1829	1.1483	347.0	212.0	59.3	15S	123W
1647	138	2186 Feb 04	02:01:15	246	2301	146	P	a-	0.8402	1.3080	0.3244	273.8	120.1	–	17N	26W
1648	138	2186 Jul 31	11:07:15	246	2307	151	N	t-	-1.1630	0.7589	-0.3102	252.7	–	–	19S	164W
1649	138	2186 Dec 26	06:46:26	247	2312	118	N	-a	-1.2018	0.6443	-0.3389	205.8	–	–	22N	100W
1650	138	2187 Jan 24	17:35:20	247	2313	156	N	a-	1.4758	0.1354	-0.8355	97.6	–	–	21N	100E
1651	138	2187 Jun 20	22:44:13	248	2318	123	P	-t	0.8929	1.2372	0.2025	294.5	104.6	–	23S	21E
1652	138	2187 Dec 15	18:58:37	249	2324	128	P	a-	-0.5595	1.8473	0.8155	323.2	184.1	–	23N	75E
1653	138	2188 Jun 09	08:12:51	250	2330	133	T+	pp	0.0887	2.6856	1.7045	333.3	218.0	99.8	23S	122W
1654	138	2188 Dec 04	00:15:39	250	2336	138	T+	pp	0.1394	2.6448	1.5602	369.0	229.6	98.9	22N	5W
1655	138	2189 May 29	23:34:01	251	2342	143	P	a-	-0.6505	1.6375	0.6909	288.9	164.1	–	22S	7E
1656	138	2189 Nov 22	23:54:07	252	2348	148	P	t-	0.8349	1.3765	0.2764	321.8	125.1	–	21N	1W
1657	139	2190 Apr 20	08:03:24	253	2353	115	N	-a	1.2034	0.6398	-0.3401	208.4	–	–	11S	120W
1658	139	2190 May 19	16:35:25	253	2354	153	N	a-	-1.3715	0.3184	-0.6356	147.9	–	–	21S	111E
1659	139	2190 Oct 13	10:43:57	254	2359	120	N	-h	-1.3480	0.3980	-0.6284	177.0	–	–	7N	163W
1660	139	2190 Nov 12	01:00:51	254	2360	158	N	h-	1.4894	0.1574	-0.9066	118.0	–	–	19N	19W
1661	139	2191 Apr 09	18:42:01	255	2365	125	P	-a	0.5107	1.9399	0.9022	335.0	194.9	–	7S	81E
1662	139	2191 Oct 02	22:45:48	255	2371	130	P	-a	-0.5729	1.7926	0.8206	302.7	177.4	–	3N	17E
1663	139	2192 Mar 28	21:56:24	256	2377	135	T-	pp	-0.2202	2.4967	1.4120	371.2	228.8	91.6	4S	33E
1664	139	2192 Sep 21	15:02:17	257	2383	140	T+	p-	0.1453	2.5668	1.6154	316.6	209.1	94.4	0S	134E
1665	139	2193 Mar 17	21:34:31	258	2389	145	P	t-	-0.9274	1.1996	0.1139	303.1	81.6	–	0N	39E
1666	139	2193 Sep 11	06:57:00	259	2395	150	P	a-	0.8828	1.2257	0.2505	270.5	108.1	–	4S	104W
1667	139	2194 Feb 05	11:34:57	260	2400	117	N	-a	1.2339	0.6028	-0.4145	208.6	–	–	17N	169W
1668	139	2194 Aug 02	05:18:43	260	2406	122	N	-t	-1.0540	0.9479	-0.0993	269.7	–	–	19S	77W
1669	140	2195 Jan 26	00:58:49	261	2412	127	P	-a	0.5140	1.9028	0.9269	303.8	182.7	–	19N	10W
1670	140	2195 Jul 22	06:49:10	262	2418	132	T	pt	-0.3087	2.3270	1.2568	367.8	224.6	77.4	20S	99W
1671	140	2196 Jan 15	16:41:55	263	2424	137	T-	p-	-0.1537	2.5641	1.5877	320.4	209.1	93.1	21N	113E
1672	140	2196 Jul 10	08:26:05	264	2430	142	P	t-	0.4577	2.0407	0.9960	347.4	205.8	–	22S	124W
1673	140	2197 Jan 04	06:04:04	265	2436	147	P	a-	-0.8601	1.2895	0.2704	283.9	114.1	–	22N	89W
1674	140	2197 May 31	07:36:03	265	2441	114	N	-a	-1.3955	0.2817	-0.6872	142.4	–	–	23S	113W
1675	140	2197 Jun 29	16:22:51	266	2442	152	N	a-	1.1911	0.6680	-0.3232	217.9	–	–	22S	116E
1676	140	2197 Nov 24	19:17:16	266	2447	119	N	-t	1.3723	0.3870	-0.7061	187.1	–	–	22S	68E
1677	140	2198 May 20	23:50:32	267	2453	124	P	-a	-0.6437	1.6492	0.7041	288.5	164.8	–	21S	3E
1678	140	2198 Nov 13	18:34:27	268	2459	129	P	-t	0.6945	1.6306	0.5377	337.8	166.7	–	19N	78E
1679	140	2199 May 10	16:25:22	269	2465	134	T+	pp	0.0792	2.6951	1.7297	324.9	214.1	98.8	18S	114E
1680	140	2199 Nov 02	21:27:11	270	2471	139	T-	pp	-0.0339	2.8187	1.7731	355.0	226.1	102.7	15N	35E

Cat Num	Canon Plate	Calendar Date	TD of Greatest Eclipse	ΔT s	Luna Num	Saros Num	Ecl Type	QSE	Gamma	Pen Mag	Um Mag	Phase ---- Durations ----			Greatest in Zenith	
												Pen m	Par m	Total m	Lat	Long
1681	141	2200 Apr 30	04:44:34	271	2477	144	P	t-	0.8550	1.2987	0.2798	291.2	118.6	-	14S	70W
1682	141	2200 Oct 23	07:44:44	272	2483	149	P	a-	-0.7411	1.4917	0.5045	290.5	147.8	-	11N	119W
1683	141	2201 Mar 20	16:55:03	272	2488	116	N	-t	-1.2929	0.5323	-0.5602	217.9	-	-	1S	109E
1684	141	2201 Sep 13	15:03:16	273	2494	121	N	-a	1.1598	0.7059	-0.2464	210.8	-	-	3S	134E
1685	141	2201 Oct 12	23:14:06	273	2495	159	N	a-	-1.4002	0.2670	-0.6896	134.9	-	-	6N	10E
1686	141	2202 Mar 09	16:51:36	274	2500	126	P	-t	-0.5824	1.8288	0.7505	343.7	187.8	-	4N	111E
1687	141	2202 Sep 03	06:05:57	275	2506	131	T	-a	0.4623	2.0031	1.0163	319.6	194.9	19.6	7S	91W
1688	141	2203 Feb 26	22:20:38	276	2512	136	T+	p-	0.1500	2.5964	1.5692	344.0	219.5	96.1	9N	29E
1689	141	2203 Aug 23	15:15:11	277	2518	141	T	pp	-0.3039	2.3203	1.2806	352.3	218.6	78.1	12S	133E
1690	141	2204 Feb 16	10:41:26	278	2524	146	P	a-	0.8286	1.3276	0.3475	274.6	123.7	-	13N	156W
1691	141	2204 Aug 11	17:37:23	279	2530	151	N	t-	-1.0820	0.9088	-0.1627	272.7	-	-	16S	98E
1692	141	2205 Jan 06	15:34:56	279	2535	118	N	-a	-1.2080	0.6341	-0.3511	204.8	-	-	21N	129E
1693	142	2205 Feb 05	02:23:29	280	2536	156	N	a-	1.4700	0.1458	-0.8244	101.2	-	-	18N	31W
1694	142	2205 Jul 02	05:29:54	280	2541	123	P	-t	0.9714	1.0912	0.0602	279.8	58.0	-	22S	80W
1695	142	2205 Dec 27	03:28:47	281	2547	128	P	-a	-0.5666	1.8364	0.8008	323.9	183.4	-	23N	51W
1696	142	2206 Jun 21	15:28:26	282	2553	133	T+	pp	0.1626	2.5480	1.5710	330.6	215.5	95.4	23S	130E
1697	142	2206 Dec 16	08:19:07	283	2559	138	T+	pp	0.1275	2.6685	1.5803	370.4	230.3	99.8	23N	125W
1698	142	2207 Jun 11	07:07:39	284	2565	143	P	a-	-0.5812	1.7635	0.8193	294.6	174.8	-	24S	106W
1699	142	2207 Dec 05	07:45:23	285	2571	148	P	t-	0.8170	1.4102	0.3084	324.4	131.4	-	23N	118W
1700	142	2208 May 01	15:49:07	286	2576	115	N	-a	1.2584	0.5390	-0.4409	193.7	-	-	14S	124E
1701	142	2208 May 31	00:10:35	286	2577	153	N	a-	-1.3103	0.4306	-0.5233	170.5	-	-	23S	2W
1702	142	2208 Oct 24	18:36:04	287	2582	120	N	-h	-1.3789	0.3411	-0.6851	164.2	-	-	11N	79E
1703	142	2208 Nov 23	09:01:57	287	2583	158	N	h-	1.4660	0.2003	-0.8634	132.3	-	-	22N	138W
1704	142	2209 Apr 21	02:12:20	288	2588	125	P	-h	0.5617	1.8463	0.8086	331.8	188.2	-	11S	32W
1705	143	2209 Oct 14	06:49:53	288	2594	130	P	-a	-0.6120	1.7213	0.7487	298.7	171.1	-	7N	104W
1706	143	2210 Apr 10	05:13:49	289	2600	135	T-	pp	-0.1736	2.5812	1.4986	372.8	231.4	97.3	8S	77W
1707	143	2210 Oct 03	23:03:49	290	2606	140	T+	p-	0.0988	2.6538	1.6994	317.7	210.2	96.8	4N	12E
1708	143	2211 Mar 30	05:02:58	291	2612	145	P	t-	-0.8883	1.2689	0.1881	308.5	103.6	-	4S	74W
1709	143	2211 Sep 23	14:39:32	292	2618	150	P	a-	0.8314	1.3226	0.3422	279.0	125.0	-	1N	139E
1710	143	2212 Feb 17	20:03:18	293	2623	117	N	-a	1.2416	0.5863	-0.4264	205.3	-	-	13N	64E
1711	143	2212 Mar 18	09:06:43	293	2624	155	N	a-	-1.5477	0.0364	-0.9995	55.7	-	-	0S	134W
1712	143	2212 Aug 13	12:02:10	294	2629	122	N	-t	-1.1349	0.8015	-0.2499	252.7	-	-	15S	178W
1713	143	2213 Feb 06	09:44:33	295	2635	127	P	-a	0.5218	1.8872	0.9137	302.7	181.7	-	16N	141W
1714	143	2213 Aug 02	13:16:19	296	2641	132	T	-t	-0.3946	2.1698	1.0987	363.2	216.8	50.6	18S	164E
1715	143	2214 Jan 27	01:30:46	297	2647	137	T-	p-	-0.1479	2.5748	1.5979	321.0	209.5	93.6	18N	18W
1716	143	2214 Jul 22	15:06:54	298	2653	142	T	t-	0.3734	2.1942	1.1519	351.5	214.2	60.4	20S	136E
1717	144	2215 Jan 16	14:40:00	299	2659	147	P	a-	-0.8578	1.2951	0.2733	285.3	115.0	-	20N	143E
1718	144	2215 Jun 12	14:59:57	299	2664	114	N	-a	-1.4595	0.1623	-0.8024	108.9	-	-	25S	136E
1719	144	2215 Jul 11	23:30:23	300	2665	152	N	a-	1.1114	0.8125	-0.1753	235.9	-	-	21S	10E
1720	144	2215 Dec 07	03:12:05	300	2670	119	N	-t	1.3892	0.3578	-0.7388	180.8	-	-	24N	49W
1721	144	2216 Jun 01	07:27:36	301	2676	124	P	-a	-0.7097	1.5271	0.5839	281.7	153.0	-	23S	111W
1722	144	2216 Nov 25	02:22:56	302	2682	129	P	-t	0.7144	1.5946	0.5005	335.2	161.6	-	21N	38W
1723	144	2217 May 22	00:01:35	303	2688	134	T+	pp	0.0167	2.8100	1.8444	326.1	215.2	100.4	20S	0E
1724	144	2217 Nov 14	05:29:02	304	2694	139	T-	pp	-0.0100	2.8624	1.8172	354.0	225.5	102.6	18N	85W
1725	144	2218 May 11	12:05:34	305	2700	144	P	t-	0.7981	1.4036	0.3839	300.1	137.2	-	17S	179E
1726	144	2218 Nov 03	16:00:25	306	2706	149	P	a-	-0.7113	1.5465	0.5590	293.1	153.9	-	14N	117E
1727	144	2219 Apr 01	00:18:14	307	2711	116	N	-t	-1.3322	0.4588	-0.6308	203.6	-	-	5S	3W
1728	144	2219 Sep 24	22:55:51	308	2717	121	N	-a	1.2117	0.6126	-0.3435	198.6	-	-	2N	15E
1729	145	2219 Oct 24	07:29:33	308	2718	159	N	a-	-1.3663	0.3304	-0.6288	149.3	-	-	10N	115W
1730	145	2220 Mar 20	00:32:40	309	2723	126	P	-t	-0.6115	1.7728	0.6998	339.5	182.6	-	0S	5W
1731	145	2220 Sep 13	13:36:52	310	2729	131	P	-a	0.5229	1.8948	0.9023	316.7	188.0	-	3S	156E
1732	145	2221 Mar 09	06:32:19	311	2735	136	T+	p-	0.1290	2.6321	1.6106	342.8	219.7	97.5	5N	94W
1733	145	2221 Sep 02	22:13:42	312	2741	141	T-	pp	-0.2348	2.4498	1.4048	356.8	223.5	89.7	8S	28E
1734	145	2222 Feb 26	19:17:36	313	2747	146	P	a-	0.8137	1.3531	0.3767	275.7	128.0	-	9N	75E
1735	145	2222 Aug 23	00:12:08	314	2753	151	Nx	t-	-1.0043	1.0526	-0.0214	289.5	-	-	12S	1W
1736	145	2223 Jan 18	00:22:31	314	2758	118	N	-a	-1.2145	0.6229	-0.3639	203.7	-	-	20N	2W
1737	145	2223 Feb 16	11:07:59	315	2759	156	N	a-	1.4617	0.1606	-0.8087	106.1	-	-	14N	162W
1738	145	2223 Jul 13	12:17:52	315	2764	123	N	-t	1.0486	0.9478	-0.0797	263.7	-	-	21S	178E
1739	145	2224 Jan 07	11:58:46	316	2770	128	P	-a	-0.5732	1.8260	0.7870	324.6	182.8	-	22N	177W
1740	145	2224 Jul 01	22:43:13	317	2776	133	T+	-p	0.2379	2.4081	1.4347	327.1	211.8	87.7	23S	22E

Cat Num	Canon Plate	Calendar Date	TD of Greatest Eclipse	ΔT s	Luna Num	Saros Num	Ecl Type	QSE	Gamma	Pen Mag	Um Mag	Pen m	Par m	Total m	Greatest in Zenith Lat	Long
1741	146	2224 Dec 26	16:25:17	318	2782	138	T+	pp	0.1183	2.6869	1.5956	371.6	230.9	100.5	23N	115E
1742	146	2225 Jun 21	14:38:56	319	2788	143	P	a-	-0.5097	1.8936	0.9512	299.8	184.0	-	24S	142E
1743	146	2225 Dec 15	15:41:08	320	2794	148	P	t-	0.8027	1.4370	0.3344	326.4	136.2	-	24N	125E
1744	146	2226 May 12	23:26:44	321	2799	115	N	-a	1.3191	0.4277	-0.5526	174.9	-	-	17S	9E
1745	146	2226 Jun 11	07:41:29	321	2800	153	N	a-	-1.2460	0.5488	-0.4056	190.7	-	-	24S	114W
1746	146	2226 Nov 05	02:38:02	322	2805	120	N	-h	-1.4025	0.2978	-0.7282	153.6	-	-	14N	42W
1747	146	2226 Dec 04	17:10:19	322	2806	158	N	h-	1.4479	0.2330	-0.8300	141.9	-	-	24N	101E
1748	146	2227 May 02	09:32:27	323	2811	125	P	-t	0.6204	1.7387	0.7008	327.4	179.0	-	15S	142W
1749	146	2227 Oct 25	15:02:23	324	2817	130	P	-a	-0.6445	1.6621	0.6886	295.2	165.4	-	11N	132E
1750	146	2228 Apr 20	12:20:31	325	2823	135	T-	pp	-0.1184	2.6813	1.6008	374.1	233.6	102.1	12S	176E
1751	146	2228 Oct 14	07:13:09	326	2829	140	T+	pp	0.0586	2.7291	1.7714	318.6	210.8	98.0	8N	110W
1752	146	2229 Apr 09	12:21:26	327	2835	145	P	t-	-0.8403	1.3544	0.2786	314.7	124.2	-	8S	176E
1753	147	2229 Oct 03	22:29:30	328	2841	150	P	a-	0.7866	1.4077	0.4217	286.1	137.4	-	5N	21E
1754	147	2230 Feb 28	04:27:12	329	2846	117	N	-a	1.2538	0.5613	-0.4462	200.6	-	-	9N	62W
1755	147	2230 Mar 29	16:58:21	329	2847	155	N	a-	-1.5105	0.1014	-0.9282	92.1	-	-	5S	107E
1756	147	2230 Aug 24	18:48:10	330	2852	122	N	-t	-1.2127	0.6610	-0.3949	233.5	-	-	12S	81E
1757	147	2231 Feb 17	18:27:46	331	2858	127	P	-a	0.5321	1.8669	0.8961	301.4	180.3	-	13N	88E
1758	147	2231 Aug 13	19:45:54	332	2864	132	P	-t	-0.4786	2.0163	0.9439	357.5	206.9	-	15S	66E
1759	147	2232 Feb 07	10:17:44	333	2870	137	T-	p-	-0.1410	2.5876	1.6106	321.6	210.0	94.1	15N	150W
1760	147	2232 Aug 01	21:49:49	334	2876	142	T	t-	0.2898	2.3465	1.3062	354.4	220.4	81.1	18S	36E
1761	147	2233 Jan 26	23:15:03	335	2882	147	P	a-	-0.8553	1.3007	0.2768	286.7	116.0	-	18N	15E
1762	147	2233 Jun 22	22:22:33	336	2887	114	Ne	-a	-1.5250	0.0404	-0.9209	54.8	-	-	25S	27E
1763	147	2233 Jul 22	06:40:41	336	2888	152	N	a-	1.0329	0.9552	-0.0297	251.0	-	-	19S	97W
1764	147	2233 Dec 17	11:10:38	337	2893	119	N	-t	1.4028	0.3343	-0.7652	175.4	-	-	25N	167W
1765	148	2234 Jun 12	15:02:55	338	2899	124	P	-a	-0.7774	1.4022	0.4603	273.9	138.5	-	24S	136E
1766	148	2234 Dec 06	10:17:26	339	2905	129	P	-t	0.7301	1.5662	0.4715	332.9	157.3	-	23N	155W
1767	148	2235 Jun 02	07:32:47	340	2911	134	T-	pp	-0.0495	2.7500	1.7838	326.9	215.5	100.1	22S	112W
1768	148	2235 Nov 25	13:38:15	341	2917	139	T+	pp	0.0086	2.8647	1.8200	352.9	224.9	102.4	21N	153E
1769	148	2236 May 21	19:18:51	342	2923	144	P	t-	0.7352	1.5194	0.4987	309.2	154.2	-	20S	71E
1770	148	2236 Nov 14	00:24:12	343	2929	149	P	a-	-0.6879	1.5896	0.6019	294.9	158.2	-	17N	8W
1771	148	2237 Apr 11	07:30:44	344	2934	116	N	-t	-1.3796	0.3703	-0.7163	184.3	-	-	9S	111W
1772	148	2237 May 10	23:45:33	344	2935	154	N	t-	1.5297	0.0864	-0.9831	90.2	-	-	16S	4E
1773	148	2237 Oct 05	06:57:01	345	2940	121	N	-a	1.2564	0.5325	-0.4275	187.0	-	-	6N	106W
1774	148	2237 Nov 03	15:53:39	345	2941	159	N	a-	-1.3394	0.3810	-0.5806	159.6	-	-	14N	119E
1775	148	2238 Mar 31	08:05:24	346	2946	126	P	-t	-0.6477	1.7035	0.6361	334.4	175.6	-	5S	119W
1776	148	2238 Sep 24	21:14:02	347	2952	131	P	-a	0.5775	1.7975	0.7992	313.8	180.6	-	1N	41E
1777	149	2239 Mar 20	14:37:27	348	2958	136	T+	p-	0.1017	2.6792	1.6636	341.6	219.9	99.1	0N	144E
1778	149	2239 Sep 14	05:17:33	349	2964	141	T-	pp	-0.1708	2.5702	1.5195	360.3	227.0	97.0	4S	79W
1779	149	2240 Mar 09	03:46:50	350	2970	146	P	a-	0.7925	1.3899	0.4176	277.5	133.8	-	5N	52W
1780	149	2240 Sep 02	06:52:16	351	2976	151	P	t-	-0.9305	1.1895	0.1126	303.6	81.8	-	9S	101W
1781	149	2241 Jan 28	09:08:45	352	2981	118	N	-a	-1.2221	0.6096	-0.3784	202.2	-	-	17N	133W
1782	149	2241 Feb 26	19:46:43	352	2982	156	N	a-	1.4489	0.1834	-0.7847	113.2	-	-	10N	68E
1783	149	2241 Jul 23	19:08:09	353	2987	123	N	-t	1.1246	0.8070	-0.2177	246.0	-	-	19S	76E
1784	149	2242 Jan 17	20:28:26	354	2993	128	P	-a	-0.5794	1.8159	0.7742	325.3	182.2	-	20N	57E
1785	149	2242 Jul 13	05:59:11	355	2999	133	T	-p	0.3129	2.2688	1.2984	323.0	206.7	76.2	22S	87W
1786	149	2243 Jan 07	00:33:44	356	3005	138	T+	pp	0.1116	2.7004	1.6069	372.6	231.4	101.0	23N	6W
1787	149	2243 Jul 02	22:07:19	357	3011	143	T	a-	-0.4355	2.0293	1.0880	304.4	191.8	43.2	23S	31E
1788	149	2243 Dec 26	23:42:16	358	3017	148	P	t-	0.7922	1.4563	0.3533	327.6	139.5	-	24N	6E
1789	150	2244 May 23	06:56:59	359	3022	115	N	-a	1.3851	0.3070	-0.6741	150.3	-	-	19S	103W
1790	150	2244 Jun 21	15:07:42	359	3023	153	N	a-	-1.1783	0.6735	-0.2820	209.1	-	-	25S	135E
1791	150	2244 Nov 15	10:48:55	360	3028	120	N	-a	-1.4201	0.2651	-0.7604	144.9	-	-	17N	164W
1792	150	2244 Dec 15	01:25:19	360	3029	158	N	a-	1.4341	0.2578	-0.8040	148.5	-	-	25N	21W
1793	150	2245 May 12	16:43:42	361	3034	125	P	-t	0.6856	1.6193	0.5809	321.7	166.7	-	18S	110E
1794	150	2245 Nov 04	23:23:16	362	3040	130	P	-a	-0.6708	1.6142	0.6399	292.1	160.4	-	15N	7E
1795	150	2246 May 01	19:20:11	363	3046	135	T-	pp	-0.0575	2.7920	1.7137	375.0	235.2	105.2	15S	71E
1796	150	2246 Oct 25	15:28:37	364	3052	140	T+	pp	0.0236	2.7950	1.8339	319.3	211.1	98.6	12N	125E
1797	150	2247 Apr 20	19:34:23	366	3058	145	P	t-	-0.7870	1.4495	0.3790	321.0	142.4	-	12S	67E
1798	150	2247 Oct 15	06:25:29	367	3064	150	P	a-	0.7471	1.4829	0.4912	292.3	147.1	-	9N	99W
1799	150	2248 Mar 10	12:44:46	367	3069	117	N	-a	1.2717	0.5256	-0.4765	194.0	-	-	5N	173E
1800	150	2248 Apr 09	00:42:27	368	3070	155	N	a-	-1.4663	0.1793	-0.8441	121.0	-	-	9S	9W

Cat Num	Canon Plate	Calendar Date	TD of Greatest Eclipse	ΔT s	Luna Num	Saros Num	Ecl Type	QSE	Gamma	Pen Mag	Um Mag	Phase ---- Durations ---- Pen m	Par m	Total m	Greatest in Zenith Lat	Long
1801	151	2248 Sep 04	01:38:57	369	3075	122	N	-t	-1.2858	0.5295	-0.5313	212.4	-	-	8S	23W
1802	151	2248 Oct 03	15:52:01	369	3076	160	Nb	t-	1.5365	0.0613	-0.9833	73.4	-	-	5N	120E
1803	151	2249 Feb 28	03:04:45	370	3081	127	P	-a	0.5480	1.8362	0.8685	299.6	178.2	-	9N	41W
1804	151	2249 Aug 24	02:22:14	371	3087	132	P	-t	-0.5572	1.8728	0.7990	351.0	195.3	-	12S	33W
1805	151	2250 Feb 17	18:58:32	372	3093	137	T-	p-	-0.1291	2.6094	1.6326	322.3	210.7	95.0	12N	80E
1806	151	2250 Aug 13	04:39:38	373	3099	142	T+	pp	0.2108	2.4908	1.4520	356.1	224.5	92.9	15S	67W
1807	151	2251 Feb 07	07:45:39	374	3105	147	P	a-	-0.8497	1.3118	0.2863	288.5	118.2	-	15N	112W
1808	151	2251 Aug 02	13:53:15	375	3111	152	P	a-	0.9549	1.0971	0.1146	263.9	75.6	-	17S	155E
1809	151	2251 Dec 28	19:12:50	376	3116	119	N	-t	1.4132	0.3162	-0.7854	171.2	-	-	25N	74E
1810	151	2252 Jun 22	22:33:27	377	3122	124	P	-a	-0.8494	1.2697	0.3286	264.7	119.3	-	24S	24E
1811	151	2252 Dec 16	18:18:40	378	3128	129	P	-t	0.7406	1.5468	0.4521	331.1	154.3	-	24N	86E
1812	151	2253 Jun 12	14:57:11	379	3134	134	T-	-p	-0.1210	2.6195	1.6520	327.0	214.8	97.6	23S	137E
1813	152	2253 Dec 05	21:55:59	380	3140	139	T+	pp	0.0213	2.8409	1.7973	351.7	224.2	102.0	22N	30E
1814	152	2254 Jun 02	02:24:39	381	3146	144	P	t-	0.6670	1.6452	0.6232	318.0	169.5	-	21S	35W
1815	152	2254 Nov 25	08:54:58	382	3152	149	P	a-	-0.6696	1.6231	0.6354	296.1	161.3	-	20N	135W
1816	152	2255 Apr 22	14:36:06	383	3157	116	N	-t	-1.4324	0.2717	-0.8116	159.2	-	-	13S	142E
1817	152	2255 May 22	06:33:14	384	3158	154	N	t-	1.4630	0.2083	-0.8603	138.8	-	-	19S	97W
1818	152	2255 Oct 16	15:04:23	384	3163	121	N	-a	1.2959	0.4621	-0.5021	175.8	-	-	10N	132E
1819	152	2255 Nov 15	00:24:35	385	3164	159	N	a-	-1.3181	0.4213	-0.5428	167.2	-	-	17N	8W
1820	152	2256 Apr 10	15:31:03	386	3169	126	P	-t	-0.6905	1.6221	0.5606	328.2	166.5	-	9S	129E
1821	152	2256 Oct 05	04:57:12	387	3175	131	P	-a	0.6264	1.7108	0.7064	311.0	173.0	-	5N	76W
1822	152	2257 Mar 30	22:36:42	388	3181	136	T+	pp	0.0686	2.7368	1.7273	340.3	220.0	100.4	4S	24E
1823	152	2257 Sep 24	12:27:34	389	3187	141	T-	pp	-0.1123	2.6803	1.6239	363.2	229.4	101.4	1N	173E
1824	152	2258 Mar 20	12:10:19	390	3193	146	P	a-	0.7663	1.4358	0.4677	279.9	140.3	-	1N	179W
1825	153	2258 Sep 13	13:39:53	391	3199	151	P	t-	-0.8623	1.3160	0.2362	315.2	116.4	-	4S	156E
1826	153	2259 Feb 08	17:51:41	392	3204	118	N	-a	-1.2321	0.5917	-0.3971	200.0	-	-	14N	97E
1827	153	2259 Mar 10	04:19:53	392	3205	156	N	a-	1.4323	0.2132	-0.7536	121.9	-	-	6N	60W
1828	153	2259 Aug 04	02:01:59	393	3210	123	N	-t	1.1982	0.6707	-0.3516	226.4	-	-	16S	27W
1829	153	2259 Sep 02	14:47:57	393	3211	161	Nb	t-	-1.5669	0.0100	-1.0434	30.4	-	-	9S	140E
1830	153	2260 Jan 29	04:55:22	394	3216	128	P	-a	-0.5872	1.8027	0.7589	325.8	181.4	-	18N	69W
1831	153	2260 Jul 23	13:17:09	395	3222	133	T	-p	0.3868	2.1322	1.1642	318.2	200.5	59.0	19S	164E
1832	153	2261 Jan 17	08:40:06	397	3228	138	T+	pp	0.1036	2.7157	1.6208	373.5	232.0	101.5	21N	126W
1833	153	2261 Jul 13	05:36:18	398	3234	143	T	p-	-0.3617	2.1644	1.2236	308.3	198.1	66.0	22S	81W
1834	153	2262 Jan 06	07:45:00	399	3240	148	P	t-	0.7832	1.4726	0.3702	328.4	142.3	-	23N	113W
1835	153	2262 Jun 03	14:20:48	400	3245	115	N	-a	1.4556	0.1784	-0.8039	116.4	-	-	21S	146E
1836	153	2262 Jul 02	22:31:30	400	3246	153	N	a-	-1.1090	0.8015	-0.1555	225.8	-	-	24S	25E
1837	154	2262 Nov 26	19:06:56	401	3251	120	N	-a	-1.4328	0.2416	-0.7832	138.2	-	-	20N	72E
1838	154	2262 Dec 26	09:43:58	401	3252	158	N	a-	1.4227	0.2779	-0.7821	153.4	-	-	25N	144W
1839	154	2263 May 23	23:46:24	402	3257	125	P	-t	0.7568	1.4891	0.4499	314.3	150.2	-	20S	5E
1840	154	2263 Nov 16	07:52:13	403	3263	130	P	-a	-0.6909	1.5778	0.6027	289.6	156.3	-	18N	120W
1841	154	2264 May 12	02:08:52	404	3269	135	T+	pp	0.0121	2.8742	1.7979	375.3	235.8	106.2	18S	31W
1842	154	2264 Nov 04	23:52:49	405	3275	140	T-	pp	-0.0039	2.8329	1.8684	319.9	211.2	98.6	16N	1W
1843	154	2265 May 01	02:38:34	407	3281	145	P	t-	-0.7261	1.5587	0.4934	327.5	159.3	-	16S	39W
1844	154	2265 Oct 25	14:28:58	408	3287	150	P	a-	0.7146	1.5455	0.5480	297.4	154.4	-	13N	140E
1845	154	2266 Mar 21	20:56:21	409	3292	117	N	-a	1.2951	0.4800	-0.5166	185.5	-	-	1N	50E
1846	154	2266 Apr 20	08:20:16	409	3293	155	N	a-	-1.4163	0.2678	-0.7492	146.0	-	-	13S	124W
1847	154	2266 Sep 15	08:35:39	410	3298	122	N	-t	-1.3530	0.4087	-0.6572	189.4	-	-	4S	128W
1848	154	2266 Oct 14	23:22:59	410	3299	160	N	t-	1.4969	0.1371	-0.9137	109.6	-	-	10N	7E
1849	155	2267 Mar 11	11:37:13	411	3304	127	P	-a	0.5679	1.7980	0.8336	297.5	175.6	-	4N	170W
1850	155	2267 Sep 04	09:02:59	412	3310	132	P	-t	-0.6322	1.7360	0.6604	343.7	181.7	-	8S	134W
1851	155	2268 Feb 29	03:35:26	413	3316	137	T-	p-	-0.1142	2.6365	1.6602	323.0	211.4	96.0	8N	49W
1852	155	2268 Aug 23	11:34:50	414	3322	142	T+	pp	0.1351	2.6290	1.5915	356.8	226.9	99.8	11S	171W
1853	155	2269 Feb 17	16:11:17	415	3328	147	P	a-	-0.8406	1.3290	0.3023	290.8	121.5	-	11N	122E
1854	155	2269 Aug 12	21:11:37	417	3334	152	P	a-	0.8806	1.2325	0.2517	274.6	109.6	-	14S	45E
1855	155	2270 Jan 08	03:16:21	418	3339	119	N	-t	1.4225	0.2999	-0.8031	167.2	-	-	23N	46W
1856	155	2270 Jul 04	06:03:42	419	3345	124	P	-a	-0.9215	1.1374	0.1965	254.3	94.1	-	24S	88W
1857	155	2270 Dec 28	02:22:42	420	3351	129	P	-t	0.7494	1.5304	0.4364	329.4	151.7	-	24N	34W
1858	155	2271 Jun 23	22:18:46	421	3357	134	T-	-p	-0.1944	2.4858	1.5166	326.5	212.9	92.3	24S	28E
1859	155	2271 Dec 17	06:18:50	422	3363	139	T+	pp	0.0303	2.8235	1.7815	350.5	223.6	101.7	23N	94W
1860	155	2272 Jun 12	09:23:35	423	3369	144	P	t-	0.5938	1.7804	0.7565	326.6	183.3	-	23S	139W

Cat Num	Canon Plate	Calendar Date	TD of Greatest Eclipse	ΔT s	Luna Num	Saros Num	Ecl Type	QSE	Gamma	Pen Mag	Um Mag	Phase ---- Durations ---- Pen m	Par m	Total m	Greatest in Zenith Lat	Long
1861	156	2272 Dec 05	17:32:31	425	3375	149	P	a-	-0.6565	1.6471	0.6597	296.8	163.4	–	22N	96E
1862	156	2273 May 02	21:31:51	426	3380	116	N	-t	-1.4926	0.1598	-0.9205	123.2	–	–	17S	38E
1863	156	2273 Jun 01	13:13:38	426	3381	154	N	t-	1.3903	0.3413	-0.7267	175.8	–	–	21S	163E
1864	156	2273 Oct 26	23:19:48	427	3386	121	N	-a	1.3289	0.4037	-0.5647	165.6	–	–	14N	7E
1865	156	2273 Nov 25	09:01:54	427	3387	159	N	a-	-1.3020	0.4520	-0.5144	172.8	–	–	19N	137W
1866	156	2274 Apr 21	22:48:59	428	3392	126	P	-t	-0.7402	1.5280	0.4723	320.8	154.6	–	13S	19E
1867	156	2274 Oct 16	12:48:08	429	3398	131	P	-a	0.6684	1.6369	0.6264	308.4	165.5	–	10N	166E
1868	156	2275 Apr 11	06:28:07	430	3404	136	T+	pp	0.0283	2.8078	1.8044	339.0	220.0	101.3	8S	95W
1869	156	2275 Oct 05	19:44:06	431	3410	141	T-	pp	-0.0599	2.7794	1.7172	365.4	230.8	103.8	5N	63E
1870	156	2276 Mar 30	20:26:06	433	3416	146	P	a-	0.7334	1.4941	0.5302	282.9	147.8	–	3S	57E
1871	156	2276 Sep 23	20:35:24	434	3422	151	P	t-	-0.8004	1.4311	0.3482	324.7	138.9	–	0S	51E
1872	156	2277 Feb 19	02:29:14	435	3427	118	N	-a	-1.2460	0.5662	-0.4229	196.6	–	–	10N	32W
1873	157	2277 Mar 20	12:44:40	435	3428	156	N	a-	1.4094	0.2544	-0.7108	132.7	–	–	1N	173E
1874	157	2277 Aug 14	09:01:19	436	3433	123	N	-t	1.2679	0.5419	-0.4785	205.3	–	–	13S	133W
1875	157	2277 Sep 12	21:49:42	436	3434	161	N	t-	-1.4999	0.1329	-0.9206	109.2	–	–	5S	34E
1876	157	2278 Feb 08	13:19:09	437	3439	128	P	-a	-0.5966	1.7863	0.7409	326.1	180.3	–	14N	165E
1877	157	2278 Aug 03	20:37:40	438	3445	133	T	-a	0.4592	1.9983	1.0321	312.8	193.1	27.1	17S	54E
1878	157	2279 Jan 28	16:45:41	439	3451	138	T+	pp	0.0954	2.7312	1.6355	374.3	232.5	102.1	18N	114E
1879	157	2279 Jul 24	13:05:07	441	3457	143	T	p-	-0.2877	2.3002	1.3594	311.5	203.1	79.9	20S	167E
1880	157	2280 Jan 17	15:49:31	442	3463	148	P	t-	0.7749	1.4871	0.3861	329.1	144.8	–	21N	127E
1881	157	2280 Jun 13	21:38:08	443	3468	115	Ne	-a	1.5304	0.0420	-0.9420	57.4	–	–	22S	38E
1882	157	2280 Jul 13	05:52:35	443	3469	153	N	a-	-1.0377	0.9335	-0.0259	241.0	–	–	23S	85W
1883	157	2280 Dec 07	03:32:38	444	3474	120	N	-a	-1.4403	0.2273	-0.7964	133.8	–	–	21N	53W
1884	157	2281 Jan 05	18:06:45	444	3475	158	N	a-	1.4137	0.2932	-0.7643	156.8	–	–	24N	91E
1885	158	2281 Jun 03	06:42:42	445	3480	125	P	-t	0.8323	1.3512	0.3109	305.2	127.9	–	22S	99W
1886	158	2281 Nov 26	16:27:11	446	3486	130	P	-a	-0.7065	1.5494	0.5737	287.6	153.0	–	20N	112E
1887	158	2282 May 23	08:52:42	448	3492	135	T+	pp	0.0856	2.7384	1.6640	374.7	235.1	104.4	21S	132W
1888	158	2282 Nov 16	08:23:04	449	3498	140	T-	pp	-0.0261	2.7939	1.8261	320.4	211.2	98.4	19N	128W
1889	158	2283 May 12	09:37:19	450	3504	145	P	t-	-0.6596	1.6780	0.6178	333.8	174.4	–	19S	144W
1890	158	2283 Nov 05	22:38:42	451	3510	150	P	a-	0.6877	1.5977	0.5945	301.7	160.1	–	16N	18E
1891	158	2284 Apr 01	05:01:10	452	3515	117	N	-a	1.3247	0.4228	-0.5681	174.3	–	–	4S	72W
1892	158	2284 Apr 30	15:51:40	452	3516	155	N	a-	-1.3601	0.3679	-0.6430	168.8	–	–	16S	123E
1893	158	2284 Sep 25	15:39:32	454	3521	122	N	-t	-1.4139	0.2995	-0.7715	164.3	–	–	0N	126E
1894	158	2284 Oct 25	07:01:33	454	3522	160	N	t-	1.4633	0.2017	-0.8552	132.7	–	–	14N	108W
1895	158	2285 Mar 21	20:01:07	455	3527	127	P	-a	0.5954	1.7458	0.7847	294.6	171.7	–	0S	64E
1896	158	2285 Sep 14	15:53:25	456	3533	132	P	-t	-0.6997	1.6132	0.5357	336.2	166.9	–	4S	123E
1897	159	2286 Mar 11	12:04:37	457	3539	137	T-	pp	-0.0928	2.6753	1.6997	323.8	212.3	97.3	4N	177W
1898	159	2286 Sep 03	18:37:54	458	3545	142	T+	pp	0.0648	2.7576	1.7209	356.7	227.8	103.2	7S	82E
1899	159	2287 Mar 01	00:30:01	460	3551	147	P	a-	-0.8265	1.3554	0.3279	293.7	126.4	–	7N	3W
1900	159	2287 Aug 24	04:35:07	461	3557	152	P	a-	0.8094	1.3624	0.3829	283.5	132.2	–	10S	66W
1901	159	2288 Jan 19	11:19:31	462	3562	119	N	-t	1.4317	0.2832	-0.8203	162.8	–	–	22N	165W
1902	159	2288 Jul 14	13:31:30	463	3568	124	P	-a	-0.9955	1.0018	0.0604	242.4	53.1	–	22S	161E
1903	159	2288 Aug 12	20:15:28	463	3569	162	Nb	a-	1.4946	0.0877	-0.8570	78.6	–	–	13S	59E
1904	159	2289 Jan 07	10:30:56	464	3574	129	P	-t	0.7553	1.5187	0.4263	327.9	150.0	–	23N	154W
1905	159	2289 Jul 04	05:36:25	466	3580	134	T-	-p	-0.2703	2.3476	1.3760	325.2	209.7	83.3	23S	81W
1906	159	2289 Dec 27	14:46:23	467	3586	139	T+	pp	0.0364	2.8113	1.7713	349.2	222.9	101.4	23N	141E
1907	159	2290 Jun 23	16:17:39	468	3592	144	P	t-	0.5172	1.9222	0.8960	334.5	195.3	–	23S	118E
1908	159	2290 Dec 17	02:15:35	469	3598	149	P	a-	-0.6473	1.6636	0.6768	297.0	164.7	–	23N	33W
1909	160	2291 May 14	04:20:24	470	3603	116	Ne	-t	-1.5581	0.0379	-1.0392	60.6	–	–	20S	64W
1910	160	2291 Jun 12	19:47:40	470	3604	154	N	t-	1.3123	0.4841	-0.5835	206.8	–	–	22S	65E
1911	160	2291 Nov 07	07:41:43	471	3609	121	N	-a	1.3565	0.3553	-0.6174	156.5	–	–	18N	118W
1912	160	2291 Dec 06	17:45:09	472	3610	159	N	a-	-1.2909	0.4735	-0.4950	176.6	–	–	21N	93E
1913	160	2292 May 02	06:00:51	473	3615	126	P	-t	-0.7956	1.4233	0.3734	312.1	139.2	–	16S	89W
1914	160	2292 Oct 26	20:45:26	474	3621	131	P	-a	0.7042	1.5743	0.5576	306.1	158.4	–	13N	46E
1915	160	2293 Apr 21	14:13:28	475	3627	136	T-	pp	-0.0180	2.8237	1.8263	337.3	219.5	101.4	12S	148E
1916	160	2293 Oct 16	03:08:17	476	3633	141	T-	pp	-0.0144	2.8659	1.7979	367.2	231.6	104.6	9N	49W
1917	160	2294 Apr 11	04:36:13	478	3639	146	P	a-	0.6956	1.5614	0.6015	286.2	155.5	–	8S	67W
1918	160	2294 Oct 05	03:38:22	479	3645	151	P	t-	-0.7443	1.5357	0.4498	332.6	155.4	–	4N	55W
1919	160	2295 Mar 02	11:01:07	480	3650	118	N	-a	-1.2643	0.5329	-0.4564	191.7	–	–	6N	161W
1920	160	2295 Mar 31	21:02:52	480	3651	156	N	a-	1.3817	0.3046	-0.6592	144.7	–	–	3S	48E

Cat Num	Canon Plate	Calendar Date	TD of Greatest Eclipse	ΔT s	Luna Num	Saros Num	Ecl Type	QSE	Gamma	Pen Mag	Um Mag	Pen m	Par m	Total m	Lat	Long
1921	161	2295 Aug 25	16:07:03	481	3656	123	N	-t	1.3329	0.4218	-0.5971	182.6	–	–	9S	121E
1922	161	2295 Sep 24	05:00:03	481	3657	161	N	t-	-1.4388	0.2451	-0.8085	146.4	–	–	1S	75W
1923	161	2296 Feb 19	21:35:59	483	3662	128	P	-a	-0.6112	1.7599	0.7134	325.7	178.2	–	11N	41E
1924	161	2296 Aug 14	04:03:00	484	3668	133	P	-a	0.5283	1.8710	0.9060	307.0	184.6	–	14S	58W
1925	161	2297 Feb 08	00:46:04	485	3674	138	T+	pp	0.0832	2.7536	1.6579	375.0	233.1	102.8	15N	6W
1926	161	2297 Aug 03	20:37:09	486	3680	143	T-	p-	-0.2162	2.4318	1.4901	314.0	206.8	88.9	17S	54E
1927	161	2298 Jan 27	23:51:15	488	3686	148	P	t-	0.7640	1.5060	0.4071	329.9	148.0	–	19N	7E
1928	161	2298 Jul 24	13:14:15	489	3692	153	P	a-	-0.9674	1.0640	0.1018	254.6	70.0	–	21S	165E
1929	161	2298 Dec 18	12:03:41	490	3697	120	N	-a	-1.4440	0.2196	-0.8025	131.2	–	–	22N	180W
1930	161	2299 Jan 17	02:30:29	490	3698	158	N	a-	1.4049	0.3077	-0.7467	159.9	–	–	22N	33W
1931	161	2299 Jun 14	13:31:01	491	3703	125	P	-t	0.9132	1.2036	0.1618	293.8	94.6	–	22S	160E
1932	161	2299 Dec 08	01:09:07	492	3709	130	P	-a	-0.7168	1.5307	0.5547	286.1	150.7	–	22N	17W
1933	162	2300 Jun 03	15:28:05	494	3715	135	T+	pp	0.1655	2.5910	1.5182	373.2	232.9	99.0	22S	130E
1934	162	2300 Nov 27	17:00:33	495	3721	140	T-	-p	-0.0422	2.7659	1.7950	320.9	211.2	98.1	21N	104E
1935	162	2301 May 23	16:29:16	496	3727	145	P	t-	-0.5869	1.8090	0.7537	339.7	187.8	–	21S	114E
1936	162	2301 Nov 17	06:56:02	498	3733	150	P	a-	0.6679	1.6369	0.6283	305.2	164.1	–	19N	106W
1937	162	2302 Apr 13	12:59:54	499	3738	117	N	-a	1.3599	0.3554	-0.6299	160.2	–	–	8S	168E
1938	162	2302 May 12	23:17:52	499	3739	155	N	a-	-1.2986	0.4777	-0.5271	189.5	–	–	19S	11E
1939	162	2302 Oct 07	22:49:34	500	3744	122	N	-t	-1.4691	0.2008	-0.8753	136.2	–	–	4N	17E
1940	162	2302 Nov 06	14:46:23	500	3745	160	N	t-	1.4353	0.2562	-0.8066	149.4	–	–	17N	136E
1941	162	2303 Apr 03	04:19:40	501	3750	127	P	-a	0.6276	1.6851	0.7273	291.3	166.8	–	4S	62W
1942	162	2303 Sep 26	22:50:54	502	3756	132	P	-t	-0.7616	1.5007	0.4211	328.5	150.6	–	1N	18E
1943	162	2304 Mar 22	20:26:41	504	3762	137	T-	pp	-0.0661	2.7240	1.7492	324.7	213.2	98.4	1S	57E
1944	162	2304 Sep 15	01:48:58	505	3768	142	T+	pp	0.0003	2.8756	1.8395	355.8	227.6	103.9	3S	26W
1945	163	2305 Mar 12	08:41:34	506	3774	147	P	a-	-0.8072	1.3910	0.3630	297.3	132.7	–	3N	126W
1946	163	2305 Sep 04	12:05:49	508	3780	152	P	a-	0.7436	1.4829	0.5042	290.7	148.5	–	7S	180W
1947	163	2306 Jan 30	19:20:02	509	3785	119	N	-t	1.4428	0.2628	-0.8405	157.3	–	–	19N	76E
1948	163	2306 Mar 01	13:42:51	509	3786	157	N	t-	-1.5675	0.0241	-1.0594	47.8	–	–	7N	159E
1949	163	2306 Jul 26	21:01:27	510	3791	124	N	-a	-1.0676	0.8701	-0.0725	229.3	–	–	20S	49E
1950	163	2306 Aug 25	03:53:20	510	3792	162	N	a-	1.4297	0.2074	-0.7382	119.4	–	–	10S	56W
1951	163	2307 Jan 19	18:39:13	511	3797	129	P	-t	0.7617	1.5059	0.4156	326.2	148.1	–	21N	85E
1952	163	2307 Jul 16	12:51:47	513	3803	134	T	-a	-0.3476	2.2074	1.2329	323.2	204.9	69.1	22S	171E
1953	163	2308 Jan 08	23:16:24	514	3809	139	T+	pp	0.0413	2.8010	1.7637	347.9	222.3	101.1	22N	14E
1954	163	2308 Jul 04	23:07:47	515	3815	144	T	t-	0.4377	2.0694	1.0404	341.7	205.6	32.0	22S	16E
1955	163	2308 Dec 28	11:01:32	516	3821	149	P	a-	-0.6401	1.6763	0.6906	297.0	165.7	–	23N	163W
1956	163	2309 Jun 24	02:17:41	518	3827	154	N	t-	1.2308	0.6338	-0.4339	233.5	–	–	22S	32W
1957	164	2309 Nov 18	16:10:55	519	3832	121	N	-a	1.3783	0.3174	-0.6594	148.8	–	–	21N	115E
1958	164	2309 Dec 18	02:32:40	519	3833	159	N	a-	-1.2831	0.4888	-0.4815	179.3	–	–	22N	37W
1959	164	2310 May 14	13:06:25	520	3838	126	P	-t	-0.8566	1.3085	0.2643	301.9	118.7	–	19S	165E
1960	164	2310 Nov 08	04:49:16	521	3844	131	P	-a	0.7340	1.5227	0.5001	304.3	151.8	–	17N	74W
1961	164	2311 May 03	21:52:06	523	3850	136	T-	pp	-0.0706	2.7241	1.7326	335.4	218.5	100.3	16S	33E
1962	164	2311 Oct 28	10:40:16	524	3856	141	T+	pp	0.0241	2.8508	1.7772	368.7	231.9	104.5	13N	162W
1963	164	2312 Apr 22	12:37:08	525	3862	146	P	a-	0.6499	1.6433	0.6874	290.1	163.8	–	12S	173E
1964	164	2312 Oct 16	10:51:22	527	3868	151	P	L-	-0.6960	1.6258	0.5369	330.7	167.4	–	0N	164W
1965	164	2313 Mar 13	19:25:44	528	3873	118	N	-a	-1.2881	0.4891	-0.5001	184.9	–	–	2N	73E
1966	164	2313 Apr 12	05:12:29	528	3874	156	N	a-	1.3474	0.3668	-0.5955	158.1	–	–	7S	75W
1967	164	2313 Sep 05	23:20:22	529	3879	123	N	-t	1.3926	0.3118	-0.7061	158.0	–	–	5S	11E
1968	164	2313 Oct 05	12:20:13	529	3880	161	N	t-	-1.3843	0.3452	-0.7087	171.7	–	–	3N	175E
1969	165	2314 Mar 03	05:46:47	530	3885	128	P	-a	-0.6302	1.7255	0.6784	324.9	175.3	–	7N	82W
1970	165	2314 Aug 26	11:33:38	532	3891	133	P	-a	0.5936	1.7508	0.7865	300.8	175.1	–	10S	171W
1971	165	2315 Feb 20	08:42:48	533	3897	138	T+	pp	0.0684	2.7805	1.6854	375.6	233.7	103.6	11N	125W
1972	165	2315 Aug 16	04:10:27	534	3903	143	T-	p-	-0.1459	2.5616	1.6186	315.8	209.4	94.7	14S	59W
1973	165	2316 Feb 09	07:52:24	536	3909	148	P	t-	0.7523	1.5261	0.4299	330.6	151.4	–	16N	112W
1974	165	2316 Aug 04	20:36:17	537	3915	153	P	a-	-0.8980	1.1931	0.2274	266.7	103.1	–	18S	55E
1975	165	2316 Dec 29	20:38:45	538	3920	120	N	-a	-1.4453	0.2162	-0.8039	129.8	–	–	22N	53E
1976	165	2317 Jan 28	10:53:58	538	3921	158	N	a-	1.3953	0.3234	-0.7273	163.0	–	–	20N	158W
1977	165	2317 Jun 25	20:15:56	540	3926	125	P	-t	0.9956	1.0533	0.0096	280.3	23.7	–	22S	59E
1978	165	2317 Dec 19	09:55:14	541	3932	130	P	-a	-0.7237	1.5180	0.5419	285.0	149.0	–	23N	147W
1979	165	2318 Jun 14	22:00:41	542	3938	135	T+	pp	0.2477	2.4395	1.3681	370.5	228.8	88.9	23S	32E
1980	165	2318 Dec 09	01:41:59	544	3944	140	T-	-p	-0.0547	2.7445	1.7707	321.5	211.2	97.8	23N	25W

Cat Num	Canon Plate	Calendar Date	TD of Greatest Eclipse	ΔT s	Luna Num	Saros Num	Ecl Type	QSE	Gamma	Pen Mag	Um Mag	Pen m	Par m	Total m	Lat	Long
1981	166	2319 Jun 03	23:18:18	545	3950	145	P	t-	-0.5110	1.9460	0.8954	344.9	199.2	–	23S	12E
1982	166	2319 Nov 28	15:18:34	546	3956	150	P	a-	0.6528	1.6670	0.6533	308.1	167.1	–	22N	129E
1983	166	2320 Apr 23	20:50:32	547	3961	117	N	-a	1.4022	0.2750	-0.7047	141.4	–	–	11S	50E
1984	166	2320 May 23	06:38:10	548	3962	155	N	a-	-1.2312	0.5985	-0.4007	208.7	–	–	22S	98W
1985	166	2320 Oct 18	06:08:41	549	3967	122	N	-t	-1.5163	0.1167	-0.9644	104.9	–	–	8N	93W
1986	166	2320 Nov 16	22:38:56	549	3968	160	N	t-	1.4138	0.2983	-0.7700	161.2	–	–	20N	18E
1987	166	2321 Apr 13	12:29:34	550	3973	127	P	-a	0.6672	1.6109	0.6562	287.2	160.3	–	8S	175E
1988	166	2321 Oct 07	05:58:35	551	3979	132	P	-t	-0.8152	1.4033	0.3218	321.0	133.5	–	5N	90W
1989	166	2322 Apr 03	04:39:44	553	3985	137	T-	pp	-0.0322	2.7857	1.8116	325.5	214.0	99.4	5S	67W
1990	166	2322 Sep 26	09:09:54	554	3991	142	T-	pp	-0.0568	2.7718	1.7359	354.4	226.6	102.8	1N	137W
1991	166	2323 Mar 23	16:43:40	556	3997	147	P	h-	-0.7810	1.4393	0.4111	301.7	140.6	–	1S	113E
1992	166	2323 Sep 15	19:43:07	557	4003	152	P	a-	0.6823	1.5951	0.6168	296.6	160.9	–	3S	65E
1993	167	2324 Feb 11	03:17:28	558	4008	119	N	-t	1.4561	0.2378	-0.8645	150.0	–	–	16N	43W
1994	167	2324 Mar 11	21:29:27	558	4009	157	N	t-	-1.5451	0.0647	-1.0179	78.1	–	–	2N	42E
1995	167	2324 Aug 06	04:31:50	559	4014	124	N	-a	-1.1393	0.7395	-0.2049	214.5	–	–	18S	64W
1996	167	2324 Sep 04	11:36:02	560	4015	162	N	a-	1.3683	0.3207	-0.6264	146.9	–	–	6S	172W
1997	167	2325 Jan 30	02:46:49	561	4020	129	P	-t	0.7693	1.4906	0.4033	324.3	145.9	–	18N	36W
1998	167	2325 Jul 26	20:06:27	562	4026	134	T	-a	-0.4246	2.0679	1.0897	320.3	198.7	45.0	20S	63E
1999	167	2326 Jan 19	07:48:31	564	4032	139	T+	pp	0.0455	2.7918	1.7576	346.5	221.8	100.9	20N	112W
2000	167	2326 Jul 16	05:54:46	565	4038	144	T	p-	0.3565	2.2201	1.1879	348.0	214.1	65.9	21S	85W
2001	167	2327 Jan 08	19:50:18	566	4044	149	P	a-	-0.6349	1.6851	0.7009	296.8	166.3	–	22N	66E
2002	167	2327 Jul 05	08:44:31	568	4050	154	N	t-	1.1464	0.7889	-0.2791	256.8	–	–	22S	128W
2003	167	2327 Nov 30	00:45:49	569	4055	121	N	-a	1.3950	0.2886	-0.6920	142.6	–	–	23N	12W
2004	167	2327 Dec 29	11:23:31	569	4056	159	N	a-	-1.2785	0.4979	-0.4738	181.0	–	–	22N	168W
2005	168	2328 May 24	20:06:38	570	4061	126	P	-t	-0.9226	1.1847	0.1460	290.0	89.5	–	22S	60E
2006	168	2328 Nov 18	12:59:37	572	4067	131	P	-a	0.7575	1.4824	0.4541	303.0	146.1	–	20N	164E
2007	168	2329 May 14	05:26:10	573	4073	136	T-	pp	-0.1279	2.6162	1.6302	333.0	216.9	97.6	19S	80W
2008	168	2329 Nov 07	18:18:32	574	4079	141	T+	pp	0.0568	2.7934	1.7146	369.9	231.9	103.7	16N	84E
2009	168	2330 May 03	20:33:06	576	4085	146	P	a-	0.5998	1.7334	0.7811	294.0	171.8	–	15S	54E
2010	168	2330 Oct 27	18:12:55	577	4091	151	P	t-	-0.6542	1.7039	0.6122	343.6	176.5	–	12N	85E
2011	168	2331 Mar 25	03:42:17	578	4096	118	N	-a	-1.3180	0.4341	-0.5548	175.6	–	–	3S	52W
2012	168	2331 Apr 23	13:14:06	578	4097	156	N	a-	1.3071	0.4402	-0.5210	172.2	–	–	11S	164E
2013	168	2331 Sep 17	06:41:30	580	4102	123	N	-t	1.4466	0.2123	-0.8048	131.1	–	–	1S	100W
2014	168	2331 Oct 16	19:49:56	580	4103	161	N	t-	-1.3366	0.4330	-0.6212	190.2	–	–	8N	62E
2015	168	2332 Mar 13	13:48:33	581	4108	128	P	-a	-0.6557	1.6788	0.6313	323.3	171.0	–	2N	157E
2016	168	2332 Sep 05	19:11:20	582	4114	133	P	a-	0.6533	1.6411	0.6770	294.5	165.0	–	6S	74E
2017	169	2333 Mar 02	16:30:26	584	4120	138	T+	pp	0.0466	2.8198	1.7260	376.0	234.3	104.5	7N	118E
2018	169	2333 Aug 26	11:49:38	585	4126	143	T-	pp	-0.0806	2.6822	1.7373	317.1	210.8	97.9	10S	174W
2019	169	2334 Feb 19	15:48:17	587	4132	148	P	t-	0.7362	1.5539	0.4613	331.7	155.8	–	12N	129E
2020	169	2334 Aug 16	03:59:51	588	4138	153	P	a-	-0.8304	1.3191	0.3493	277.4	125.9	–	15S	56W
2021	169	2335 Jan 10	05:15:59	589	4143	120	N	-a	-1.4455	0.2147	-0.8029	128.9	–	–	21N	75W
2022	169	2335 Feb 08	19:15:18	589	4144	158	N	a-	1.3834	0.3430	-0.7033	167.0	–	–	16N	77E
2023	169	2335 Jul 07	02:55:54	591	4149	125	N	-t	1.0807	0.8983	-0.1477	263.9	–	–	22S	40W
2024	169	2335 Dec 30	18:45:23	592	4155	130	P	-a	-0.7279	1.5101	0.5345	284.1	148.0	–	22N	82E
2025	169	2336 Jun 25	04:27:13	593	4161	135	T	-t	0.3347	2.2793	1.2089	366.5	222.5	71.0	23S	63W
2026	169	2336 Dec 19	10:28:54	595	4167	140	T-	-p	-0.0624	2.7315	1.7552	322.0	211.3	97.6	23N	156W
2027	169	2337 Jun 14	06:03:16	596	4173	145	T	t-	-0.4307	2.0911	1.0448	349.3	208.8	34.0	24S	88W
2028	169	2337 Dec 08	23:45:52	598	4179	150	P	a-	0.6423	1.6887	0.6702	310.5	169.2	–	23N	4E
2029	170	2338 May 05	04:35:59	599	4184	117	N	-a	1.4491	0.1861	-0.7883	116.9	–	–	15S	67W
2030	170	2338 Jun 03	13:55:26	599	4185	155	N	a-	-1.1603	0.7260	-0.2679	225.9	–	–	23S	153E
2031	170	2338 Oct 29	13:35:07	600	4190	122	N	-t	-1.5569	0.0447	-1.0413	65.5	–	–	12N	155E
2032	170	2338 Nov 28	06:37:23	601	4191	160	N	t-	1.3976	0.3306	-0.7427	169.8	–	–	22N	100W
2033	170	2339 Apr 24	20:32:43	602	4196	127	P	-a	0.7125	1.5262	0.5746	282.1	151.9	–	12S	54E
2034	170	2339 Oct 18	13:14:22	603	4202	132	P	-t	-0.8626	1.3174	0.2339	313.8	115.2	–	9N	161E
2035	170	2340 Apr 13	12:45:16	605	4208	137	T+	pp	0.0074	2.8309	1.8575	326.2	214.6	99.9	9S	171E
2036	170	2340 Oct 06	16:39:54	606	4214	142	T-	pp	-0.1075	2.6788	1.6431	352.7	224.9	100.4	5N	110E
2037	170	2341 Apr 03	00:36:58	607	4220	147	P	h-	-0.7481	1.4998	0.4713	306.7	149.7	–	6S	6W
2038	170	2341 Sep 26	03:29:15	609	4226	152	P	a-	0.6276	1.6955	0.7172	301.2	170.2	–	2N	52W
2039	170	2342 Feb 21	11:09:46	610	4231	119	N	-t	1.4736	0.2050	-0.8957	139.7	–	–	12N	161W
2040	170	2342 Mar 23	05:08:14	610	4232	157	N	t-	-1.5166	0.1164	-0.9652	104.5	–	–	2S	74W

Cat Num	Canon Plate	Calendar Date	TD of Greatest Eclipse	ΔT s	Luna Num	Saros Num	Ecl Type	QSE	Gamma	Pen Mag	Um Mag	Pen m	Par m	Total m	Lat	Long
2041	171	2342 Aug 17	12:05:11	611	4237	124	N	-a	-1.2083	0.6140	-0.3327	198.3	–	–	15S	177W
2042	171	2342 Sep 15	19:24:20	612	4238	162	N	a-	1.3113	0.4263	-0.5227	167.7	–	–	2S	70E
2043	171	2343 Feb 10	10:51:39	613	4243	129	P	-t	0.7796	1.4697	0.3860	321.8	142.8	–	15N	157W
2044	171	2343 Aug 07	03:21:50	614	4249	134	P	-a	-0.5005	1.9307	0.9484	316.6	190.8	–	17S	46W
2045	171	2344 Jan 30	16:18:40	616	4255	139	T+	pp	0.0518	2.7782	1.7479	345.1	221.2	100.6	18N	121E
2046	171	2344 Jul 26	12:40:59	617	4261	144	T	pp	0.2752	2.3711	1.3352	353.3	220.8	83.8	19S	174E
2047	171	2345 Jan 19	04:38:49	619	4267	149	P	a-	-0.6290	1.6949	0.7126	296.7	167.1	–	20N	65W
2048	171	2345 Jul 15	15:10:58	620	4273	154	N	t-	1.0613	0.9453	-0.1234	276.9	–	–	20S	136E
2049	171	2345 Dec 10	09:24:57	621	4278	121	N	-a	1.4085	0.2658	-0.7185	137.5	–	–	24N	141W
2050	171	2346 Jan 08	20:14:44	622	4279	159	N	a-	-1.2743	0.5060	-0.4666	182.5	–	–	21N	60E
2051	171	2346 Jun 05	03:03:17	623	4284	126	P	-t	-0.9922	1.0545	0.0209	276.3	34.3	–	23S	43W
2052	171	2346 Nov 29	21:15:59	624	4290	131	P	-a	0.7757	1.4516	0.4179	302.2	141.3	–	22N	40E
2053	172	2347 May 25	12:53:34	626	4296	136	T-	pp	-0.1917	2.4965	1.5159	330.1	214.2	92.6	21S	169E
2054	172	2347 Nov 19	02:04:58	627	4302	141	T+	pp	0.0825	2.7489	1.6651	371.0	231.8	102.7	19N	32W
2055	172	2348 May 14	04:21:13	629	4308	146	P	a-	0.5425	1.8369	0.8878	298.1	179.7	–	18S	63W
2056	172	2348 Nov 07	01:44:24	630	4314	151	P	t-	-0.6202	1.7675	0.6733	347.3	183.1	–	16N	28W
2057	172	2349 Apr 04	11:49:53	631	4319	118	N	-a	-1.3548	0.3665	-0.6222	162.8	–	–	7S	174W
2058	172	2349 May 03	21:07:25	631	4320	156	N	a-	1.2603	0.5255	-0.4347	186.9	–	–	15S	45E
2059	172	2349 Sep 27	14:12:28	633	4325	123	N	-h	1.4936	0.1259	-0.8907	101.4	–	–	3N	147E
2060	172	2349 Oct 27	03:30:27	633	4326	161	N	h-	-1.2963	0.5069	-0.5475	203.9	–	–	11N	54W
2061	172	2350 Mar 24	21:42:57	634	4331	128	P	-h	-0.6866	1.6222	0.5746	321.0	165.1	–	2S	38E
2062	172	2350 Sep 17	02:54:53	636	4337	133	P	-a	0.7088	1.5395	0.5752	288.2	154.3	–	2S	43W
2063	172	2351 Mar 14	00:12:40	637	4343	138	T+	pp	0.0206	2.8666	1.7744	376.4	234.8	105.1	3N	2E
2064	172	2351 Sep 06	19:32:41	639	4349	143	T-	pp	-0.0188	2.7970	1.8495	317.8	211.4	99.1	6S	69E
2065	173	2352 Mar 01	23:39:17	640	4355	148	P	t-	0.7155	1.5898	0.5013	333.2	161.2	–	8N	11E
2066	173	2352 Aug 26	11:26:40	641	4361	153	P	a-	-0.7660	1.4395	0.4652	286.9	143.2	–	11S	168W
2067	173	2353 Jan 20	13:54:27	643	4366	120	N	-a	-1.4454	0.2132	-0.8012	128.0	–	–	19N	156E
2068	173	2353 Feb 19	03:33:51	643	4367	158	N	a-	1.3686	0.3677	-0.6737	171.8	–	–	13N	47W
2069	173	2353 Jul 17	09:35:19	644	4372	125	N	-t	1.1653	0.7444	-0.3043	244.8	–	–	20S	140W
2070	173	2354 Jan 10	03:35:56	646	4378	130	P	-a	-0.7321	1.5019	0.5271	283.3	147.0	–	21N	50W
2071	173	2354 Jul 06	10:53:56	647	4384	135	T	-t	0.4215	2.1197	1.0501	361.3	214.0	36.6	22S	159W
2072	173	2354 Dec 30	19:17:26	649	4390	140	T-	-p	-0.0685	2.7214	1.7429	322.6	211.4	97.5	23N	74E
2073	173	2355 Jun 25	12:46:18	650	4396	145	T	t-	-0.3479	2.2409	1.1986	352.8	216.4	68.0	24S	172E
2074	173	2355 Dec 20	08:16:42	652	4402	150	P	a-	0.6355	1.7034	0.6806	312.5	170.7	–	24N	122W
2075	173	2356 May 15	12:14:45	653	4407	117	N	-a	1.5017	0.0871	-0.8823	80.4	–	–	18S	179E
2076	173	2356 Jun 13	21:09:22	653	4408	155	N	a-	-1.0859	0.8601	-0.1291	241.5	–	–	24S	45E
2077	174	2356 Dec 08	14:40:34	655	4414	160	N	t-	1.3857	0.3546	-0.7232	176.1	–	–	24N	140E
2078	174	2357 May 05	04:27:44	656	4419	127	P	-a	0.7647	1.4292	0.4802	276.0	140.9	–	15S	65W
2079	174	2357 Oct 28	20:41:13	657	4425	132	P	-t	-0.9010	1.2478	0.1625	307.5	96.9	–	13N	49E
2080	174	2358 Apr 24	20:41:45	659	4431	137	T+	pp	0.0542	2.7449	1.7720	326.8	214.8	99.5	13S	52E
2081	174	2358 Oct 18	00:19:34	660	4437	142	T-	pp	-0.1509	2.5990	1.5634	350.8	223.0	97.2	9N	6W
2082	174	2359 Apr 14	08:20:05	662	4443	147	P	t-	-0.7077	1.5738	0.5452	312.4	159.6	–	10S	122W
2083	174	2359 Oct 07	11:23:42	663	4449	152	P	a-	0.5791	1.7846	0.8059	304.8	177.3	–	6N	171W
2084	174	2360 Mar 03	18:54:40	665	4454	119	N	-t	1.4964	0.1620	-0.9365	124.6	–	–	0N	03E
2085	174	2360 Apr 02	12:35:47	665	4455	157	N	t-	-1.4797	0.1833	-0.8967	130.5	–	–	6S	174E
2086	174	2360 Aug 27	19:41:57	666	4460	124	N	-a	-1.2742	0.4948	-0.4550	180.4	–	–	11S	68E
2087	174	2360 Sep 26	03:19:51	666	4461	162	N	a-	1.2601	0.5213	-0.4301	183.8	–	–	2N	50W
2088	174	2361 Feb 20	18:53:07	668	4466	129	P	-t	0.7931	1.4427	0.3633	318.8	138.7	–	11N	83E
2089	175	2361 Aug 17	10:38:40	669	4472	134	P	-a	-0.5741	1.7981	0.8112	312.2	181.3	–	14S	155W
2090	175	2362 Feb 10	00:47:26	671	4478	139	T+	pp	0.0599	2.7611	1.7351	343.6	220.6	100.3	15N	6W
2091	175	2362 Aug 06	19:27:11	672	4484	144	T+	pp	0.1948	2.5208	1.4808	357.6	225.8	94.9	16S	73E
2092	175	2363 Jan 30	13:27:20	674	4490	149	P	a-	-0.6231	1.7046	0.7246	296.5	167.9	–	17N	164E
2093	175	2363 Jul 26	21:36:01	675	4496	154	P	t-	0.9749	1.1045	0.0347	294.6	45.9	–	19S	40E
2094	175	2363 Dec 21	18:08:30	676	4501	121	N	-a	1.4180	0.2498	-0.7377	133.8	–	–	25N	90E
2095	175	2364 Jan 20	05:07:04	677	4502	159	N	a-	-1.2715	0.5115	-0.4617	183.5	–	–	19N	72W
2096	175	2364 Jun 15	09:57:14	678	4507	126	N	-t	-1.0646	0.9191	-0.1097	260.5	–	–	24S	146W
2097	175	2364 Dec 10	05:36:16	679	4513	131	P	-a	0.7899	1.4281	0.3895	301.9	137.4	–	24N	83W
2098	175	2365 Jun 04	20:18:36	681	4519	136	T-	-p	-0.2581	2.3722	1.3963	326.6	210.5	84.9	23S	58E
2099	175	2365 Nov 29	09:57:06	682	4525	141	T+	pp	0.1031	2.7132	1.6250	371.9	231.7	101.7	22N	150W
2100	175	2366 May 25	12:05:07	684	4531	146	T	a-	0.4817	1.9469	1.0007	302.1	187.0	4.1	20S	179W

Cat Num	Canon Plate	Calendar Date	TD of Greatest Eclipse	ΔT s	Luna Num	Saros Num	Ecl Type	QSE	Gamma	Pen Mag	Um Mag	Pen m	Par m	Total m	Lat	Long
2101	176	2366 Nov 18	09:23:05	686	4537	151	P	t-	-0.5917	1.8208	0.7245	350.1	188.1	–	19N	142W
2102	176	2367 Apr 15	19:48:53	687	4542	118	N	-a	-1.3977	0.2876	-0.7010	145.7	–	–	11S	65E
2103	176	2367 May 15	04:53:36	687	4543	156	N	a-	1.2082	0.6208	-0.3389	201.6	–	–	18S	71W
2104	176	2367 Oct 08	21:52:36	688	4548	123	N	-h	1.5337	0.0521	-0.9642	65.5	–	–	7N	31E
2105	176	2367 Nov 07	11:20:25	689	4549	161	N	h-	-1.2631	0.5679	-0.4866	213.9	–	–	15N	171W
2106	176	2368 Apr 04	05:25:30	690	4554	128	P	-h	-0.7261	1.5496	0.5021	317.4	156.6	–	6S	78W
2107	176	2368 Sep 27	10:47:19	691	4560	133	P	-a	0.7571	1.4511	0.4861	282.2	143.5	–	3N	161W
2108	176	2369 Mar 24	07:44:14	693	4566	138	T-	pp	-0.0135	2.8785	1.7885	376.5	235.1	105.4	1S	112W
2109	176	2369 Sep 17	03:22:08	694	4572	143	T+	pp	0.0374	2.7642	1.8139	318.2	211.3	98.8	2S	49W
2110	176	2370 Mar 13	07:22:51	696	4578	148	P	t-	0.6883	1.6374	0.5535	335.3	167.6	–	4N	105W
2111	176	2370 Sep 06	18:57:22	698	4584	153	P	a-	-0.7056	1.5529	0.5736	295.2	156.7	–	7S	78E
2112	176	2371 Jan 31	22:31:46	699	4589	120	N	-a	-1.4467	0.2089	-0.8019	126.3	–	–	16N	28E
2113	177	2371 Mar 02	11:47:04	699	4590	158	N	a-	1.3489	0.4011	-0.6349	178.1	–	–	9N	171W
2114	177	2371 Jul 28	16:11:28	700	4595	125	N	-t	1.2512	0.5884	-0.4635	221.7	–	–	18S	122E
2115	177	2371 Aug 27	05:10:45	701	4596	163	No	t-	-1.5155	0.0933	-0.9385	89.8	–	–	12S	74W
2116	177	2372 Jan 21	12:27:43	702	4601	130	P	-a	-0.7354	1.4953	0.5217	282.5	146.2	–	19N	178E
2117	177	2372 Jul 16	17:18:28	703	4607	135	P	-t	0.5096	1.9580	0.8886	354.7	202.8	–	21S	105E
2118	177	2373 Jan 10	04:07:32	705	4613	140	T-	-p	-0.0728	2.7143	1.7342	323.2	211.6	97.4	22N	57W
2119	177	2373 Jul 05	19:28:56	707	4619	145	T-	t-	-0.2641	2.3929	1.3541	355.2	222.1	85.7	23S	72E
2120	177	2373 Dec 30	16:50:26	708	4625	150	P	a-	0.6322	1.7114	0.6848	314.1	171.6	–	24N	111E
2121	177	2374 Jun 25	04:21:35	710	4631	155	P	a-	-1.0090	0.9990	0.0141	255.4	27.0	–	24S	62W
2122	177	2374 Dec 19	22:47:51	711	4637	160	N	t-	1.3776	0.3716	-0.7102	180.5	–	–	25N	20E
2123	177	2375 May 16	12:17:11	713	4642	127	P	-a	0.8214	1.3240	0.3773	268.8	126.9	–	18S	178E
2124	177	2375 Nov 09	04:16:34	714	4648	132	P	-t	-0.9330	1.1898	0.1030	301.9	77.7	–	16N	65W
2125	178	2376 May 05	04:29:54	716	4654	137	T+	-p	0.1074	2.6471	1.6744	327.0	214.5	97.8	16S	65W
2126	178	2376 Oct 28	08:08:59	717	4660	142	T-	pp	-0.1871	2.5325	1.4970	348.8	220.9	93.7	13N	123W
2127	178	2377 Apr 24	15:54:41	719	4666	147	P	t-	-0.6611	1.6595	0.6307	318.6	169.9	–	14S	124E
2128	178	2377 Oct 17	19:26:07	720	4672	152	P	a-	0.5368	1.8624	0.8834	307.5	182.7	–	10N	68E
2129	178	2378 Mar 15	02:32:25	722	4677	119	N	-t	1.5246	0.1089	-0.9869	102.6	–	–	4N	32W
2130	178	2378 Apr 13	19:55:13	722	4678	157	N	t-	-1.4366	0.2617	-0.8168	155.0	–	–	10S	64E
2131	178	2378 Sep 08	03:23:54	723	4683	124	N	-a	-1.3354	0.3841	-0.5690	161.0	–	–	7S	48W
2132	178	2378 Oct 07	11:22:19	723	4684	162	N	a-	1.2148	0.6058	-0.3482	196.6	–	–	7N	171W
2133	178	2379 Mar 04	02:48:34	725	4689	129	P	-t	0.8121	1.4056	0.3310	314.9	132.8	–	7N	36W
2134	178	2379 Aug 28	17:58:09	726	4695	134	P	-a	-0.6446	1.6712	0.6792	307.2	170.1	–	10S	94E
2135	178	2380 Feb 21	09:11:42	728	4701	139	T+	pp	0.0726	2.7354	1.7143	342.0	219.9	99.9	11N	132W
2136	178	2380 Aug 17	02:16:10	730	4707	144	T+	pp	0.1171	2.6655	1.6209	360.9	229.1	101.5	13S	30W
2137	179	2381 Feb 09	22:11:30	731	4713	149	P	a-	-0.6131	1.7214	0.7443	296.7	169.4	–	14N	33E
2138	179	2381 Aug 06	04:04:38	733	4719	154	P	t-	0.8908	1.2595	0.1882	309.6	104.6	–	16S	57W
2139	179	2382 Jan 01	02:54:07	734	4724	121	N	-a	1.4263	0.2361	-0.7541	130.6	–	–	24N	40W
2140	179	2382 Jan 30	13:57:08	734	4725	159	N	a-	-1.2668	0.5201	-0.4532	185.1	–	–	16N	156E
2141	179	2382 Jun 26	16:49:14	736	4730	126	N	-t	-1.1392	0.7801	-0.2444	242.4	–	–	24S	112E
2142	179	2382 Dec 21	14:00:39	737	4736	131	P	-a	0.8002	1.4113	0.3684	301.9	134.4	–	24N	152E
2143	179	2383 Jun 16	03:39:21	739	4742	136	T	-p	-0.3291	2.2398	1.2682	322.3	205.5	73.0	24S	51W
2144	179	2383 Dec 10	17:55:39	740	4748	141	T+	pp	0.1179	2.6880	1.5961	372.7	231.6	100.8	23N	92E
2145	179	2384 Jun 04	19:42:05	742	4754	146	T	a-	0.4149	2.0684	1.1245	305.9	193.6	50.8	22S	67E
2146	179	2384 Nov 28	17:11:02	744	4760	151	P	t-	-0.5706	1.8604	0.7626	352.0	191.5	–	21N	102E
2147	179	2385 Apr 26	03:39:09	745	4765	118	N	-a	-1.4472	0.1969	-0.7917	121.9	–	–	15S	53W
2148	179	2385 May 25	12:32:57	745	4766	156	N	a-	1.1510	0.7257	-0.2339	216.2	–	–	20S	174E
2149	180	2385 Nov 17	19:18:56	747	4772	161	N	h-	-1.2359	0.6177	-0.4366	221.4	–	–	18N	70E
2150	180	2386 Apr 15	12:59:58	748	4777	128	P	-h	-0.7715	1.4662	0.4188	312.6	145.3	–	11S	168E
2151	180	2386 Oct 08	18:46:45	750	4783	133	P	-a	0.8003	1.3724	0.4065	276.5	132.6	–	7N	78E
2152	180	2387 Apr 04	15:07:50	751	4789	138	T-	pp	-0.0541	2.8029	1.7152	376.3	235.0	104.9	6S	137E
2153	180	2387 Sep 28	11:16:55	753	4795	143	T+	-p	0.0891	2.6712	1.7175	318.3	210.7	97.3	2N	168W
2154	180	2388 Mar 23	15:00:15	755	4801	148	P	t-	0.6554	1.6952	0.6163	337.7	174.8	–	1S	140E
2155	180	2388 Sep 17	02:33:16	756	4807	153	P	a-	-0.6501	1.6574	0.6728	302.3	167.5	–	3S	36W
2156	180	2389 Feb 11	07:06:04	757	4812	120	N	-a	-1.4511	0.1989	-0.8078	123.0	–	–	13N	100W
2157	180	2389 Mar 12	19:54:35	758	4813	158	N	a-	1.3239	0.4442	-0.5861	185.9	–	–	4N	67E
2158	180	2389 Aug 07	22:50:33	759	4818	125	N	-t	1.3335	0.4392	-0.6163	194.9	–	–	15S	22E
2159	180	2389 Sep 06	12:15:04	759	4819	163	N	t-	-1.4545	0.2081	-0.8292	133.4	–	–	8S	179E
2160	180	2390 Jan 31	21:17:33	761	4824	130	P	-a	-0.7404	1.4852	0.5133	281.6	145.1	–	17N	47E

Cat Num	Canon Plate	Calendar Date	TD of Greatest Eclipse	ΔT s	Luna Num	Saros Num	Ecl Type	QSE	Gamma	Pen Mag	Um Mag	Pen m	Par m	Total m	Lat	Long
2161	181	2390 Jul 27	23:44:45	762	4830	135	P	-t	0.5961	1.7991	0.7298	346.8	188.9	–	18S	9E
2162	181	2391 Jan 21	12:56:41	764	4836	140	T-	-p	-0.0776	2.7062	1.7249	323.7	211.8	97.3	20N	172E
2163	181	2391 Jul 17	02:12:49	766	4842	145	T-	pp	-0.1807	2.5444	1.5087	356.5	225.9	96.4	21S	28W
2164	181	2392 Jan 11	01:23:55	767	4848	150	P	a-	0.6291	1.7187	0.6889	315.7	172.4	–	23N	16W
2165	181	2392 Jul 05	11:33:10	769	4854	155	P	a-	-0.9306	1.1410	0.1598	267.7	88.7	–	24S	169W
2166	181	2392 Dec 30	06:57:19	770	4860	160	N	t-	1.3717	0.3839	-0.7010	183.8	–	–	24N	101W
2167	181	2393 May 26	20:00:14	772	4865	127	P	-a	0.8835	1.2091	0.2642	260.3	108.0	–	20S	63E
2168	181	2393 Nov 19	12:00:29	773	4871	132	P	-t	-0.9584	1.1438	0.0560	297.1	57.5	–	19N	180E
2169	181	2394 May 16	12:09:59	775	4877	137	T+	-p	0.1667	2.5384	1.5655	326.7	213.3	94.3	19S	180W
2170	181	2394 Nov 08	16:08:08	777	4883	142	T-	pp	-0.2159	2.4795	1.4443	346.9	218.9	90.3	16N	117E
2171	181	2395 May 05	23:17:47	778	4889	147	P	t-	-0.6059	1.7609	0.7317	325.1	180.5	–	17S	13E
2172	181	2395 Oct 29	03:37:43	780	4895	152	P	a-	0.5017	1.9271	0.9475	309.5	186.7	–	14N	55W
2173	182	2396 Mar 25	10:01:26	781	4900	119	Ne	-t	1.5593	0.0436	-1.0490	65.2	–	–	1S	145W
2174	182	2396 Apr 24	03:03:40	782	4901	157	N	t-	-1.3852	0.3551	-0.7217	179.2	–	–	14S	44W
2175	182	2396 Sep 18	11:11:25	783	4906	124	N	-a	-1.3918	0.2826	-0.6744	139.7	–	–	3S	165W
2176	182	2396 Oct 17	19:32:41	783	4907	162	N	a-	1.1760	0.6784	-0.2785	206.7	–	–	11N	66E
2177	182	2397 Mar 14	10:38:04	785	4912	129	P	-t	0.8364	1.3584	0.2891	310.1	124.6	–	3N	154W
2178	182	2397 Sep 08	01:22:03	786	4918	134	P	-a	-0.7105	1.5530	0.5555	301.8	157.4	–	6S	17W
2179	182	2398 Mar 03	17:32:53	788	4924	139	T+	pp	0.0885	2.7036	1.6877	340.3	219.2	99.2	7N	103E
2180	182	2398 Aug 28	09:06:26	790	4930	144	T+	pp	0.0414	2.8069	1.7575	363.4	231.0	104.6	10S	133W
2181	182	2399 Feb 21	06:53:32	791	4936	149	P	a-	-0.6013	1.7416	0.7676	297.1	171.2	–	10N	97W
2182	182	2399 Aug 17	10:35:25	793	4942	154	P	t-	0.8081	1.4122	0.3391	322.4	137.3	–	13S	155W
2183	182	2400 Jan 12	11:40:47	794	4947	121	N	-a	1.4331	0.2247	-0.7678	127.9	–	–	23N	170W
2184	182	2400 Feb 10	22:44:24	795	4948	159	N	a-	-1.2606	0.5315	-0.4416	187.1	–	–	13N	25E
2185	183	2400 Jul 06	23:41:22	796	4953	126	N	-t	-1.2141	0.6408	-0.3799	221.8	–	–	24S	10E
2186	183	2400 Aug 05	12:01:16	796	4954	164	Nb	t-	1.5295	0.0757	-0.9721	82.9	–	–	15S	176W
2187	183	2400 Dec 31	22:26:33	798	4959	131	P	-a	0.8086	1.3979	0.3512	302.0	132.0	–	24N	27E
2188	183	2401 Jun 26	10:59:49	799	4965	136	T	-p	-0.4007	2.1065	1.1386	317.3	199.2	54.6	24S	161W
2189	183	2401 Dec 21	01:56:06	801	4971	141	T+	pp	0.1307	2.6662	1.5711	373.5	231.4	99.9	24N	26W
2190	183	2402 Jun 16	03:16:58	803	4977	146	T	p-	0.3462	2.1935	1.2514	309.2	199.2	69.4	23S	46W
2191	183	2402 Dec 10	01:04:26	804	4983	151	P	t-	-0.5534	1.8924	0.7936	353.3	194.1	–	22N	15W
2192	183	2403 May 07	11:19:37	806	4988	118	N	-a	-1.5037	0.0933	-0.8955	85.0	–	–	18S	168W
2193	183	2403 Jun 05	20:05:08	806	4989	156	N	a-	1.0885	0.8406	-0.1194	230.5	–	–	21S	62E
2194	183	2403 Nov 29	03:25:43	808	4995	161	N	a-	-1.2146	0.6565	-0.3972	226.7	–	–	20N	51W
2195	183	2404 Apr 25	20:22:54	809	5000	128	P	-t	-0.8256	1.3670	0.3196	306.2	129.2	–	14S	57E
2196	183	2404 Oct 19	02:55:16	811	5006	133	P	-a	0.8363	1.3069	0.3400	271.5	122.2	–	11N	44W
2197	184	2405 Apr 14	22:20:33	812	5012	138	T-	pp	-0.1034	2.7112	1.6261	375.6	234.3	103.0	10S	28E
2198	184	2405 Oct 08	19:19:55	814	5018	143	T+	-p	0.1336	2.5912	1.6340	318.2	209.8	95.1	6N	70E
2199	184	2406 Apr 03	22:29:29	816	5024	148	P	t-	0.6153	1.7660	0.6925	340.5	182.6	–	5S	27E
2200	184	2406 Sep 28	10:14:01	817	5030	153	P	a-	-0.5994	1.7533	0.7629	308.6	176.2	–	2N	152W
2201	184	2407 Feb 22	15:37:06	819	5035	120	N	-a	-1.4585	0.1830	-0.8192	117.7	–	–	9N	132E
2202	184	2407 Mar 24	03:55:50	819	5036	158	N	a-	1.2931	0.4975	-0.5267	194.9	–	–	0S	54W
2203	184	2407 Aug 19	05:30:17	820	5041	125	N	-t	1.4138	0.2938	-0.7656	162.1	–	–	12S	78W
2204	184	2407 Sep 17	19:23:23	821	5042	163	N	t-	-1.3973	0.3160	-0.7272	163.5	–	–	3S	72E
2205	184	2408 Feb 12	06:04:34	822	5047	130	P	-a	-0.7480	1.4704	0.5006	280.3	143.5	–	13N	85W
2206	184	2408 Aug 07	06:12:57	824	5053	135	P	-t	0.6809	1.6438	0.5740	337.7	171.8	–	16S	88W
2207	184	2409 Jan 31	21:44:38	825	5059	140	T-	-p	-0.0828	2.6971	1.7149	324.3	212.1	97.3	17N	40E
2208	184	2409 Jul 27	08:59:04	827	5065	145	T-	pp	-0.0982	2.6944	1.6613	356.8	227.9	102.2	19S	129W
2209	185	2410 Jan 21	09:56:46	829	5071	150	P	a-	0.6263	1.7251	0.6927	317.1	173.3	–	20N	143W
2210	185	2410 Jul 16	18:45:57	831	5077	155	P	a-	-0.8523	1.2830	0.3050	278.3	119.7	–	22S	84E
2211	185	2411 Jan 10	15:08:14	832	5083	160	N	t-	1.3675	0.3929	-0.6945	186.3	–	–	23N	138E
2212	185	2411 Jun 07	03:37:46	834	5088	127	P	-a	0.9499	1.0865	0.1431	250.1	80.8	–	22S	51W
2213	185	2411 Jul 06	10:22:41	834	5089	165	Nb	a-	-1.5405	0.0028	-0.9403	14.2	–	–	24S	151W
2214	185	2411 Nov 30	19:52:22	835	5094	132	P	-t	-0.9775	1.1091	0.0205	293.2	34.9	–	21N	63E
2215	185	2412 May 26	19:43:24	837	5100	137	T+	-p	0.2307	2.4214	1.4479	325.9	211.2	88.2	21S	67E
2216	185	2412 Nov 19	00:15:24	839	5106	142	T-	-p	-0.2386	2.4377	1.4029	345.1	217.1	87.1	19N	4W
2217	185	2413 May 16	06:33:35	840	5112	147	P	t-	-0.5457	1.8718	0.8420	331.6	190.6	–	20S	96W
2218	185	2413 Nov 08	11:57:23	842	5118	152	P	a-	0.4733	1.9795	0.9994	310.8	189.5	–	17N	180E
2219	185	2414 May 05	10:04:11	844	5124	157	N	t-	-1.3275	0.4602	-0.6150	202.2	–	–	17S	149W
2220	185	2414 Sep 29	19:04:39	845	5129	124	N	-a	-1.4432	0.1904	-0.7708	115.9	–	–	1N	76E

Cat Num	Canon Plate	Calendar Date	TD of Greatest Eclipse	ΔT s	Luna Num	Saros Num	Ecl Type	QSE	Gamma	Pen Mag	Um Mag	Pen m	Par m	Total m	Lat	Long
2221	186	2414 Oct 29	03:49:49	846	5130	162	N	a-	1.1430	0.7405	-0.2194	214.8	–	–	14N	59W
2222	186	2415 Mar 25	18:20:35	847	5135	129	P	-t	0.8668	1.2996	0.2360	304.1	113.2	–	1S	90E
2223	186	2415 Sep 19	08:51:05	849	5141	134	P	-a	-0.7714	1.4443	0.4410	296.2	143.2	–	2S	130W
2224	186	2416 Mar 14	01:45:54	850	5147	139	T+	pp	0.1119	2.6579	1.6476	338.4	218.2	98.1	3N	21W
2225	186	2416 Sep 07	16:02:32	852	5153	144	T-	pp	-0.0289	2.8326	1.7780	365.0	231.5	104.9	6S	123E
2226	186	2417 Mar 03	15:29:01	854	5159	149	P	a-	-0.5837	1.7722	0.8015	297.9	173.7	–	6N	134E
2227	186	2417 Aug 27	17:11:32	856	5165	154	P	t-	0.7295	1.5574	0.4823	333.1	160.1	–	9S	106E
2228	186	2418 Jan 22	20:25:47	857	5170	121	N	-a	1.4411	0.2109	-0.7834	124.4	–	–	21N	60E
2229	186	2418 Feb 21	07:26:22	857	5171	159	N	a-	-1.2504	0.5498	-0.4227	190.1	–	–	9N	105W
2230	186	2418 Jul 18	06:34:23	859	5176	126	N	-t	-1.2888	0.5020	-0.5153	198.2	–	–	22S	93W
2231	186	2418 Aug 16	18:46:33	859	5177	164	N	t-	1.4488	0.2231	-0.8234	140.1	–	–	12S	83E
2232	186	2419 Jan 12	06:53:22	861	5182	131	P	-a	0.8155	1.3868	0.3369	302.3	129.9	–	22N	98W
2233	187	2419 Jul 07	18:17:22	862	5188	136	T	-a	-0.4754	1.9678	1.0031	311.5	191.3	8.5	23S	91E
2234	187	2420 Jan 01	10:00:56	864	5194	141	T+	pp	0.1394	2.6514	1.5538	374.1	231.4	99.2	23N	146W
2235	187	2420 Jun 26	10:47:39	866	5200	146	T	p-	0.2737	2.3260	1.3850	312.1	203.9	82.0	23S	157W
2236	187	2420 Dec 20	09:03:38	867	5206	151	P	t-	-0.5406	1.9160	0.8169	354.1	195.9	–	23N	133W
2237	187	2421 Jun 16	03:32:45	869	5212	156	P	a-	1.0225	0.9621	0.0011	244.1	7.5	–	22S	49W
2238	187	2421 Dec 09	11:40:02	871	5218	161	N	a-	-1.1984	0.6857	-0.3670	230.3	–	–	22N	173W
2239	187	2422 May 07	03:37:47	872	5223	128	P	-t	-0.8853	1.2576	0.2102	298.2	106.8	–	18S	52W
2240	187	2422 Oct 30	11:10:43	874	5229	133	P	-a	0.8669	1.2513	0.2831	267.0	112.2	–	15S	168W
2241	187	2423 Apr 26	05:25:44	876	5235	138	T-	pp	-0.1586	2.6086	1.5262	374.4	232.8	99.1	14S	78W
2242	187	2423 Oct 20	03:29:18	878	5241	143	T+	-p	0.1723	2.5221	1.5611	318.0	208.6	92.3	10N	52W
2243	187	2424 Apr 14	05:51:06	879	5247	148	P	t-	0.5686	1.8491	0.7810	343.6	190.6	–	9S	84W
2244	187	2424 Oct 08	18:01:43	881	5253	153	P	a-	-0.5553	1.8372	0.8410	313.9	183.0	–	6N	90E
2245	188	2425 Mar 05	00:03:12	883	5258	120	N	-a	-1.4702	0.1591	-0.8382	109.6	–	–	5N	5E
2246	188	2425 Apr 03	11:50:58	883	5259	158	N	a-	1.2569	0.5610	-0.4571	204.8	–	–	4S	173W
2247	188	2425 Aug 29	12:14:29	884	5264	125	N	-t	1.4895	0.1572	-0.9064	120.4	–	–	8S	180W
2248	188	2425 Sep 28	02:37:33	885	5265	163	N	t-	-1.3452	0.4145	-0.6346	186.3	–	–	1N	38W
2249	188	2426 Feb 22	14:46:51	886	5270	130	P	-a	-0.7595	1.4480	0.4805	278.6	141.0	–	9N	145E
2250	188	2426 Aug 18	12:46:03	888	5276	135	P	-t	0.7615	1.4963	0.4258	327.6	151.4	–	12S	173E
2251	188	2427 Feb 12	06:28:07	890	5282	140	T-	-p	-0.0913	2.6816	1.6990	324.8	212.3	97.1	14N	90W
2252	188	2427 Aug 07	15:48:56	891	5288	145	T-	pp	-0.0180	2.8405	1.8096	356.2	228.3	104.4	16S	128E
2253	188	2428 Feb 01	18:26:26	893	5294	150	P	a-	0.6218	1.7345	0.7000	318.7	174.4	–	18N	90E
2254	188	2428 Jul 27	02:01:19	895	5300	155	P	a-	-0.7754	1.4229	0.4474	287.4	141.5	–	20S	25W
2255	188	2429 Jan 20	23:16:44	897	5306	160	N	t-	1.3620	0.4039	-0.6853	189.1	–	–	21N	17E
2256	188	2429 Jun 17	11:11:33	898	5311	127	P	-a	1.0192	0.9591	0.0163	238.3	27.8	–	22S	164W
2257	189	2429 Jul 16	17:51:15	898	5312	165	N	a-	-1.4688	0.1338	-0.8085	96.6	–	–	23S	98E
2258	189	2429 Dec 11	03:51:43	900	5317	132	Nx	-t	-0.9905	1.0853	-0.0033	290.2	–	–	22N	56W
2259	189	2430 Jun 07	03:09:29	902	5323	137	T	-p	0.3000	2.2946	1.3201	324.4	207.8	78.4	22S	44W
2260	189	2430 Nov 30	08:31:14	903	5329	142	T-	-p	-0.2549	2.4075	1.3735	343.4	215.5	84.6	21N	127W
2261	189	2431 May 27	13:39:32	905	5335	147	P	t-	-0.4783	1.9960	0.9652	338.1	200.2	–	22S	158E
2262	189	2431 Nov 19	20:25:35	907	5341	152	T	a-	0.4513	2.0201	1.0395	311.7	191.4	29.6	20N	53E
2263	189	2432 May 15	16:54:27	909	5347	157	N	t-	-1.2616	0.5803	-0.4933	224.7	–	–	20S	109E
2264	189	2432 Oct 10	03:05:16	910	5352	124	N	-a	-1.4883	0.1098	-0.8559	88.9	–	–	6N	45W
2265	189	2432 Nov 08	12:15:12	911	5353	162	N	a-	1.1169	0.7900	-0.1729	220.9	–	–	18N	175E
2266	189	2433 Apr 05	01:56:43	912	5358	129	P	-t	0.9031	1.2300	0.1723	296.9	97.3	–	5S	24W
2267	189	2433 Sep 29	16:24:44	914	5364	134	P	-a	-0.8274	1.3446	0.3352	290.5	127.2	–	2N	116E
2268	189	2434 Mar 25	09:54:37	916	5370	139	T+	pp	0.1395	2.6043	1.5998	336.3	217.0	96.4	2S	143W
2269	190	2434 Sep 18	23:02:34	917	5376	144	T-	pp	-0.0951	2.7137	1.6538	365.9	231.0	102.8	2S	17E
2270	190	2435 Mar 14	23:59:26	919	5382	149	P	a-	-0.5618	1.8104	0.8434	299.0	176.8	–	2N	6E
2271	190	2435 Sep 07	23:52:35	921	5388	154	P	t-	0.6545	1.6960	0.6187	342.0	177.3	–	5S	5E
2272	190	2436 Feb 03	05:08:59	922	5393	121	N	-a	1.4503	0.1947	-0.8009	120.0	–	–	18N	70W
2273	190	2436 Mar 03	16:03:11	923	5394	159	N	a-	-1.2366	0.5746	-0.3970	194.1	–	–	5N	125E
2274	190	2436 Jul 28	13:31:08	924	5399	126	N	-t	-1.3611	0.3678	-0.6466	171.1	–	–	20S	163E
2275	190	2436 Aug 27	01:39:03	925	5400	164	N	t-	1.3725	0.3626	-0.6830	175.8	–	–	9S	21W
2276	190	2437 Jan 22	15:17:33	926	5405	131	P	-a	0.8240	1.3725	0.3200	302.3	127.3	–	20N	137E
2277	190	2437 Jul 18	01:38:00	928	5411	136	P	-a	-0.5483	1.8329	0.8707	305.1	182.0	–	21S	19W
2278	190	2438 Jan 11	18:05:29	930	5417	141	T+	pp	0.1484	2.6358	1.5365	374.6	231.4	98.5	22N	94E
2279	190	2438 Jul 07	18:17:18	931	5423	146	T+	p-	0.2003	2.4604	1.5200	314.3	207.5	90.6	22S	91E
2280	190	2438 Dec 31	17:06:04	933	5429	151	P	t-	-0.5300	1.9353	0.8366	354.5	197.3	–	23N	108E

Cat Num	Canon Plate	Calendar Date	TD of Greatest Eclipse	ΔT s	Luna Num	Saros Num	Ecl Type	QSE	Gamma	Pen Mag	Um Mag	Phase Durations Pen m	Par m	Total m	Greatest in Zenith Lat	Long
2281	191	2439 Jun 27	10:55:57	935	5435	156	P	a-	0.9532	1.0902	0.1276	257.0	78.2	–	22S	159W
2282	191	2439 Dec 20	19:59:35	937	5441	161	N	a-	-1.1859	0.7080	-0.3433	232.8	–	–	22N	63E
2283	191	2440 May 17	10:41:47	938	5446	128	P	-t	-0.9528	1.1338	0.0862	287.9	69.8	–	20S	157W
2284	191	2440 Nov 09	19:35:16	940	5452	133	P	-a	0.8905	1.2086	0.2392	263.3	103.7	–	18N	66E
2285	191	2441 May 06	12:21:24	942	5458	138	T-	pp	-0.2214	2.4920	1.4123	372.4	230.0	92.2	17S	178E
2286	191	2441 Oct 30	11:45:55	944	5464	143	T+	-p	0.2048	2.4644	1.4996	317.9	207.5	89.3	14N	177W
2287	191	2442 Apr 25	13:05:11	946	5470	148	P	t-	0.5147	1.9450	0.8826	346.7	198.6	–	13S	167E
2288	191	2442 Oct 20	01:55:56	947	5476	153	P	a-	-0.5172	1.9101	0.9079	318.4	188.4	–	10N	29W
2289	191	2443 Mar 16	08:22:51	949	5481	120	N	-a	-1.4878	0.1241	-0.8679	96.7	–	–	0N	120W
2290	191	2443 Apr 14	19:37:49	949	5482	158	N	a-	1.2129	0.6386	-0.3733	215.8	–	–	8S	70E
2291	191	2443 Sep 09	19:02:36	951	5487	125	Ne	-t	1.5610	0.0282	-1.0399	51.7	–	–	4S	77E
2292	191	2443 Oct 09	09:58:19	951	5488	163	N	t-	-1.2988	0.5028	-0.5523	204.4	–	–	5N	148W
2293	192	2444 Mar 04	23:24:11	953	5493	130	P	-a	-0.7755	1.4174	0.4526	276.4	137.3	–	5N	15E
2294	192	2444 Aug 28	19:24:49	954	5499	135	P	-t	0.8376	1.3571	0.2856	316.8	126.5	–	8S	73E
2295	192	2445 Feb 22	15:07:07	956	5505	140	T-	-p	-0.1033	2.6597	1.6770	325.3	212.4	96.7	10N	140E
2296	192	2445 Aug 17	22:44:45	958	5511	145	T+	pp	0.0583	2.7657	1.7365	354.6	227.3	103.3	13S	24E
2297	192	2446 Feb 12	02:53:06	960	5517	150	P	a-	0.6155	1.7468	0.7107	320.4	176.0	–	14N	36W
2298	192	2446 Aug 07	09:19:04	962	5523	155	P	a-	-0.6995	1.5610	0.5876	295.0	158.2	–	17S	134W
2299	192	2447 Feb 01	07:24:27	964	5529	160	N	t-	1.3563	0.4149	-0.6753	191.9	–	–	18N	104W
2300	192	2447 Jun 28	18:42:10	965	5534	127	N	-a	1.0907	0.8278	-0.1148	224.7	–	–	22S	85E
2301	192	2447 Jul 28	01:20:15	965	5535	165	N	a-	-1.3975	0.2646	-0.6774	134.1	–	–	20S	14W
2302	192	2447 Dec 22	11:56:09	967	5540	132	Nx	-t	-1.0002	1.0673	-0.0208	287.8	–	–	22N	176W
2303	192	2448 Jun 17	10:30:30	969	5546	137	T	-a	0.3730	2.1615	1.1853	322.1	202.9	62.6	23S	153W
2304	192	2448 Dec 10	16:53:18	971	5552	142	T-	-p	-0.2667	2.3852	1.3523	341.8	214.2	82.6	23N	109E
2305	193	2449 Jun 06	20:39:59	972	5558	147	T	t-	-0.4068	2.1278	1.0957	344.1	208.8	48.3	23S	54E
2306	193	2449 Nov 30	04:59:04	974	5564	152	T	a-	0.4334	2.0530	1.0722	312.2	192.9	39.5	22N	74W
2307	193	2450 May 26	23:38:30	976	5570	157	N	t-	-1.1907	0.7098	-0.3625	245.6	–	–	22S	9E
2308	193	2450 Oct 21	11:12:20	978	5575	124	N	-a	-1.5281	0.0393	-0.9310	53.6	–	–	9N	167W
2309	193	2450 Nov 19	20:46:38	978	5576	162	N	a-	1.0959	0.8298	-0.1359	225.7	–	–	21N	48E
2310	193	2451 Apr 16	09:23:54	980	5581	129	P	-t	0.9472	1.1461	0.0945	288.0	72.7	–	9S	137W
2311	193	2451 Oct 11	00:05:23	981	5587	134	P	-a	-0.8769	1.2570	0.2413	285.0	109.8	–	6N	0W
2312	193	2452 Apr 04	17:54:42	983	5593	139	T+	pp	0.1748	2.5365	1.5379	334.0	215.4	93.7	6S	96E
2313	193	2452 Sep 29	06:10:27	985	5599	144	T-	pp	-0.1543	2.6079	1.5425	366.3	229.6	98.7	3N	91W
2314	193	2453 Mar 25	08:21:31	987	5605	149	P	a-	-0.5329	1.8616	0.8983	300.6	180.5	–	3S	120W
2315	193	2453 Sep 18	06:42:15	989	5611	154	P	t-	0.5863	1.8224	0.7427	349.1	190.2	–	1S	98W
2316	193	2454 Feb 13	13:48:11	990	5616	121	N	-a	1.4626	0.1727	-0.8240	113.5	–	–	14N	161E
2317	194	2454 Mar 15	00:33:00	991	5617	159	N	a-	-1.2176	0.6091	-0.3615	199.4	–	–	1N	3W
2318	194	2454 Aug 08	20:30:21	992	5622	126	N	-t	-1.4321	0.2364	-0.7756	138.3	–	–	17S	59E
2319	194	2454 Sep 07	08:37:30	993	5623	164	N	t-	1.2998	0.4957	-0.5493	202.3	–	–	5S	126W
2320	194	2455 Feb 02	23:40:14	994	5628	131	P	-a	0.8332	1.3567	0.3023	302.1	124.4	–	17N	13E
2321	194	2455 Jul 29	08:58:49	996	5634	136	P	-a	-0.6218	1.6970	0.7368	297.8	170.9	–	19S	128W
2322	194	2456 Jan 23	02:10:07	998	5640	141	T+	pp	0.1568	2.6207	1.5206	375.0	231.3	97.9	20N	26W
2323	194	2456 Jul 18	01:45:41	1000	5646	146	T+	p-	0.1257	2.5974	1.6568	316.0	210.0	96.1	21S	20W
2324	194	2457 Jan 11	01:11:46	1002	5652	151	P	t-	-0.5215	1.9504	0.8527	354.6	198.4	–	21N	12W
2325	194	2457 Jul 07	18:16:30	1003	5658	156	P	a-	-0.8822	1.2214	0.2568	268.9	109.2	–	22S	91E
2326	194	2457 Dec 31	04:23:19	1005	5664	161	N	a-	-1.1760	0.7251	-0.3241	234.4	–	–	22N	61W
2327	194	2458 May 28	17:39:24	1007	5669	128	Nx	-t	-1.0245	1.0024	-0.0457	275.3	–	–	23S	99E
2328	194	2458 Nov 21	04:06:20	1009	5675	133	P	-a	0.9092	1.1748	0.2043	260.3	96.2	–	21N	61W
2329	195	2459 May 17	19:09:12	1011	5681	138	T	pt	-0.2904	2.3640	1.2868	369.5	225.8	80.8	20S	76E
2330	195	2459 Nov 10	20:09:30	1013	5687	143	T+	-p	0.2313	2.4178	1.4492	317.8	206.4	86.3	18N	58E
2331	195	2460 May 05	20:13:02	1014	5693	148	P	t-	0.4549	2.0519	0.9950	349.7	206.0	–	16S	60E
2332	195	2460 Oct 30	09:56:52	1016	5699	153	P	a-	-0.4853	1.9717	0.9636	322.3	192.7	–	14N	149W
2333	195	2461 Mar 26	16:36:08	1018	5704	120	N	-a	-1.5111	0.0788	-0.9080	77.1	–	–	4S	116E
2334	195	2461 Apr 25	03:19:08	1018	5705	158	N	a-	1.1634	0.7262	-0.2796	227.1	–	–	12S	46W
2335	195	2461 Oct 19	17:26:44	1020	5711	163	N	t-	-1.2587	0.5793	-0.4817	218.7	–	–	9N	99E
2336	195	2462 Mar 16	07:55:12	1022	5716	130	P	-a	-0.7967	1.3771	0.4150	273.4	132.2	–	1N	113W
2337	195	2462 Sep 09	02:10:00	1024	5722	135	P	-t	0.9085	1.2277	0.1550	305.4	94.9	–	4S	29W
2338	195	2463 Mar 05	23:39:33	1026	5728	140	T-	-p	-0.1202	2.6286	1.6461	325.7	212.5	96.1	6N	12E
2339	195	2463 Aug 29	05:47:13	1027	5734	145	T+	pp	0.1297	2.6341	1.6062	352.4	225.1	99.7	9S	82W
2340	195	2464 Feb 23	11:12:17	1029	5740	150	P	a-	0.6041	1.7684	0.7312	322.6	178.4	–	10N	160W

Cat Num	Canon Plate	Calendar Date	TD of Greatest Eclipse	ΔT s	Luna Num	Saros Num	Ecl Type	QSE	Gamma	Pen Mag	Um Mag	Pen m	Par m	Total m	Lat	Long
2341	196	2464 Aug 17	16:42:25	1031	5746	155	P	a-	-0.6277	1.6922	0.7202	301.3	171.0	–	13S	115E
2342	196	2465 Feb 11	15:26:51	1033	5752	160	N	t-	1.3471	0.4320	-0.6586	195.9	–	–	15N	136E
2343	196	2465 Jul 09	02:10:47	1035	5757	127	N	-a	1.1636	0.6942	-0.2489	208.8	–	–	21S	27W
2344	196	2465 Aug 07	08:51:22	1035	5758	165	N	a-	-1.3276	0.3930	-0.5494	161.4	–	–	17S	127W
2345	196	2466 Jan 01	20:04:16	1037	5763	132	Nx	-t	-1.0071	1.0540	-0.0328	285.7	–	–	22N	64E
2346	196	2466 Jun 28	17:46:37	1039	5769	137	T	-a	0.4491	2.0230	1.0447	318.8	196.2	32.2	23S	99E
2347	196	2466 Dec 22	01:21:40	1040	5775	142	T	-p	-0.2740	2.3710	1.3397	340.4	213.2	81.3	23N	17W
2348	196	2467 Jun 18	03:31:36	1042	5781	147	T	p-	-0.3290	2.2714	1.2375	349.6	216.3	72.9	24S	48W
2349	196	2467 Dec 11	13:39:53	1044	5787	152	T	a-	0.4214	2.0752	1.0944	312.4	193.7	44.8	23N	157E
2350	196	2468 Jun 06	06:15:11	1046	5793	157	N	t-	-1.1139	0.8500	-0.2212	265.2	–	–	24S	90W
2351	196	2468 Nov 30	05:24:26	1048	5799	162	N	a-	1.0806	0.8594	-0.1091	229.3	–	–	23N	80W
2352	196	2469 Apr 26	16:45:32	1050	5804	129	P	-t	0.9961	1.0533	0.0077	277.7	20.9	–	13S	113E
2353	197	2469 Oct 21	07:52:37	1052	5810	134	P	-a	-0.9197	1.1815	0.1596	279.9	90.6	–	10N	117W
2354	197	2470 Apr 16	01:49:48	1054	5816	139	T+	-p	0.2151	2.4597	1.4670	331.4	213.2	89.8	10S	23W
2355	197	2470 Oct 10	13:23:38	1055	5822	144	T-	pp	-0.2084	2.5113	1.4404	366.3	227.6	93.0	7N	160E
2356	197	2471 Apr 05	16:38:07	1057	5828	149	P	a-	-0.4993	1.9215	0.9620	302.5	184.6	–	7S	115E
2357	197	2471 Sep 29	13:39:36	1059	5834	154	P	t-	0.5238	1.9384	0.8561	354.8	200.0	–	3N	157E
2358	197	2472 Feb 24	22:21:42	1061	5839	121	N	-a	1.4791	0.1427	-0.8546	103.7	–	–	11N	33E
2359	197	2472 Mar 25	08:55:08	1061	5840	159	N	a-	-1.1927	0.6542	-0.3153	206.0	–	–	3S	129W
2360	197	2472 Aug 19	03:36:28	1063	5845	126	N	-t	-1.4982	0.1142	-0.8959	96.8	–	–	14S	48W
2361	197	2472 Sep 17	15:45:48	1063	5846	164	N	t-	1.2338	0.6167	-0.4280	222.4	–	–	1S	126E
2362	197	2473 Feb 13	07:57:34	1065	5851	131	P	-a	0.8462	1.3335	0.2776	301.2	120.0	–	14N	111W
2363	197	2473 Aug 08	16:24:05	1067	5857	136	P	-a	-0.6920	1.5675	0.6086	290.0	158.2	–	16S	120E
2364	197	2474 Feb 02	10:11:04	1069	5863	141	T+	pp	0.1682	2.6000	1.4997	375.1	231.1	96.9	17N	145W
2365	198	2474 Jul 29	09:15:37	1071	5869	146	T+	pp	0.0523	2.7324	1.7911	317.0	211.3	98.9	18S	133W
2366	198	2475 Jan 22	09:16:57	1073	5875	151	P	t-	-0.5121	1.9665	0.8709	354.6	199.5	–	19N	132W
2367	198	2475 Jul 19	01:34:31	1075	5881	156	P	a-	0.8097	1.3560	0.3886	280.0	132.1	–	20S	18W
2368	198	2476 Jan 11	12:49:29	1076	5887	161	N	a-	-1.1672	0.7398	-0.3067	235.6	–	–	21N	174E
2369	198	2476 Jun 08	00:28:50	1078	5892	128	N	-t	-1.1021	0.8606	-0.1884	259.6	–	–	24S	3W
2370	198	2476 Dec 01	12:44:16	1080	5898	133	P	-a	0.9229	1.1502	0.1788	258.0	90.2	–	23N	171E
2371	198	2477 May 28	01:49:58	1082	5904	138	T	-t	-0.3653	2.2254	1.1506	365.4	219.6	61.5	22S	23W
2372	198	2477 Nov 21	04:40:33	1084	5910	143	T+	-p	0.2516	2.3824	1.4101	317.9	205.5	83.8	20N	69W
2373	198	2478 May 17	03:13:37	1086	5916	148	T	t-	-0.3883	2.1716	1.1200	352.5	212.9	54.3	19S	45W
2374	198	2478 Nov 10	18:04:52	1088	5922	153	T	p-	-0.4598	2.0214	1.0075	325.6	195.9	13.4	17N	89E
2375	198	2479 Apr 07	00:42:34	1089	5927	120	Ne	-a	-1.5403	0.0223	-0.9591	41.1	–	–	8S	6W
2376	198	2479 May 06	10:53:13	1090	5928	158	N	a-	1.1070	0.8266	-0.1731	238.8	–	–	16S	159W
2377	199	2479 Oct 31	01:02:53	1092	5934	163	N	t-	-1.2253	0.6434	-0.4234	229.9	–	–	13N	15W
2378	199	2480 Mar 26	16:18:41	1093	5939	130	P	-a	-0.8242	1.3251	0.3658	269.6	125.1	–	4S	121E
2379	199	2480 Sep 19	09:03:31	1095	5945	135	P	-t	0.9727	1.1107	0.0366	293.9	46.8	–	0S	133W
2380	199	2481 Mar 16	08:05:58	1097	5951	140	T-	-p	-0.1415	2.5892	1.6071	325.9	212.4	95.0	1N	115W
2381	199	2481 Sep 08	12:56:07	1099	5957	145	T+	pp	0.1967	2.5107	1.4838	349.5	221.9	93.7	5S	170E
2382	199	2482 Mar 05	19:26:13	1101	5963	150	P	a-	0.5889	1.7965	0.7586	325.0	181.4	–	6N	76E
2383	199	2482 Aug 29	00:10:15	1103	5969	155	P	a-	-0.5588	1.8180	0.8469	306.4	181.0	–	10S	3E
2384	199	2483 Feb 22	23:24:23	1105	5975	160	N	t-	1.3340	0.4558	-0.6345	201.1	–	–	11N	17E
2385	199	2483 Jul 20	09:38:02	1107	5980	127	N	-a	1.2374	0.5594	-0.3848	190.2	–	–	19S	138W
2386	199	2483 Aug 18	16:25:11	1107	5981	165	N	a-	-1.2597	0.5182	-0.4252	183.1	–	–	14S	120E
2387	199	2484 Jan 13	04:14:52	1109	5986	132	Nx	-t	-1.0125	1.0429	-0.0419	283.8	–	–	21N	57W
2388	199	2484 Jul 09	01:00:41	1111	5992	137	P	-a	0.5261	1.8831	0.9020	314.6	187.6	–	22S	9W
2389	200	2485 Jan 01	09:52:19	1113	5998	142	T	-p	-0.2801	2.3588	1.3297	338.9	212.3	80.2	23N	143W
2390	200	2485 Jun 28	10:20:44	1115	6004	147	T-	pp	-0.2498	2.4177	1.3817	354.4	222.4	87.8	23S	149W
2391	200	2485 Dec 21	22:24:26	1117	6010	152	T	a-	0.4123	2.0915	1.1111	312.3	194.2	48.3	24N	28E
2392	200	2486 Jun 17	12:46:53	1119	6016	157	N	t-	-1.0329	0.9983	-0.0721	283.2	–	–	24S	173E
2393	200	2486 Dec 11	14:07:09	1121	6022	162	N	a-	1.0695	0.8810	-0.0899	231.9	–	–	24N	151E
2394	200	2487 May 07	23:59:40	1122	6027	129	N	-t	1.0517	0.9483	-0.0913	265.2	–	–	16S	4E
2395	200	2487 Nov 01	15:47:25	1124	6033	134	P	-a	-0.9560	1.1180	0.0900	275.4	68.9	–	14N	124E
2396	200	2488 Apr 26	09:36:09	1126	6039	139	T+	-p	0.2634	2.3681	1.3811	328.2	210.3	83.7	14S	140W
2397	200	2488 Oct 20	20:46:18	1128	6045	144	T-	-p	-0.2544	2.4296	1.3534	366.0	225.3	86.3	11N	49E
2398	200	2489 Apr 16	00:46:36	1130	6051	149	T	a-	-0.4585	1.9946	1.0386	304.6	189.1	29.0	11S	7W
2399	200	2489 Oct 09	20:45:33	1132	6057	154	P	t-	0.4679	2.0423	0.9575	359.3	207.5	–	7N	50E
2400	200	2490 Mar 07	06:48:58	1134	6062	121	N	-a	1.5005	0.1037	-0.8939	88.9	–	–	6N	94W

Cat Num	Canon Plate	Calendar Date	TD of Greatest Eclipse	ΔT s	Luna Num	Saros Num	Ecl Type	QSE	Gamma	Pen Mag	Um Mag	Phase ---- Durations ----			Greatest in Zenith	
												Pen m	Par m	Total m	Lat	Long
2401	201	2490 Apr 05	17:09:25	1134	6063	159	N	a-	-1.1619	0.7102	-0.2582	213.8	–	–	8S	107E
2402	201	2490 Sep 28	23:02:19	1136	6069	164	N	t-	1.1733	0.7278	-0.3169	238.3	–	–	4N	16E
2403	201	2491 Feb 24	16:09:25	1138	6074	131	P	-a	0.8631	1.3029	0.2462	299.7	113.8	–	10N	126E
2404	201	2491 Aug 19	23:52:19	1140	6080	136	P	-a	-0.7603	1.4419	0.4837	281.7	143.5	–	13S	8E
2405	201	2492 Feb 13	18:09:19	1142	6086	141	T+	pp	0.1814	2.5753	1.4756	375.1	230.8	95.6	13N	96E
2406	201	2492 Aug 08	16:47:16	1144	6092	146	T-	pp	-0.0196	2.7932	1.8505	317.4	211.6	99.4	16S	115E
2407	201	2493 Feb 01	17:21:20	1146	6098	151	P	t-	-0.5016	1.9846	0.8916	354.6	200.8	–	16N	107E
2408	201	2493 Jul 29	08:53:03	1148	6104	156	P	a-	0.7379	1.4892	0.5185	289.9	150.0	–	18S	127W
2409	201	2494 Jan 21	21:17:43	1150	6110	161	N	a-	-1.1593	0.7526	-0.2906	236.5	–	–	19N	48E
2410	201	2494 Jun 19	07:12:40	1152	6115	128	N	-t	-1.1830	0.7126	-0.3376	240.4	–	–	24S	103W
2411	201	2494 Jul 18	19:45:11	1152	6116	166	Nb	t-	1.5604	0.0071	-1.0169	24.9	–	–	19S	70E
2412	201	2494 Dec 12	21:27:42	1154	6121	133	P	-a	0.9325	1.1330	0.1609	256.3	85.7	–	24N	41E
2413	202	2495 Jun 08	08:25:19	1156	6127	138	T	-t	-0.4447	2.0786	1.0059	360.1	211.2	12.8	23S	121W
2414	202	2495 Dec 02	13:16:55	1158	6133	143	T+	-p	0.2671	2.3556	1.3798	318.1	204.8	81.6	22N	163E
2415	202	2496 May 27	10:09:52	1160	6139	148	T	t-	0.3172	2.2994	1.2531	354.7	218.7	75.3	21S	148W
2416	202	2496 Nov 21	02:19:03	1162	6145	153	T	p-	-0.4399	2.0606	1.0412	328.5	198.5	31.2	20N	34W
2417	202	2497 May 16	18:23:07	1164	6151	158	N	a-	1.0464	0.9350	-0.0589	250.0	–	–	18S	89E
2418	202	2497 Nov 10	08:44:48	1166	6157	163	N	t-	-1.1970	0.6982	-0.3741	239.1	–	–	16N	130W
2419	202	2498 Apr 07	00:35:15	1168	6162	130	P	-a	-0.8577	1.2622	0.3058	264.9	115.4	–	8S	4W
2420	202	2498 Sep 30	16:05:34	1170	6168	135	Nx	-t	1.0301	1.0061	-0.0695	282.5	–	–	4N	121E
2421	202	2499 Mar 27	16:22:53	1172	6174	140	T-	-p	-0.1705	2.5358	1.5542	326.0	211.9	93.1	3S	120E
2422	202	2499 Sep 19	20:14:16	1174	6180	145	T+	pp	0.2569	2.3999	1.3736	346.4	218.1	85.8	1S	60E
2423	202	2500 Mar 17	03:30:26	1176	6186	150	P	h-	0.5665	1.8379	0.7997	328.0	185.5	–	2N	46W
2424	202	2500 Sep 09	07:45:58	1178	6192	155	P	a-	-0.4957	1.9336	0.9629	310.4	188.6	–	6S	112W

Appendix B

Lunar Eclipse Figures: 1501 to 2500

Key to Lunar Eclipse Figures

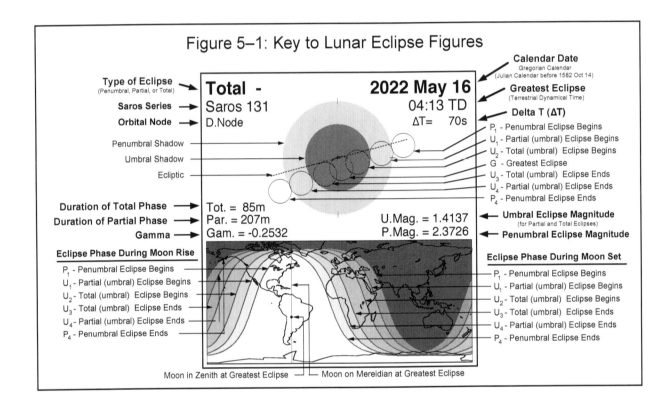

Figure 5–1: Key to Lunar Eclipse Figures

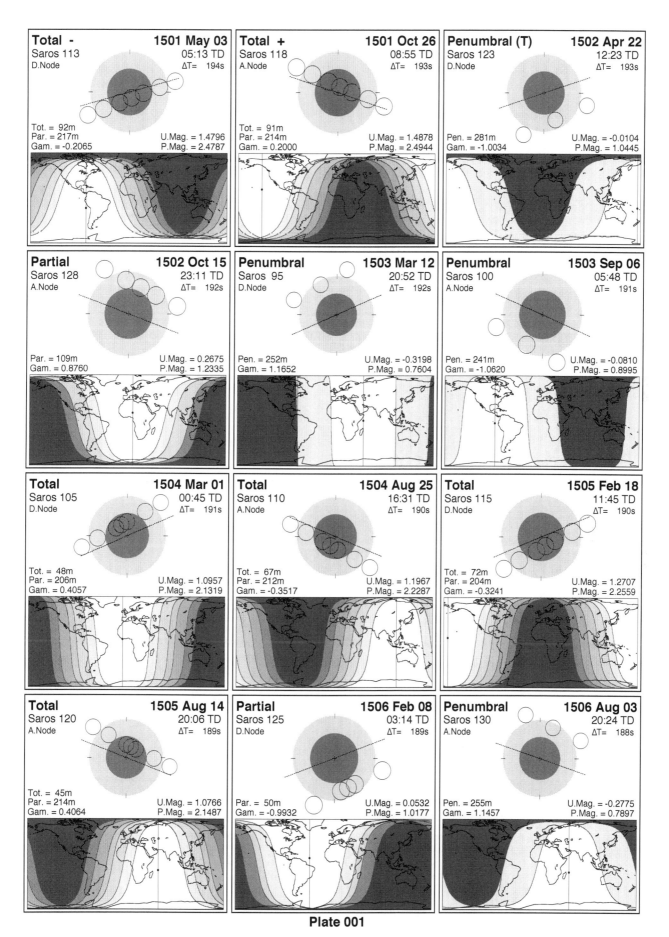

Total -   **1501 May 03**
Saros 113   05:13 TD
D.Node   ΔT=   194s

Tot. = 92m
Par. = 217m   U.Mag. = 1.4796
Gam. = -0.2065   P.Mag. = 2.4787

Total +   **1501 Oct 26**
Saros 118   08:55 TD
A.Node   ΔT=   193s

Tot. = 91m
Par. = 214m   U.Mag. = 1.4878
Gam. = 0.2000   P.Mag. = 2.4944

Penumbral (T)   **1502 Apr 22**
Saros 123   12:23 TD
D.Node   ΔT=   193s

Pen. = 281m
                                  U.Mag. = -0.0104
Gam. = -1.0034   P.Mag. = 1.0445

Partial   **1502 Oct 15**
Saros 128   23:11 TD
A.Node   ΔT=   192s

Par. = 109m
Gam. = 0.8760   U.Mag. = 0.2675
                                  P.Mag. = 1.2335

Penumbral   **1503 Mar 12**
Saros 95   20:52 TD
D.Node   ΔT=   192s

Pen. = 252m
Gam. = 1.1652   U.Mag. = -0.3198
                                  P.Mag. = 0.7604

Penumbral   **1503 Sep 06**
Saros 100   05:48 TD
A.Node   ΔT=   191s

Pen. = 241m
Gam. = -1.0620   U.Mag. = -0.0810
                                  P.Mag. = 0.8995

Total   **1504 Mar 01**
Saros 105   00:45 TD
D.Node   ΔT=   191s

Tot. = 48m
Par. = 206m   U.Mag. = 1.0957
Gam. = 0.4057   P.Mag. = 2.1319

Total   **1504 Aug 25**
Saros 110   16:31 TD
A.Node   ΔT=   190s

Tot. = 67m
Par. = 212m   U.Mag. = 1.1967
Gam. = -0.3517   P.Mag. = 2.2287

Total   **1505 Feb 18**
Saros 115   11:45 TD
D.Node   ΔT=   190s

Tot. = 72m
Par. = 204m   U.Mag. = 1.2707
Gam. = -0.3241   P.Mag. = 2.2559

Total   **1505 Aug 14**
Saros 120   20:06 TD
A.Node   ΔT=   189s

Tot. = 45m
Par. = 214m   U.Mag. = 1.0766
Gam. = 0.4064   P.Mag. = 2.1487

Partial   **1506 Feb 08**
Saros 125   03:14 TD
D.Node   ΔT=   189s

Par. = 50m
Gam. = -0.9932   U.Mag. = 0.0532
                                  P.Mag. = 1.0177

Penumbral   **1506 Aug 03**
Saros 130   20:24 TD
A.Node   ΔT=   188s

Pen. = 255m
Gam. = 1.1457   U.Mag. = -0.2775
                                  P.Mag. = 0.7897

Plate 001

97

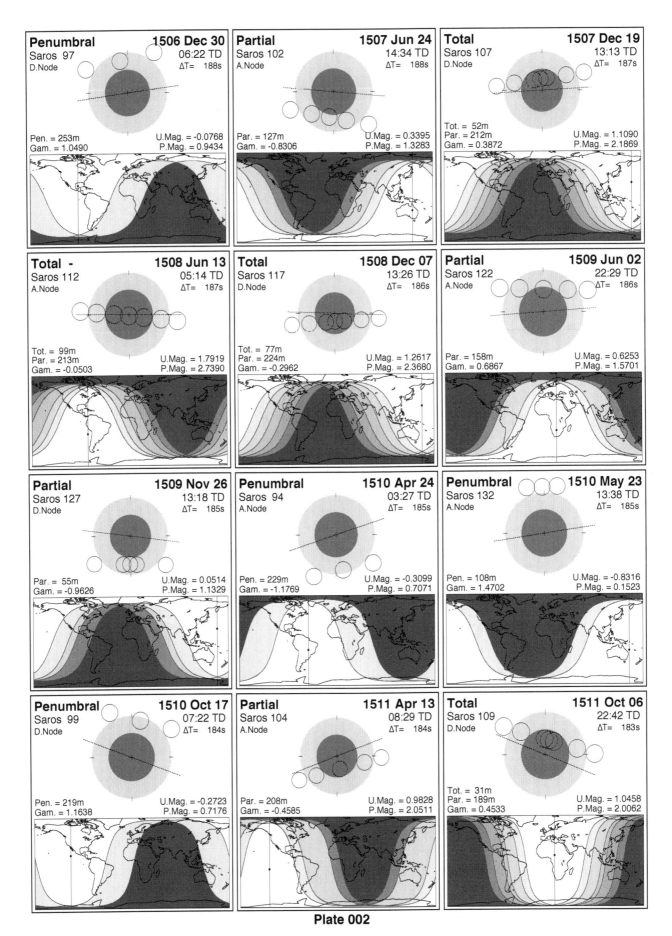

Penumbral   **1506 Dec 30**
Saros 97   06:22 TD
D.Node   ΔT= 188s

Pen. = 253m   U.Mag. = -0.0768
Gam. = 1.0490   P.Mag. = 0.9434

Partial   **1507 Jun 24**
Saros 102   14:34 TD
A.Node   ΔT= 188s

Par. = 127m   U.Mag. = 0.3395
Gam. = -0.8306   P.Mag. = 1.3283

Total   **1507 Dec 19**
Saros 107   13:13 TD
D.Node   ΔT= 187s

Tot. = 52m
Par. = 212m   U.Mag. = 1.1090
Gam. = 0.3872   P.Mag. = 2.1869

Total -   **1508 Jun 13**
Saros 112   05:14 TD
A.Node   ΔT= 187s

Tot. = 99m
Par. = 213m   U.Mag. = 1.7919
Gam. = -0.0503   P.Mag. = 2.7390

Total   **1508 Dec 07**
Saros 117   13:26 TD
D.Node   ΔT= 186s

Tot. = 77m
Par. = 224m   U.Mag. = 1.2617
Gam. = -0.2962   P.Mag. = 2.3680

Partial   **1509 Jun 02**
Saros 122   22:29 TD
A.Node   ΔT= 186s

Par. = 158m   U.Mag. = 0.6253
Gam. = 0.6867   P.Mag. = 1.5701

Partial   **1509 Nov 26**
Saros 127   13:18 TD
D.Node   ΔT= 185s

Par. = 55m   U.Mag. = 0.0514
Gam. = -0.9626   P.Mag. = 1.1329

Penumbral   **1510 Apr 24**
Saros 94   03:27 TD
A.Node   ΔT= 185s

Pen. = 229m   U.Mag. = -0.3099
Gam. = -1.1769   P.Mag. = 0.7071

Penumbral   **1510 May 23**
Saros 132   13:38 TD
A.Node   ΔT= 185s

Pen. = 108m   U.Mag. = -0.8316
Gam. = 1.4702   P.Mag. = 0.1523

Penumbral   **1510 Oct 17**
Saros 99   07:22 TD
D.Node   ΔT= 184s

Pen. = 219m   U.Mag. = -0.2723
Gam. = 1.1638   P.Mag. = 0.7176

Partial   **1511 Apr 13**
Saros 104   08:29 TD
A.Node   ΔT= 184s

Par. = 208m   U.Mag. = 0.9828
Gam. = -0.4585   P.Mag. = 2.0511

Total   **1511 Oct 06**
Saros 109   22:42 TD
D.Node   ΔT= 183s

Tot. = 31m
Par. = 189m   U.Mag. = 1.0458
Gam. = 0.4533   P.Mag. = 2.0062

Plate 002

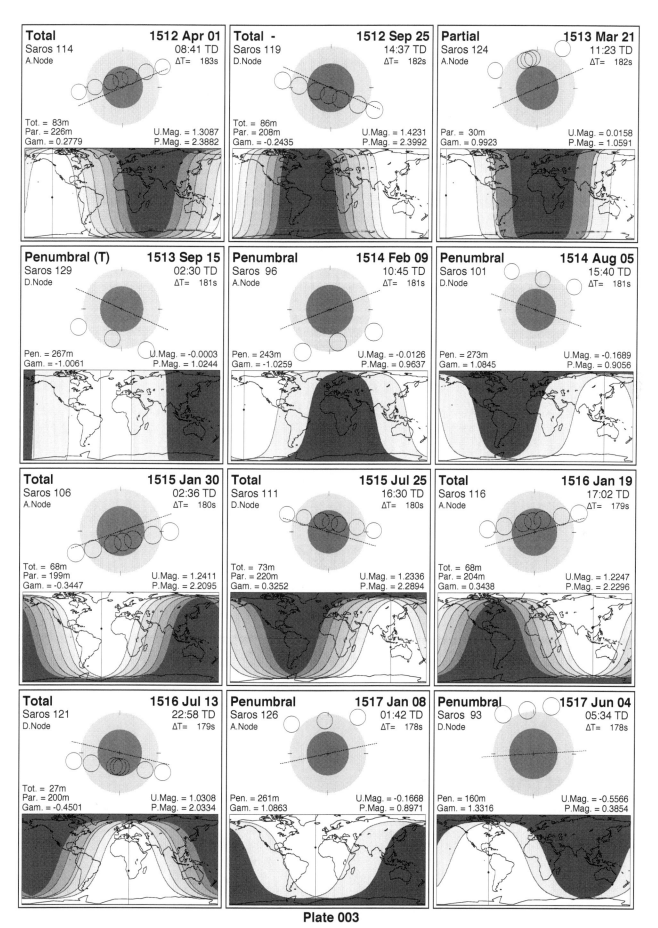

Total   **1512 Apr 01**
Saros 114   08:41 TD
A.Node   ΔT= 183s
Tot. = 83m
Par. = 226m   U.Mag. = 1.3087
Gam. = 0.2779   P.Mag. = 2.3882

Total -   **1512 Sep 25**
Saros 119   14:37 TD
D.Node   ΔT= 182s
Tot. = 86m
Par. = 208m   U.Mag. = 1.4231
Gam. = -0.2435   P.Mag. = 2.3992

Partial   **1513 Mar 21**
Saros 124   11:23 TD
A.Node   ΔT= 182s
Par. = 30m
Gam. = 0.9923   U.Mag. = 0.0158
    P.Mag. = 1.0591

Penumbral (T)   **1513 Sep 15**
Saros 129   02:30 TD
D.Node   ΔT= 181s
Pen. = 267m
Gam. = -1.0061   U.Mag. = -0.0003
    P.Mag. = 1.0244

Penumbral   **1514 Feb 09**
Saros 96   10:45 TD
A.Node   ΔT= 181s
Pen. = 243m
Gam. = -1.0259   U.Mag. = -0.0126
    P.Mag. = 0.9637

Penumbral   **1514 Aug 05**
Saros 101   15:40 TD
D.Node   ΔT= 181s
Pen. = 273m
Gam. = 1.0845   U.Mag. = -0.1689
    P.Mag. = 0.9056

Total   **1515 Jan 30**
Saros 106   02:36 TD
A.Node   ΔT= 180s
Tot. = 68m
Par. = 199m   U.Mag. = 1.2411
Gam. = -0.3447   P.Mag. = 2.2095

Total   **1515 Jul 25**
Saros 111   16:30 TD
D.Node   ΔT= 180s
Tot. = 73m
Par. = 220m   U.Mag. = 1.2336
Gam. = 0.3252   P.Mag. = 2.2894

Total   **1516 Jan 19**
Saros 116   17:02 TD
A.Node   ΔT= 179s
Tot. = 68m
Par. = 204m   U.Mag. = 1.2247
Gam. = 0.3438   P.Mag. = 2.2296

Total   **1516 Jul 13**
Saros 121   22:58 TD
D.Node   ΔT= 179s
Tot. = 27m
Par. = 200m   U.Mag. = 1.0308
Gam. = -0.4501   P.Mag. = 2.0334

Penumbral   **1517 Jan 08**
Saros 126   01:42 TD
A.Node   ΔT= 178s
Pen. = 261m
Gam. = 1.0863   U.Mag. = -0.1668
    P.Mag. = 0.8971

Penumbral   **1517 Jun 04**
Saros 93   05:34 TD
D.Node   ΔT= 178s
Pen. = 160m
Gam. = 1.3316   U.Mag. = -0.5566
    P.Mag. = 0.3854

Plate 003

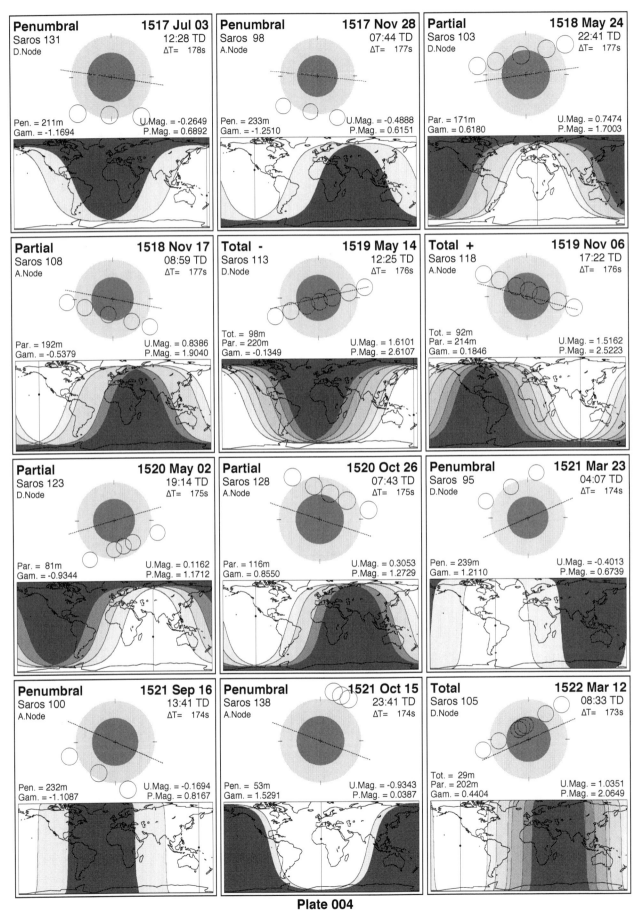

Plate 004

100

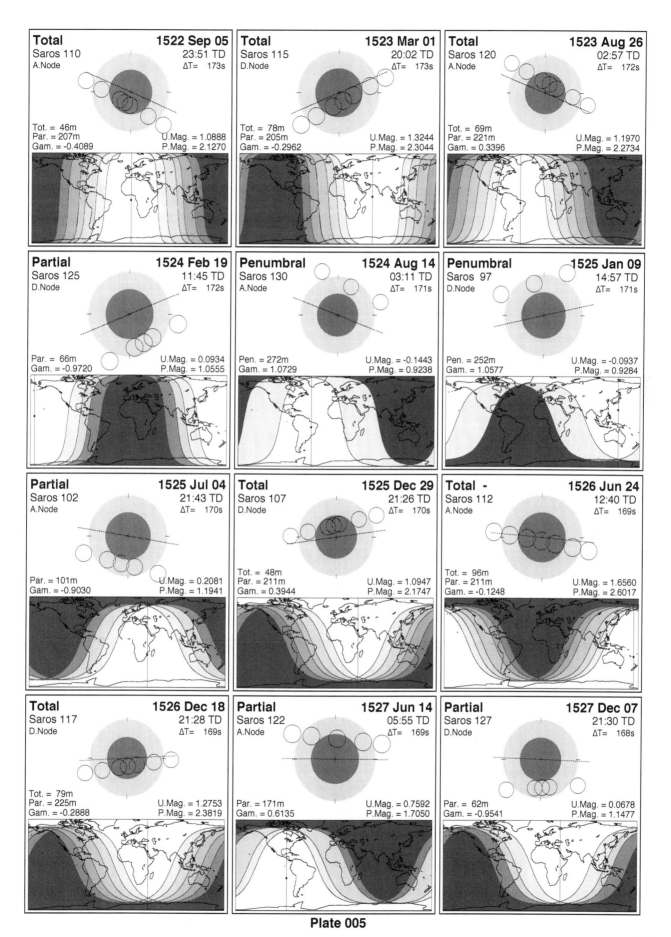

Total **1522 Sep 05** Saros 110 23:51 TD A.Node ΔT= 173s Tot. = 46m Par. = 207m Gam. = -0.4089 U.Mag. = 1.0888 P.Mag. = 2.1270	**Total** **1523 Mar 01** Saros 115 20:02 TD D.Node ΔT= 173s Tot. = 78m Par. = 205m Gam. = -0.2962 U.Mag. = 1.3244 P.Mag. = 2.3044	**Total** **1523 Aug 26** Saros 120 02:57 TD A.Node ΔT= 172s Tot. = 69m Par. = 221m Gam. = 0.3396 U.Mag. = 1.1970 P.Mag. = 2.2734
Partial **1524 Feb 19** Saros 125 11:45 TD D.Node ΔT= 172s Par. = 66m Gam. = -0.9720 U.Mag. = 0.0934 P.Mag. = 1.0555	**Penumbral** **1524 Aug 14** Saros 130 03:11 TD A.Node ΔT= 171s Pen. = 272m Gam. = 1.0729 U.Mag. = -0.1443 P.Mag. = 0.9238	**Penumbral** **1525 Jan 09** Saros 97 14:57 TD D.Node ΔT= 171s Pen. = 252m Gam. = 1.0577 U.Mag. = -0.0937 P.Mag. = 0.9284
Partial **1525 Jul 04** Saros 102 21:43 TD A.Node ΔT= 170s Par. = 101m Gam. = -0.9030 U.Mag. = 0.2081 P.Mag. = 1.1941	**Total** **1525 Dec 29** Saros 107 21:26 TD D.Node ΔT= 170s Tot. = 48m Par. = 211m Gam. = 0.3944 U.Mag. = 1.0947 P.Mag. = 2.1747	**Total -** **1526 Jun 24** Saros 112 12:40 TD A.Node ΔT= 169s Tot. = 96m Par. = 211m Gam. = -0.1248 U.Mag. = 1.6560 P.Mag. = 2.6017
Total **1526 Dec 18** Saros 117 21:28 TD D.Node ΔT= 169s Tot. = 79m Par. = 225m Gam. = -0.2888 U.Mag. = 1.2753 P.Mag. = 2.3819	**Partial** **1527 Jun 14** Saros 122 05:55 TD A.Node ΔT= 169s Par. = 171m Gam. = 0.6135 U.Mag. = 0.7592 P.Mag. = 1.7050	**Partial** **1527 Dec 07** Saros 127 21:30 TD D.Node ΔT= 168s Par. = 62m Gam. = -0.9541 U.Mag. = 0.0678 P.Mag. = 1.1477

Plate 005

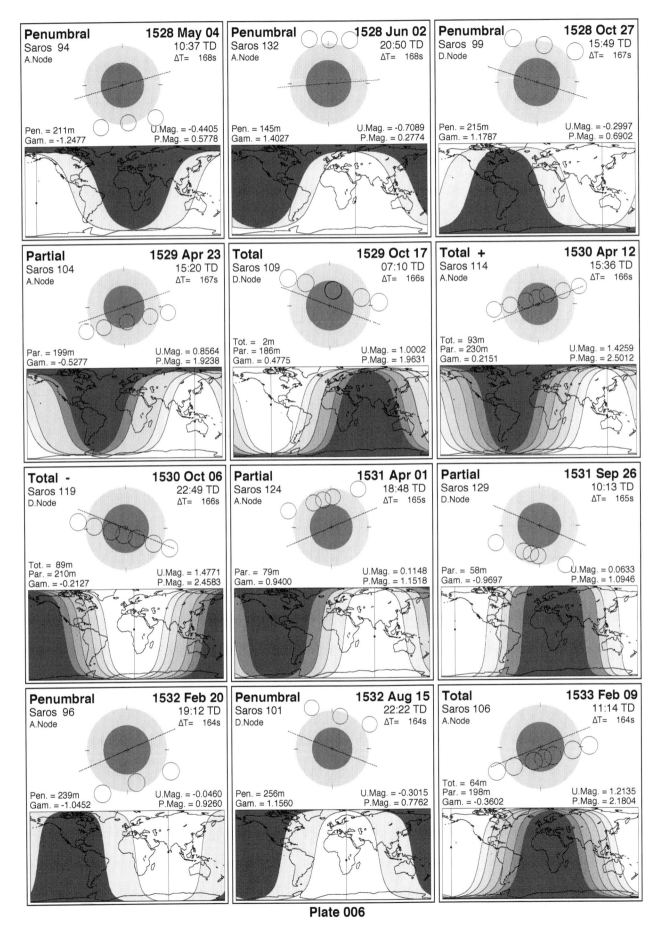

Penumbral   **1528 May 04**
Saros 94   10:37 TD
A.Node   ΔT= 168s
Pen. = 211m   U.Mag. = -0.4405
Gam. = -1.2477   P.Mag. = 0.5778

Penumbral   **1528 Jun 02**
Saros 132   20:50 TD
A.Node   ΔT= 168s
Pen. = 145m   U.Mag. = -0.7089
Gam. = 1.4027   P.Mag. = 0.2774

Penumbral   **1528 Oct 27**
Saros 99   15:49 TD
D.Node   ΔT= 167s
Pen. = 215m   U.Mag. = -0.2997
Gam. = 1.1787   P.Mag. = 0.6902

Partial   **1529 Apr 23**
Saros 104   15:20 TD
A.Node   ΔT= 167s
Par. = 199m   U.Mag. = 0.8564
Gam. = -0.5277   P.Mag. = 1.9238

Total   **1529 Oct 17**
Saros 109   07:10 TD
D.Node   ΔT= 166s
Tot. = 2m   U.Mag. = 1.0002
Par. = 186m   P.Mag. = 1.9631
Gam. = 0.4775

Total +   **1530 Apr 12**
Saros 114   15:36 TD
A.Node   ΔT= 166s
Tot. = 93m   U.Mag. = 1.4259
Par. = 230m   P.Mag. = 2.5012
Gam. = 0.2151

Total -   **1530 Oct 06**
Saros 119   22:49 TD
D.Node   ΔT= 166s
Tot. = 89m   U.Mag. = 1.4771
Par. = 210m   P.Mag. = 2.4583
Gam. = -0.2127

Partial   **1531 Apr 01**
Saros 124   18:48 TD
A.Node   ΔT= 165s
Par. = 79m   U.Mag. = 0.1148
Gam. = 0.9400   P.Mag. = 1.1518

Partial   **1531 Sep 26**
Saros 129   10:13 TD
D.Node   ΔT= 165s
Par. = 58m   U.Mag. = 0.0633
Gam. = -0.9697   P.Mag. = 1.0946

Penumbral   **1532 Feb 20**
Saros 96   19:12 TD
A.Node   ΔT= 164s
Pen. = 239m   U.Mag. = -0.0460
Gam. = -1.0452   P.Mag. = 0.9260

Penumbral   **1532 Aug 15**
Saros 101   22:22 TD
D.Node   ΔT= 164s
Pen. = 256m   U.Mag. = -0.3015
Gam. = 1.1560   P.Mag. = 0.7762

Total   **1533 Feb 09**
Saros 106   11:14 TD
A.Node   ΔT= 164s
Tot. = 64m   U.Mag. = 1.2135
Par. = 198m   P.Mag. = 2.1804
Gam. = -0.3602

Plate 006

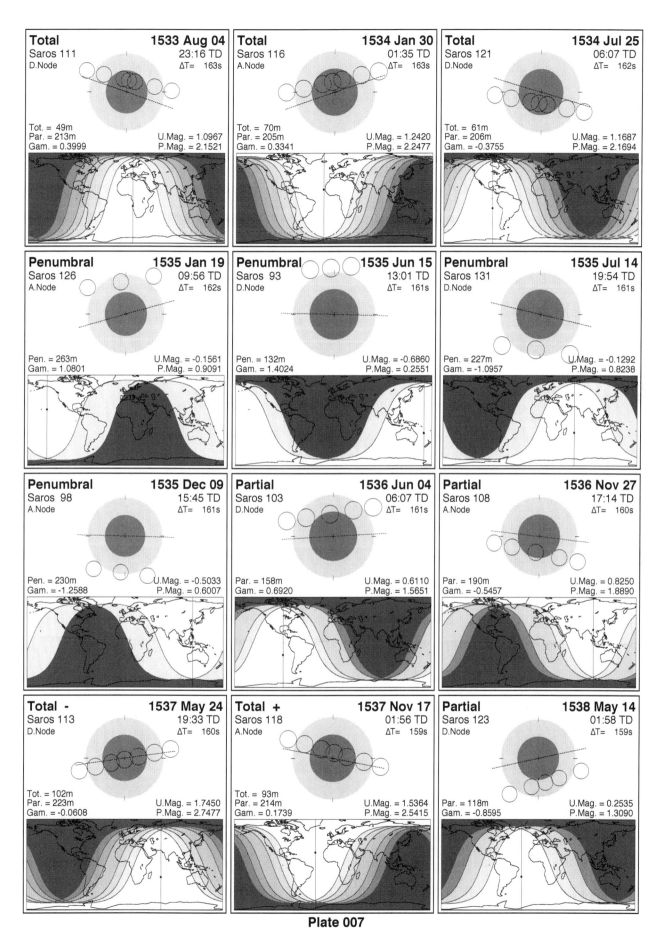

Total 1533 Aug 04	**Total** 1534 Jan 30	**Total** 1534 Jul 25
Saros 111	Saros 116	Saros 121
23:16 TD	01:35 TD	06:07 TD
D.Node ΔT= 163s	A.Node ΔT= 163s	D.Node ΔT= 162s
Tot. = 49m	Tot. = 70m	Tot. = 61m
Par. = 213m	Par. = 205m	Par. = 206m
Gam. = 0.3999	Gam. = 0.3341	Gam. = -0.3755
U.Mag. = 1.0967	U.Mag. = 1.2420	U.Mag. = 1.1687
P.Mag. = 2.1521	P.Mag. = 2.2477	P.Mag. = 2.1694

Penumbral 1535 Jan 19	**Penumbral** 1535 Jun 15	**Penumbral** 1535 Jul 14
Saros 126	Saros 93	Saros 131
09:56 TD	13:01 TD	19:54 TD
A.Node ΔT= 162s	D.Node ΔT= 161s	D.Node ΔT= 161s
Pen. = 263m	Pen. = 132m	Pen. = 227m
Gam. = 1.0801	Gam. = 1.4024	Gam. = -1.0957
U.Mag. = -0.1561	U.Mag. = -0.6860	U.Mag. = -0.1292
P.Mag. = 0.9091	P.Mag. = 0.2551	P.Mag. = 0.8238

Penumbral 1535 Dec 09	**Partial** 1536 Jun 04	**Partial** 1536 Nov 27
Saros 98	Saros 103	Saros 108
15:45 TD	06:07 TD	17:14 TD
A.Node ΔT= 161s	D.Node ΔT= 161s	A.Node ΔT= 160s
Pen. = 230m	Par. = 158m	Par. = 190m
Gam. = -1.2588	Gam. = 0.6920	Gam. = -0.5457
U.Mag. = -0.5033	U.Mag. = 0.6110	U.Mag. = 0.8250
P.Mag. = 0.6007	P.Mag. = 1.5651	P.Mag. = 1.8890

Total - 1537 May 24	**Total +** 1537 Nov 17	**Partial** 1538 May 14
Saros 113	Saros 118	Saros 123
19:33 TD	01:56 TD	01:58 TD
D.Node ΔT= 160s	A.Node ΔT= 159s	D.Node ΔT= 159s
Tot. = 102m	Tot. = 93m	Par. = 118m
Par. = 223m	Par. = 214m	Gam. = -0.8595
Gam. = -0.0608	Gam. = 0.1739	
U.Mag. = 1.7450	U.Mag. = 1.5364	U.Mag. = 0.2535
P.Mag. = 2.7477	P.Mag. = 2.5415	P.Mag. = 1.3090

Plate 007

103

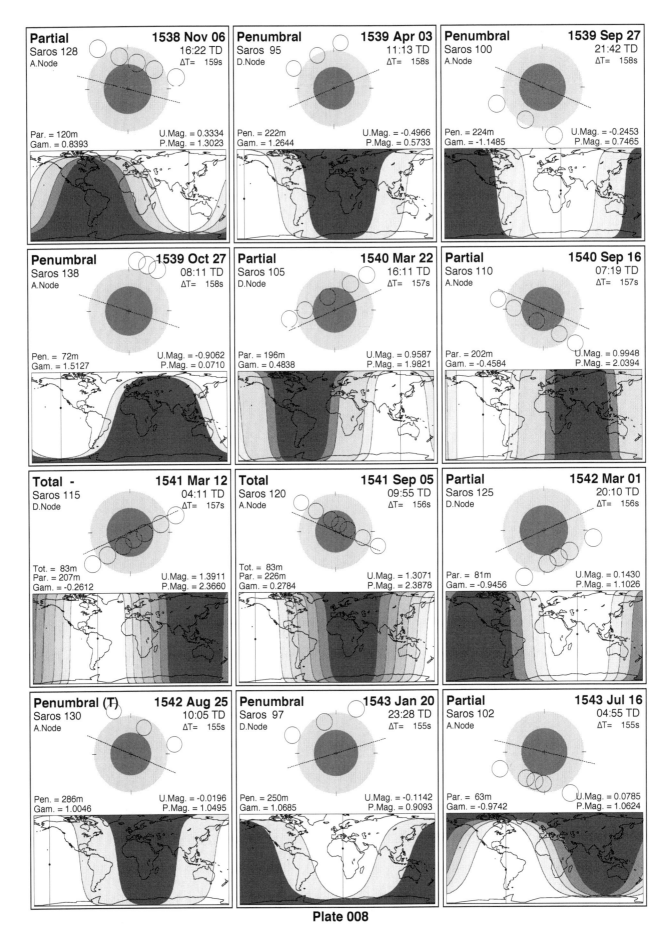

Partial   **1538 Nov 06**
Saros 128   16:22 TD
A.Node   ΔT= 159s
Par. = 120m   U.Mag. = 0.3334
Gam. = 0.8393   P.Mag. = 1.3023

Penumbral   **1539 Apr 03**
Saros 95   11:13 TD
D.Node   ΔT= 158s
Pen. = 222m   U.Mag. = -0.4966
Gam. = 1.2644   P.Mag. = 0.5733

Penumbral   **1539 Sep 27**
Saros 100   21:42 TD
A.Node   ΔT= 158s
Pen. = 224m   U.Mag. = -0.2453
Gam. = -1.1485   P.Mag. = 0.7465

Penumbral   **1539 Oct 27**
Saros 138   08:11 TD
A.Node   ΔT= 158s
Pen. = 72m   U.Mag. = -0.9062
Gam. = 1.5127   P.Mag. = 0.0710

Partial   **1540 Mar 22**
Saros 105   16:11 TD
D.Node   ΔT= 157s
Par. = 196m   U.Mag. = 0.9587
Gam. = 0.4838   P.Mag. = 1.9821

Partial   **1540 Sep 16**
Saros 110   07:19 TD
A.Node   ΔT= 157s
Par. = 202m   U.Mag. = 0.9948
Gam. = -0.4584   P.Mag. = 2.0394

Total -   **1541 Mar 12**
Saros 115   04:11 TD
D.Node   ΔT= 157s
Tot. = 83m
Par. = 207m   U.Mag. = 1.3911
Gam. = -0.2612   P.Mag. = 2.3660

Total   **1541 Sep 05**
Saros 120   09:55 TD
A.Node   ΔT= 156s
Tot. = 83m
Par. = 226m   U.Mag. = 1.3071
Gam. = 0.2784   P.Mag. = 2.3878

Partial   **1542 Mar 01**
Saros 125   20:10 TD
D.Node   ΔT= 156s
Par. = 81m   U.Mag. = 0.1430
Gam. = -0.9456   P.Mag. = 1.1026

Penumbral (T)   **1542 Aug 25**
Saros 130   10:05 TD
A.Node   ΔT= 155s
Pen. = 286m   U.Mag. = -0.0196
Gam. = 1.0046   P.Mag. = 1.0495

Penumbral   **1543 Jan 20**
Saros 97   23:28 TD
D.Node   ΔT= 155s
Pen. = 250m   U.Mag. = -0.1142
Gam. = 1.0685   P.Mag. = 0.9093

Partial   **1543 Jul 16**
Saros 102   04:55 TD
A.Node   ΔT= 155s
Par. = 63m   U.Mag. = 0.0785
Gam. = -0.9742   P.Mag. = 1.0624

Plate 008

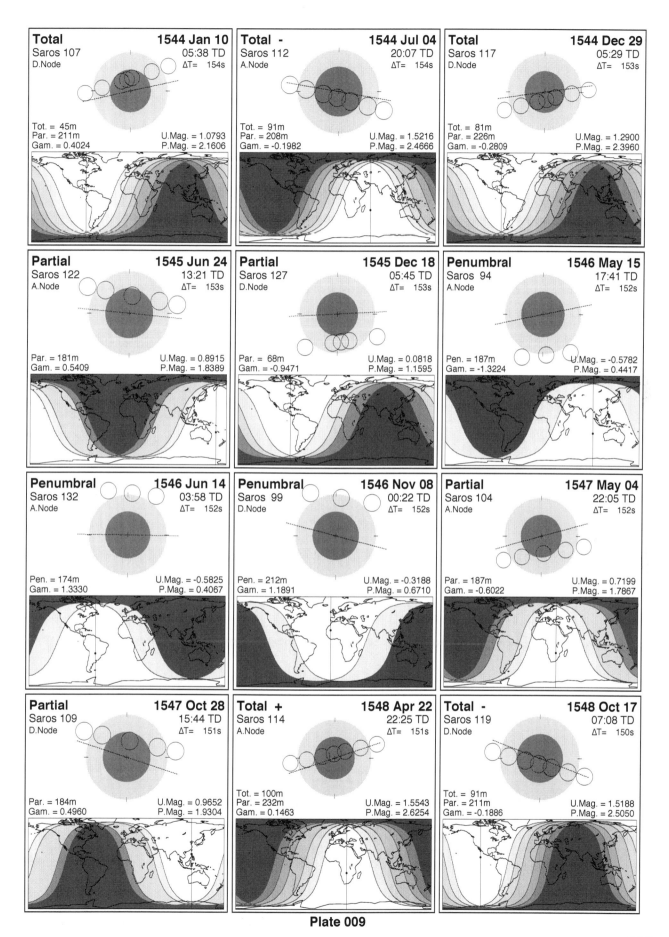

Total 1544 Jan 10 Saros 107 — 05:38 TD D.Node — ΔT= 154s Tot. = 45m Par. = 211m — U.Mag. = 1.0793 Gam. = 0.4024 — P.Mag. = 2.1606	**Total -** 1544 Jul 04 Saros 112 — 20:07 TD A.Node — ΔT= 154s Tot. = 91m Par. = 208m — U.Mag. = 1.5216 Gam. = -0.1982 — P.Mag. = 2.4666	**Total** 1544 Dec 29 Saros 117 — 05:29 TD D.Node — ΔT= 153s Tot. = 81m Par. = 226m — U.Mag. = 1.2900 Gam. = -0.2809 — P.Mag. = 2.3960
Partial 1545 Jun 24 Saros 122 — 13:21 TD A.Node — ΔT= 153s Par. = 181m — U.Mag. = 0.8915 Gam. = 0.5409 — P.Mag. = 1.8389	**Partial** 1545 Dec 18 Saros 127 — 05:45 TD D.Node — ΔT= 153s Par. = 68m — U.Mag. = 0.0818 Gam. = -0.9471 — P.Mag. = 1.1595	**Penumbral** 1546 May 15 Saros 94 — 17:41 TD A.Node — ΔT= 152s Pen. = 187m — U.Mag. = -0.5782 Gam. = -1.3224 — P.Mag. = 0.4417
Penumbral 1546 Jun 14 Saros 132 — 03:58 TD A.Node — ΔT= 152s Pen. = 174m — U.Mag. = -0.5825 Gam. = 1.3330 — P.Mag. = 0.4067	**Penumbral** 1546 Nov 08 Saros 99 — 00:22 TD D.Node — ΔT= 152s Pen. = 212m — U.Mag. = -0.3188 Gam. = 1.1891 — P.Mag. = 0.6710	**Partial** 1547 May 04 Saros 104 — 22:05 TD A.Node — ΔT= 152s Par. = 187m — U.Mag. = 0.7199 Gam. = -0.6022 — P.Mag. = 1.7867
Partial 1547 Oct 28 Saros 109 — 15:44 TD D.Node — ΔT= 151s Par. = 184m — U.Mag. = 0.9652 Gam. = 0.4960 — P.Mag. = 1.9304	**Total +** 1548 Apr 22 Saros 114 — 22:25 TD A.Node — ΔT= 151s Tot. = 100m Par. = 232m — U.Mag. = 1.5543 Gam. = 0.1463 — P.Mag. = 2.6254	**Total -** 1548 Oct 17 Saros 119 — 07:08 TD D.Node — ΔT= 150s Tot. = 91m Par. = 211m — U.Mag. = 1.5188 Gam. = -0.1886 — P.Mag. = 2.5050

Plate 009

105

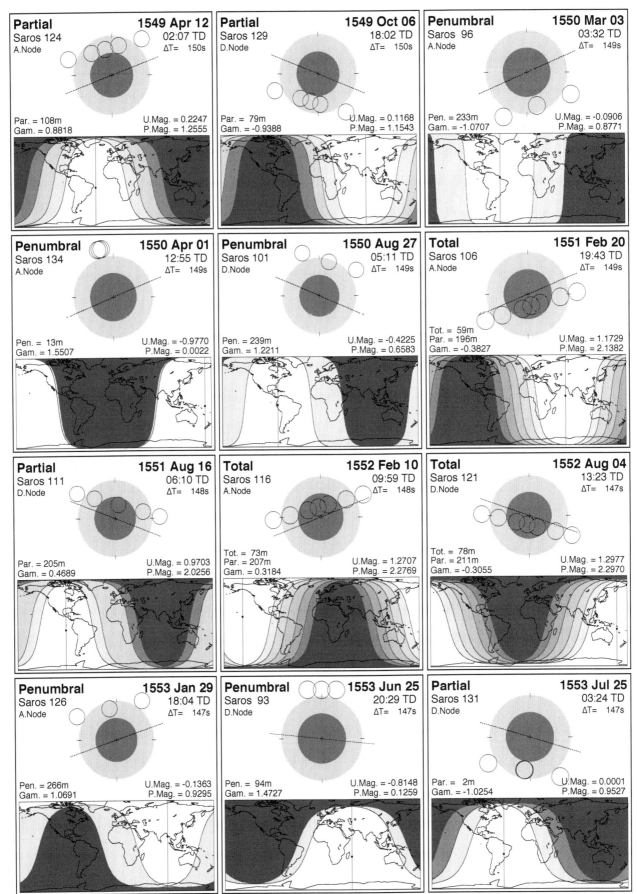

Partial   **1549 Apr 12**
Saros 124   02:07 TD
A.Node   ΔT= 150s
Par. = 108m   U.Mag. = 0.2247
Gam. = 0.8818   P.Mag. = 1.2555

Partial   **1549 Oct 06**
Saros 129   18:02 TD
D.Node   ΔT= 150s
Par. = 79m   U.Mag. = 0.1168
Gam. = -0.9388   P.Mag. = 1.1543

Penumbral   **1550 Mar 03**
Saros 96   03:32 TD
A.Node   ΔT= 149s
Pen. = 233m   U.Mag. = -0.0906
Gam. = -1.0707   P.Mag. = 0.8771

Penumbral   **1550 Apr 01**
Saros 134   12:55 TD
A.Node   ΔT= 149s
Pen. = 13m   U.Mag. = -0.9770
Gam. = 1.5507   P.Mag. = 0.0022

Penumbral   **1550 Aug 27**
Saros 101   05:11 TD
D.Node   ΔT= 149s
Pen. = 239m   U.Mag. = -0.4225
Gam. = 1.2211   P.Mag. = 0.6583

Total   **1551 Feb 20**
Saros 106   19:43 TD
A.Node   ΔT= 149s
Tot. = 59m
Par. = 196m   U.Mag. = 1.1729
Gam. = -0.3827   P.Mag. = 2.1382

Partial   **1551 Aug 16**
Saros 111   06:10 TD
D.Node   ΔT= 148s
Par. = 205m   U.Mag. = 0.9703
Gam. = 0.4689   P.Mag. = 2.0256

Total   **1552 Feb 10**
Saros 116   09:59 TD
A.Node   ΔT= 148s
Tot. = 73m
Par. = 207m   U.Mag. = 1.2707
Gam. = 0.3184   P.Mag. = 2.2769

Total   **1552 Aug 04**
Saros 121   13:23 TD
D.Node   ΔT= 147s
Tot. = 78m
Par. = 211m   U.Mag. = 1.2977
Gam. = -0.3055   P.Mag. = 2.2970

Penumbral   **1553 Jan 29**
Saros 126   18:04 TD
A.Node   ΔT= 147s
Pen. = 266m   U.Mag. = -0.1363
Gam. = 1.0691   P.Mag. = 0.9295

Penumbral   **1553 Jun 25**
Saros 93   20:29 TD
D.Node   ΔT= 147s
Pen. = 94m   U.Mag. = -0.8148
Gam. = 1.4727   P.Mag. = 0.1259

Partial   **1553 Jul 25**
Saros 131   03:24 TD
D.Node   ΔT= 147s
Par. = 2m   U.Mag. = 0.0001
Gam. = -1.0254   P.Mag. = 0.9527

Plate 010

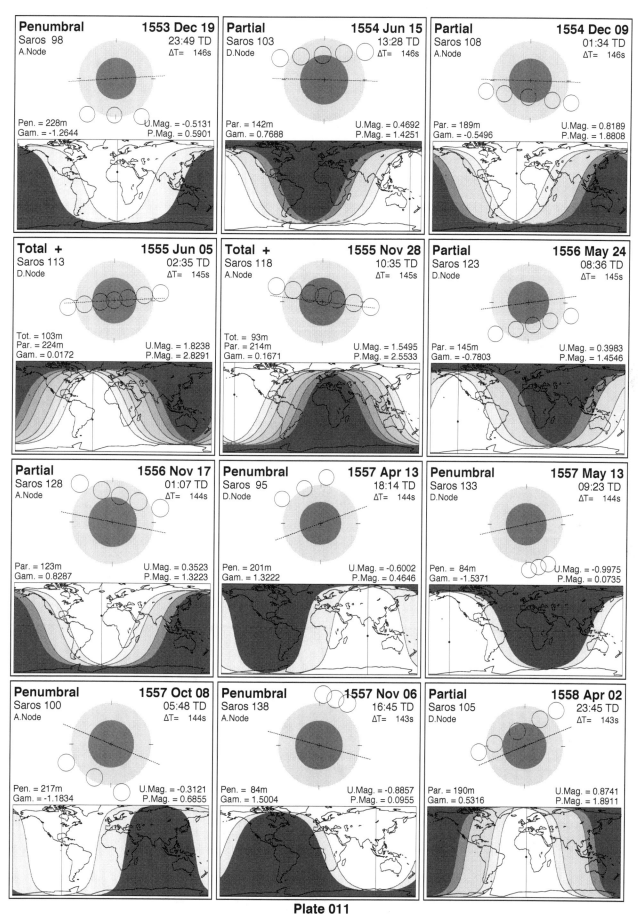

Penumbral	**1553 Dec 19**
Saros 98	23:49 TD
A.Node	ΔT= 146s
Pen. = 228m	U.Mag. = -0.5131
Gam. = -1.2644	P.Mag. = 0.5901

Partial	**1554 Jun 15**
Saros 103	13:28 TD
D.Node	ΔT= 146s
Par. = 142m	U.Mag. = 0.4692
Gam. = 0.7688	P.Mag. = 1.4251

Partial	**1554 Dec 09**
Saros 108	01:34 TD
A.Node	ΔT= 146s
Par. = 189m	U.Mag. = 0.8189
Gam. = -0.5496	P.Mag. = 1.8808

Total +	**1555 Jun 05**
Saros 113	02:35 TD
D.Node	ΔT= 145s
Tot. = 103m	
Par. = 224m	U.Mag. = 1.8238
Gam. = 0.0172	P.Mag. = 2.8291

Total +	**1555 Nov 28**
Saros 118	10:35 TD
A.Node	ΔT= 145s
Tot. = 93m	
Par. = 214m	U.Mag. = 1.5495
Gam. = 0.1671	P.Mag. = 2.5533

Partial	**1556 May 24**
Saros 123	08:36 TD
D.Node	ΔT= 145s
Par. = 145m	U.Mag. = 0.3983
Gam. = -0.7803	P.Mag. = 1.4546

Partial	**1556 Nov 17**
Saros 128	01:07 TD
A.Node	ΔT= 144s
Par. = 123m	U.Mag. = 0.3523
Gam. = 0.8287	P.Mag. = 1.3223

Penumbral	**1557 Apr 13**
Saros 95	18:14 TD
D.Node	ΔT= 144s
Pen. = 201m	U.Mag. = -0.6002
Gam. = 1.3222	P.Mag. = 0.4646

Penumbral	**1557 May 13**
Saros 133	09:23 TD
D.Node	ΔT= 144s
Pen. = 84m	U.Mag. = -0.9975
Gam. = -1.5371	P.Mag. = 0.0735

Penumbral	**1557 Oct 08**
Saros 100	05:48 TD
A.Node	ΔT= 144s
Pen. = 217m	U.Mag. = -0.3121
Gam. = -1.1834	P.Mag. = 0.6855

Penumbral	**1557 Nov 06**
Saros 138	16:45 TD
A.Node	ΔT= 143s
Pen. = 84m	U.Mag. = -0.8857
Gam. = 1.5004	P.Mag. = 0.0955

Partial	**1558 Apr 02**
Saros 105	23:45 TD
D.Node	ΔT= 143s
Par. = 190m	U.Mag. = 0.8741
Gam. = 0.5316	P.Mag. = 1.8911

Plate 011

107

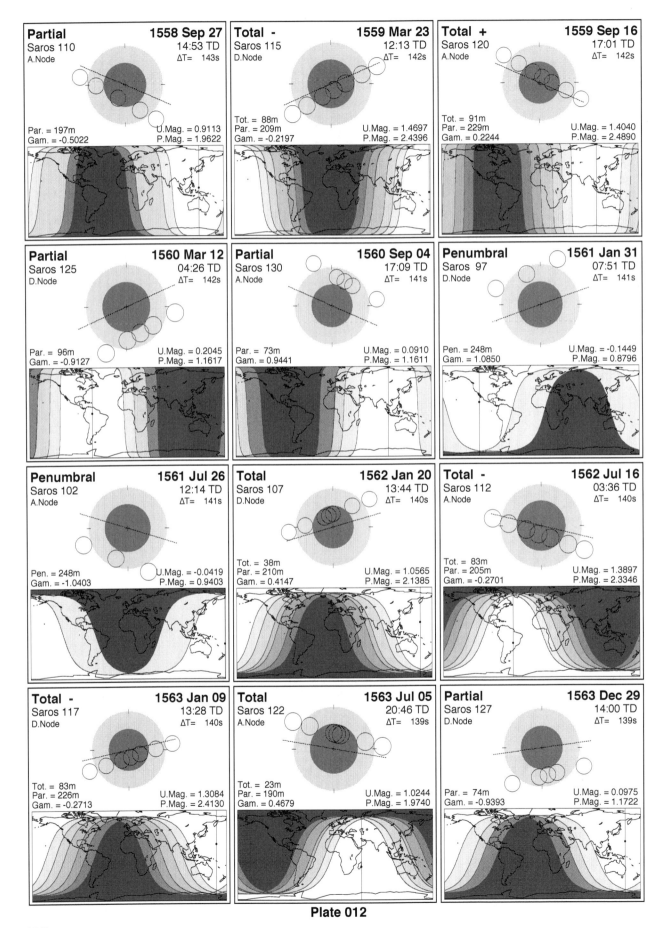

Partial 1558 Sep 27	**Total -** 1559 Mar 23	**Total +** 1559 Sep 16
Saros 110 / 14:53 TD	Saros 115 / 12:13 TD	Saros 120 / 17:01 TD
A.Node / ΔT= 143s	D.Node / ΔT= 142s	A.Node / ΔT= 142s
	Tot. = 88m	Tot. = 91m
Par. = 197m	Par. = 209m	Par. = 229m
Gam. = -0.5022 / U.Mag. = 0.9113 / P.Mag. = 1.9622	Gam. = -0.2197 / U.Mag. = 1.4697 / P.Mag. = 2.4396	Gam. = 0.2244 / U.Mag. = 1.4040 / P.Mag. = 2.4890
Partial 1560 Mar 12	**Partial** 1560 Sep 04	**Penumbral** 1561 Jan 31
Saros 125 / 04:26 TD	Saros 130 / 17:09 TD	Saros 97 / 07:51 TD
D.Node / ΔT= 142s	A.Node / ΔT= 141s	D.Node / ΔT= 141s
Par. = 96m	Par. = 73m	Pen. = 248m
Gam. = -0.9127 / U.Mag. = 0.2045 / P.Mag. = 1.1617	Gam. = 0.9441 / U.Mag. = 0.0910 / P.Mag. = 1.1611	Gam. = 1.0850 / U.Mag. = -0.1449 / P.Mag. = 0.8796
Penumbral 1561 Jul 26	**Total** 1562 Jan 20	**Total -** 1562 Jul 16
Saros 102 / 12:14 TD	Saros 107 / 13:44 TD	Saros 112 / 03:36 TD
A.Node / ΔT= 141s	D.Node / ΔT= 140s	A.Node / ΔT= 140s
	Tot. = 38m	Tot. = 83m
Pen. = 248m	Par. = 210m	Par. = 205m
Gam. = -1.0403 / U.Mag. = -0.0419 / P.Mag. = 0.9403	Gam. = 0.4147 / U.Mag. = 1.0565 / P.Mag. = 2.1385	Gam. = -0.2701 / U.Mag. = 1.3897 / P.Mag. = 2.3346
Total - 1563 Jan 09	**Total** 1563 Jul 05	**Partial** 1563 Dec 29
Saros 117 / 13:28 TD	Saros 122 / 20:46 TD	Saros 127 / 14:00 TD
D.Node / ΔT= 140s	A.Node / ΔT= 139s	D.Node / ΔT= 139s
Tot. = 83m	Tot. = 23m	
Par. = 226m	Par. = 190m	Par. = 74m
Gam. = -0.2713 / U.Mag. = 1.3084 / P.Mag. = 2.4130	Gam. = 0.4679 / U.Mag. = 1.0244 / P.Mag. = 1.9740	Gam. = -0.9393 / U.Mag. = 0.0975 / P.Mag. = 1.1722

Plate 012

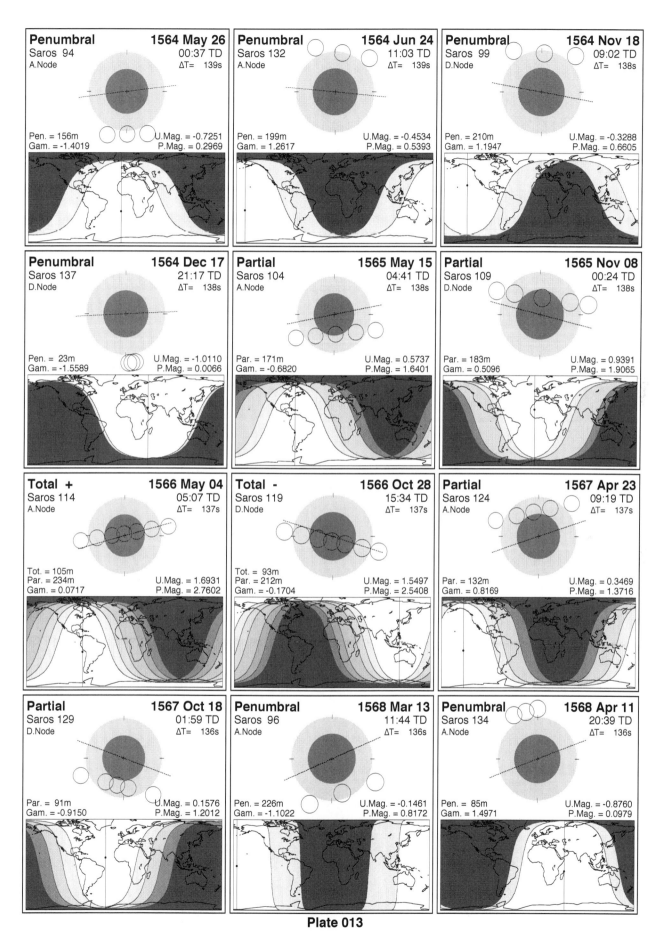

Penumbral	1564 May 26
Saros 94	00:37 TD
A.Node	ΔT= 139s
Pen. = 156m	U.Mag. = -0.7251
Gam. = -1.4019	P.Mag. = 0.2969

Penumbral	1564 Jun 24
Saros 132	11:03 TD
A.Node	ΔT= 139s
Pen. = 199m	U.Mag. = -0.4534
Gam. = 1.2617	P.Mag. = 0.5393

Penumbral	1564 Nov 18
Saros 99	09:02 TD
D.Node	ΔT= 138s
Pen. = 210m	U.Mag. = -0.3288
Gam. = 1.1947	P.Mag. = 0.6605

Penumbral	1564 Dec 17
Saros 137	21:17 TD
D.Node	ΔT= 138s
Pen. = 23m	U.Mag. = -1.0110
Gam. = -1.5589	P.Mag. = 0.0066

Partial	1565 May 15
Saros 104	04:41 TD
A.Node	ΔT= 138s
Par. = 171m	U.Mag. = 0.5737
Gam. = -0.6820	P.Mag. = 1.6401

Partial	1565 Nov 08
Saros 109	00:24 TD
D.Node	ΔT= 138s
Par. = 183m	U.Mag. = 0.9391
Gam. = 0.5096	P.Mag. = 1.9065

Total +	1566 May 04
Saros 114	05:07 TD
A.Node	ΔT= 137s
Tot. = 105m	
Par. = 234m	U.Mag. = 1.6931
Gam. = 0.0717	P.Mag. = 2.7602

Total -	1566 Oct 28
Saros 119	15:34 TD
D.Node	ΔT= 137s
Tot. = 93m	
Par. = 212m	U.Mag. = 1.5497
Gam. = -0.1704	P.Mag. = 2.5408

Partial	1567 Apr 23
Saros 124	09:19 TD
A.Node	ΔT= 137s
Par. = 132m	U.Mag. = 0.3469
Gam. = 0.8169	P.Mag. = 1.3716

Partial	1567 Oct 18
Saros 129	01:59 TD
D.Node	ΔT= 136s
Par. = 91m	U.Mag. = 0.1576
Gam. = -0.9150	P.Mag. = 1.2012

Penumbral	1568 Mar 13
Saros 96	11:44 TD
A.Node	ΔT= 136s
Pen. = 226m	U.Mag. = -0.1461
Gam. = -1.1022	P.Mag. = 0.8172

Penumbral	1568 Apr 11
Saros 134	20:39 TD
A.Node	ΔT= 136s
Pen. = 85m	U.Mag. = -0.8760
Gam. = 1.4971	P.Mag. = 0.0979

Plate 013

109

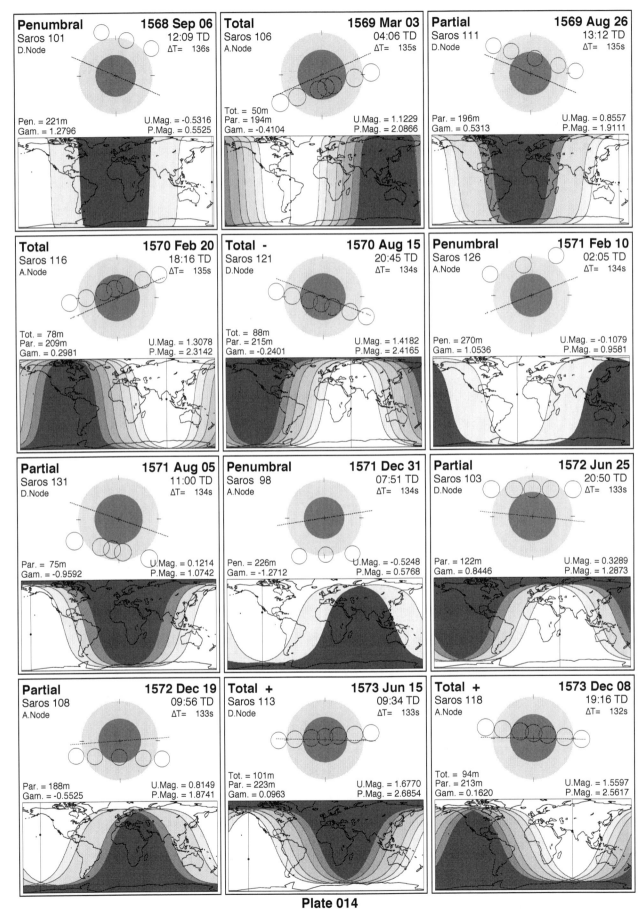

Penumbral   **1568 Sep 06**
Saros 101   12:09 TD
D.Node   ΔT= 136s

Pen. = 221m   U.Mag. = -0.5316
Gam. = 1.2796   P.Mag. = 0.5525

Total   **1569 Mar 03**
Saros 106   04:06 TD
A.Node   ΔT= 135s

Tot. = 50m
Par. = 194m   U.Mag. = 1.1229
Gam. = -0.4104   P.Mag. = 2.0866

Partial   **1569 Aug 26**
Saros 111   13:12 TD
D.Node   ΔT= 135s

Par. = 196m   U.Mag. = 0.8557
Gam. = 0.5313   P.Mag. = 1.9111

Total   **1570 Feb 20**
Saros 116   18:16 TD
A.Node   ΔT= 135s

Tot. = 78m
Par. = 209m   U.Mag. = 1.3078
Gam. = 0.2981   P.Mag. = 2.3142

Total -   **1570 Aug 15**
Saros 121   20:45 TD
D.Node   ΔT= 134s

Tot. = 88m
Par. = 215m   U.Mag. = 1.4182
Gam. = -0.2401   P.Mag. = 2.4165

Penumbral   **1571 Feb 10**
Saros 126   02:05 TD
A.Node   ΔT= 134s

Pen. = 270m   U.Mag. = -0.1079
Gam. = 1.0536   P.Mag. = 0.9581

Partial   **1571 Aug 05**
Saros 131   11:00 TD
D.Node   ΔT= 134s

Par. = 75m   U.Mag. = 0.1214
Gam. = -0.9592   P.Mag. = 1.0742

Penumbral   **1571 Dec 31**
Saros 98   07:51 TD
A.Node   ΔT= 134s

Pen. = 226m   U.Mag. = -0.5248
Gam. = -1.2712   P.Mag. = 0.5768

Partial   **1572 Jun 25**
Saros 103   20:50 TD
D.Node   ΔT= 133s

Par. = 122m   U.Mag. = 0.3289
Gam. = 0.8446   P.Mag. = 1.2873

Partial   **1572 Dec 19**
Saros 108   09:56 TD
A.Node   ΔT= 133s

Par. = 188m   U.Mag. = 0.8149
Gam. = -0.5525   P.Mag. = 1.8741

Total +   **1573 Jun 15**
Saros 113   09:34 TD
D.Node   ΔT= 133s

Tot. = 101m
Par. = 223m   U.Mag. = 1.6770
Gam. = 0.0963   P.Mag. = 2.6854

Total +   **1573 Dec 08**
Saros 118   19:16 TD
A.Node   ΔT= 132s

Tot. = 94m
Par. = 213m   U.Mag. = 1.5597
Gam. = 0.1620   P.Mag. = 2.5617

Plate 014

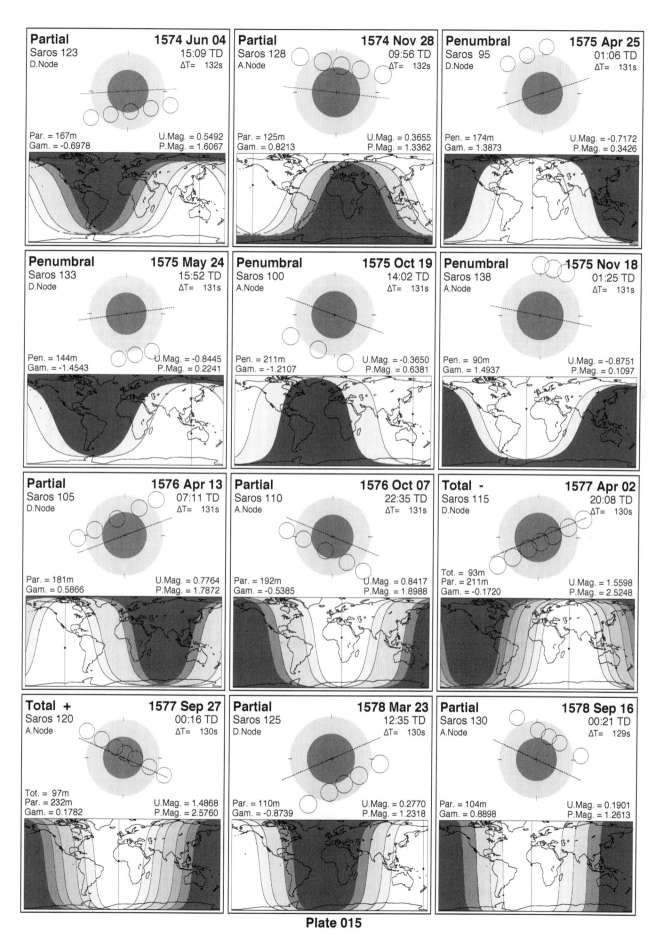

Partial — 1574 Jun 04
Saros 123 — 15:09 TD
D.Node — ΔT= 132s
Par. = 167m — U.Mag. = 0.5492
Gam. = -0.6978 — P.Mag. = 1.6067

Partial — 1574 Nov 28
Saros 128 — 09:56 TD
A.Node — ΔT= 132s
Par. = 125m — U.Mag. = 0.3655
Gam. = 0.8213 — P.Mag. = 1.3362

Penumbral — 1575 Apr 25
Saros 95 — 01:06 TD
D.Node — ΔT= 131s
Pen. = 174m — U.Mag. = -0.7172
Gam. = 1.3873 — P.Mag. = 0.3426

Penumbral — 1575 May 24
Saros 133 — 15:52 TD
D.Node — ΔT= 131s
Pen. = 144m — U.Mag. = -0.8445
Gam. = -1.4543 — P.Mag. = 0.2241

Penumbral — 1575 Oct 19
Saros 100 — 14:02 TD
A.Node — ΔT= 131s
Pen. = 211m — U.Mag. = -0.3650
Gam. = -1.2107 — P.Mag. = 0.6381

Penumbral — 1575 Nov 18
Saros 138 — 01:25 TD
A.Node — ΔT= 131s
Pen. = 90m — U.Mag. = -0.8751
Gam. = 1.4937 — P.Mag. = 0.1097

Partial — 1576 Apr 13
Saros 105 — 07:11 TD
D.Node — ΔT= 131s
Par. = 181m — U.Mag. = 0.7764
Gam. = 0.5866 — P.Mag. = 1.7872

Partial — 1576 Oct 07
Saros 110 — 22:35 TD
A.Node — ΔT= 131s
Par. = 192m — U.Mag. = 0.8417
Gam. = -0.5385 — P.Mag. = 1.8988

Total - — 1577 Apr 02
Saros 115 — 20:08 TD
D.Node — ΔT= 130s
Tot. = 93m
Par. = 211m — U.Mag. = 1.5598
Gam. = -0.1720 — P.Mag. = 2.5248

Total + — 1577 Sep 27
Saros 120 — 00:16 TD
A.Node — ΔT= 130s
Tot. = 97m
Par. = 232m — U.Mag. = 1.4868
Gam. = 0.1782 — P.Mag. = 2.5760

Partial — 1578 Mar 23
Saros 125 — 12:35 TD
D.Node — ΔT= 130s
Par. = 110m — U.Mag. = 0.2770
Gam. = -0.8739 — P.Mag. = 1.2318

Partial — 1578 Sep 16
Saros 130 — 00:21 TD
A.Node — ΔT= 129s
Par. = 104m — U.Mag. = 0.1901
Gam. = 0.8898 — P.Mag. = 1.2613

Plate 015

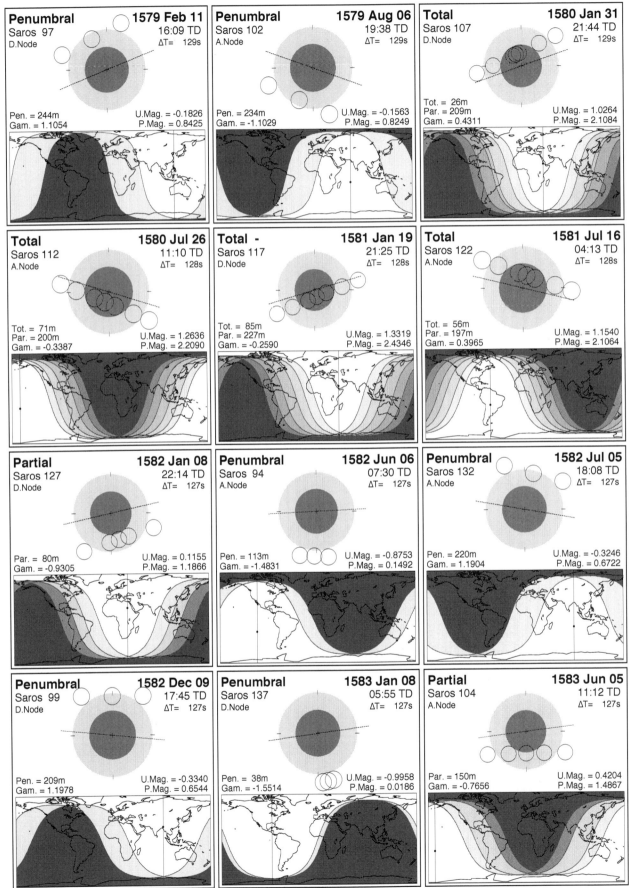

Penumbral   **1579 Feb 11**
Saros 97   16:09 TD
D.Node   ΔT= 129s

Pen. = 244m   U.Mag. = -0.1826
Gam. = 1.1054   P.Mag. = 0.8425

Penumbral   **1579 Aug 06**
Saros 102   19:38 TD
A.Node   ΔT= 129s

Pen. = 234m   U.Mag. = -0.1563
Gam. = -1.1029   P.Mag. = 0.8249

Total   **1580 Jan 31**
Saros 107   21:44 TD
D.Node   ΔT= 129s

Tot. = 26m
Par. = 209m   U.Mag. = 1.0264
Gam. = 0.4311   P.Mag. = 2.1084

Total   **1580 Jul 26**
Saros 112   11:10 TD
A.Node   ΔT= 128s

Tot. = 71m
Par. = 200m   U.Mag. = 1.2636
Gam. = -0.3387   P.Mag. = 2.2090

Total -   **1581 Jan 19**
Saros 117   21:25 TD
D.Node   ΔT= 128s

Tot. = 85m
Par. = 227m   U.Mag. = 1.3319
Gam. = -0.2590   P.Mag. = 2.4346

Total   **1581 Jul 16**
Saros 122   04:13 TD
A.Node   ΔT= 128s

Tot. = 56m
Par. = 197m   U.Mag. = 1.1540
Gam. = 0.3965   P.Mag. = 2.1064

Partial   **1582 Jan 08**
Saros 127   22:14 TD
D.Node   ΔT= 127s

Par. = 80m   U.Mag. = 0.1155
Gam. = -0.9305   P.Mag. = 1.1866

Penumbral   **1582 Jun 06**
Saros 94   07:30 TD
A.Node   ΔT= 127s

Pen. = 113m   U.Mag. = -0.8753
Gam. = -1.4831   P.Mag. = 0.1492

Penumbral   **1582 Jul 05**
Saros 132   18:08 TD
A.Node   ΔT= 127s

Pen. = 220m   U.Mag. = -0.3246
Gam. = 1.1904   P.Mag. = 0.6722

Penumbral   **1582 Dec 09**
Saros 99   17:45 TD
D.Node   ΔT= 127s

Pen. = 209m   U.Mag. = -0.3340
Gam. = 1.1978   P.Mag. = 0.6544

Penumbral   **1583 Jan 08**
Saros 137   05:55 TD
D.Node   ΔT= 127s

Pen. = 38m   U.Mag. = -0.9958
Gam. = -1.5514   P.Mag. = 0.0186

Partial   **1583 Jun 05**
Saros 104   11:12 TD
A.Node   ΔT= 127s

Par. = 150m   U.Mag. = 0.4204
Gam. = -0.7656   P.Mag. = 1.4867

Plate 016

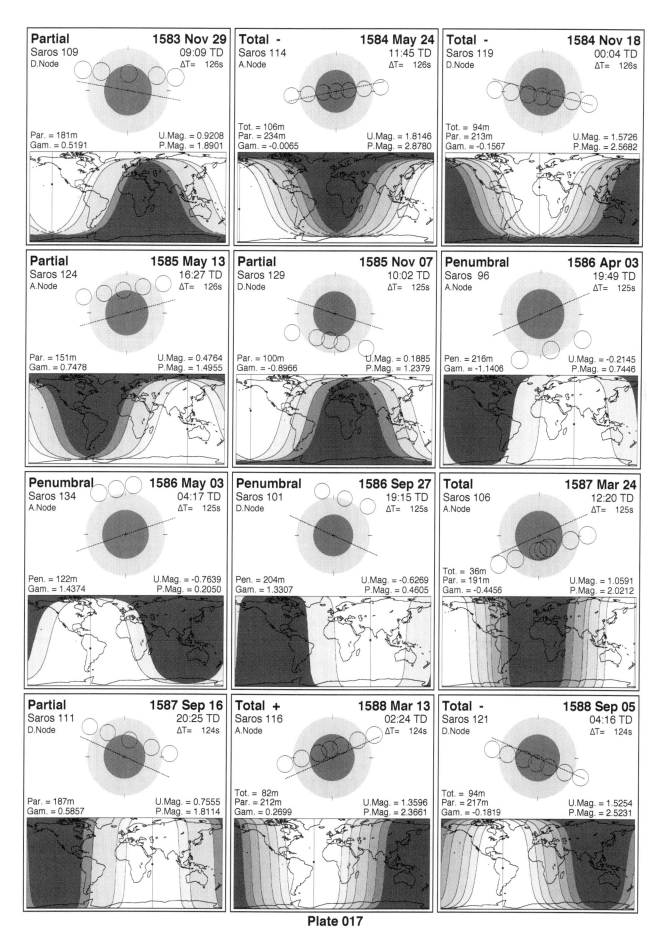

Partial   **1583 Nov 29**
Saros 109   09:09 TD
D.Node   ΔT= 126s
Par. = 181m   U.Mag. = 0.9208
Gam. = 0.5191   P.Mag. = 1.8901

Total -   **1584 May 24**
Saros 114   11:45 TD
A.Node   ΔT= 126s
Tot. = 106m
Par. = 234m   U.Mag. = 1.8146
Gam. = -0.0065   P.Mag. = 2.8780

Total -   **1584 Nov 18**
Saros 119   00:04 TD
D.Node   ΔT= 126s
Tot. = 94m
Par. = 213m   U.Mag. = 1.5726
Gam. = -0.1567   P.Mag. = 2.5682

Partial   **1585 May 13**
Saros 124   16:27 TD
A.Node   ΔT= 126s
Par. = 151m   U.Mag. = 0.4764
Gam. = 0.7478   P.Mag. = 1.4955

Partial   **1585 Nov 07**
Saros 129   10:02 TD
D.Node   ΔT= 125s
Par. = 100m   U.Mag. = 0.1885
Gam. = -0.8966   P.Mag. = 1.2379

Penumbral   **1586 Apr 03**
Saros 96   19:49 TD
A.Node   ΔT= 125s
Pen. = 216m   U.Mag. = -0.2145
Gam. = -1.1406   P.Mag. = 0.7446

Penumbral   **1586 May 03**
Saros 134   04:17 TD
A.Node   ΔT= 125s
Pen. = 122m   U.Mag. = -0.7639
Gam. = 1.4374   P.Mag. = 0.2050

Penumbral   **1586 Sep 27**
Saros 101   19:15 TD
D.Node   ΔT= 125s
Pen. = 204m   U.Mag. = -0.6269
Gam. = 1.3307   P.Mag. = 0.4605

Total   **1587 Mar 24**
Saros 106   12:20 TD
A.Node   ΔT= 125s
Tot. = 36m
Par. = 191m   U.Mag. = 1.0591
Gam. = -0.4456   P.Mag. = 2.0212

Partial   **1587 Sep 16**
Saros 111   20:25 TD
D.Node   ΔT= 124s
Par. = 187m   U.Mag. = 0.7555
Gam. = 0.5857   P.Mag. = 1.8114

Total +   **1588 Mar 13**
Saros 116   02:24 TD
A.Node   ΔT= 124s
Tot. = 82m
Par. = 212m   U.Mag. = 1.3596
Gam. = 0.2699   P.Mag. = 2.3661

Total -   **1588 Sep 05**
Saros 121   04:16 TD
D.Node   ΔT= 124s
Tot. = 94m
Par. = 217m   U.Mag. = 1.5254
Gam. = -0.1819   P.Mag. = 2.5231

Plate 017

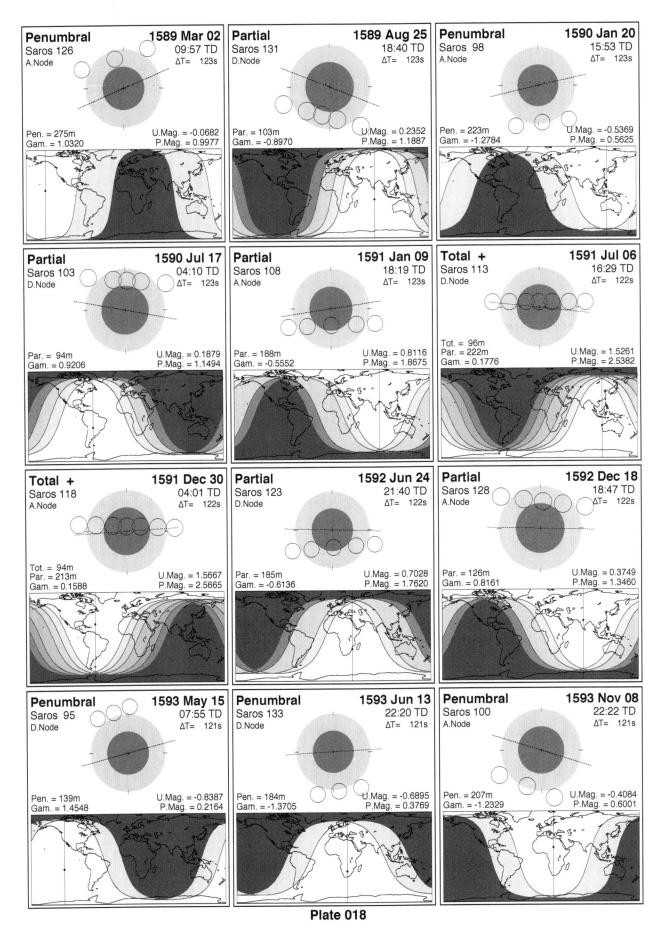

Penumbral   **1589 Mar 02**
Saros 126   09:57 TD
A.Node   ΔT= 123s

Pen. = 275m   U.Mag. = -0.0682
Gam. = 1.0320   P.Mag. = 0.9977

Partial   **1589 Aug 25**
Saros 131   18:40 TD
D.Node   ΔT= 123s

Par. = 103m   U.Mag. = 0.2352
Gam. = -0.8970   P.Mag. = 1.1887

Penumbral   **1590 Jan 20**
Saros 98   15:53 TD
A.Node   ΔT= 123s

Pen. = 223m   U.Mag. = -0.5369
Gam. = -1.2784   P.Mag. = 0.5625

Partial   **1590 Jul 17**
Saros 103   04:10 TD
D.Node   ΔT= 123s

Par. = 94m   U.Mag. = 0.1879
Gam. = 0.9206   P.Mag. = 1.1494

Partial   **1591 Jan 09**
Saros 108   18:19 TD
A.Node   ΔT= 123s

Par. = 188m   U.Mag. = 0.8116
Gam. = -0.5552   P.Mag. = 1.8675

Total +   **1591 Jul 06**
Saros 113   16:29 TD
D.Node   ΔT= 122s

Tot. = 96m
Par. = 222m   U.Mag. = 1.5261
Gam. = 0.1776   P.Mag. = 2.5382

Total +   **1591 Dec 30**
Saros 118   04:01 TD
A.Node   ΔT= 122s

Tot. = 94m
Par. = 213m   U.Mag. = 1.5667
Gam. = 0.1588   P.Mag. = 2.5665

Partial   **1592 Jun 24**
Saros 123   21:40 TD
D.Node   ΔT= 122s

Par. = 185m   U.Mag. = 0.7028
Gam. = -0.6136   P.Mag. = 1.7620

Partial   **1592 Dec 18**
Saros 128   18:47 TD
A.Node   ΔT= 122s

Par. = 126m   U.Mag. = 0.3749
Gam. = 0.8161   P.Mag. = 1.3460

Penumbral   **1593 May 15**
Saros 95   07:55 TD
D.Node   ΔT= 121s

Pen. = 139m   U.Mag. = -0.8387
Gam. = 1.4548   P.Mag. = 0.2164

Penumbral   **1593 Jun 13**
Saros 133   22:20 TD
D.Node   ΔT= 121s

Pen. = 184m   U.Mag. = -0.6895
Gam. = -1.3705   P.Mag. = 0.3769

Penumbral   **1593 Nov 08**
Saros 100   22:22 TD
A.Node   ΔT= 121s

Pen. = 207m   U.Mag. = -0.4084
Gam. = -1.2329   P.Mag. = 0.6001

Plate 018

114

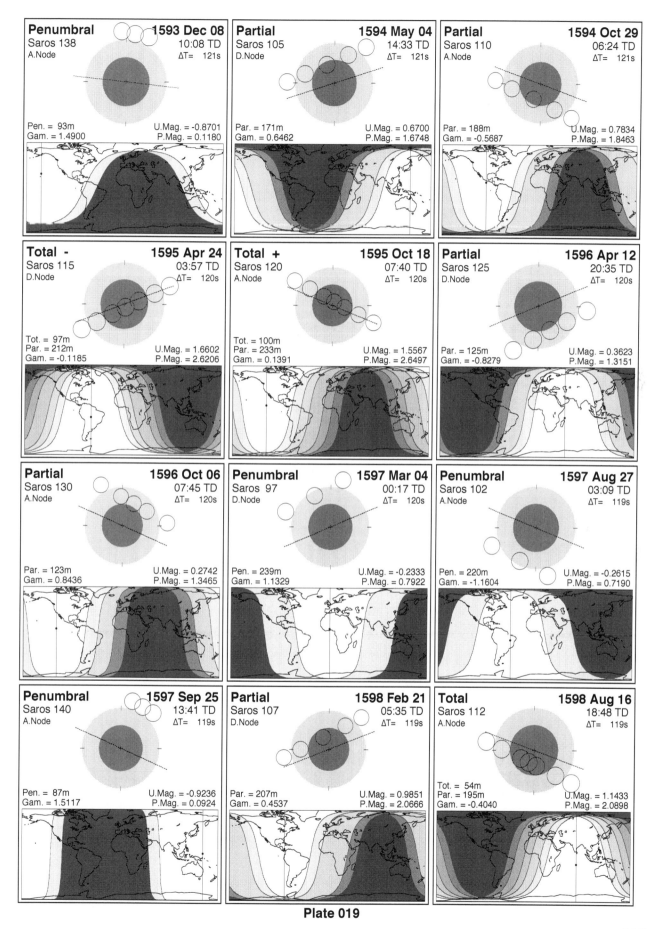

Penumbral   **1593 Dec 08**
Saros 138   10:08 TD
A.Node   ΔT= 121s

Pen. = 93m   U.Mag. = -0.8701
Gam. = 1.4900   P.Mag. = 0.1180

Partial   **1594 May 04**
Saros 105   14:33 TD
D.Node   ΔT= 121s

Par. = 171m   U.Mag. = 0.6700
Gam. = 0.6462   P.Mag. = 1.6748

Partial   **1594 Oct 29**
Saros 110   06:24 TD
A.Node   ΔT= 121s

Par. = 188m   U.Mag. = 0.7834
Gam. = -0.5687   P.Mag. = 1.8463

Total -   **1595 Apr 24**
Saros 115   03:57 TD
D.Node   ΔT= 120s

Tot. = 97m
Par. = 212m   U.Mag. = 1.6602
Gam. = -0.1185   P.Mag. = 2.6206

Total +   **1595 Oct 18**
Saros 120   07:40 TD
A.Node   ΔT= 120s

Tot. = 100m
Par. = 233m   U.Mag. = 1.5567
Gam. = 0.1391   P.Mag. = 2.6497

Partial   **1596 Apr 12**
Saros 125   20:35 TD
D.Node   ΔT= 120s

Par. = 125m   U.Mag. = 0.3623
Gam. = -0.8279   P.Mag. = 1.3151

Partial   **1596 Oct 06**
Saros 130   07:45 TD
A.Node   ΔT= 120s

Par. = 123m   U.Mag. = 0.2742
Gam. = 0.8436   P.Mag. = 1.3465

Penumbral   **1597 Mar 04**
Saros 97   00:17 TD
D.Node   ΔT= 120s

Pen. = 239m   U.Mag. = -0.2333
Gam. = 1.1329   P.Mag. = 0.7922

Penumbral   **1597 Aug 27**
Saros 102   03:09 TD
A.Node   ΔT= 119s

Pen. = 220m   U.Mag. = -0.2615
Gam. = -1.1604   P.Mag. = 0.7190

Penumbral   **1597 Sep 25**
Saros 140   13:41 TD
A.Node   ΔT= 119s

Pen. = 87m   U.Mag. = -0.9236
Gam. = 1.5117   P.Mag. = 0.0924

Partial   **1598 Feb 21**
Saros 107   05:35 TD
D.Node   ΔT= 119s

Par. = 207m   U.Mag. = 0.9851
Gam. = 0.4537   P.Mag. = 2.0666

Total   **1598 Aug 16**
Saros 112   18:48 TD
A.Node   ΔT= 119s

Tot. = 54m
Par. = 195m   U.Mag. = 1.1433
Gam. = -0.4040   P.Mag. = 2.0898

Plate 019

115

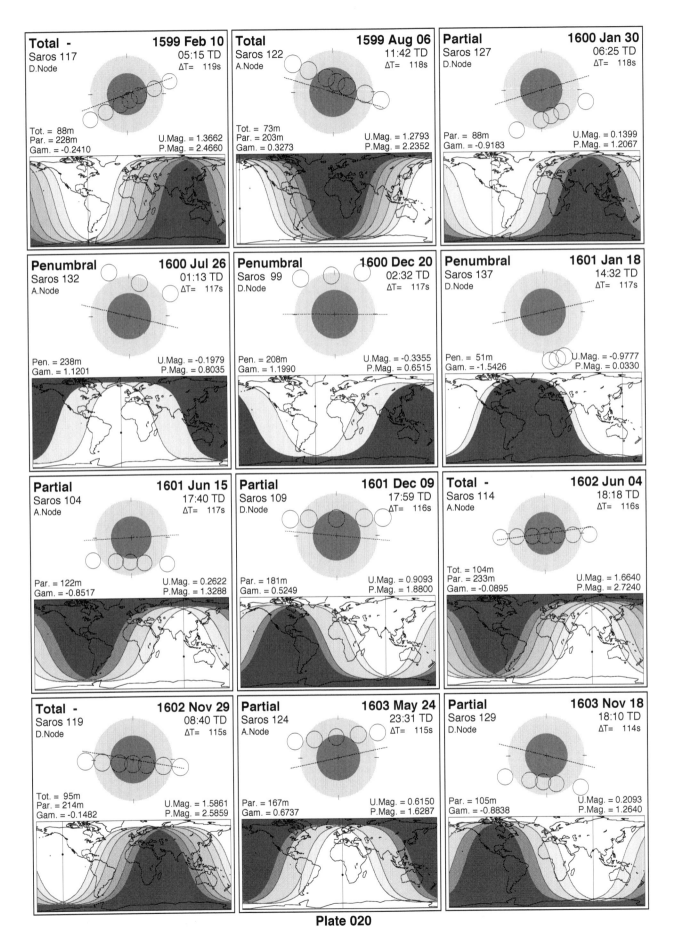

Total - **1599 Feb 10**	
Saros 117 05:15 TD	
D.Node ΔT= 119s	
Tot. = 88m	
Par. = 228m U.Mag. = 1.3662	
Gam. = -0.2410 P.Mag. = 2.4660	

Total **1599 Aug 06**	
Saros 122 11:42 TD	
A.Node ΔT= 118s	
Tot. = 73m	
Par. = 203m U.Mag. = 1.2793	
Gam. = 0.3273 P.Mag. = 2.2352	

Partial **1600 Jan 30**	
Saros 127 06:25 TD	
D.Node ΔT= 118s	
Par. = 88m U.Mag. = 0.1399	
Gam. = -0.9183 P.Mag. = 1.2067	

Penumbral **1600 Jul 26**	
Saros 132 01:13 TD	
A.Node ΔT= 117s	
Pen. = 238m U.Mag. = -0.1979	
Gam. = 1.1201 P.Mag. = 0.8035	

Penumbral **1600 Dec 20**	
Saros 99 02:32 TD	
D.Node ΔT= 117s	
Pen. = 208m U.Mag. = -0.3355	
Gam. = 1.1990 P.Mag. = 0.6515	

Penumbral **1601 Jan 18**	
Saros 137 14:32 TD	
D.Node ΔT= 117s	
Pen. = 51m U.Mag. = -0.9777	
Gam. = -1.5426 P.Mag. = 0.0330	

Partial **1601 Jun 15**	
Saros 104 17:40 TD	
A.Node ΔT= 117s	
Par. = 122m U.Mag. = 0.2622	
Gam. = -0.8517 P.Mag. = 1.3288	

Partial **1601 Dec 09**	
Saros 109 17:59 TD	
D.Node ΔT= 116s	
Par. = 181m U.Mag. = 0.9093	
Gam. = 0.5249 P.Mag. = 1.8800	

Total - **1602 Jun 04**	
Saros 114 18:18 TD	
A.Node ΔT= 116s	
Tot. = 104m	
Par. = 233m U.Mag. = 1.6640	
Gam. = -0.0895 P.Mag. = 2.7240	

Total - **1602 Nov 29**	
Saros 119 08:40 TD	
D.Node ΔT= 115s	
Tot. = 95m	
Par. = 214m U.Mag. = 1.5861	
Gam. = -0.1482 P.Mag. = 2.5859	

Partial **1603 May 24**	
Saros 124 23:31 TD	
A.Node ΔT= 115s	
Par. = 167m U.Mag. = 0.6150	
Gam. = 0.6737 P.Mag. = 1.6287	

Partial **1603 Nov 18**	
Saros 129 18:10 TD	
D.Node ΔT= 114s	
Par. = 105m U.Mag. = 0.2093	
Gam. = -0.8838 P.Mag. = 1.2640	

Plate 020

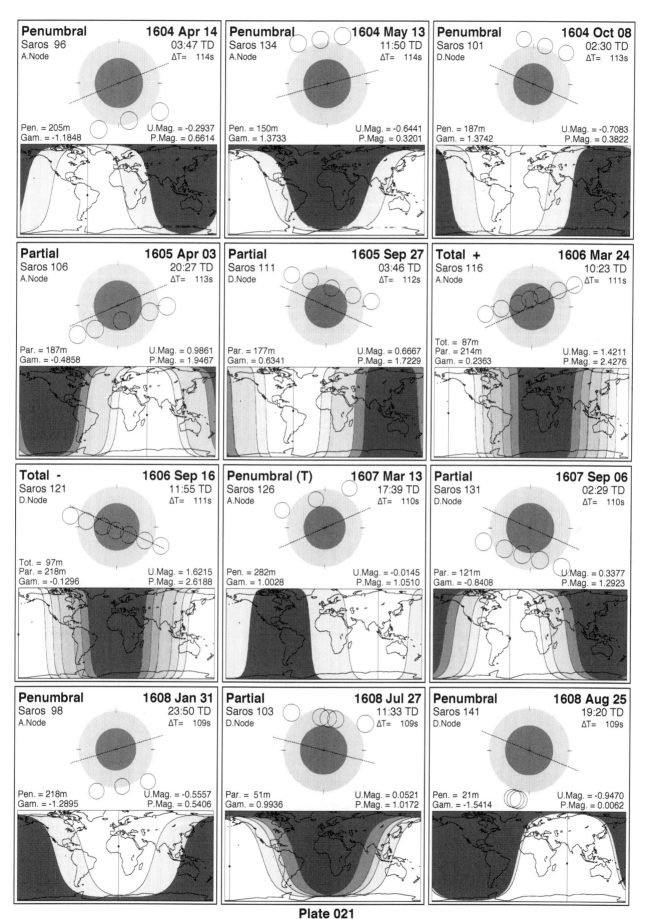

Penumbral	**1604 Apr 14**
Saros 96	03:47 TD
A.Node	ΔT= 114s
Pen. = 205m	U.Mag. = -0.2937
Gam. = -1.1848	P.Mag. = 0.6614

Penumbral	**1604 May 13**
Saros 134	11:50 TD
A.Node	ΔT= 114s
Pen. = 150m	U.Mag. = -0.6441
Gam. = 1.3733	P.Mag. = 0.3201

Penumbral	**1604 Oct 08**
Saros 101	02:30 TD
D.Node	ΔT= 113s
Pen. = 187m	U.Mag. = -0.7083
Gam. = 1.3742	P.Mag. = 0.3822

Partial	**1605 Apr 03**
Saros 106	20:27 TD
A.Node	ΔT= 113s
Par. = 187m	U.Mag. = 0.9861
Gam. = -0.4858	P.Mag. = 1.9467

Partial	**1605 Sep 27**
Saros 111	03:46 TD
D.Node	ΔT= 112s
Par. = 177m	U.Mag. = 0.6667
Gam. = 0.6341	P.Mag. = 1.7229

Total +	**1606 Mar 24**
Saros 116	10:23 TD
A.Node	ΔT= 111s
Tot. = 87m	
Par. = 214m	U.Mag. = 1.4211
Gam. = 0.2363	P.Mag. = 2.4276

Total -	**1606 Sep 16**
Saros 121	11:55 TD
D.Node	ΔT= 111s
Tot. = 97m	
Par. = 218m	U.Mag. = 1.6215
Gam. = -0.1296	P.Mag. = 2.6188

Penumbral (T)	**1607 Mar 13**
Saros 126	17:39 TD
A.Node	ΔT= 110s
Pen. = 282m	U.Mag. = -0.0145
Gam. = 1.0028	P.Mag. = 1.0510

Partial	**1607 Sep 06**
Saros 131	02:29 TD
D.Node	ΔT= 110s
Par. = 121m	U.Mag. = 0.3377
Gam. = -0.8408	P.Mag. = 1.2923

Penumbral	**1608 Jan 31**
Saros 98	23:50 TD
A.Node	ΔT= 109s
Pen. = 218m	U.Mag. = -0.5557
Gam. = -1.2895	P.Mag. = 0.5406

Partial	**1608 Jul 27**
Saros 103	11:33 TD
D.Node	ΔT= 109s
Par. = 51m	U.Mag. = 0.0521
Gam. = 0.9936	P.Mag. = 1.0172

Penumbral	**1608 Aug 25**
Saros 141	19:20 TD
D.Node	ΔT= 109s
Pen. = 21m	U.Mag. = -0.9470
Gam. = -1.5414	P.Mag. = 0.0062

Plate 021

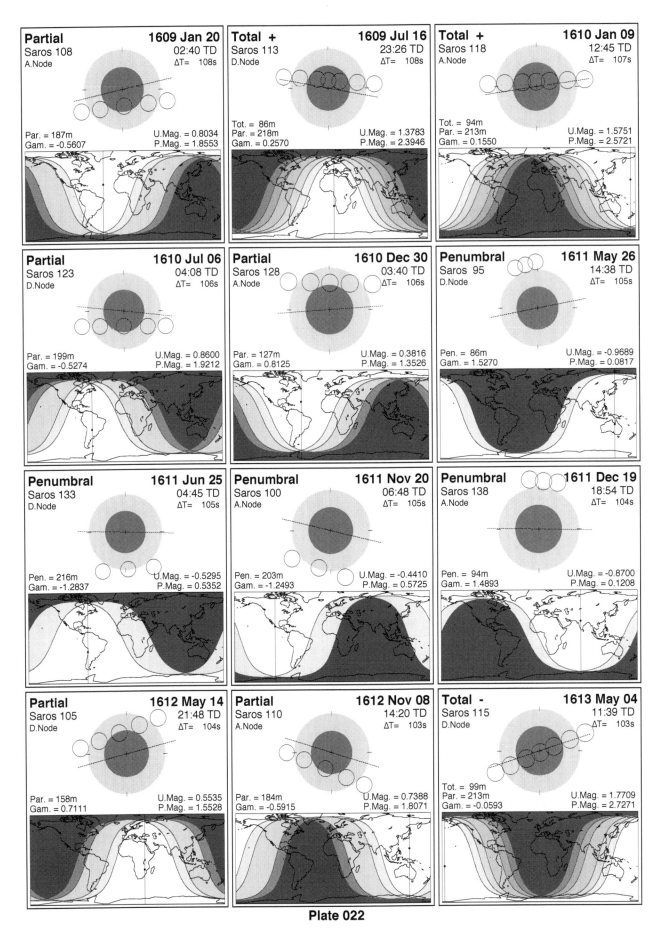

Partial **1609 Jan 20** Saros 108 02:40 TD A.Node ΔT= 108s Par. = 187m U.Mag. = 0.8034 Gam. = -0.5607 P.Mag. = 1.8553	**Total +** **1609 Jul 16** Saros 113 23:26 TD D.Node ΔT= 108s Tot. = 86m Par. = 218m U.Mag. = 1.3783 Gam. = 0.2570 P.Mag. = 2.3946	**Total +** **1610 Jan 09** Saros 118 12:45 TD A.Node ΔT= 107s Tot. = 94m Par. = 213m U.Mag. = 1.5751 Gam. = 0.1550 P.Mag. = 2.5721
Partial **1610 Jul 06** Saros 123 04:08 TD D.Node ΔT= 106s Par. = 199m U.Mag. = 0.8600 Gam. = -0.5274 P.Mag. = 1.9212	**Partial** **1610 Dec 30** Saros 128 03:40 TD A.Node ΔT= 106s Par. = 127m U.Mag. = 0.3816 Gam. = 0.8125 P.Mag. = 1.3526	**Penumbral** **1611 May 26** Saros 95 14:38 TD D.Node ΔT= 105s Pen. = 86m U.Mag. = -0.9689 Gam. = 1.5270 P.Mag. = 0.0817
Penumbral **1611 Jun 25** Saros 133 04:45 TD D.Node ΔT= 105s Pen. = 216m U.Mag. = -0.5295 Gam. = -1.2837 P.Mag. = 0.5352	**Penumbral** **1611 Nov 20** Saros 100 06:48 TD A.Node ΔT= 105s Pen. = 203m U.Mag. = -0.4410 Gam. = -1.2493 P.Mag. = 0.5725	**Penumbral** **1611 Dec 19** Saros 138 18:54 TD A.Node ΔT= 104s Pen. = 94m U.Mag. = -0.8700 Gam. = 1.4893 P.Mag. = 0.1208
Partial **1612 May 14** Saros 105 21:48 TD D.Node ΔT= 104s Par. = 158m U.Mag. = 0.5535 Gam. = 0.7111 P.Mag. = 1.5528	**Partial** **1612 Nov 08** Saros 110 14:20 TD A.Node ΔT= 103s Par. = 184m U.Mag. = 0.7388 Gam. = -0.5915 P.Mag. = 1.8071	**Total -** **1613 May 04** Saros 115 11:39 TD D.Node ΔT= 103s Tot. = 99m Par. = 213m U.Mag. = 1.7709 Gam. = -0.0593 P.Mag. = 2.7271

Plate 022

118

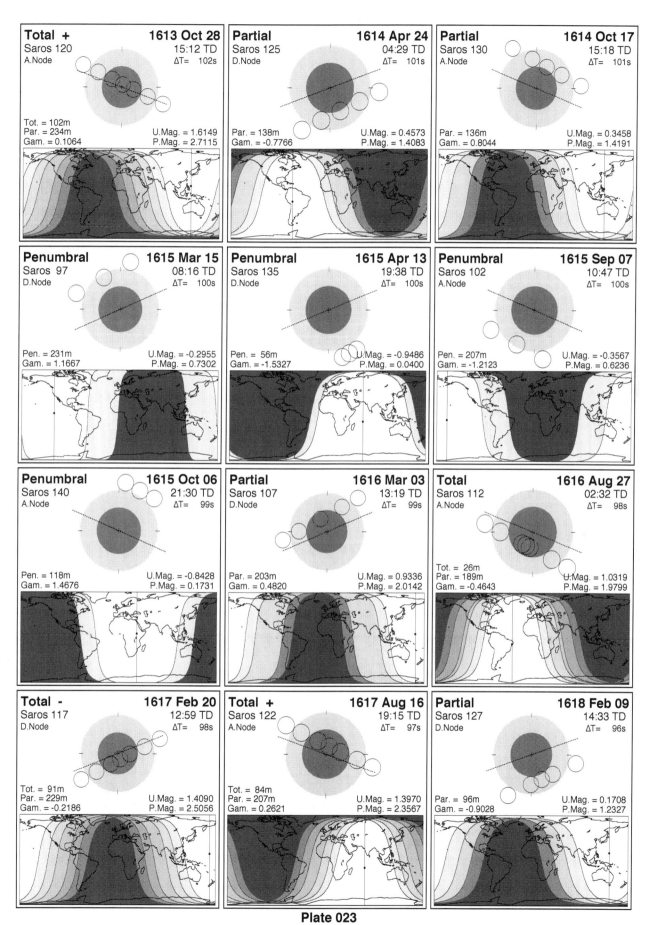

Total +   **1613 Oct 28**
Saros 120   15:12 TD
A.Node   ΔT= 102s

Tot. = 102m
Par. = 234m
Gam. = 0.1064   U.Mag. = 1.6149   P.Mag. = 2.7115

Partial   **1614 Apr 24**
Saros 125   04:29 TD
D.Node   ΔT= 101s

Par. = 138m
Gam. = -0.7766   U.Mag. = 0.4573   P.Mag. = 1.4083

Partial   **1614 Oct 17**
Saros 130   15:18 TD
A.Node   ΔT= 101s

Par. = 136m
Gam. = 0.8044   U.Mag. = 0.3458   P.Mag. = 1.4191

Penumbral   **1615 Mar 15**
Saros 97   08:16 TD
D.Node   ΔT= 100s

Pen. = 231m
Gam. = 1.1667   U.Mag. = -0.2955   P.Mag. = 0.7302

Penumbral   **1615 Apr 13**
Saros 135   19:38 TD
D.Node   ΔT= 100s

Pen. = 56m
Gam. = -1.5327   U.Mag. = -0.9486   P.Mag. = 0.0400

Penumbral   **1615 Sep 07**
Saros 102   10:47 TD
A.Node   ΔT= 100s

Pen. = 207m
Gam. = -1.2123   U.Mag. = -0.3567   P.Mag. = 0.6236

Penumbral   **1615 Oct 06**
Saros 140   21:30 TD
A.Node   ΔT= 99s

Pen. = 118m
Gam. = 1.4676   U.Mag. = -0.8428   P.Mag. = 0.1731

Partial   **1616 Mar 03**
Saros 107   13:19 TD
D.Node   ΔT= 99s

Par. = 203m
Gam. = 0.4820   U.Mag. = 0.9336   P.Mag. = 2.0142

Total   **1616 Aug 27**
Saros 112   02:32 TD
A.Node   ΔT= 98s

Tot. = 26m
Par. = 189m
Gam. = -0.4643   U.Mag. = 1.0319   P.Mag. = 1.9799

Total -   **1617 Feb 20**
Saros 117   12:59 TD
D.Node   ΔT= 98s

Tot. = 91m
Par. = 229m
Gam. = -0.2186   U.Mag. = 1.4090   P.Mag. = 2.5056

Total +   **1617 Aug 16**
Saros 122   19:15 TD
A.Node   ΔT= 97s

Tot. = 84m
Par. = 207m
Gam. = 0.2621   U.Mag. = 1.3970   P.Mag. = 2.3567

Partial   **1618 Feb 09**
Saros 127   14:33 TD
D.Node   ΔT= 96s

Par. = 96m
Gam. = -0.9028   U.Mag. = 0.1708   P.Mag. = 1.2327

Plate 023

119

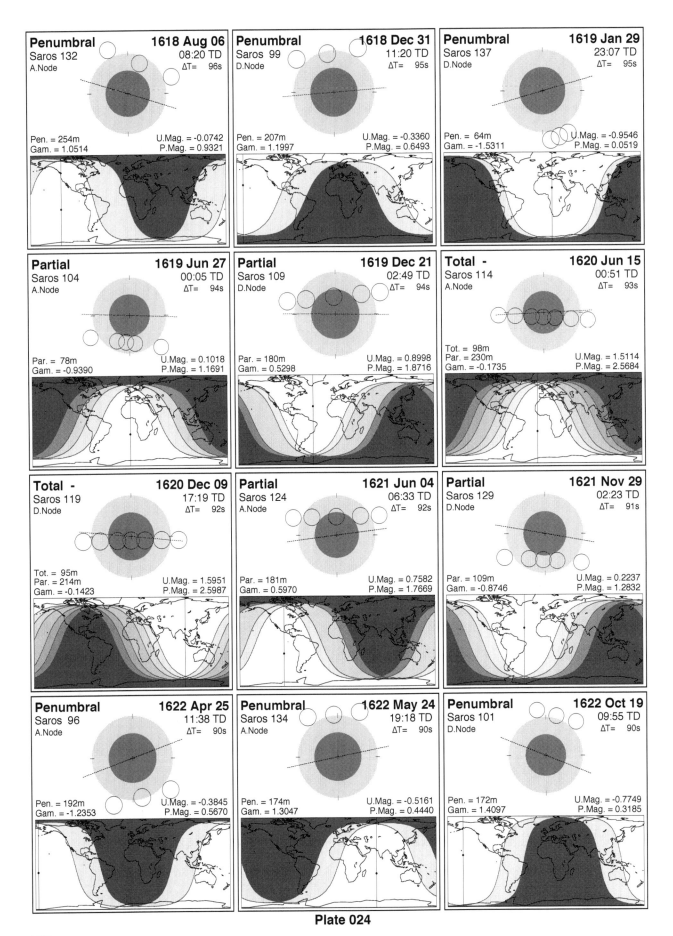

Penumbral   **1618 Aug 06**
Saros 132   08:20 TD
A.Node   ΔT= 96s
Pen. = 254m   U.Mag. = -0.0742
Gam. = 1.0514   P.Mag. = 0.9321

Penumbral   **1618 Dec 31**
Saros 99   11:20 TD
D.Node   ΔT= 95s
Pen. = 207m   U.Mag. = -0.3360
Gam. = 1.1997   P.Mag. = 0.6493

Penumbral   **1619 Jan 29**
Saros 137   23:07 TD
D.Node   ΔT= 95s
Pen. = 64m   U.Mag. = -0.9546
Gam. = -1.5311   P.Mag. = 0.0519

Partial   **1619 Jun 27**
Saros 104   00:05 TD
A.Node   ΔT= 94s
Par. = 78m   U.Mag. = 0.1018
Gam. = -0.9390   P.Mag. = 1.1691

Partial   **1619 Dec 21**
Saros 109   02:49 TD
D.Node   ΔT= 94s
Par. = 180m   U.Mag. = 0.8998
Gam. = 0.5298   P.Mag. = 1.8716

Total -   **1620 Jun 15**
Saros 114   00:51 TD
A.Node   ΔT= 93s
Tot. = 98m
Par. = 230m   U.Mag. = 1.5114
Gam. = -0.1735   P.Mag. = 2.5684

Total -   **1620 Dec 09**
Saros 119   17:19 TD
D.Node   ΔT= 92s
Tot. = 95m
Par. = 214m   U.Mag. = 1.5951
Gam. = -0.1423   P.Mag. = 2.5987

Partial   **1621 Jun 04**
Saros 124   06:33 TD
A.Node   ΔT= 92s
Par. = 181m   U.Mag. = 0.7582
Gam. = 0.5970   P.Mag. = 1.7669

Partial   **1621 Nov 29**
Saros 129   02:23 TD
D.Node   ΔT= 91s
Par. = 109m   U.Mag. = 0.2237
Gam. = -0.8746   P.Mag. = 1.2832

Penumbral   **1622 Apr 25**
Saros 96   11:38 TD
A.Node   ΔT= 90s
Pen. = 192m   U.Mag. = -0.3845
Gam. = -1.2353   P.Mag. = 0.5670

Penumbral   **1622 May 24**
Saros 134   19:18 TD
A.Node   ΔT= 90s
Pen. = 174m   U.Mag. = -0.5161
Gam. = 1.3047   P.Mag. = 0.4440

Penumbral   **1622 Oct 19**
Saros 101   09:55 TD
D.Node   ΔT= 90s
Pen. = 172m   U.Mag. = -0.7749
Gam. = 1.4097   P.Mag. = 0.3185

Plate 024

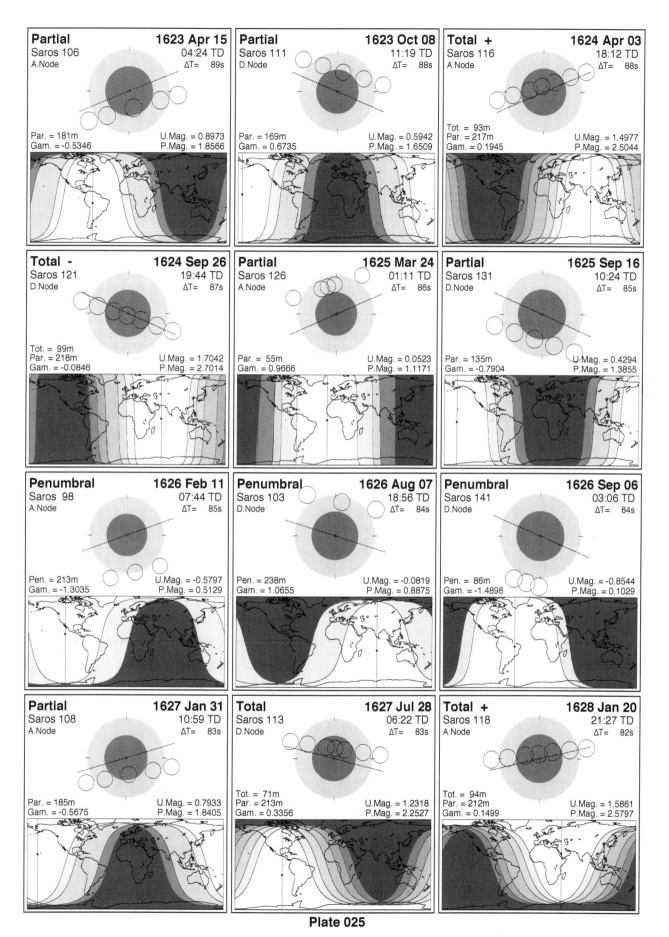

Partial — **1623 Apr 15**
Saros 106 — 04:24 TD
A.Node — ΔT= 89s
Par. = 181m
Gam. = -0.5346
U.Mag. = 0.8973
P.Mag. = 1.8566

Partial — **1623 Oct 08**
Saros 111 — 11:19 TD
D.Node — ΔT= 88s
Par. = 169m
Gam. = 0.6735
U.Mag. = 0.5942
P.Mag. = 1.6509

Total + — **1624 Apr 03**
Saros 116 — 18:12 TD
A.Node — ΔT= 88s
Tot. = 93m
Par. = 217m
Gam. = 0.1945
U.Mag. = 1.4977
P.Mag. = 2.5044

Total - — **1624 Sep 26**
Saros 121 — 19:44 TD
D.Node — ΔT= 87s
Tot. = 99m
Par. = 218m
Gam. = -0.0846
U.Mag. = 1.7042
P.Mag. = 2.7014

Partial — **1625 Mar 24**
Saros 126 — 01:11 TD
A.Node — ΔT= 86s
Par. = 55m
Gam. = 0.9666
U.Mag. = 0.0523
P.Mag. = 1.1171

Partial — **1625 Sep 16**
Saros 131 — 10:24 TD
D.Node — ΔT= 85s
Par. = 135m
Gam. = -0.7904
U.Mag. = 0.4294
P.Mag. = 1.3855

Penumbral — **1626 Feb 11**
Saros 98 — 07:44 TD
A.Node — ΔT= 85s
Pen. = 213m
Gam. = -1.3035
U.Mag. = -0.5797
P.Mag. = 0.5129

Penumbral — **1626 Aug 07**
Saros 103 — 18:56 TD
D.Node — ΔT= 84s
Pen. = 238m
Gam. = 1.0655
U.Mag. = -0.0819
P.Mag. = 0.8875

Penumbral — **1626 Sep 06**
Saros 141 — 03:06 TD
D.Node — ΔT= 84s
Pen. = 86m
Gam. = -1.4898
U.Mag. = -0.8544
P.Mag. = 0.1029

Partial — **1627 Jan 31**
Saros 108 — 10:59 TD
A.Node — ΔT= 83s
Par. = 185m
Gam. = -0.5675
U.Mag. = 0.7933
P.Mag. = 1.8405

Total — **1627 Jul 28**
Saros 113 — 06:22 TD
D.Node — ΔT= 83s
Tot. = 71m
Par. = 213m
Gam. = 0.3356
U.Mag. = 1.2318
P.Mag. = 2.2527

Total + — **1628 Jan 20**
Saros 118 — 21:27 TD
A.Node — ΔT= 82s
Tot. = 94m
Par. = 212m
Gam. = 0.1499
U.Mag. = 1.5861
P.Mag. = 2.5797

Plate 025

121

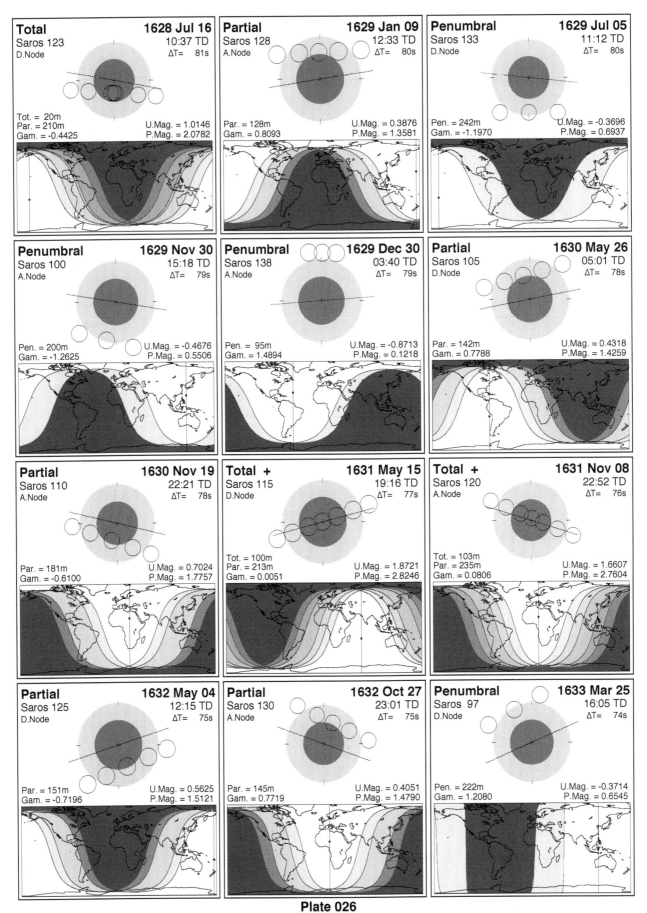

Total 1628 Jul 16	
Saros 123 10:37 TD	
D.Node ΔT= 81s	
Tot. = 20m	
Par. = 210m U.Mag. = 1.0146	
Gam. = -0.4425 P.Mag. = 2.0782	

| **Partial** 1629 Jan 09 |
| Saros 128 12:33 TD |
| A.Node ΔT= 80s |
| Par. = 128m U.Mag. = 0.3876 |
| Gam. = 0.8093 P.Mag. = 1.3581 |

| **Penumbral** 1629 Jul 05 |
| Saros 133 11:12 TD |
| D.Node ΔT= 80s |
| Pen. = 242m U.Mag. = -0.3696 |
| Gam. = -1.1970 P.Mag. = 0.6937 |

| **Penumbral** 1629 Nov 30 |
| Saros 100 15:18 TD |
| A.Node ΔT= 79s |
| Pen. = 200m U.Mag. = -0.4676 |
| Gam. = -1.2625 P.Mag. = 0.5506 |

| **Penumbral** 1629 Dec 30 |
| Saros 138 03:40 TD |
| A.Node ΔT= 79s |
| Pen. = 95m U.Mag. = -0.8713 |
| Gam. = 1.4894 P.Mag. = 0.1218 |

| **Partial** 1630 May 26 |
| Saros 105 05:01 TD |
| D.Node ΔT= 78s |
| Par. = 142m U.Mag. = 0.4318 |
| Gam. = 0.7788 P.Mag. = 1.4259 |

| **Partial** 1630 Nov 19 |
| Saros 110 22:21 TD |
| A.Node ΔT= 78s |
| Par. = 181m U.Mag. = 0.7024 |
| Gam. = -0.6100 P.Mag. = 1.7757 |

| **Total +** 1631 May 15 |
| Saros 115 19:16 TD |
| D.Node ΔT= 77s |
| Tot. = 100m |
| Par. = 213m U.Mag. = 1.8721 |
| Gam. = 0.0051 P.Mag. = 2.8246 |

| **Total +** 1631 Nov 08 |
| Saros 120 22:52 TD |
| A.Node ΔT= 76s |
| Tot. = 103m |
| Par. = 235m U.Mag. = 1.6607 |
| Gam. = 0.0806 P.Mag. = 2.7604 |

| **Partial** 1632 May 04 |
| Saros 125 12:15 TD |
| D.Node ΔT= 75s |
| Par. = 151m U.Mag. = 0.5625 |
| Gam. = -0.7196 P.Mag. = 1.5121 |

| **Partial** 1632 Oct 27 |
| Saros 130 23:01 TD |
| A.Node ΔT= 75s |
| Par. = 145m U.Mag. = 0.4051 |
| Gam. = 0.7719 P.Mag. = 1.4790 |

| **Penumbral** 1633 Mar 25 |
| Saros 97 16:05 TD |
| D.Node ΔT= 74s |
| Pen. = 222m U.Mag. = -0.3714 |
| Gam. = 1.2080 P.Mag. = 0.6545 |

Plate 026

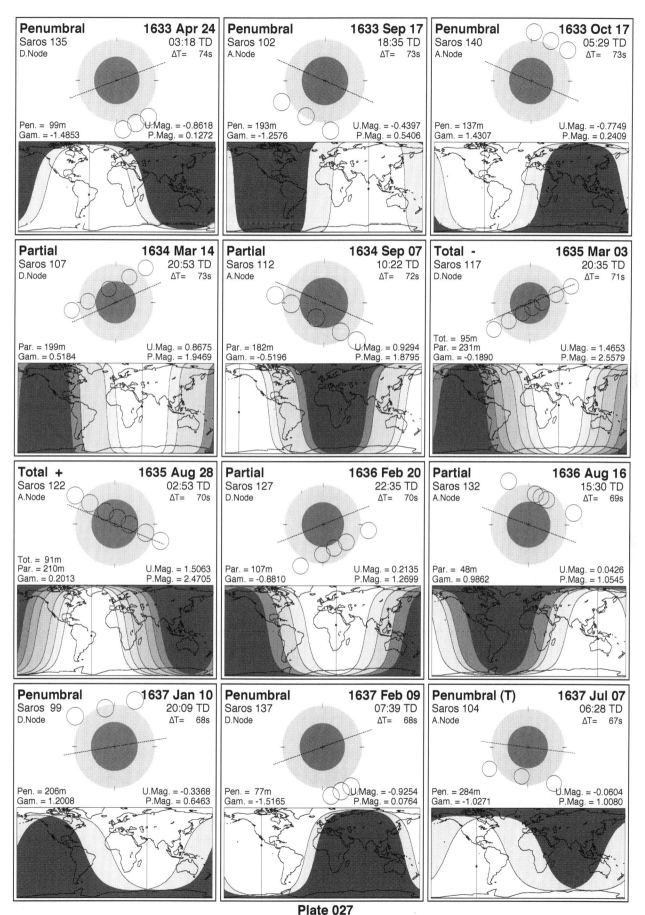

Penumbral   **1633 Apr 24**
Saros 135   03:18 TD
D.Node   ΔT= 74s
Pen. = 99m   U.Mag. = -0.8618
Gam. = -1.4853   P.Mag. = 0.1272

Penumbral   **1633 Sep 17**
Saros 102   18:35 TD
A.Node   ΔT= 73s
Pen. = 193m   U.Mag. = -0.4397
Gam. = -1.2576   P.Mag. = 0.5406

Penumbral   **1633 Oct 17**
Saros 140   05:29 TD
A.Node   ΔT= 73s
Pen. = 137m   U.Mag. = -0.7749
Gam. = 1.4307   P.Mag. = 0.2409

Partial   **1634 Mar 14**
Saros 107   20:53 TD
D.Node   ΔT= 73s
Par. = 199m   U.Mag. = 0.8675
Gam. = 0.5184   P.Mag. = 1.9469

Partial   **1634 Sep 07**
Saros 112   10:22 TD
A.Node   ΔT= 72s
Par. = 182m   U.Mag. = 0.9294
Gam. = -0.5196   P.Mag. = 1.8795

Total -   **1635 Mar 03**
Saros 117   20:35 TD
D.Node   ΔT= 71s
Tot. = 95m
Par. = 231m   U.Mag. = 1.4653
Gam. = -0.1890   P.Mag. = 2.5579

Total +   **1635 Aug 28**
Saros 122   02:53 TD
A.Node   ΔT= 70s
Tot. = 91m
Par. = 210m   U.Mag. = 1.5063
Gam. = 0.2013   P.Mag. = 2.4705

Partial   **1636 Feb 20**
Saros 127   22:35 TD
D.Node   ΔT= 70s
Par. = 107m   U.Mag. = 0.2135
Gam. = -0.8810   P.Mag. = 1.2699

Partial   **1636 Aug 16**
Saros 132   15:30 TD
A.Node   ΔT= 69s
Par. = 48m   U.Mag. = 0.0426
Gam. = 0.9862   P.Mag. = 1.0545

Penumbral   **1637 Jan 10**
Saros 99   20:09 TD
D.Node   ΔT= 68s
Pen. = 206m   U.Mag. = -0.3368
Gam. = 1.2008   P.Mag. = 0.6463

Penumbral   **1637 Feb 09**
Saros 137   07:39 TD
D.Node   ΔT= 68s
Pen. = 77m   U.Mag. = -0.9254
Gam. = -1.5165   P.Mag. = 0.0764

Penumbral (T)   **1637 Jul 07**
Saros 104   06:28 TD
A.Node   ΔT= 67s
Pen. = 284m   U.Mag. = -0.0604
Gam. = -1.0271   P.Mag. = 1.0080

Plate 027

123

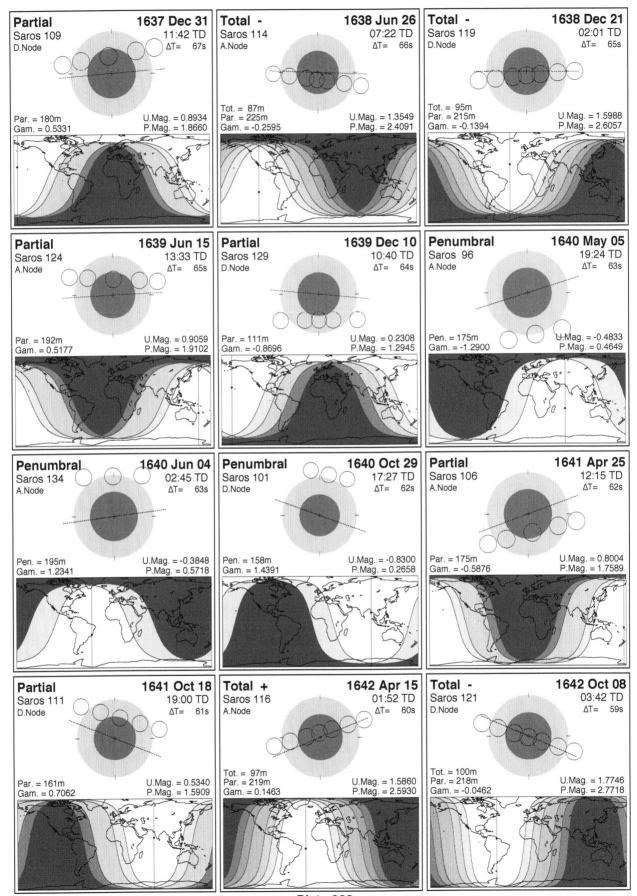

Partial **1637 Dec 31** Saros 109 11:42 TD D.Node ΔT= 67s Par. = 180m U.Mag. = 0.8934 Gam. = 0.5331 P.Mag. = 1.8660	**Total -** **1638 Jun 26** Saros 114 07:22 TD A.Node ΔT= 66s Tot. = 87m Par. = 225m U.Mag. = 1.3549 Gam. = -0.2595 P.Mag. = 2.4091	**Total -** **1638 Dec 21** Saros 119 02:01 TD D.Node ΔT= 65s Tot. = 95m Par. = 215m U.Mag. = 1.5988 Gam. = -0.1394 P.Mag. = 2.6057
Partial **1639 Jun 15** Saros 124 13:33 TD A.Node ΔT= 65s Par. = 192m U.Mag. = 0.9059 Gam. = 0.5177 P.Mag. = 1.9102	**Partial** **1639 Dec 10** Saros 129 10:40 TD D.Node ΔT= 64s Par. = 111m U.Mag. = 0.2308 Gam. = -0.8696 P.Mag. = 1.2945	**Penumbral** **1640 May 05** Saros 96 19:24 TD A.Node ΔT= 63s Pen. = 175m U.Mag. = -0.4833 Gam. = -1.2900 P.Mag. = 0.4649
Penumbral **1640 Jun 04** Saros 134 02:45 TD A.Node ΔT= 63s Pen. = 195m U.Mag. = -0.3848 Gam. = 1.2341 P.Mag. = 0.5718	**Penumbral** **1640 Oct 29** Saros 101 17:27 TD D.Node ΔT= 62s Pen. = 158m U.Mag. = -0.8300 Gam. = 1.4391 P.Mag. = 0.2658	**Partial** **1641 Apr 25** Saros 106 12:15 TD A.Node ΔT= 62s Par. = 175m U.Mag. = 0.8004 Gam. = -0.5876 P.Mag. = 1.7589
Partial **1641 Oct 18** Saros 111 19:00 TD D.Node ΔT= 61s Par. = 161m U.Mag. = 0.5340 Gam. = 0.7062 P.Mag. = 1.5909	**Total +** **1642 Apr 15** Saros 116 01:52 TD A.Node ΔT= 60s Tot. = 97m Par. = 219m U.Mag. = 1.5860 Gam. = 0.1463 P.Mag. = 2.5930	**Total -** **1642 Oct 08** Saros 121 03:42 TD D.Node ΔT= 59s Tot. = 100m Par. = 218m U.Mag. = 1.7746 Gam. = -0.0462 P.Mag. = 2.7718

Plate 028

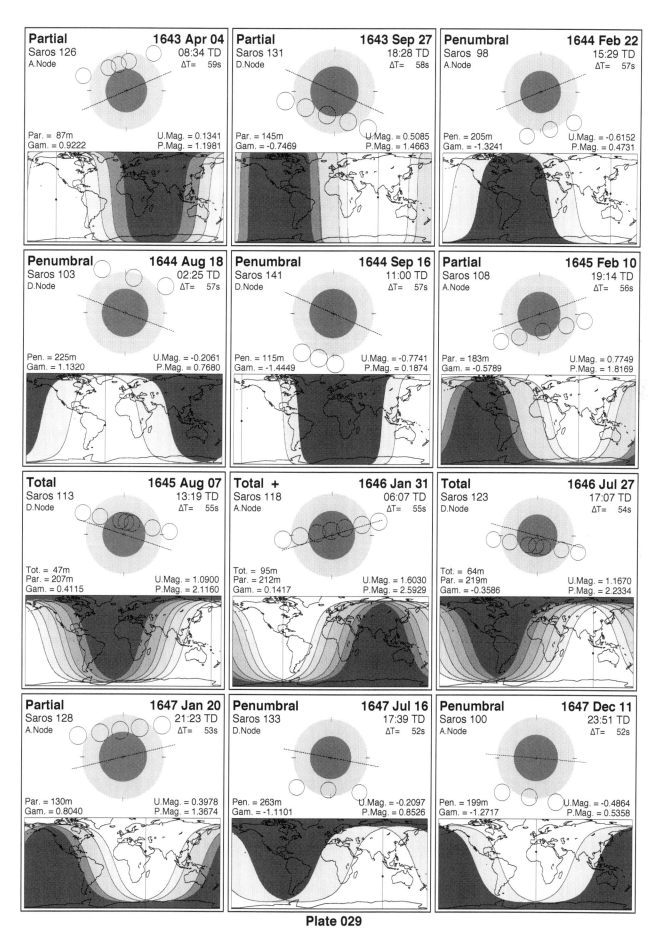

Partial   **1643 Apr 04**
Saros 126   08:34 TD
A.Node   ΔT= 59s

Par. = 87m   U.Mag. = 0.1341
Gam. = 0.9222   P.Mag. = 1.1981

Partial   **1643 Sep 27**
Saros 131   18:28 TD
D.Node   ΔT= 58s

Par. = 145m   U.Mag. = 0.5085
Gam. = -0.7469   P.Mag. = 1.4663

Penumbral   **1644 Feb 22**
Saros 98   15:29 TD
A.Node   ΔT= 57s

Pen. = 205m   U.Mag. = -0.6152
Gam. = -1.3241   P.Mag. = 0.4731

Penumbral   **1644 Aug 18**
Saros 103   02:25 TD
D.Node   ΔT= 57s

Pen. = 225m   U.Mag. = -0.2061
Gam. = 1.1320   P.Mag. = 0.7680

Penumbral   **1644 Sep 16**
Saros 141   11:00 TD
D.Node   ΔT= 57s

Pen. = 115m   U.Mag. = -0.7741
Gam. = -1.4449   P.Mag. = 0.1874

Partial   **1645 Feb 10**
Saros 108   19:14 TD
A.Node   ΔT= 56s

Par. = 183m   U.Mag. = 0.7749
Gam. = -0.5789   P.Mag. = 1.8169

Total   **1645 Aug 07**
Saros 113   13:19 TD
D.Node   ΔT= 55s

Tot. = 47m
Par. = 207m   U.Mag. = 1.0900
Gam. = 0.4115   P.Mag. = 2.1160

Total +   **1646 Jan 31**
Saros 118   06:07 TD
A.Node   ΔT= 55s

Tot. = 95m
Par. = 212m   U.Mag. = 1.6030
Gam. = 0.1417   P.Mag. = 2.5929

Total   **1646 Jul 27**
Saros 123   17:07 TD
D.Node   ΔT= 54s

Tot. = 64m
Par. = 219m   U.Mag. = 1.1670
Gam. = -0.3586   P.Mag. = 2.2334

Partial   **1647 Jan 20**
Saros 128   21:23 TD
A.Node   ΔT= 53s

Par. = 130m   U.Mag. = 0.3978
Gam. = 0.8040   P.Mag. = 1.3674

Penumbral   **1647 Jul 16**
Saros 133   17:39 TD
D.Node   ΔT= 52s

Pen. = 263m   U.Mag. = -0.2097
Gam. = -1.1101   P.Mag. = 0.8526

Penumbral   **1647 Dec 11**
Saros 100   23:51 TD
A.Node   ΔT= 52s

Pen. = 199m   U.Mag. = -0.4864
Gam. = -1.2717   P.Mag. = 0.5358

Plate 029

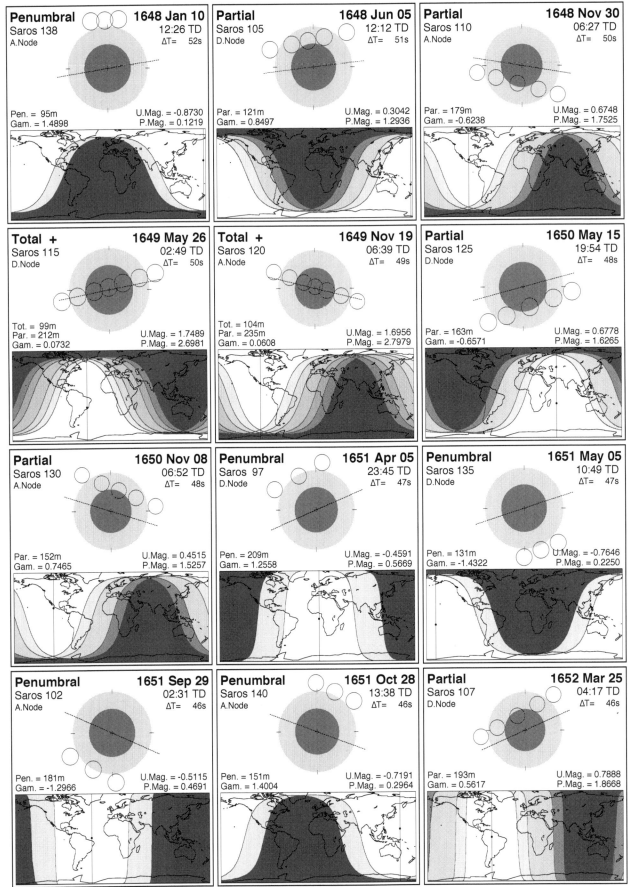

Penumbral   **1648 Jan 10**
Saros 138   12:26 TD
A.Node   ΔT= 52s
Pen. = 95m   U.Mag. = -0.8730
Gam. = 1.4898   P.Mag. = 0.1219

Partial   **1648 Jun 05**
Saros 105   12:12 TD
D.Node   ΔT= 51s
Par. = 121m   U.Mag. = 0.3042
Gam. = 0.8497   P.Mag. = 1.2936

Partial   **1648 Nov 30**
Saros 110   06:27 TD
A.Node   ΔT= 50s
Par. = 179m   U.Mag. = 0.6748
Gam. = -0.6238   P.Mag. = 1.7525

Total +   **1649 May 26**
Saros 115   02:49 TD
D.Node   ΔT= 50s
Tot. = 99m
Par. = 212m   U.Mag. = 1.7489
Gam. = 0.0732   P.Mag. = 2.6981

Total +   **1649 Nov 19**
Saros 120   06:39 TD
A.Node   ΔT= 49s
Tot. = 104m
Par. = 235m   U.Mag. = 1.6956
Gam. = 0.0608   P.Mag. = 2.7979

Partial   **1650 May 15**
Saros 125   19:54 TD
D.Node   ΔT= 48s
Par. = 163m   U.Mag. = 0.6778
Gam. = -0.6571   P.Mag. = 1.6265

Partial   **1650 Nov 08**
Saros 130   06:52 TD
A.Node   ΔT= 48s
Par. = 152m   U.Mag. = 0.4515
Gam. = 0.7465   P.Mag. = 1.5257

Penumbral   **1651 Apr 05**
Saros 97   23:45 TD
D.Node   ΔT= 47s
Pen. = 209m   U.Mag. = -0.4591
Gam. = 1.2558   P.Mag. = 0.5669

Penumbral   **1651 May 05**
Saros 135   10:49 TD
D.Node   ΔT= 47s
Pen. = 131m   U.Mag. = -0.7646
Gam. = -1.4322   P.Mag. = 0.2250

Penumbral   **1651 Sep 29**
Saros 102   02:31 TD
A.Node   ΔT= 46s
Pen. = 181m   U.Mag. = -0.5115
Gam. = -1.2966   P.Mag. = 0.4691

Penumbral   **1651 Oct 28**
Saros 140   13:38 TD
A.Node   ΔT= 46s
Pen. = 151m   U.Mag. = -0.7191
Gam. = 1.4004   P.Mag. = 0.2964

Partial   **1652 Mar 25**
Saros 107   04:17 TD
D.Node   ΔT= 46s
Par. = 193m   U.Mag. = 0.7888
Gam. = 0.5617   P.Mag. = 1.8668

Plate 030

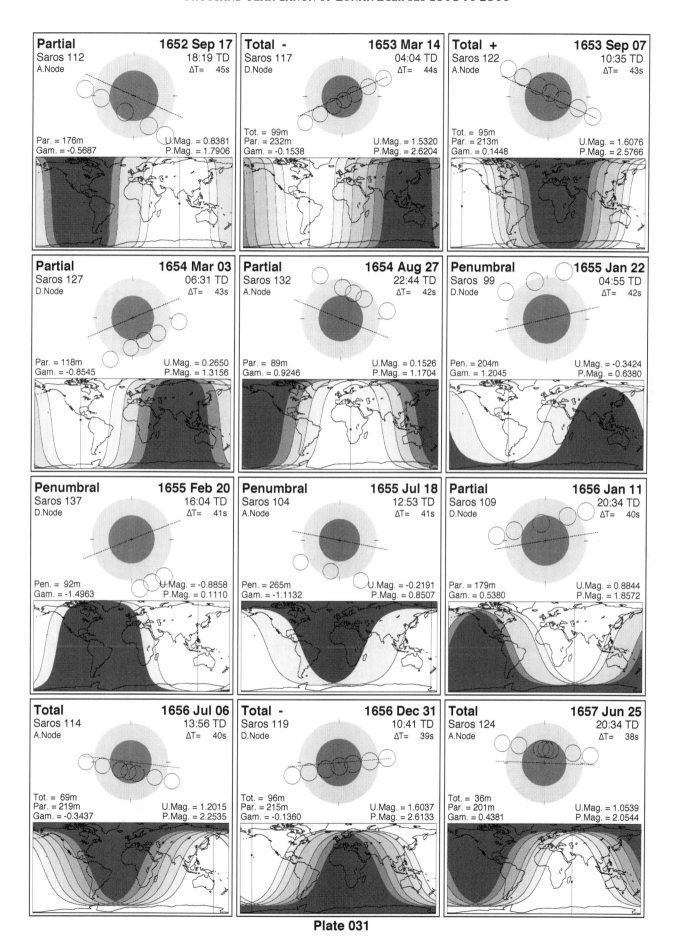

Partial **1652 Sep 17**	**Total -** **1653 Mar 14**	**Total +** **1653 Sep 07**
Saros 112 18:19 TD	Saros 117 04:04 TD	Saros 122 10:35 TD
A.Node ΔT= 45s	D.Node ΔT= 44s	A.Node ΔT= 43s
Par. = 176m U.Mag. = 0.8381	Tot. = 99m U.Mag. = 1.5320	Tot. = 95m U.Mag. = 1.6076
Gam. = -0.5687 P.Mag. = 1.7906	Par. = 232m P.Mag. = 2.6204	Par. = 213m P.Mag. = 2.5766
	Gam. = -0.1538	Gam. = 0.1448
Partial **1654 Mar 03**	**Partial** **1654 Aug 27**	**Penumbral** **1655 Jan 22**
Saros 127 06:31 TD	Saros 132 22:44 TD	Saros 99 04:55 TD
D.Node ΔT= 43s	A.Node ΔT= 42s	D.Node ΔT= 42s
Par. = 118m U.Mag. = 0.2650	Par. = 89m U.Mag. = 0.1526	Pen. = 204m U.Mag. = -0.3424
Gam. = -0.8545 P.Mag. = 1.3156	Gam. = 0.9246 P.Mag. = 1.1704	Gam. = 1.2045 P.Mag. = 0.6380
Penumbral **1655 Feb 20**	**Penumbral** **1655 Jul 18**	**Partial** **1656 Jan 11**
Saros 137 16:04 TD	Saros 104 12:53 TD	Saros 109 20:34 TD
D.Node ΔT= 41s	A.Node ΔT= 41s	D.Node ΔT= 40s
Pen. = 92m U.Mag. = -0.8858	Pen. = 265m U.Mag. = -0.2191	Par. = 179m U.Mag. = 0.8844
Gam. = -1.4963 P.Mag. = 0.1110	Gam. = -1.1132 P.Mag. = 0.8507	Gam. = 0.5380 P.Mag. = 1.8572
Total **1656 Jul 06**	**Total -** **1656 Dec 31**	**Total** **1657 Jun 25**
Saros 114 13:56 TD	Saros 119 10:41 TD	Saros 124 20:34 TD
A.Node ΔT= 40s	D.Node ΔT= 39s	A.Node ΔT= 38s
Tot. = 69m U.Mag. = 1.2015	Tot. = 96m U.Mag. = 1.6037	Tot. = 36m U.Mag. = 1.0539
Par. = 219m P.Mag. = 2.2535	Par. = 215m P.Mag. = 2.6133	Par. = 201m P.Mag. = 2.0544
Gam. = -0.3437	Gam. = -0.1360	Gam. = 0.4381

Plate 031

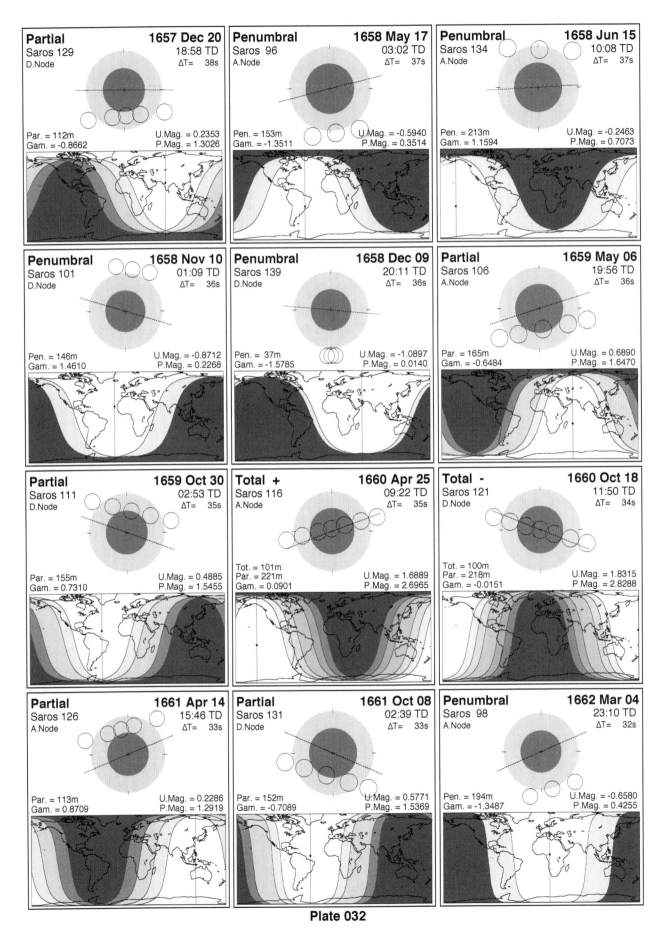

Partial   **1657 Dec 20**
Saros 129   18:58 TD
D.Node   ΔT= 38s

Par. = 112m   U.Mag. = 0.2353
Gam. = -0.8662   P.Mag. = 1.3026

Penumbral   **1658 May 17**
Saros 96   03:02 TD
A.Node   ΔT= 37s

Pen. = 153m   U.Mag. = -0.5940
Gam. = -1.3511   P.Mag. = 0.3514

Penumbral   **1658 Jun 15**
Saros 134   10:08 TD
A.Node   ΔT= 37s

Pen. = 213m   U.Mag. = -0.2463
Gam. = 1.1594   P.Mag. = 0.7073

Penumbral   **1658 Nov 10**
Saros 101   01:09 TD
D.Node   ΔT= 36s

Pen. = 146m   U.Mag. = -0.8712
Gam. = 1.4610   P.Mag. = 0.2268

Penumbral   **1658 Dec 09**
Saros 139   20:11 TD
D.Node   ΔT= 36s

Pen. = 37m   U.Mag. = -1.0897
Gam. = -1.5785   P.Mag. = 0.0140

Partial   **1659 May 06**
Saros 106   19:56 TD
A.Node   ΔT= 36s

Par. = 165m   U.Mag. = 0.6890
Gam. = -0.6484   P.Mag. = 1.6470

Partial   **1659 Oct 30**
Saros 111   02:53 TD
D.Node   ΔT= 35s

Par. = 155m   U.Mag. = 0.4885
Gam. = 0.7310   P.Mag. = 1.5455

Total +   **1660 Apr 25**
Saros 116   09:22 TD
A.Node   ΔT= 35s

Tot. = 101m
Par. = 221m   U.Mag. = 1.6889
Gam. = 0.0901   P.Mag. = 2.6965

Total -   **1660 Oct 18**
Saros 121   11:50 TD
D.Node   ΔT= 34s

Tot. = 100m
Par. = 218m   U.Mag. = 1.8315
Gam. = -0.0151   P.Mag. = 2.8288

Partial   **1661 Apr 14**
Saros 126   15:46 TD
A.Node   ΔT= 33s

Par. = 113m   U.Mag. = 0.2286
Gam. = 0.8709   P.Mag. = 1.2919

Partial   **1661 Oct 08**
Saros 131   02:39 TD
D.Node   ΔT= 33s

Par. = 152m   U.Mag. = 0.5771
Gam. = -0.7089   P.Mag. = 1.5369

Penumbral   **1662 Mar 04**
Saros 98   23:10 TD
A.Node   ΔT= 32s

Pen. = 194m   U.Mag. = -0.6580
Gam. = -1.3487   P.Mag. = 0.4255

Plate 032

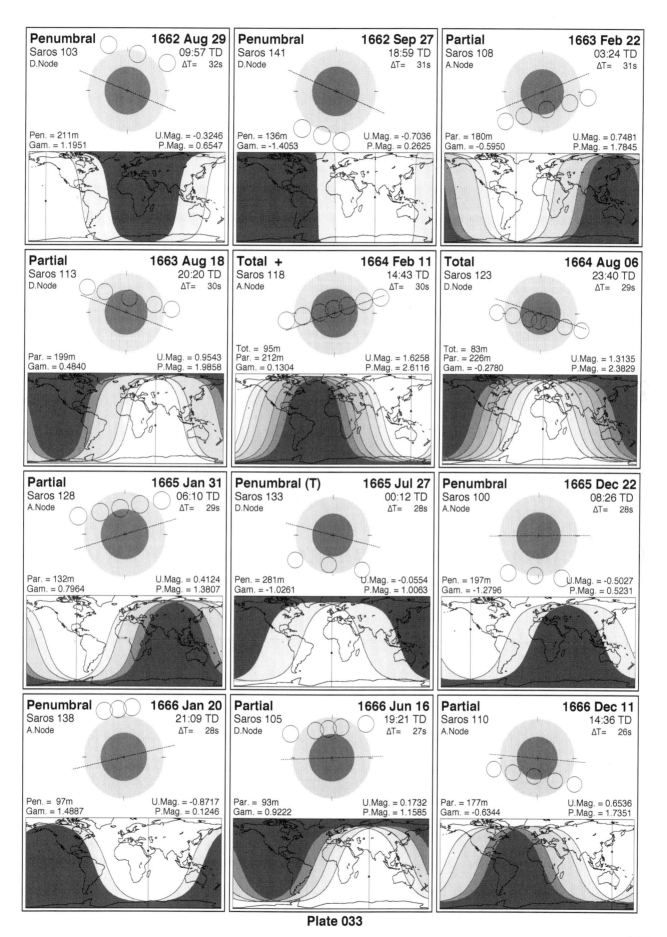

Penumbral   **1662 Aug 29**
Saros 103   09:57 TD
D.Node   ΔT= 32s

Pen. = 211m   U.Mag. = -0.3246
Gam. = 1.1951   P.Mag. = 0.6547

Penumbral   **1662 Sep 27**
Saros 141   18:59 TD
D.Node   ΔT= 31s

Pen. = 136m   U.Mag. = -0.7036
Gam. = -1.4053   P.Mag. = 0.2625

Partial   **1663 Feb 22**
Saros 108   03:24 TD
A.Node   ΔT= 31s

Par. = 180m   U.Mag. = 0.7481
Gam. = -0.5950   P.Mag. = 1.7845

Partial   **1663 Aug 18**
Saros 113   20:20 TD
D.Node   ΔT= 30s

Par. = 199m   U.Mag. = 0.9543
Gam. = 0.4840   P.Mag. = 1.9858

Total +   **1664 Feb 11**
Saros 118   14:43 TD
A.Node   ΔT= 30s

Tot. = 95m
Par. = 212m   U.Mag. = 1.6258
Gam. = 0.1304   P.Mag. = 2.6116

Total   **1664 Aug 06**
Saros 123   23:40 TD
D.Node   ΔT= 29s

Tot. = 83m
Par. = 226m   U.Mag. = 1.3135
Gam. = -0.2780   P.Mag. = 2.3829

Partial   **1665 Jan 31**
Saros 128   06:10 TD
A.Node   ΔT= 29s

Par. = 132m   U.Mag. = 0.4124
Gam. = 0.7964   P.Mag. = 1.3807

Penumbral (T)   **1665 Jul 27**
Saros 133   00:12 TD
D.Node   ΔT= 28s

Pen. = 281m   U.Mag. = -0.0554
Gam. = -1.0261   P.Mag. = 1.0063

Penumbral   **1665 Dec 22**
Saros 100   08:26 TD
A.Node   ΔT= 28s

Pen. = 197m   U.Mag. = -0.5027
Gam. = -1.2796   P.Mag. = 0.5231

Penumbral   **1666 Jan 20**
Saros 138   21:09 TD
A.Node   ΔT= 28s

Pen. = 97m   U.Mag. = -0.8717
Gam. = 1.4887   P.Mag. = 0.1246

Partial   **1666 Jun 16**
Saros 105   19:21 TD
D.Node   ΔT= 27s

Par. = 93m   U.Mag. = 0.1732
Gam. = 0.9222   P.Mag. = 1.1585

Partial   **1666 Dec 11**
Saros 110   14:36 TD
A.Node   ΔT= 26s

Par. = 177m   U.Mag. = 0.6536
Gam. = -0.6344   P.Mag. = 1.7351

Plate 033

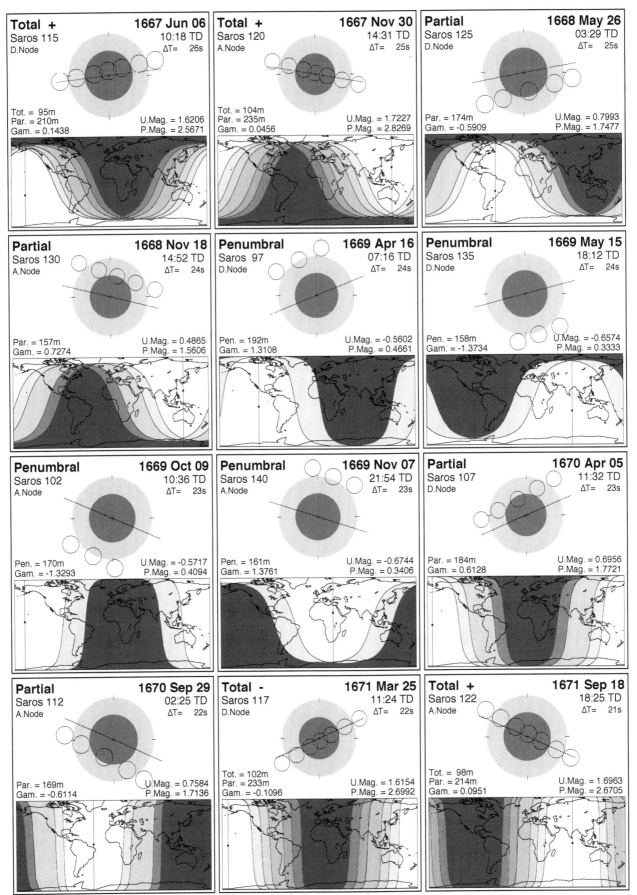

Total + 1667 Jun 06	**Total +** 1667 Nov 30
Saros 115 10:18 TD	Saros 120 14:31 TD
D.Node ΔT= 26s	A.Node ΔT= 25s
Tot. = 95m	Tot. = 104m
Par. = 210m U.Mag. = 1.6206	Par. = 235m U.Mag. = 1.7227
Gam. = 0.1438 P.Mag. = 2.5671	Gam. = 0.0456 P.Mag. = 2.8269

Partial 1668 May 26
Saros 125 03:29 TD
D.Node ΔT= 25s
Par. = 174m U.Mag. = 0.7993
Gam. = -0.5909 P.Mag. = 1.7477

Partial 1668 Nov 18
Saros 130 14:52 TD
A.Node ΔT= 24s
Par. = 157m U.Mag. = 0.4865
Gam. = 0.7274 P.Mag. = 1.5606

Penumbral 1669 Apr 16
Saros 97 07:16 TD
D.Node ΔT= 24s
Pen. = 192m U.Mag. = -0.5602
Gam. = 1.3108 P.Mag. = 0.4661

Penumbral 1669 May 15
Saros 135 18:12 TD
D.Node ΔT= 24s
Pen. = 158m U.Mag. = -0.6574
Gam. = -1.3734 P.Mag. = 0.3333

Penumbral 1669 Oct 09
Saros 102 10:36 TD
A.Node ΔT= 23s
Pen. = 170m U.Mag. = -0.5717
Gam. = -1.3293 P.Mag. = 0.4094

Penumbral 1669 Nov 07
Saros 140 21:54 TD
A.Node ΔT= 23s
Pen. = 161m U.Mag. = -0.6744
Gam. = 1.3761 P.Mag. = 0.3406

Partial 1670 Apr 05
Saros 107 11:32 TD
D.Node ΔT= 23s
Par. = 184m U.Mag. = 0.6956
Gam. = 0.6128 P.Mag. = 1.7721

Partial 1670 Sep 29
Saros 112 02:25 TD
A.Node ΔT= 22s
Par. = 169m U.Mag. = 0.7584
Gam. = -0.6114 P.Mag. = 1.7136

Total - 1671 Mar 25
Saros 117 11:24 TD
D.Node ΔT= 22s
Tot. = 102m
Par. = 233m U.Mag. = 1.6154
Gam. = -0.1096 P.Mag. = 2.6992

Total + 1671 Sep 18
Saros 122 18:25 TD
A.Node ΔT= 21s
Tot. = 98m
Par. = 214m U.Mag. = 1.6963
Gam. = 0.0951 P.Mag. = 2.6705

Plate 034

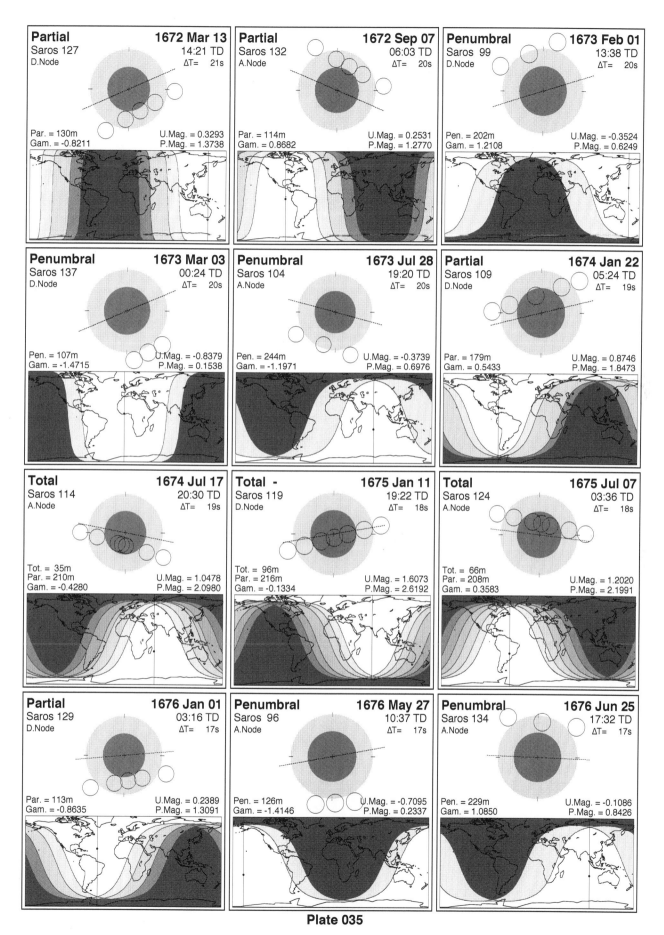

Partial **1672 Mar 13** Saros 127 14:21 TD D.Node ΔT= 21s Par. = 130m Gam. = -0.8211 U.Mag. = 0.3293 P.Mag. = 1.3738	**Partial** **1672 Sep 07** Saros 132 06:03 TD A.Node ΔT= 20s Par. = 114m Gam. = 0.8682 U.Mag. = 0.2531 P.Mag. = 1.2770	**Penumbral** **1673 Feb 01** Saros 99 13:38 TD D.Node ΔT= 20s Pen. = 202m Gam. = 1.2108 U.Mag. = -0.3524 P.Mag. = 0.6249
Penumbral **1673 Mar 03** Saros 137 00:24 TD D.Node ΔT= 20s Pen. = 107m Gam. = -1.4715 U.Mag. = -0.8379 P.Mag. = 0.1538	**Penumbral** **1673 Jul 28** Saros 104 19:20 TD A.Node ΔT= 20s Pen. = 244m Gam. = -1.1971 U.Mag. = -0.3739 P.Mag. = 0.6976	**Partial** **1674 Jan 22** Saros 109 05:24 TD D.Node ΔT= 19s Par. = 179m Gam. = 0.5433 U.Mag. = 0.8746 P.Mag. = 1.8473
Total **1674 Jul 17** Saros 114 20:30 TD A.Node ΔT= 19s Tot. = 35m Par. = 210m Gam. = -0.4280 U.Mag. = 1.0478 P.Mag. = 2.0980	**Total -** **1675 Jan 11** Saros 119 19:22 TD D.Node ΔT= 18s Tot. = 96m Par. = 216m Gam. = -0.1334 U.Mag. = 1.6073 P.Mag. = 2.6192	**Total** **1675 Jul 07** Saros 124 03:36 TD A.Node ΔT= 18s Tot. = 66m Par. = 208m Gam. = 0.3583 U.Mag. = 1.2020 P.Mag. = 2.1991
Partial **1676 Jan 01** Saros 129 03:16 TD D.Node ΔT= 17s Par. = 113m Gam. = -0.8635 U.Mag. = 0.2389 P.Mag. = 1.3091	**Penumbral** **1676 May 27** Saros 96 10:37 TD A.Node ΔT= 17s Pen. = 126m Gam. = -1.4146 U.Mag. = -0.7095 P.Mag. = 0.2337	**Penumbral** **1676 Jun 25** Saros 134 17:32 TD A.Node ΔT= 17s Pen. = 229m Gam. = 1.0850 U.Mag. = -0.1086 P.Mag. = 0.8426

Plate 035

131

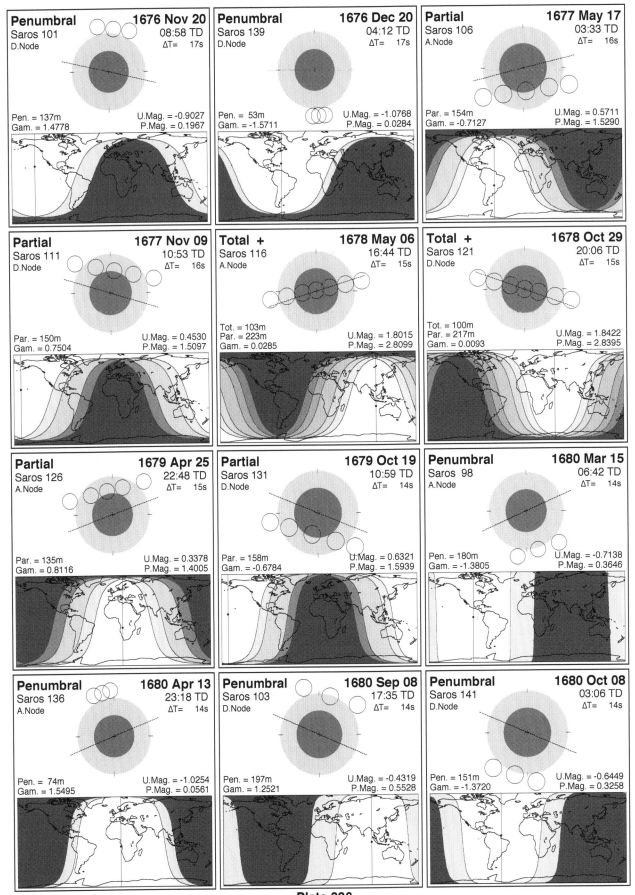

Penumbral	1676 Nov 20
Saros 101	08:58 TD
D.Node	ΔT= 17s

| Pen. = 137m | U.Mag. = -0.9027 |
| Gam. = 1.4778 | P.Mag. = 0.1967 |

Penumbral	1676 Dec 20
Saros 139	04:12 TD
D.Node	ΔT= 17s

| Pen. = 53m | U.Mag. = -1.0768 |
| Gam. = -1.5711 | P.Mag. = 0.0284 |

Partial	1677 May 17
Saros 106	03:33 TD
A.Node	ΔT= 16s

| Par. = 154m | U.Mag. = 0.5711 |
| Gam. = -0.7127 | P.Mag. = 1.5290 |

Partial	1677 Nov 09
Saros 111	10:53 TD
D.Node	ΔT= 16s

| Par. = 150m | U.Mag. = 0.4530 |
| Gam. = 0.7504 | P.Mag. = 1.5097 |

Total +	1678 May 06
Saros 116	16:44 TD
A.Node	ΔT= 15s

Tot. = 103m	
Par. = 223m	U.Mag. = 1.8015
Gam. = 0.0285	P.Mag. = 2.8099

Total +	1678 Oct 29
Saros 121	20:06 TD
D.Node	ΔT= 15s

Tot. = 100m	
Par. = 217m	U.Mag. = 1.8422
Gam. = 0.0093	P.Mag. = 2.8395

Partial	1679 Apr 25
Saros 126	22:48 TD
A.Node	ΔT= 15s

| Par. = 135m | U.Mag. = 0.3378 |
| Gam. = 0.8116 | P.Mag. = 1.4005 |

Partial	1679 Oct 19
Saros 131	10:59 TD
D.Node	ΔT= 14s

| Par. = 158m | U.Mag. = 0.6321 |
| Gam. = -0.6784 | P.Mag. = 1.5939 |

Penumbral	1680 Mar 15
Saros 98	06:42 TD
A.Node	ΔT= 14s

| Pen. = 180m | U.Mag. = -0.7138 |
| Gam. = -1.3805 | P.Mag. = 0.3646 |

Penumbral	1680 Apr 13
Saros 136	23:18 TD
A.Node	ΔT= 14s

| Pen. = 74m | U.Mag. = -1.0254 |
| Gam. = 1.5495 | P.Mag. = 0.0561 |

Penumbral	1680 Sep 08
Saros 103	17:35 TD
D.Node	ΔT= 14s

| Pen. = 197m | U.Mag. = -0.4319 |
| Gam. = 1.2521 | P.Mag. = 0.5528 |

Penumbral	1680 Oct 08
Saros 141	03:06 TD
D.Node	ΔT= 14s

| Pen. = 151m | U.Mag. = -0.6449 |
| Gam. = -1.3720 | P.Mag. = 0.3258 |

Plate 036

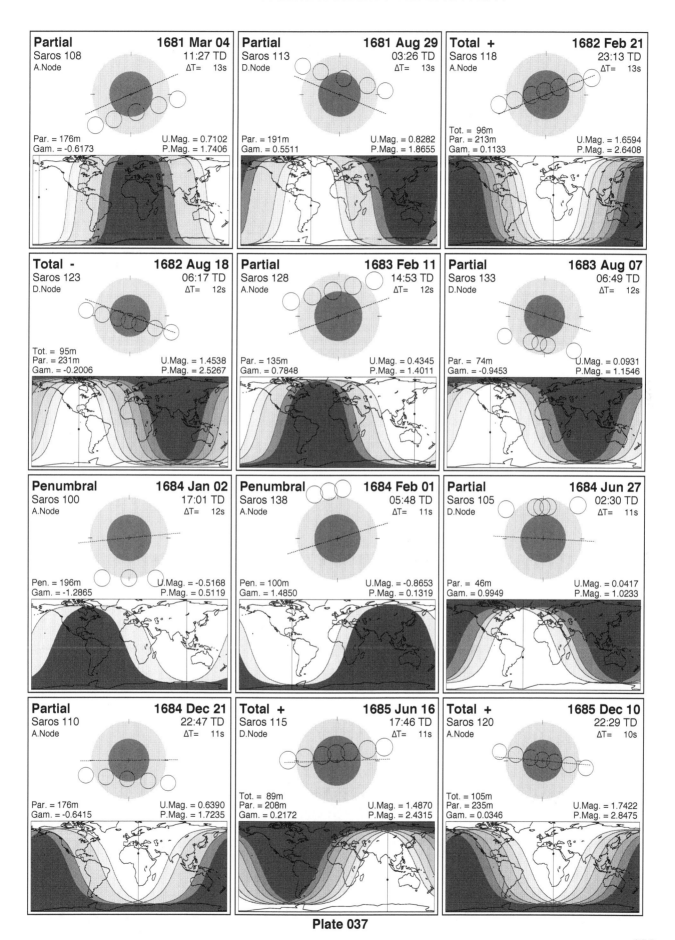

Partial **1681 Mar 04** Saros 108 11:27 TD A.Node ΔT= 13s Par. = 176m U.Mag. = 0.7102 Gam. = -0.6173 P.Mag. = 1.7406	**Partial** **1681 Aug 29** Saros 113 03:26 TD D.Node ΔT= 13s Par. = 191m U.Mag. = 0.8282 Gam. = 0.5511 P.Mag. = 1.8655	**Total +** **1682 Feb 21** Saros 118 23:13 TD A.Node ΔT= 13s Tot. = 96m Par. = 213m U.Mag. = 1.6594 Gam. = 0.1133 P.Mag. = 2.6408
Total - **1682 Aug 18** Saros 123 06:17 TD D.Node ΔT= 12s Tot. = 95m Par. = 231m U.Mag. = 1.4538 Gam. = -0.2006 P.Mag. = 2.5267	**Partial** **1683 Feb 11** Saros 128 14:53 TD A.Node ΔT= 12s Par. = 135m U.Mag. = 0.4345 Gam. = 0.7848 P.Mag. = 1.4011	**Partial** **1683 Aug 07** Saros 133 06:49 TD D.Node ΔT= 12s Par. = 74m U.Mag. = 0.0931 Gam. = -0.9453 P.Mag. = 1.1546
Penumbral **1684 Jan 02** Saros 100 17:01 TD A.Node ΔT= 12s Pen. = 196m U.Mag. = -0.5168 Gam. = -1.2865 P.Mag. = 0.5119	**Penumbral** **1684 Feb 01** Saros 138 05:48 TD A.Node ΔT= 11s Pen. = 100m U.Mag. = -0.8653 Gam. = 1.4850 P.Mag. = 0.1319	**Partial** **1684 Jun 27** Saros 105 02:30 TD D.Node ΔT= 11s Par. = 46m U.Mag. = 0.0417 Gam. = 0.9949 P.Mag. = 1.0233
Partial **1684 Dec 21** Saros 110 22:47 TD A.Node ΔT= 11s Par. = 176m U.Mag. = 0.6390 Gam. = -0.6415 P.Mag. = 1.7235	**Total +** **1685 Jun 16** Saros 115 17:46 TD D.Node ΔT= 11s Tot. = 89m Par. = 208m U.Mag. = 1.4870 Gam. = 0.2172 P.Mag. = 2.4315	**Total +** **1685 Dec 10** Saros 120 22:29 TD A.Node ΔT= 10s Tot. = 105m Par. = 235m U.Mag. = 1.7422 Gam. = 0.0346 P.Mag. = 2.8475

Plate 037

133

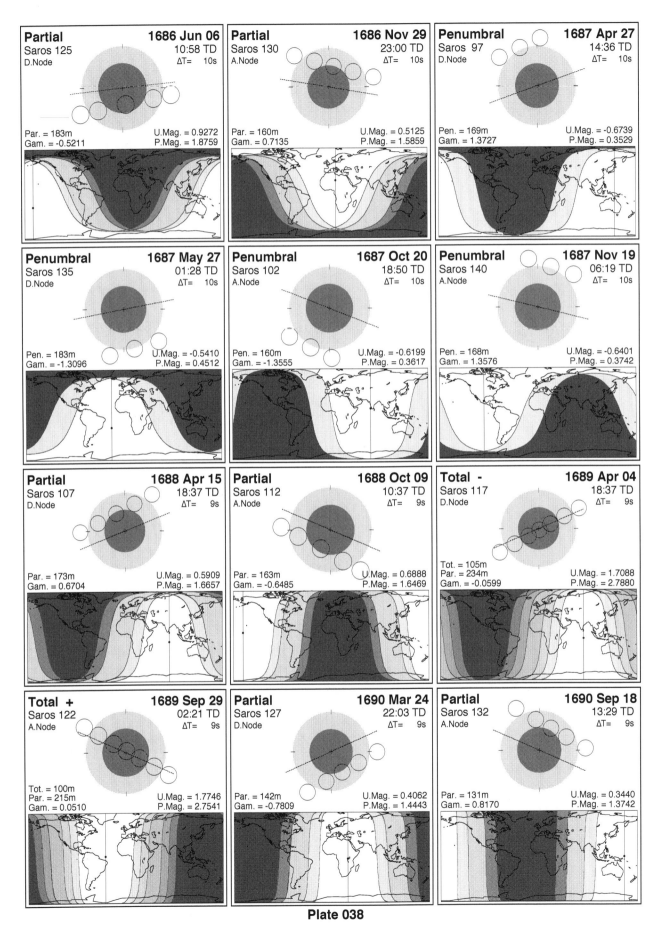

Partial   **1686 Jun 06**
Saros 125   10:58 TD
D.Node   ΔT= 10s
Par. = 183m   U.Mag. = 0.9272
Gam. = -0.5211   P.Mag. = 1.8759

Partial   **1686 Nov 29**
Saros 130   23:00 TD
A.Node   ΔT= 10s
Par. = 160m   U.Mag. = 0.5125
Gam. = 0.7135   P.Mag. = 1.5859

Penumbral   **1687 Apr 27**
Saros 97   14:36 TD
D.Node   ΔT= 10s
Pen. = 169m   U.Mag. = -0.6739
Gam. = 1.3727   P.Mag. = 0.3529

Penumbral   **1687 May 27**
Saros 135   01:28 TD
D.Node   ΔT= 10s
Pen. = 183m   U.Mag. = -0.5410
Gam. = -1.3096   P.Mag. = 0.4512

Penumbral   **1687 Oct 20**
Saros 102   18:50 TD
A.Node   ΔT= 10s
Pen. = 160m   U.Mag. = -0.6199
Gam. = -1.3555   P.Mag. = 0.3617

Penumbral   **1687 Nov 19**
Saros 140   06:19 TD
A.Node   ΔT= 10s
Pen. = 168m   U.Mag. = -0.6401
Gam. = 1.3576   P.Mag. = 0.3742

Partial   **1688 Apr 15**
Saros 107   18:37 TD
D.Node   ΔT= 9s
Par. = 173m   U.Mag. = 0.5909
Gam. = 0.6704   P.Mag. = 1.6657

Partial   **1688 Oct 09**
Saros 112   10:37 TD
A.Node   ΔT= 9s
Par. = 163m   U.Mag. = 0.6888
Gam. = -0.6485   P.Mag. = 1.6469

Total -   **1689 Apr 04**
Saros 117   18:37 TD
D.Node   ΔT= 9s
Tot. = 105m
Par. = 234m   U.Mag. = 1.7088
Gam. = -0.0599   P.Mag. = 2.7880

Total +   **1689 Sep 29**
Saros 122   02:21 TD
A.Node   ΔT= 9s
Tot. = 100m
Par. = 215m   U.Mag. = 1.7746
Gam. = 0.0510   P.Mag. = 2.7541

Partial   **1690 Mar 24**
Saros 127   22:03 TD
D.Node   ΔT= 9s
Par. = 142m   U.Mag. = 0.4062
Gam. = -0.7809   P.Mag. = 1.4443

Partial   **1690 Sep 18**
Saros 132   13:29 TD
A.Node   ΔT= 9s
Par. = 131m   U.Mag. = 0.3440
Gam. = 0.8170   P.Mag. = 1.3742

Plate 038

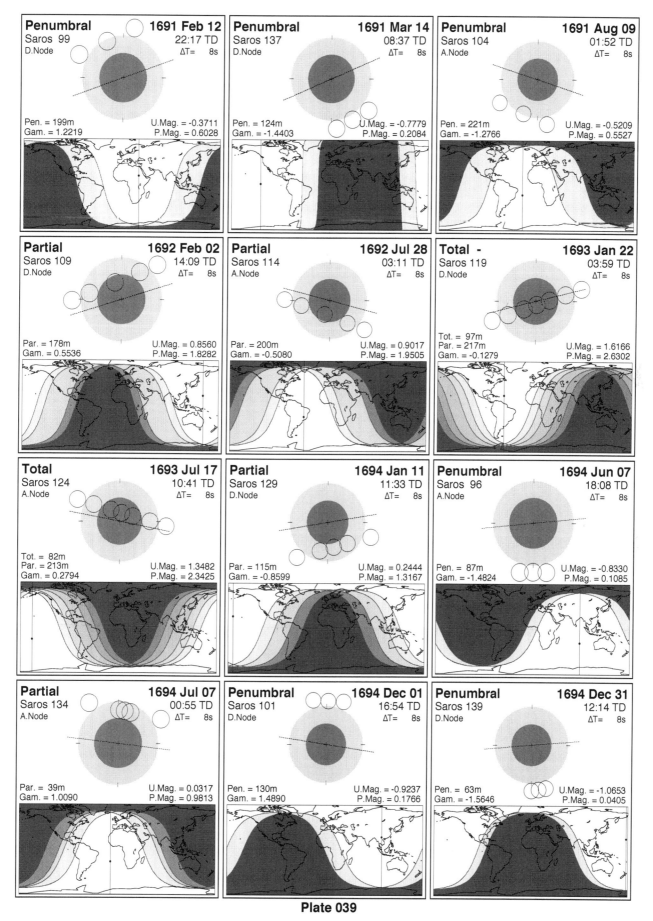

Penumbral **1691 Feb 12**	
Saros 99	22:17 TD
D.Node	ΔT= 8s
Pen. = 199m	U.Mag. = -0.3711
Gam. = 1.2219	P.Mag. = 0.6028

Penumbral **1691 Mar 14**	
Saros 137	08:37 TD
D.Node	ΔT= 8s
Pen. = 124m	U.Mag. = -0.7779
Gam. = -1.4403	P.Mag. = 0.2084

Penumbral **1691 Aug 09**	
Saros 104	01:52 TD
A.Node	ΔT= 8s
Pen. = 221m	U.Mag. = -0.5209
Gam. = -1.2766	P.Mag. = 0.5527

Partial **1692 Feb 02**	
Saros 109	14:09 TD
D.Node	ΔT= 8s
Par. = 178m	U.Mag. = 0.8560
Gam. = 0.5536	P.Mag. = 1.8282

Partial **1692 Jul 28**	
Saros 114	03:11 TD
A.Node	ΔT= 8s
Par. = 200m	U.Mag. = 0.9017
Gam. = -0.5080	P.Mag. = 1.9505

Total - **1693 Jan 22**	
Saros 119	03:59 TD
D.Node	ΔT= 8s
Tot. = 97m	
Par. = 217m	U.Mag. = 1.6166
Gam. = -0.1279	P.Mag. = 2.6302

Total **1693 Jul 17**	
Saros 124	10:41 TD
A.Node	ΔT= 8s
Tot. = 82m	
Par. = 213m	U.Mag. = 1.3482
Gam. = 0.2794	P.Mag. = 2.3425

Partial **1694 Jan 11**	
Saros 129	11:33 TD
D.Node	ΔT= 8s
Par. = 115m	U.Mag. = 0.2444
Gam. = -0.8599	P.Mag. = 1.3167

Penumbral **1694 Jun 07**	
Saros 96	18:08 TD
A.Node	ΔT= 8s
Pen. = 87m	U.Mag. = -0.8330
Gam. = -1.4824	P.Mag. = 0.1085

Partial **1694 Jul 07**	
Saros 134	00:55 TD
A.Node	ΔT= 8s
Par. = 39m	U.Mag. = 0.0317
Gam. = 1.0090	P.Mag. = 0.9813

Penumbral **1694 Dec 01**	
Saros 101	16:54 TD
D.Node	ΔT= 8s
Pen. = 130m	U.Mag. = -0.9237
Gam. = 1.4890	P.Mag. = 0.1766

Penumbral **1694 Dec 31**	
Saros 139	12:14 TD
D.Node	ΔT= 8s
Pen. = 63m	U.Mag. = -1.0653
Gam. = -1.5646	P.Mag. = 0.0405

Plate 039

135

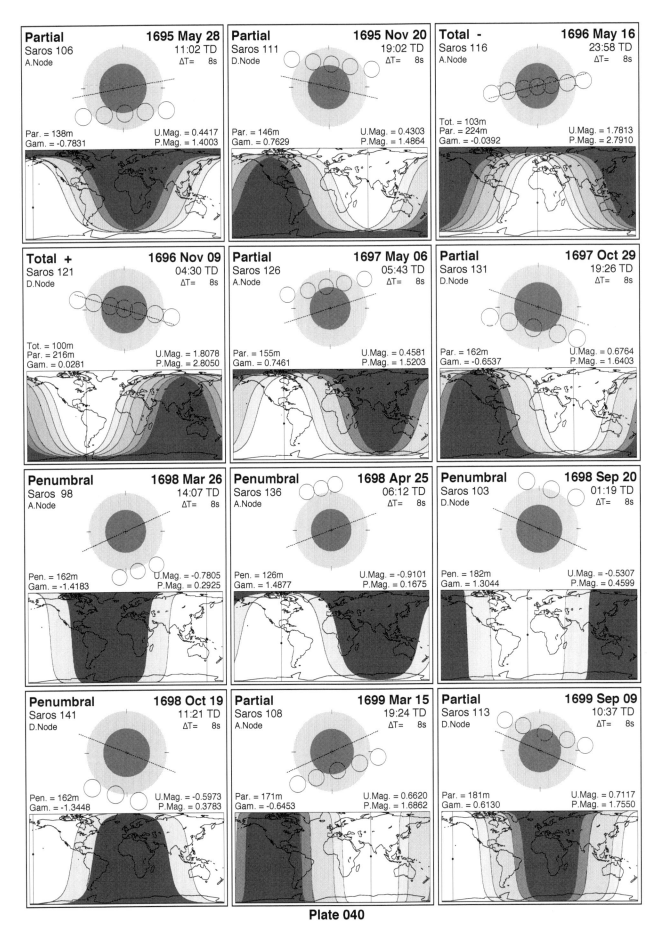

Partial	1695 May 28
Saros 106	11:02 TD
A.Node	ΔT= 8s

Par. = 138m   U.Mag. = 0.4417
Gam. = -0.7831   P.Mag. = 1.4003

Partial	1695 Nov 20
Saros 111	19:02 TD
D.Node	ΔT= 8s

Par. = 146m   U.Mag. = 0.4303
Gam. = 0.7629   P.Mag. = 1.4864

Total -	1696 May 16
Saros 116	23:58 TD
A.Node	ΔT= 8s

Tot. = 103m
Par. = 224m   U.Mag. = 1.7813
Gam. = -0.0392   P.Mag. = 2.7910

Total +	1696 Nov 09
Saros 121	04:30 TD
D.Node	ΔT= 8s

Tot. = 100m
Par. = 216m   U.Mag. = 1.8078
Gam. = 0.0281   P.Mag. = 2.8050

Partial	1697 May 06
Saros 126	05:43 TD
A.Node	ΔT= 8s

Par. = 155m   U.Mag. = 0.4581
Gam. = 0.7461   P.Mag. = 1.5203

Partial	1697 Oct 29
Saros 131	19:26 TD
D.Node	ΔT= 8s

Par. = 162m   U.Mag. = 0.6764
Gam. = -0.6537   P.Mag. = 1.6403

Penumbral	1698 Mar 26
Saros 98	14:07 TD
A.Node	ΔT= 8s

Pen. = 162m   U.Mag. = -0.7805
Gam. = -1.4183   P.Mag. = 0.2925

Penumbral	1698 Apr 25
Saros 136	06:12 TD
A.Node	ΔT= 8s

Pen. = 126m   U.Mag. = -0.9101
Gam. = 1.4877   P.Mag. = 0.1675

Penumbral	1698 Sep 20
Saros 103	01:19 TD
D.Node	ΔT= 8s

Pen. = 182m   U.Mag. = -0.5307
Gam. = 1.3044   P.Mag. = 0.4599

Penumbral	1698 Oct 19
Saros 141	11:21 TD
D.Node	ΔT= 8s

Pen. = 162m   U.Mag. = -0.5973
Gam. = -1.3448   P.Mag. = 0.3783

Partial	1699 Mar 15
Saros 108	19:24 TD
A.Node	ΔT= 8s

Par. = 171m   U.Mag. = 0.6620
Gam. = -0.6453   P.Mag. = 1.6862

Partial	1699 Sep 09
Saros 113	10:37 TD
D.Node	ΔT= 8s

Par. = 181m   U.Mag. = 0.7117
Gam. = 0.6130   P.Mag. = 1.7550

Plate 040

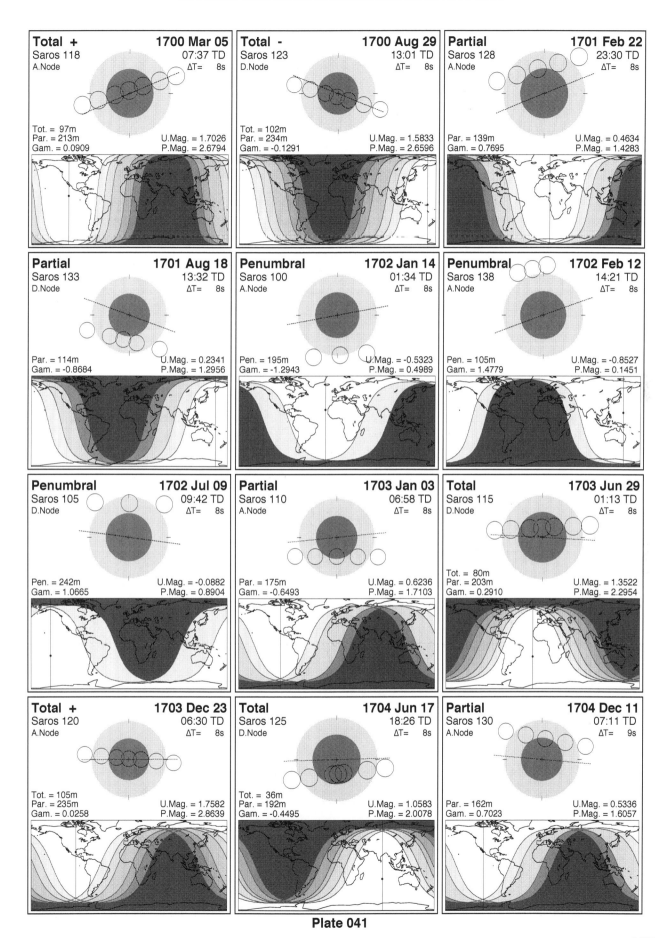

Total + **1700 Mar 05**	Saros 118 07:37 TD A.Node ΔT= 8s
Tot. = 97m Par. = 213m Gam. = 0.0909	U.Mag. = 1.7026 P.Mag. = 2.6794

Total - **1700 Aug 29**	Saros 123 13:01 TD D.Node ΔT= 8s
Tot. = 102m Par. = 234m Gam. = -0.1291	U.Mag. = 1.5833 P.Mag. = 2.6596

Partial **1701 Feb 22**	Saros 128 23:30 TD A.Node ΔT= 8s
Par. = 139m Gam. = 0.7695	U.Mag. = 0.4634 P.Mag. = 1.4283

Partial **1701 Aug 18**	Saros 133 13:32 TD D.Node ΔT= 8s
Par. = 114m Gam. = -0.8684	U.Mag. = 0.2341 P.Mag. = 1.2956

Penumbral **1702 Jan 14**	Saros 100 01:34 TD A.Node ΔT= 8s
Pen. = 195m Gam. = -1.2943	U.Mag. = -0.5323 P.Mag. = 0.4989

Penumbral **1702 Feb 12**	Saros 138 14:21 TD A.Node ΔT= 8s
Pen. = 105m Gam. = 1.4779	U.Mag. = -0.8527 P.Mag. = 0.1451

Penumbral **1702 Jul 09**	Saros 105 09:42 TD D.Node ΔT= 8s
Pen. = 242m Gam. = 1.0665	U.Mag. = -0.0882 P.Mag. = 0.8904

Partial **1703 Jan 03**	Saros 110 06:58 TD A.Node ΔT= 8s
Par. = 175m Gam. = -0.6493	U.Mag. = 0.6236 P.Mag. = 1.7103

Total **1703 Jun 29**	Saros 115 01:13 TD D.Node ΔT= 8s
Tot. = 80m Par. = 203m Gam. = 0.2910	U.Mag. = 1.3522 P.Mag. = 2.2954

Total + **1703 Dec 23**	Saros 120 06:30 TD A.Node ΔT= 8s
Tot. = 105m Par. = 235m Gam. = 0.0258	U.Mag. = 1.7582 P.Mag. = 2.8639

Total **1704 Jun 17**	Saros 125 18:26 TD D.Node ΔT= 8s
Tot. = 36m Par. = 192m Gam. = -0.4495	U.Mag. = 1.0583 P.Mag. = 2.0078

Partial **1704 Dec 11**	Saros 130 07:11 TD A.Node ΔT= 9s
Par. = 162m Gam. = 0.7023	U.Mag. = 0.5336 P.Mag. = 1.6057

Plate 041

137

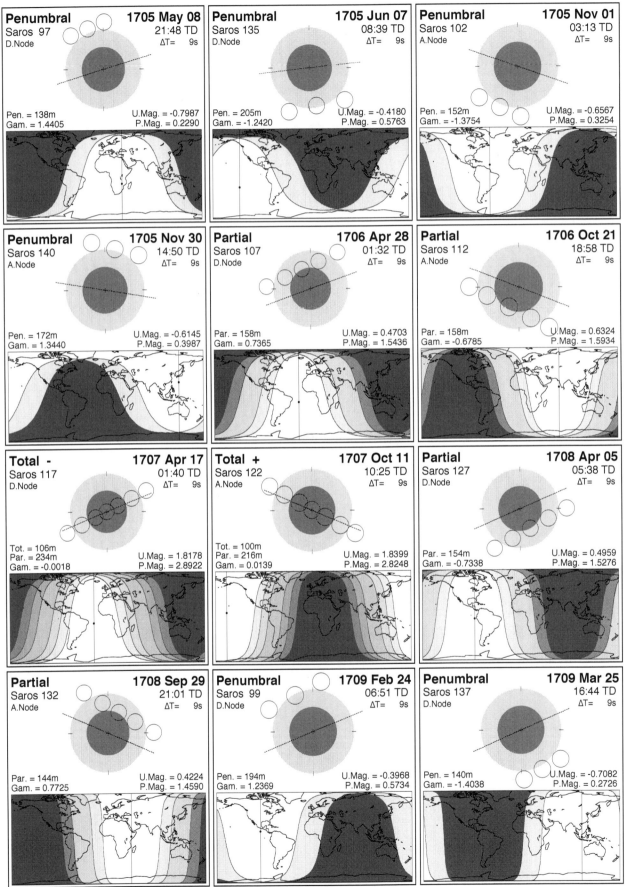

Penumbral   **1705 May 08**
Saros 97   21:48 TD
D.Node   ΔT= 9s
Pen. = 138m   U.Mag. = -0.7987
Gam. = 1.4405   P.Mag. = 0.2290

Penumbral   **1705 Jun 07**
Saros 135   08:39 TD
D.Node   ΔT= 9s
Pen. = 205m   U.Mag. = -0.4180
Gam. = -1.2420   P.Mag. = 0.5763

Penumbral   **1705 Nov 01**
Saros 102   03:13 TD
A.Node   ΔT= 9s
Pen. = 152m   U.Mag. = -0.6567
Gam. = -1.3754   P.Mag. = 0.3254

Penumbral   **1705 Nov 30**
Saros 140   14:50 TD
A.Node   ΔT= 9s
Pen. = 172m   U.Mag. = -0.6145
Gam. = 1.3440   P.Mag. = 0.3987

Partial   **1706 Apr 28**
Saros 107   01:32 TD
D.Node   ΔT= 9s
Par. = 158m   U.Mag. = 0.4703
Gam. = 0.7365   P.Mag. = 1.5436

Partial   **1706 Oct 21**
Saros 112   18:58 TD
A.Node   ΔT= 9s
Par. = 158m   U.Mag. = 0.6324
Gam. = -0.6785   P.Mag. = 1.5934

Total -   **1707 Apr 17**
Saros 117   01:40 TD
D.Node   ΔT= 9s
Tot. = 106m
Par. = 234m   U.Mag. = 1.8178
Gam. = -0.0018   P.Mag. = 2.8922

Total +   **1707 Oct 11**
Saros 122   10:25 TD
A.Node   ΔT= 9s
Tot. = 100m
Par. = 216m   U.Mag. = 1.8399
Gam. = 0.0139   P.Mag. = 2.8248

Partial   **1708 Apr 05**
Saros 127   05:38 TD
D.Node   ΔT= 9s
Par. = 154m   U.Mag. = 0.4959
Gam. = -0.7338   P.Mag. = 1.5276

Partial   **1708 Sep 29**
Saros 132   21:01 TD
A.Node   ΔT= 9s
Par. = 144m   U.Mag. = 0.4224
Gam. = 0.7725   P.Mag. = 1.4590

Penumbral   **1709 Feb 24**
Saros 99   06:51 TD
D.Node   ΔT= 9s
Pen. = 194m   U.Mag. = -0.3968
Gam. = 1.2369   P.Mag. = 0.5734

Penumbral   **1709 Mar 25**
Saros 137   16:44 TD
D.Node   ΔT= 9s
Pen. = 140m   U.Mag. = -0.7082
Gam. = -1.4038   P.Mag. = 0.2726

Plate 042

138

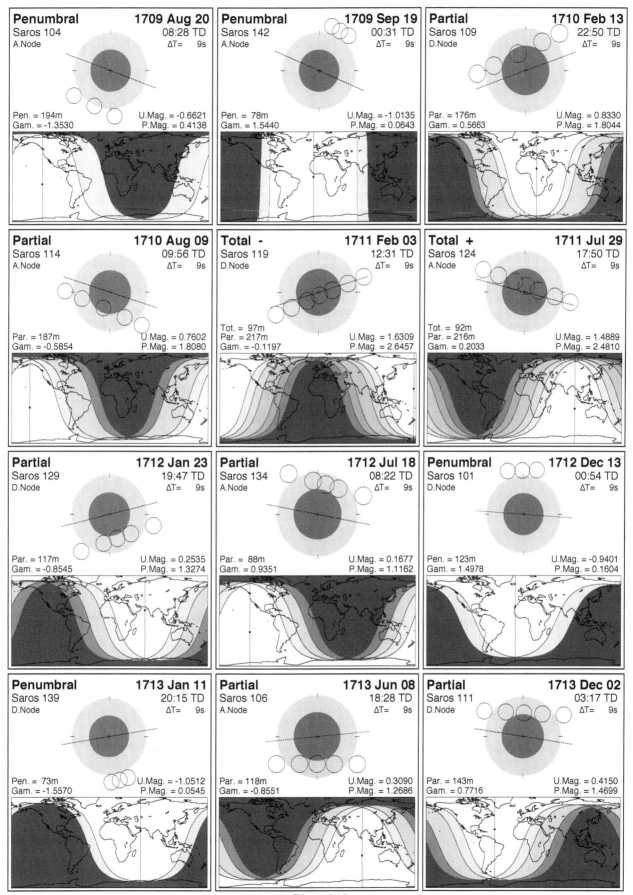

Penumbral	1709 Aug 20
Saros 104	08:28 TD
A.Node	ΔT= 9s
Pen. = 194m	U.Mag. = -0.6621
Gam. = -1.3530	P.Mag. = 0.4138

Penumbral	1709 Sep 19
Saros 142	00:31 TD
A.Node	ΔT= 9s
Pen. = 78m	U.Mag. = -1.0135
Gam. = 1.5440	P.Mag. = 0.0643

Partial	1710 Feb 13
Saros 109	22:50 TD
D.Node	ΔT= 9s
Par. = 176m	U.Mag. = 0.8330
Gam. = 0.5663	P.Mag. = 1.8044

Partial	1710 Aug 09
Saros 114	09:56 TD
A.Node	ΔT= 9s
Par. = 187m	U.Mag. = 0.7602
Gam. = -0.5854	P.Mag. = 1.8080

Total -	1711 Feb 03
Saros 119	12:31 TD
D.Node	ΔT= 9s
Tot. = 97m	
Par. = 217m	U.Mag. = 1.6309
Gam. = -0.1197	P.Mag. = 2.6457

Total +	1711 Jul 29
Saros 124	17:50 TD
A.Node	ΔT= 9s
Tot. = 92m	
Par. = 216m	U.Mag. = 1.4889
Gam. = 0.2033	P.Mag. = 2.4810

Partial	1712 Jan 23
Saros 129	19:47 TD
D.Node	ΔT= 9s
Par. = 117m	U.Mag. = 0.2535
Gam. = -0.8545	P.Mag. = 1.3274

Partial	1712 Jul 18
Saros 134	08:22 TD
A.Node	ΔT= 9s
Par. = 88m	U.Mag. = 0.1677
Gam. = 0.9351	P.Mag. = 1.1162

Penumbral	1712 Dec 13
Saros 101	00:54 TD
D.Node	ΔT= 9s
Pen. = 123m	U.Mag. = -0.9401
Gam. = 1.4978	P.Mag. = 0.1604

Penumbral	1713 Jan 11
Saros 139	20:15 TD
D.Node	ΔT= 9s
Pen. = 73m	U.Mag. = -1.0512
Gam. = -1.5570	P.Mag. = 0.0545

Partial	1713 Jun 08
Saros 106	18:28 TD
A.Node	ΔT= 9s
Par. = 118m	U.Mag. = 0.3090
Gam. = -0.8551	P.Mag. = 1.2686

Partial	1713 Dec 02
Saros 111	03:17 TD
D.Node	ΔT= 9s
Par. = 143m	U.Mag. = 0.4150
Gam. = 0.7716	P.Mag. = 1.4699

Plate 043

139

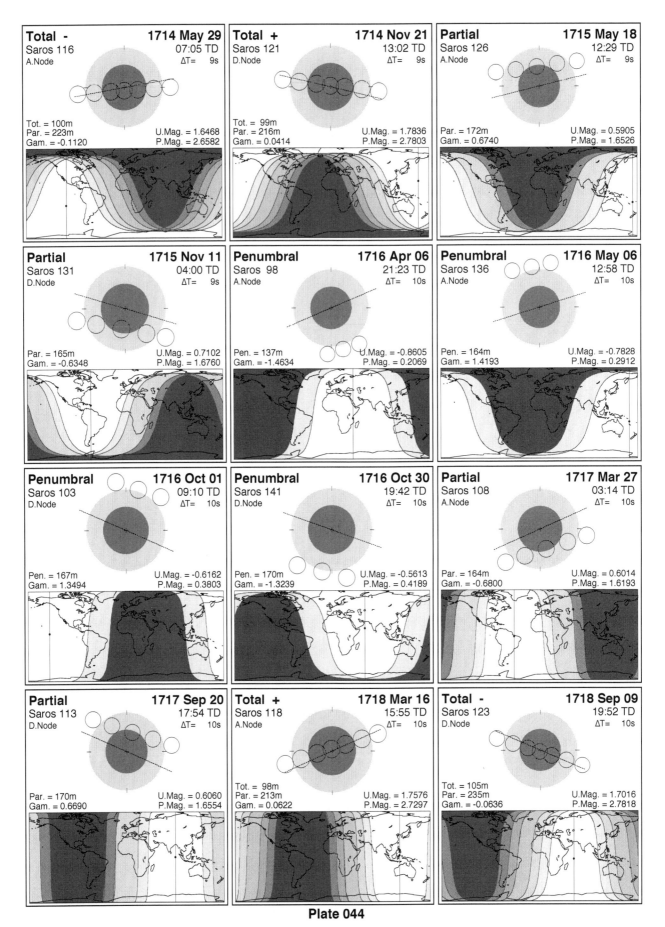

Total - **1714 May 29**
Saros 116 07:05 TD
A.Node ΔT= 9s
Tot. = 100m
Par. = 223m U.Mag. = 1.6468
Gam. = -0.1120 P.Mag. = 2.6582

Total + **1714 Nov 21**
Saros 121 13:02 TD
D.Node ΔT= 9s
Tot. = 99m
Par. = 216m U.Mag. = 1.7836
Gam. = 0.0414 P.Mag. = 2.7803

Partial **1715 May 18**
Saros 126 12:29 TD
A.Node ΔT= 9s
Par. = 172m U.Mag. = 0.5905
Gam. = 0.6740 P.Mag. = 1.6526

Partial **1715 Nov 11**
Saros 131 04:00 TD
D.Node ΔT= 9s
Par. = 165m U.Mag. = 0.7102
Gam. = -0.6348 P.Mag. = 1.6760

Penumbral **1716 Apr 06**
Saros 98 21:23 TD
A.Node ΔT= 10s
Pen. = 137m U.Mag. = -0.8605
Gam. = -1.4634 P.Mag. = 0.2069

Penumbral **1716 May 06**
Saros 136 12:58 TD
A.Node ΔT= 10s
Pen. = 164m U.Mag. = -0.7828
Gam. = 1.4193 P.Mag. = 0.2912

Penumbral **1716 Oct 01**
Saros 103 09:10 TD
D.Node ΔT= 10s
Pen. = 167m U.Mag. = -0.6162
Gam. = 1.3494 P.Mag. = 0.3803

Penumbral **1716 Oct 30**
Saros 141 19:42 TD
D.Node ΔT= 10s
Pen. = 170m U.Mag. = -0.5613
Gam. = -1.3239 P.Mag. = 0.4189

Partial **1717 Mar 27**
Saros 108 03:14 TD
A.Node ΔT= 10s
Par. = 164m U.Mag. = 0.6014
Gam. = -0.6800 P.Mag. = 1.6193

Partial **1717 Sep 20**
Saros 113 17:54 TD
D.Node ΔT= 10s
Par. = 170m U.Mag. = 0.6060
Gam. = 0.6690 P.Mag. = 1.6554

Total + **1718 Mar 16**
Saros 118 15:55 TD
A.Node ΔT= 10s
Tot. = 98m
Par. = 213m U.Mag. = 1.7576
Gam. = 0.0622 P.Mag. = 2.7297

Total - **1718 Sep 09**
Saros 123 19:52 TD
D.Node ΔT= 10s
Tot. = 105m
Par. = 235m U.Mag. = 1.7016
Gam. = -0.0636 P.Mag. = 2.7818

Plate 044

140

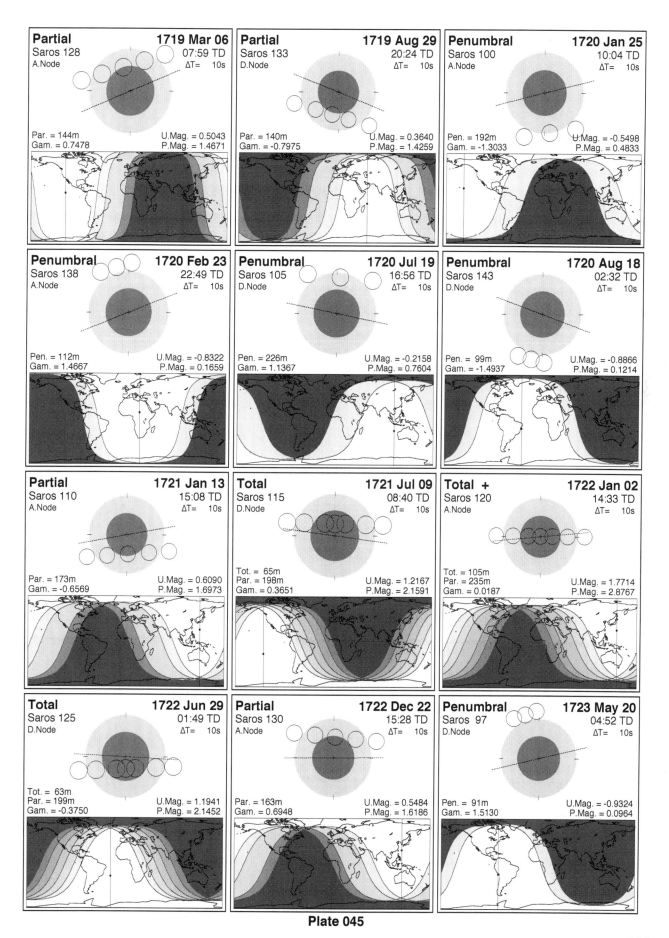

Partial   **1719 Mar 06**
Saros 128   07:59 TD
A.Node   ΔT= 10s
Par. = 144m   U.Mag. = 0.5043
Gam. = 0.7478   P.Mag. = 1.4671

Partial   **1719 Aug 29**
Saros 133   20:24 TD
D.Node   ΔT= 10s
Par. = 140m   U.Mag. = 0.3640
Gam. = -0.7975   P.Mag. = 1.4259

Penumbral   **1720 Jan 25**
Saros 100   10:04 TD
A.Node   ΔT= 10s
Pen. = 192m   U.Mag. = -0.5498
Gam. = -1.3033   P.Mag. = 0.4833

Penumbral   **1720 Feb 23**
Saros 138   22:49 TD
A.Node   ΔT= 10s
Pen. = 112m   U.Mag. = -0.8322
Gam. = 1.4667   P.Mag. = 0.1659

Penumbral   **1720 Jul 19**
Saros 105   16:56 TD
D.Node   ΔT= 10s
Pen. = 226m   U.Mag. = -0.2158
Gam. = 1.1367   P.Mag. = 0.7604

Penumbral   **1720 Aug 18**
Saros 143   02:32 TD
D.Node   ΔT= 10s
Pen. = 99m   U.Mag. = -0.8866
Gam. = -1.4937   P.Mag. = 0.1214

Partial   **1721 Jan 13**
Saros 110   15:08 TD
A.Node   ΔT= 10s
Par. = 173m   U.Mag. = 0.6090
Gam. = -0.6569   P.Mag. = 1.6973

Total   **1721 Jul 09**
Saros 115   08:40 TD
D.Node   ΔT= 10s
Tot. = 65m
Par. = 198m   U.Mag. = 1.2167
Gam. = 0.3651   P.Mag. = 2.1591

Total +   **1722 Jan 02**
Saros 120   14:33 TD
A.Node   ΔT= 10s
Tot. = 105m
Par. = 235m   U.Mag. = 1.7714
Gam. = 0.0187   P.Mag. = 2.8767

Total   **1722 Jun 29**
Saros 125   01:49 TD
D.Node   ΔT= 10s
Tot. = 63m
Par. = 199m   U.Mag. = 1.1941
Gam. = -0.3750   P.Mag. = 2.1452

Partial   **1722 Dec 22**
Saros 130   15:28 TD
A.Node   ΔT= 10s
Par. = 163m   U.Mag. = 0.5484
Gam. = 0.6948   P.Mag. = 1.6186

Penumbral   **1723 May 20**
Saros 97   04:52 TD
D.Node   ΔT= 10s
Pen. = 91m   U.Mag. = -0.9324
Gam. = 1.5130   P.Mag. = 0.0964

Plate 045

141

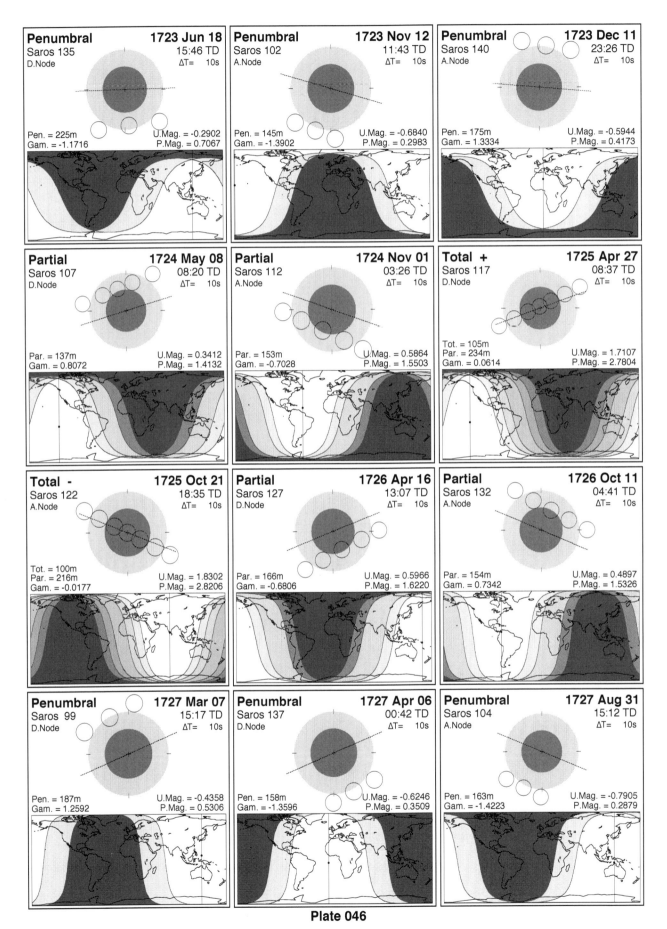

Penumbral   **1723 Jun 18**
Saros 135   15:46 TD
D.Node   ΔT=   10s

Pen. = 225m   U.Mag. = -0.2902
Gam. = -1.1716   P.Mag. = 0.7067

Penumbral   **1723 Nov 12**
Saros 102   11:43 TD
A.Node   ΔT=   10s

Pen. = 145m   U.Mag. = -0.6840
Gam. = -1.3902   P.Mag. = 0.2983

Penumbral   **1723 Dec 11**
Saros 140   23:26 TD
A.Node   ΔT=   10s

Pen. = 175m   U.Mag. = -0.5944
Gam. = 1.3334   P.Mag. = 0.4173

Partial   **1724 May 08**
Saros 107   08:20 TD
D.Node   ΔT=   10s

Par. = 137m   U.Mag. = 0.3412
Gam. = 0.8072   P.Mag. = 1.4132

Partial   **1724 Nov 01**
Saros 112   03:26 TD
A.Node   ΔT=   10s

Par. = 153m   U.Mag. = 0.5864
Gam. = -0.7028   P.Mag. = 1.5503

Total +   **1725 Apr 27**
Saros 117   08:37 TD
D.Node   ΔT=   10s

Tot. = 105m
Par. = 234m   U.Mag. = 1.7107
Gam. = 0.0614   P.Mag. = 2.7804

Total -   **1725 Oct 21**
Saros 122   18:35 TD
A.Node   ΔT=   10s

Tot. = 100m
Par. = 216m   U.Mag. = 1.8302
Gam. = -0.0177   P.Mag. = 2.8206

Partial   **1726 Apr 16**
Saros 127   13:07 TD
D.Node   ΔT=   10s

Par. = 166m   U.Mag. = 0.5966
Gam. = -0.6806   P.Mag. = 1.6220

Partial   **1726 Oct 11**
Saros 132   04:41 TD
A.Node   ΔT=   10s

Par. = 154m   U.Mag. = 0.4897
Gam. = 0.7342   P.Mag. = 1.5326

Penumbral   **1727 Mar 07**
Saros 99   15:17 TD
D.Node   ΔT=   10s

Pen. = 187m   U.Mag. = -0.4358
Gam. = 1.2592   P.Mag. = 0.5306

Penumbral   **1727 Apr 06**
Saros 137   00:42 TD
D.Node   ΔT=   10s

Pen. = 158m   U.Mag. = -0.6246
Gam. = -1.3596   P.Mag. = 0.3509

Penumbral   **1727 Aug 31**
Saros 104   15:12 TD
A.Node   ΔT=   10s

Pen. = 163m   U.Mag. = -0.7905
Gam. = -1.4223   P.Mag. = 0.2879

Plate 046

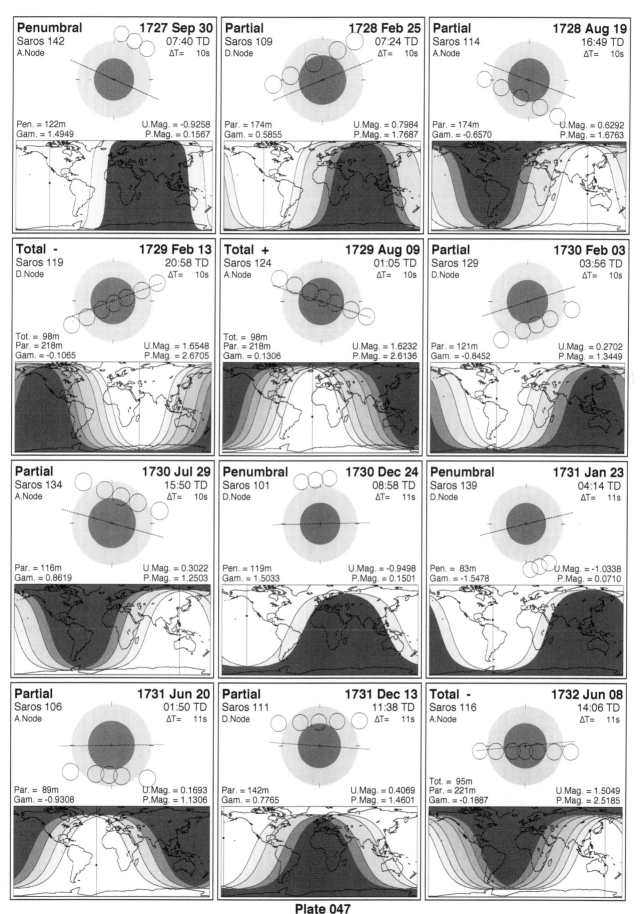

Penumbral 1727 Sep 30 Saros 142 07:40 TD A.Node ΔT= 10s Pen. = 122m U.Mag. = -0.9258 Gam. = 1.4949 P.Mag. = 0.1567	**Partial** 1728 Feb 25 Saros 109 07:24 TD D.Node ΔT= 10s Par. = 174m U.Mag. = 0.7984 Gam. = 0.5855 P.Mag. = 1.7687	**Partial** 1728 Aug 19 Saros 114 16:49 TD A.Node ΔT= 10s Par. = 174m U.Mag. = 0.6292 Gam. = -0.6570 P.Mag. = 1.6763
Total - 1729 Feb 13 Saros 119 20:58 TD D.Node ΔT= 10s Tot. = 98m Par. = 218m U.Mag. = 1.6548 Gam. = -0.1065 P.Mag. = 2.6705	**Total +** 1729 Aug 09 Saros 124 01:05 TD A.Node ΔT= 10s Tot. = 98m Par. = 218m U.Mag. = 1.6232 Gam. = 0.1306 P.Mag. = 2.6136	**Partial** 1730 Feb 03 Saros 129 03:56 TD D.Node ΔT= 10s Par. = 121m U.Mag. = 0.2702 Gam. = -0.8452 P.Mag. = 1.3449
Partial 1730 Jul 29 Saros 134 15:50 TD A.Node ΔT= 10s Par. = 116m U.Mag. = 0.3022 Gam. = 0.8619 P.Mag. = 1.2503	**Penumbral** 1730 Dec 24 Saros 101 08:58 TD D.Node ΔT= 11s Pen. = 119m U.Mag. = -0.9498 Gam. = 1.5033 P.Mag. = 0.1501	**Penumbral** 1731 Jan 23 Saros 139 04:14 TD D.Node ΔT= 11s Pen. = 83m U.Mag. = -1.0338 Gam. = -1.5478 P.Mag. = 0.0710
Partial 1731 Jun 20 Saros 106 01:50 TD A.Node ΔT= 11s Par. = 89m U.Mag. = 0.1693 Gam. = -0.9308 P.Mag. = 1.1306	**Partial** 1731 Dec 13 Saros 111 11:38 TD D.Node ΔT= 11s Par. = 142m U.Mag. = 0.4069 Gam. = 0.7765 P.Mag. = 1.4601	**Total -** 1732 Jun 08 Saros 116 14:06 TD A.Node ΔT= 11s Tot. = 95m Par. = 221m U.Mag. = 1.5049 Gam. = -0.1887 P.Mag. = 2.5185

Plate 047

143

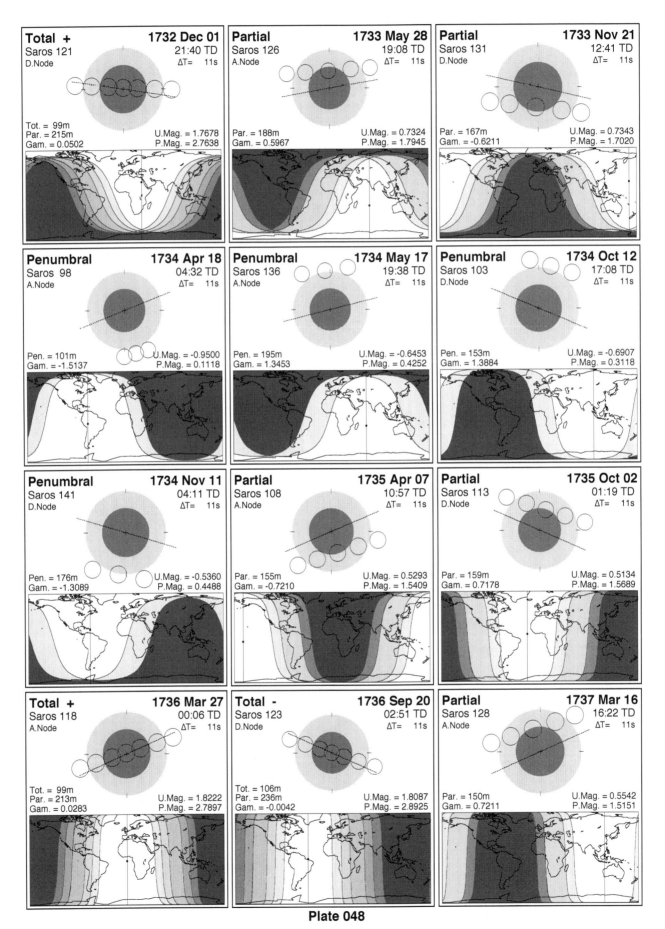

Total + **1732 Dec 01** Saros 121 21:40 TD D.Node ΔT= 11s Tot. = 99m Par. = 215m Gam. = 0.0502 U.Mag. = 1.7678 P.Mag. = 2.7638	**Partial** **1733 May 28** Saros 126 19:08 TD A.Node ΔT= 11s Par. = 188m Gam. = 0.5967 U.Mag. = 0.7324 P.Mag. = 1.7945	**Partial** **1733 Nov 21** Saros 131 12:41 TD D.Node ΔT= 11s Par. = 167m Gam. = -0.6211 U.Mag. = 0.7343 P.Mag. = 1.7020
Penumbral **1734 Apr 18** Saros 98 04:32 TD A.Node ΔT= 11s Pen. = 101m Gam. = -1.5137 U.Mag. = -0.9500 P.Mag. = 0.1118	**Penumbral** **1734 May 17** Saros 136 19:38 TD A.Node ΔT= 11s Pen. = 195m Gam. = 1.3453 U.Mag. = -0.6453 P.Mag. = 0.4252	**Penumbral** **1734 Oct 12** Saros 103 17:08 TD D.Node ΔT= 11s Pen. = 153m Gam. = 1.3884 U.Mag. = -0.6907 P.Mag. = 0.3118
Penumbral **1734 Nov 11** Saros 141 04:11 TD D.Node ΔT= 11s Pen. = 176m Gam. = -1.3089 U.Mag. = -0.5360 P.Mag. = 0.4488	**Partial** **1735 Apr 07** Saros 108 10:57 TD A.Node ΔT= 11s Par. = 155m Gam. = -0.7210 U.Mag. = 0.5293 P.Mag. = 1.5409	**Partial** **1735 Oct 02** Saros 113 01:19 TD D.Node ΔT= 11s Par. = 159m Gam. = 0.7178 U.Mag. = 0.5134 P.Mag. = 1.5689
Total + **1736 Mar 27** Saros 118 00:06 TD A.Node ΔT= 11s Tot. = 99m Par. = 213m Gam. = 0.0283 U.Mag. = 1.8222 P.Mag. = 2.7897	**Total -** **1736 Sep 20** Saros 123 02:51 TD D.Node ΔT= 11s Tot. = 106m Par. = 236m Gam. = -0.0042 U.Mag. = 1.8087 P.Mag. = 2.8925	**Partial** **1737 Mar 16** Saros 128 16:22 TD A.Node ΔT= 11s Par. = 150m Gam. = 0.7211 U.Mag. = 0.5542 P.Mag. = 1.5151

Plate 048

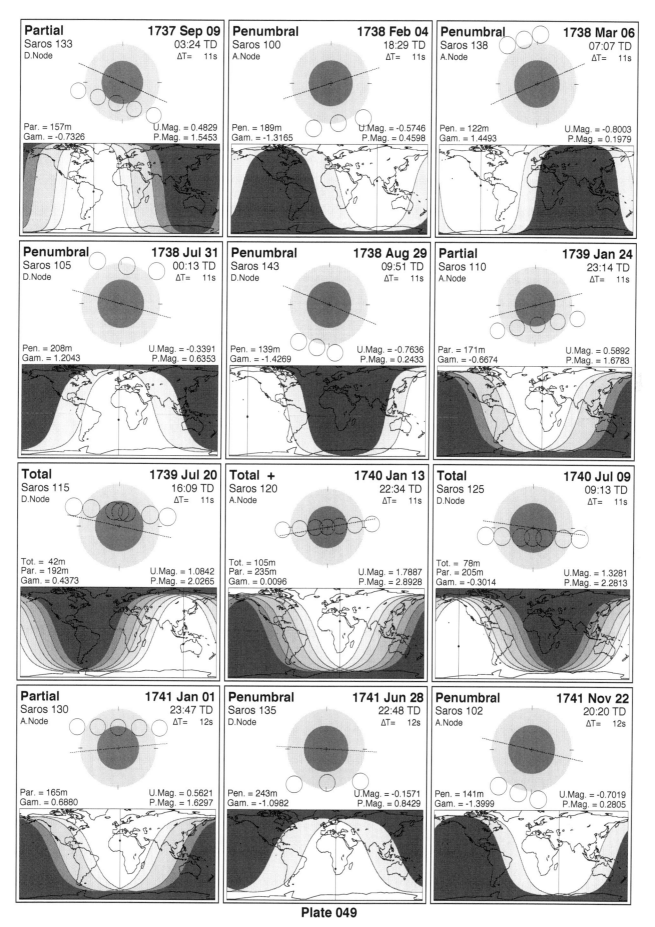

Partial **1737 Sep 09**	
Saros 133 03:24 TD	
D.Node ΔT= 11s	
Par. = 157m U.Mag. = 0.4829	
Gam. = -0.7326 P.Mag. = 1.5453	

Penumbral **1738 Feb 04**	
Saros 100 18:29 TD	
A.Node ΔT= 11s	
Pen. = 189m U.Mag. = -0.5746	
Gam. = -1.3165 P.Mag. = 0.4598	

Penumbral **1738 Mar 06**	
Saros 138 07:07 TD	
A.Node ΔT= 11s	
Pen. = 122m U.Mag. = -0.8003	
Gam. = 1.4493 P.Mag. = 0.1979	

Penumbral **1738 Jul 31**	
Saros 105 00:13 TD	
D.Node ΔT= 11s	
Pen. = 208m U.Mag. = -0.3391	
Gam. = 1.2043 P.Mag. = 0.6353	

Penumbral **1738 Aug 29**	
Saros 143 09:51 TD	
D.Node ΔT= 11s	
Pen. = 139m U.Mag. = -0.7636	
Gam. = -1.4269 P.Mag. = 0.2433	

Partial **1739 Jan 24**	
Saros 110 23:14 TD	
A.Node ΔT= 11s	
Par. = 171m U.Mag. = 0.5892	
Gam. = -0.6674 P.Mag. = 1.6783	

Total **1739 Jul 20**	
Saros 115 16:09 TD	
D.Node ΔT= 11s	
Tot. = 42m	
Par. = 192m U.Mag. = 1.0842	
Gam. = 0.4373 P.Mag. = 2.0265	

Total + **1740 Jan 13**	
Saros 120 22:34 TD	
A.Node ΔT= 11s	
Tot. = 105m	
Par. = 235m U.Mag. = 1.7887	
Gam. = 0.0096 P.Mag. = 2.8928	

Total **1740 Jul 09**	
Saros 125 09:13 TD	
D.Node ΔT= 11s	
Tot. = 78m	
Par. = 205m U.Mag. = 1.3281	
Gam. = -0.3014 P.Mag. = 2.2813	

Partial **1741 Jan 01**	
Saros 130 23:47 TD	
A.Node ΔT= 12s	
Par. = 165m U.Mag. = 0.5621	
Gam. = 0.6880 P.Mag. = 1.6297	

Penumbral **1741 Jun 28**	
Saros 135 22:48 TD	
D.Node ΔT= 12s	
Pen. = 243m U.Mag. = -0.1571	
Gam. = -1.0982 P.Mag. = 0.8429	

Penumbral **1741 Nov 22**	
Saros 102 20:20 TD	
A.Node ΔT= 12s	
Pen. = 141m U.Mag. = -0.7019	
Gam. = -1.3999 P.Mag. = 0.2805	

Plate 049

145

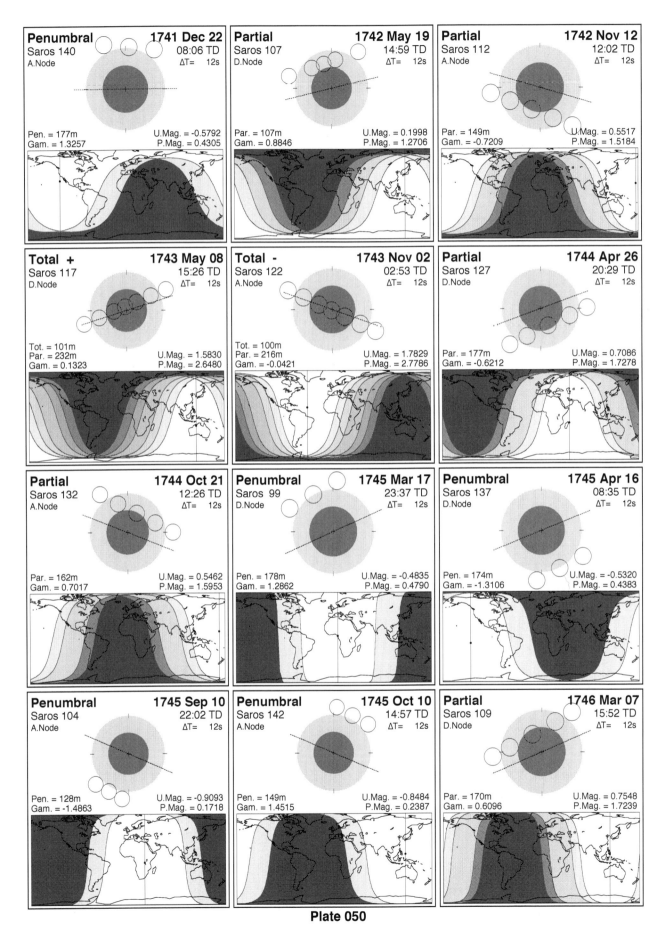

Penumbral **1741 Dec 22**	**Partial** **1742 May 19**	**Partial** **1742 Nov 12**
Saros 140 08:06 TD	Saros 107 14:59 TD	Saros 112 12:02 TD
A.Node ΔT= 12s	D.Node ΔT= 12s	A.Node ΔT= 12s
Pen. = 177m U.Mag. = -0.5792	Par. = 107m U.Mag. = 0.1998	Par. = 149m U.Mag. = 0.5517
Gam. = 1.3257 P.Mag. = 0.4305	Gam. = 0.8846 P.Mag. = 1.2706	Gam. = -0.7209 P.Mag. = 1.5184
Total + **1743 May 08**	**Total -** **1743 Nov 02**	**Partial** **1744 Apr 26**
Saros 117 15:26 TD	Saros 122 02:53 TD	Saros 127 20:29 TD
D.Node ΔT= 12s	A.Node ΔT= 12s	D.Node ΔT= 12s
Tot. = 101m	Tot. = 100m	
Par. = 232m U.Mag. = 1.5830	Par. = 216m U.Mag. = 1.7829	Par. = 177m U.Mag. = 0.7086
Gam. = 0.1323 P.Mag. = 2.6480	Gam. = -0.0421 P.Mag. = 2.7786	Gam. = -0.6212 P.Mag. = 1.7278
Partial **1744 Oct 21**	**Penumbral** **1745 Mar 17**	**Penumbral** **1745 Apr 16**
Saros 132 12:26 TD	Saros 99 23:37 TD	Saros 137 08:35 TD
A.Node ΔT= 12s	D.Node ΔT= 12s	D.Node ΔT= 12s
Par. = 162m U.Mag. = 0.5462	Pen. = 178m U.Mag. = -0.4835	Pen. = 174m U.Mag. = -0.5320
Gam. = 0.7017 P.Mag. = 1.5953	Gam. = 1.2862 P.Mag. = 0.4790	Gam. = -1.3106 P.Mag. = 0.4383
Penumbral **1745 Sep 10**	**Penumbral** **1745 Oct 10**	**Partial** **1746 Mar 07**
Saros 104 22:02 TD	Saros 142 14:57 TD	Saros 109 15:52 TD
A.Node ΔT= 12s	A.Node ΔT= 12s	D.Node ΔT= 12s
Pen. = 128m U.Mag. = -0.9093	Pen. = 149m U.Mag. = -0.8484	Par. = 170m U.Mag. = 0.7548
Gam. = -1.4863 P.Mag. = 0.1718	Gam. = 1.4515 P.Mag. = 0.2387	Gam. = 0.6096 P.Mag. = 1.7239

Plate 050

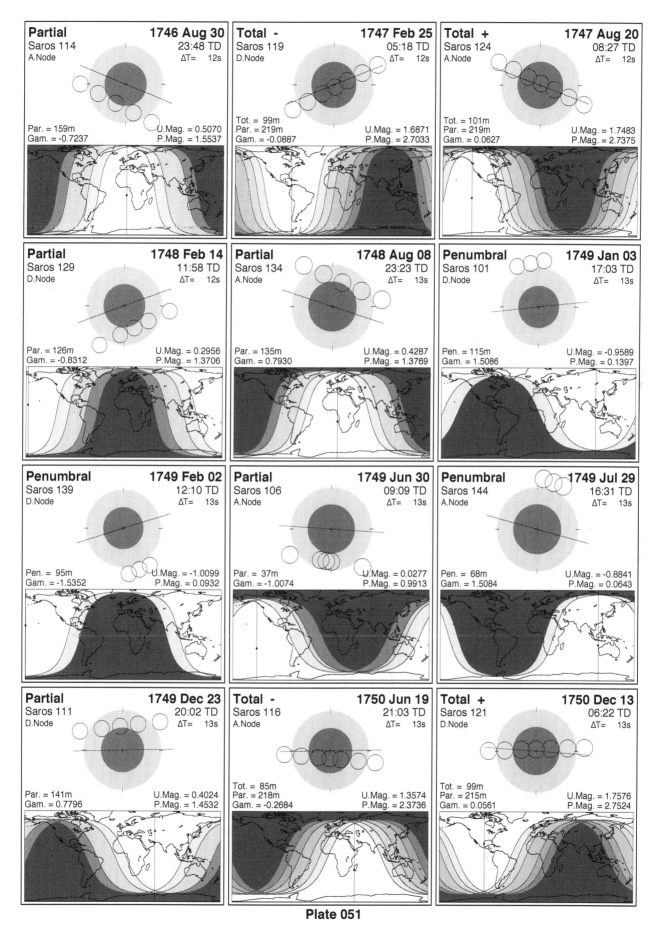

Partial   **1746 Aug 30**
Saros 114   23:48 TD
A.Node   ΔT= 12s

Par. = 159m
Gam. = -0.7237   U.Mag. = 0.5070
     P.Mag. = 1.5537

Total -   **1747 Feb 25**
Saros 119   05:18 TD
D.Node   ΔT= 12s

Tot. = 99m
Par. = 219m
Gam. = -0.0887   U.Mag. = 1.6871
     P.Mag. = 2.7033

Total +   **1747 Aug 20**
Saros 124   08:27 TD
A.Node   ΔT= 12s

Tot. = 101m
Par. = 219m
Gam. = 0.0627   U.Mag. = 1.7483
     P.Mag. = 2.7375

Partial   **1748 Feb 14**
Saros 129   11:58 TD
D.Node   ΔT= 12s

Par. = 126m
Gam. = -0.8312   U.Mag. = 0.2956
     P.Mag. = 1.3706

Partial   **1748 Aug 08**
Saros 134   23:23 TD
A.Node   ΔT= 13s

Par. = 135m
Gam. = 0.7930   U.Mag. = 0.4287
     P.Mag. = 1.3769

Penumbral   **1749 Jan 03**
Saros 101   17:03 TD
D.Node   ΔT= 13s

Pen. = 115m
Gam. = 1.5086   U.Mag. = -0.9589
     P.Mag. = 0.1397

Penumbral   **1749 Feb 02**
Saros 139   12:10 TD
D.Node   ΔT= 13s

Pen. = 95m
Gam. = -1.5352   U.Mag. = -1.0099
     P.Mag. = 0.0932

Partial   **1749 Jun 30**
Saros 106   09:09 TD
A.Node   ΔT= 13s

Par. = 37m
Gam. = -1.0074   U.Mag. = 0.0277
     P.Mag. = 0.9913

Penumbral   **1749 Jul 29**
Saros 144   16:31 TD
A.Node   ΔT= 13s

Pen. = 68m
Gam. = 1.5084   U.Mag. = -0.8841
     P.Mag. = 0.0643

Partial   **1749 Dec 23**
Saros 111   20:02 TD
D.Node   ΔT= 13s

Par. = 141m
Gam. = 0.7796   U.Mag. = 0.4024
     P.Mag. = 1.4532

Total -   **1750 Jun 19**
Saros 116   21:03 TD
A.Node   ΔT= 13s

Tot. = 85m
Par. = 218m
Gam. = -0.2684   U.Mag. = 1.3574
     P.Mag. = 2.3736

Total +   **1750 Dec 13**
Saros 121   06:22 TD
D.Node   ΔT= 13s

Tot. = 99m
Par. = 215m
Gam. = 0.0561   U.Mag. = 1.7576
     P.Mag. = 2.7524

Plate 051

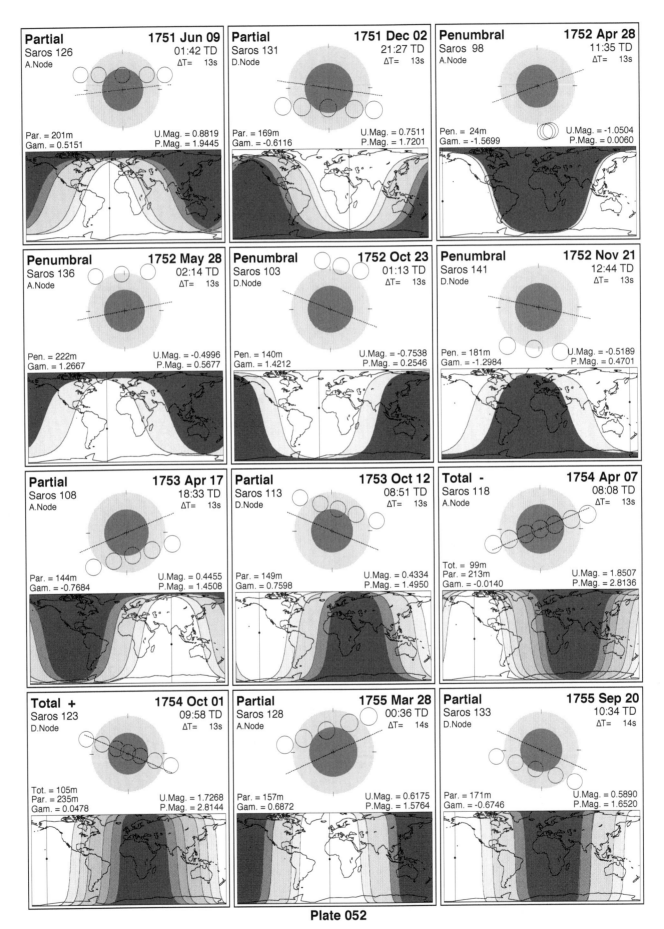

Partial   1751 Jun 09
Saros 126   01:42 TD
A.Node   ΔT=   13s
Par. = 201m   U.Mag. = 0.8819
Gam. = 0.5151   P.Mag. = 1.9445

Partial   1751 Dec 02
Saros 131   21:27 TD
D.Node   ΔT=   13s
Par. = 169m   U.Mag. = 0.7511
Gam. = -0.6116   P.Mag. = 1.7201

Penumbral   1752 Apr 28
Saros 98   11:35 TD
A.Node   ΔT=   13s
Pen. = 24m   U.Mag. = -1.0504
Gam. = -1.5699   P.Mag. = 0.0060

Penumbral   1752 May 28
Saros 136   02:14 TD
A.Node   ΔT=   13s
Pen. = 222m   U.Mag. = -0.4996
Gam. = 1.2667   P.Mag. = 0.5677

Penumbral   1752 Oct 23
Saros 103   01:13 TD
D.Node   ΔT=   13s
Pen. = 140m   U.Mag. = -0.7538
Gam. = 1.4212   P.Mag. = 0.2546

Penumbral   1752 Nov 21
Saros 141   12:44 TD
D.Node   ΔT=   13s
Pen. = 181m   U.Mag. = -0.5189
Gam. = -1.2984   P.Mag. = 0.4701

Partial   1753 Apr 17
Saros 108   18:33 TD
A.Node   ΔT=   13s
Par. = 144m   U.Mag. = 0.4455
Gam. = -0.7684   P.Mag. = 1.4508

Partial   1753 Oct 12
Saros 113   08:51 TD
D.Node   ΔT=   13s
Par. = 149m   U.Mag. = 0.4334
Gam. = 0.7598   P.Mag. = 1.4950

Total -   1754 Apr 07
Saros 118   08:08 TD
A.Node   ΔT=   13s
Tot. = 99m
Par. = 213m   U.Mag. = 1.8507
Gam. = -0.0140   P.Mag. = 2.8136

Total +   1754 Oct 01
Saros 123   09:58 TD
D.Node   ΔT=   13s
Tot. = 105m
Par. = 235m   U.Mag. = 1.7268
Gam. = 0.0478   P.Mag. = 2.8144

Partial   1755 Mar 28
Saros 128   00:36 TD
A.Node   ΔT=   14s
Par. = 157m   U.Mag. = 0.6175
Gam. = 0.6872   P.Mag. = 1.5764

Partial   1755 Sep 20
Saros 133   10:34 TD
D.Node   ΔT=   14s
Par. = 171m   U.Mag. = 0.5890
Gam. = -0.6746   P.Mag. = 1.6520

Plate 052

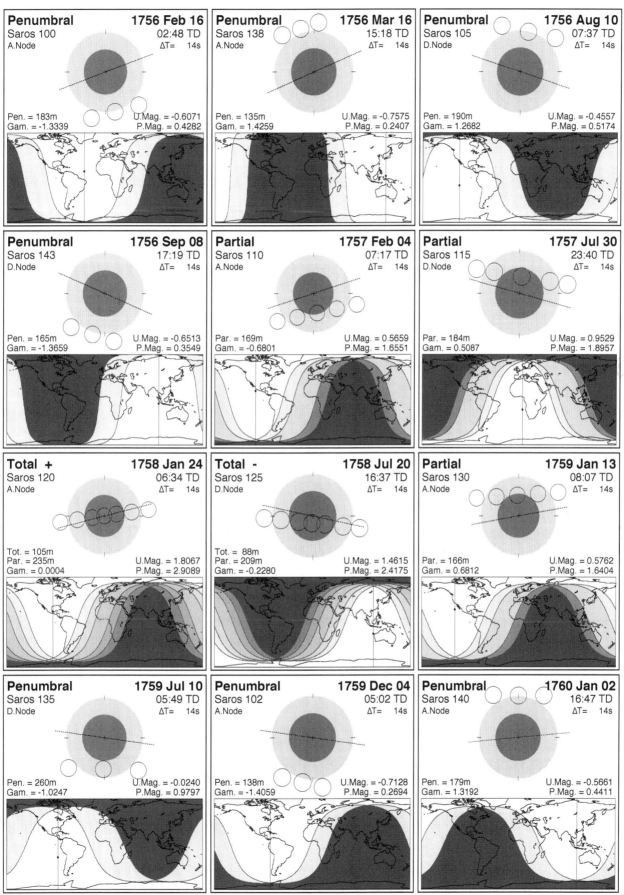

Penumbral	1756 Feb 16
Saros 100	02:48 TD
A.Node	ΔT= 14s
Pen. = 183m	U.Mag. = -0.6071
Gam. = -1.3339	P.Mag. = 0.4282

Penumbral	1756 Mar 16
Saros 138	15:18 TD
A.Node	ΔT= 14s
Pen. = 135m	U.Mag. = -0.7575
Gam. = 1.4259	P.Mag. = 0.2407

Penumbral	1756 Aug 10
Saros 105	07:37 TD
D.Node	ΔT= 14s
Pen. = 190m	U.Mag. = -0.4557
Gam. = 1.2682	P.Mag. = 0.5174

Penumbral	1756 Sep 08
Saros 143	17:19 TD
D.Node	ΔT= 14s
Pen. = 165m	U.Mag. = -0.6513
Gam. = -1.3659	P.Mag. = 0.3549

Partial	1757 Feb 04
Saros 110	07:17 TD
A.Node	ΔT= 14s
Par. = 169m	U.Mag. = 0.5659
Gam. = -0.6801	P.Mag. = 1.6551

Partial	1757 Jul 30
Saros 115	23:40 TD
D.Node	ΔT= 14s
Par. = 184m	U.Mag. = 0.9529
Gam. = 0.5087	P.Mag. = 1.8957

Total +	1758 Jan 24
Saros 120	06:34 TD
A.Node	ΔT= 14s
Tot. = 105m	
Par. = 235m	U.Mag. = 1.8067
Gam. = 0.0004	P.Mag. = 2.9089

Total -	1758 Jul 20
Saros 125	16:37 TD
D.Node	ΔT= 14s
Tot. = 88m	
Par. = 209m	U.Mag. = 1.4615
Gam. = -0.2280	P.Mag. = 2.4175

Partial	1759 Jan 13
Saros 130	08:07 TD
A.Node	ΔT= 14s
Par. = 166m	U.Mag. = 0.5762
Gam. = 0.6812	P.Mag. = 1.6404

Penumbral	1759 Jul 10
Saros 135	05:49 TD
D.Node	ΔT= 14s
Pen. = 260m	U.Mag. = -0.0240
Gam. = -1.0247	P.Mag. = 0.9797

Penumbral	1759 Dec 04
Saros 102	05:02 TD
A.Node	ΔT= 14s
Pen. = 138m	U.Mag. = -0.7128
Gam. = -1.4059	P.Mag. = 0.2694

Penumbral	1760 Jan 02
Saros 140	16:47 TD
A.Node	ΔT= 14s
Pen. = 179m	U.Mag. = -0.5661
Gam. = 1.3192	P.Mag. = 0.4411

Plate 053

149

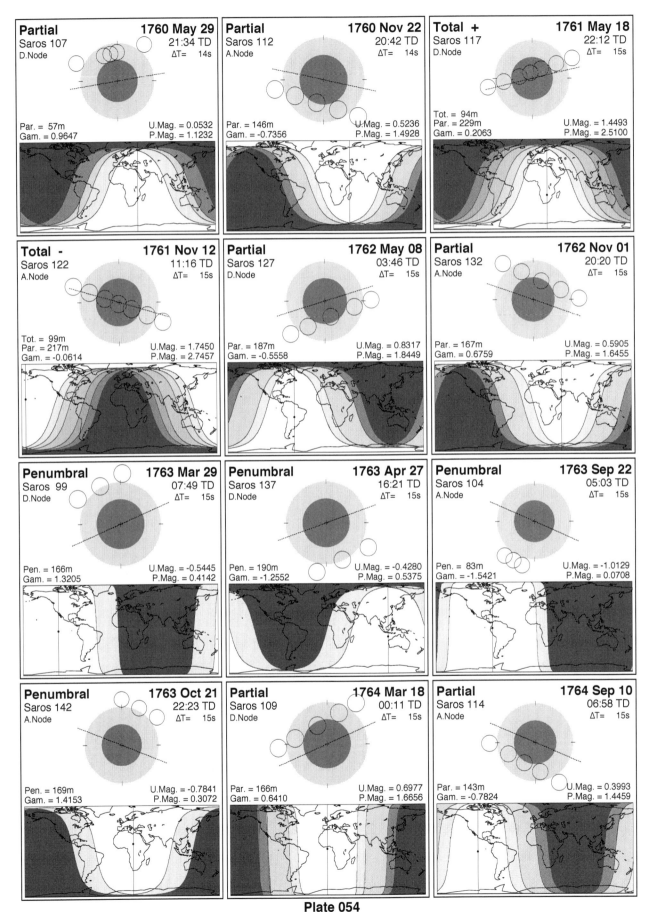

Partial	1760 May 29
Saros 107	21:34 TD
D.Node	ΔT= 14s
Par. = 57m	U.Mag. = 0.0532
Gam. = 0.9647	P.Mag. = 1.1232

Partial	1760 Nov 22
Saros 112	20:42 TD
A.Node	ΔT= 14s
Par. = 146m	U.Mag. = 0.5236
Gam. = -0.7356	P.Mag. = 1.4928

Total +	1761 May 18
Saros 117	22:12 TD
D.Node	ΔT= 15s
Tot. = 94m	
Par. = 229m	U.Mag. = 1.4493
Gam. = 0.2063	P.Mag. = 2.5100

Total -	1761 Nov 12
Saros 122	11:16 TD
A.Node	ΔT= 15s
Tot. = 99m	
Par. = 217m	U.Mag. = 1.7450
Gam. = -0.0614	P.Mag. = 2.7457

Partial	1762 May 08
Saros 127	03:46 TD
D.Node	ΔT= 15s
Par. = 187m	U.Mag. = 0.8317
Gam. = -0.5558	P.Mag. = 1.8449

Partial	1762 Nov 01
Saros 132	20:20 TD
A.Node	ΔT= 15s
Par. = 167m	U.Mag. = 0.5905
Gam. = 0.6759	P.Mag. = 1.6455

Penumbral	1763 Mar 29
Saros 99	07:49 TD
D.Node	ΔT= 15s
Pen. = 166m	U.Mag. = -0.5445
Gam. = 1.3205	P.Mag. = 0.4142

Penumbral	1763 Apr 27
Saros 137	16:21 TD
D.Node	ΔT= 15s
Pen. = 190m	U.Mag. = -0.4280
Gam. = -1.2552	P.Mag. = 0.5375

Penumbral	1763 Sep 22
Saros 104	05:03 TD
A.Node	ΔT= 15s
Pen. = 83m	U.Mag. = -1.0129
Gam. = -1.5421	P.Mag. = 0.0708

Penumbral	1763 Oct 21
Saros 142	22:23 TD
A.Node	ΔT= 15s
Pen. = 169m	U.Mag. = -0.7841
Gam. = 1.4153	P.Mag. = 0.3072

Partial	1764 Mar 18
Saros 109	00:11 TD
D.Node	ΔT= 15s
Par. = 166m	U.Mag. = 0.6977
Gam. = 0.6410	P.Mag. = 1.6656

Partial	1764 Sep 10
Saros 114	06:58 TD
A.Node	ΔT= 15s
Par. = 143m	U.Mag. = 0.3993
Gam. = -0.7824	P.Mag. = 1.4459

Plate 054

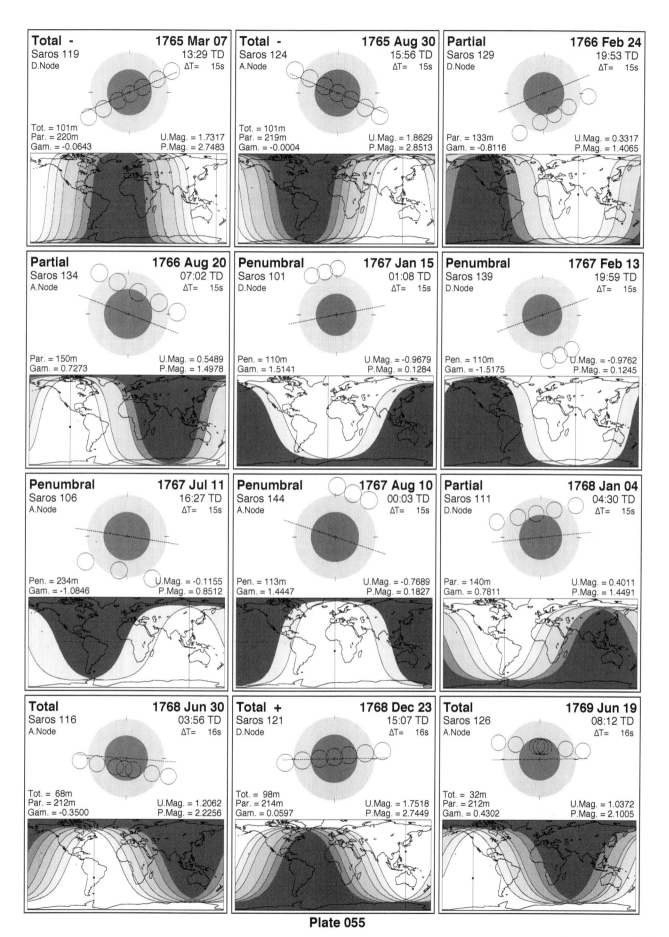

Total -   **1765 Mar 07**
Saros 119   13:29 TD
D.Node   ΔT= 15s
Tot. = 101m
Par. = 220m
Gam. = -0.0643   U.Mag. = 1.7317
     P.Mag. = 2.7483

Total -   **1765 Aug 30**
Saros 124   15:56 TD
A.Node   ΔT= 15s
Tot. = 101m
Par. = 219m
Gam. = -0.0004   U.Mag. = 1.8629
     P.Mag. = 2.8513

Partial   **1766 Feb 24**
Saros 129   19:53 TD
D.Node   ΔT= 15s
Par. = 133m
Gam. = -0.8116   U.Mag. = 0.3317
     P.Mag. = 1.4065

Partial   **1766 Aug 20**
Saros 134   07:02 TD
A.Node   ΔT= 15s
Par. = 150m
Gam. = 0.7273   U.Mag. = 0.5489
     P.Mag. = 1.4978

Penumbral   **1767 Jan 15**
Saros 101   01:08 TD
D.Node   ΔT= 15s
Pen. = 110m
Gam. = 1.5141   U.Mag. = -0.9679
     P.Mag. = 0.1284

Penumbral   **1767 Feb 13**
Saros 139   19:59 TD
D.Node   ΔT= 15s
Pen. = 110m
Gam. = -1.5175   U.Mag. = -0.9762
     P.Mag. = 0.1245

Penumbral   **1767 Jul 11**
Saros 106   16:27 TD
A.Node   ΔT= 15s
Pen. = 234m
Gam. = -1.0846   U.Mag. = -0.1155
     P.Mag. = 0.8512

Penumbral   **1767 Aug 10**
Saros 144   00:03 TD
A.Node   ΔT= 15s
Pen. = 113m
Gam. = 1.4447   U.Mag. = -0.7689
     P.Mag. = 0.1827

Partial   **1768 Jan 04**
Saros 111   04:30 TD
D.Node   ΔT= 15s
Par. = 140m
Gam. = 0.7811   U.Mag. = 0.4011
     P.Mag. = 1.4491

Total   **1768 Jun 30**
Saros 116   03:56 TD
A.Node   ΔT= 16s
Tot. = 68m
Par. = 212m
Gam. = -0.3500   U.Mag. = 1.2062
     P.Mag. = 2.2256

Total +   **1768 Dec 23**
Saros 121   15:07 TD
D.Node   ΔT= 16s
Tot. = 98m
Par. = 214m
Gam. = 0.0597   U.Mag. = 1.7518
     P.Mag. = 2.7449

Total   **1769 Jun 19**
Saros 126   08:12 TD
A.Node   ΔT= 16s
Tot. = 32m
Par. = 212m
Gam. = 0.4302   U.Mag. = 1.0372
     P.Mag. = 2.1005

Plate 055

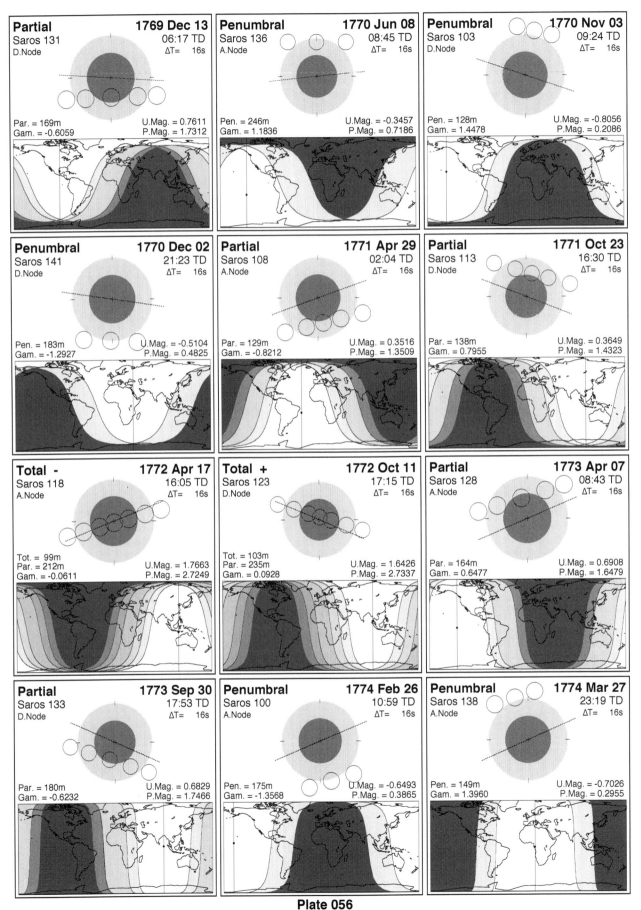

Partial 1769 Dec 13	
Saros 131	06:17 TD
D.Node	ΔT= 16s
Par. = 169m	U.Mag. = 0.7611
Gam. = -0.6059	P.Mag. = 1.7312

Penumbral 1770 Jun 08	
Saros 136	08:45 TD
A.Node	ΔT= 16s
Pen. = 246m	U.Mag. = -0.3457
Gam. = 1.1836	P.Mag. = 0.7186

Penumbral 1770 Nov 03	
Saros 103	09:24 TD
D.Node	ΔT= 16s
Pen. = 128m	U.Mag. = -0.8056
Gam. = 1.4478	P.Mag. = 0.2086

Penumbral 1770 Dec 02	
Saros 141	21:23 TD
D.Node	ΔT= 16s
Pen. = 183m	U.Mag. = -0.5104
Gam. = -1.2927	P.Mag. = 0.4825

Partial 1771 Apr 29	
Saros 108	02:04 TD
A.Node	ΔT= 16s
Par. = 129m	U.Mag. = 0.3516
Gam. = -0.8212	P.Mag. = 1.3509

Partial 1771 Oct 23	
Saros 113	16:30 TD
D.Node	ΔT= 16s
Par. = 138m	U.Mag. = 0.3649
Gam. = 0.7955	P.Mag. = 1.4323

Total - 1772 Apr 17	
Saros 118	16:05 TD
A.Node	ΔT= 16s
Tot. = 99m	
Par. = 212m	U.Mag. = 1.7663
Gam. = -0.0611	P.Mag. = 2.7249

Total + 1772 Oct 11	
Saros 123	17:15 TD
D.Node	ΔT= 16s
Tot. = 103m	
Par. = 235m	U.Mag. = 1.6426
Gam. = 0.0928	P.Mag. = 2.7337

Partial 1773 Apr 07	
Saros 128	08:43 TD
A.Node	ΔT= 16s
Par. = 164m	U.Mag. = 0.6908
Gam. = 0.6477	P.Mag. = 1.6479

Partial 1773 Sep 30	
Saros 133	17:53 TD
D.Node	ΔT= 16s
Par. = 180m	U.Mag. = 0.6829
Gam. = -0.6232	P.Mag. = 1.7466

Penumbral 1774 Feb 26	
Saros 100	10:59 TD
A.Node	ΔT= 16s
Pen. = 175m	U.Mag. = -0.6493
Gam. = -1.3568	P.Mag. = 0.3865

Penumbral 1774 Mar 27	
Saros 138	23:19 TD
A.Node	ΔT= 16s
Pen. = 149m	U.Mag. = -0.7026
Gam. = 1.3960	P.Mag. = 0.2955

Plate 056

152

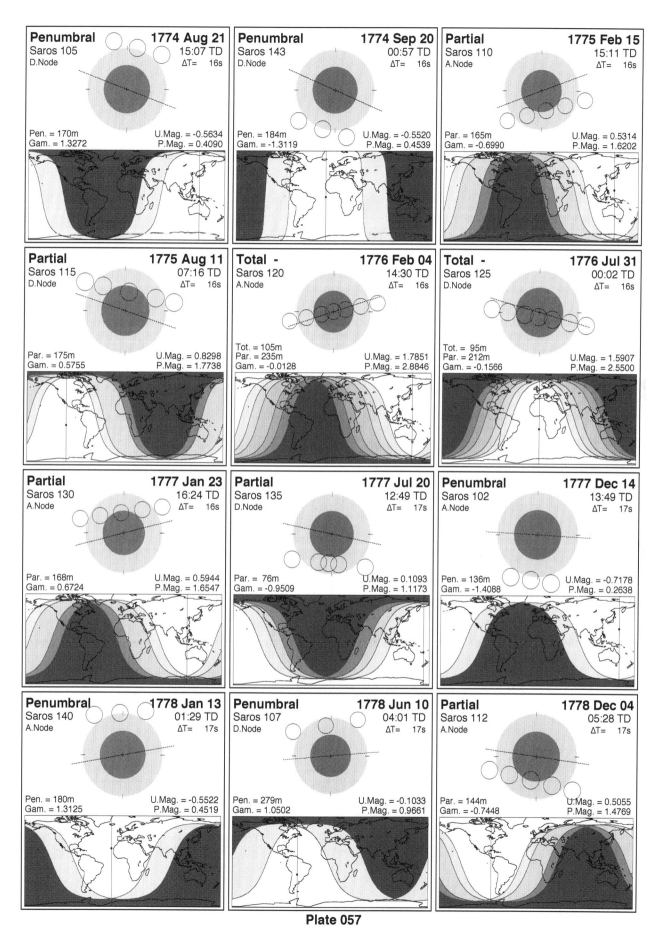

Penumbral   **1774 Aug 21**
Saros 105   15:07 TD
D.Node   ΔT= 16s
Pen. = 170m   U.Mag. = -0.5634
Gam. = 1.3272   P.Mag. = 0.4090

Penumbral   **1774 Sep 20**
Saros 143   00:57 TD
D.Node   ΔT= 16s
Pen. = 184m   U.Mag. = -0.5520
Gam. = -1.3119   P.Mag. = 0.4539

Partial   **1775 Feb 15**
Saros 110   15:11 TD
A.Node   ΔT= 16s
Par. = 165m   U.Mag. = 0.5314
Gam. = -0.6990   P.Mag. = 1.6202

Partial   **1775 Aug 11**
Saros 115   07:16 TD
D.Node   ΔT= 16s
Par. = 175m   U.Mag. = 0.8298
Gam. = 0.5755   P.Mag. = 1.7738

Total -   **1776 Feb 04**
Saros 120   14:30 TD
A.Node   ΔT= 16s
Tot. = 105m
Par. = 235m   U.Mag. = 1.7851
Gam. = -0.0128   P.Mag. = 2.8846

Total -   **1776 Jul 31**
Saros 125   00:02 TD
D.Node   ΔT= 16s
Tot. = 95m
Par. = 212m   U.Mag. = 1.5907
Gam. = -0.1566   P.Mag. = 2.5500

Partial   **1777 Jan 23**
Saros 130   16:24 TD
A.Node   ΔT= 16s
Par. = 168m   U.Mag. = 0.5944
Gam. = 0.6724   P.Mag. = 1.6547

Partial   **1777 Jul 20**
Saros 135   12:49 TD
D.Node   ΔT= 17s
Par. = 76m   U.Mag. = 0.1093
Gam. = -0.9509   P.Mag. = 1.1173

Penumbral   **1777 Dec 14**
Saros 102   13:49 TD
A.Node   ΔT= 17s
Pen. = 136m   U.Mag. = -0.7178
Gam. = -1.4088   P.Mag. = 0.2638

Penumbral   **1778 Jan 13**
Saros 140   01:29 TD
A.Node   ΔT= 17s
Pen. = 180m   U.Mag. = -0.5522
Gam. = 1.3125   P.Mag. = 0.4519

Penumbral   **1778 Jun 10**
Saros 107   04:01 TD
D.Node   ΔT= 17s
Pen. = 279m   U.Mag. = -0.1033
Gam. = 1.0502   P.Mag. = 0.9661

Partial   **1778 Dec 04**
Saros 112   05:28 TD
A.Node   ΔT= 17s
Par. = 144m   U.Mag. = 0.5055
Gam. = -0.7448   P.Mag. = 1.4769

Plate 057

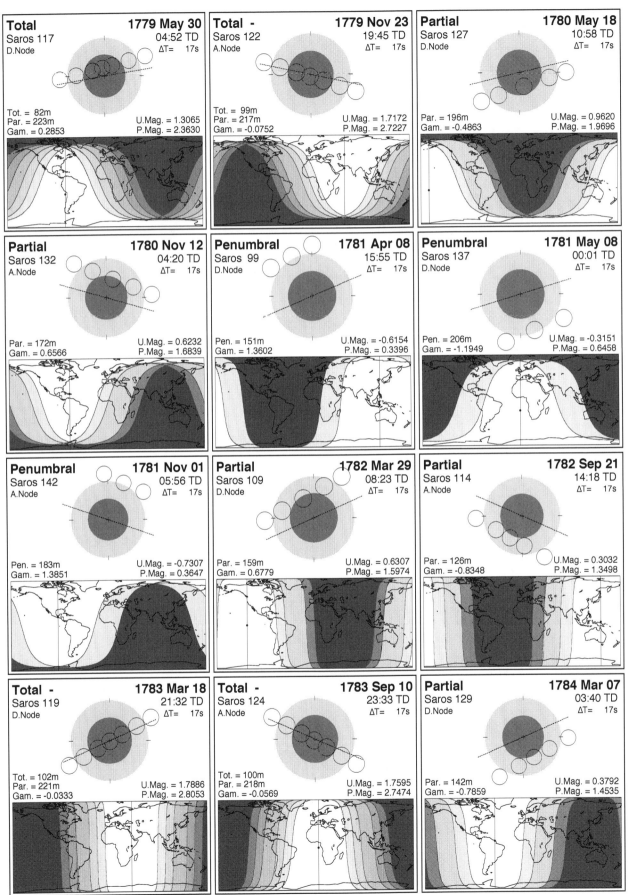

Total   **1779 May 30**
Saros 117   04:52 TD
D.Node   ΔT= 17s
Tot. = 82m
Par. = 223m   U.Mag. = 1.3065
Gam. = 0.2853   P.Mag. = 2.3630

Total -   **1779 Nov 23**
Saros 122   19:45 TD
A.Node   ΔT= 17s
Tot. = 99m
Par. = 217m   U.Mag. = 1.7172
Gam. = -0.0752   P.Mag. = 2.7227

Partial   **1780 May 18**
Saros 127   10:58 TD
D.Node   ΔT= 17s
Par. = 196m   U.Mag. = 0.9620
Gam. = -0.4863   P.Mag. = 1.9696

Partial   **1780 Nov 12**
Saros 132   04:20 TD
A.Node   ΔT= 17s
Par. = 172m   U.Mag. = 0.6232
Gam. = 0.6566   P.Mag. = 1.6839

Penumbral   **1781 Apr 08**
Saros 99   15:55 TD
D.Node   ΔT= 17s
Pen. = 151m   U.Mag. = -0.6154
Gam. = 1.3602   P.Mag. = 0.3396

Penumbral   **1781 May 08**
Saros 137   00:01 TD
D.Node   ΔT= 17s
Pen. = 206m   U.Mag. = -0.3151
Gam. = -1.1949   P.Mag. = 0.6458

Penumbral   **1781 Nov 01**
Saros 142   05:56 TD
A.Node   ΔT= 17s
Pen. = 183m   U.Mag. = -0.7307
Gam. = 1.3851   P.Mag. = 0.3647

Partial   **1782 Mar 29**
Saros 109   08:23 TD
D.Node   ΔT= 17s
Par. = 159m   U.Mag. = 0.6307
Gam. = 0.6779   P.Mag. = 1.5974

Partial   **1782 Sep 21**
Saros 114   14:18 TD
A.Node   ΔT= 17s
Par. = 126m   U.Mag. = 0.3032
Gam. = -0.8348   P.Mag. = 1.3498

Total -   **1783 Mar 18**
Saros 119   21:32 TD
D.Node   ΔT= 17s
Tot. = 102m
Par. = 221m   U.Mag. = 1.7886
Gam. = -0.0333   P.Mag. = 2.8053

Total -   **1783 Sep 10**
Saros 124   23:33 TD
A.Node   ΔT= 17s
Tot. = 100m
Par. = 218m   U.Mag. = 1.7595
Gam. = -0.0569   P.Mag. = 2.7474

Partial   **1784 Mar 07**
Saros 129   03:40 TD
D.Node   ΔT= 17s
Par. = 142m   U.Mag. = 0.3792
Gam. = -0.7859   P.Mag. = 1.4535

Plate 058

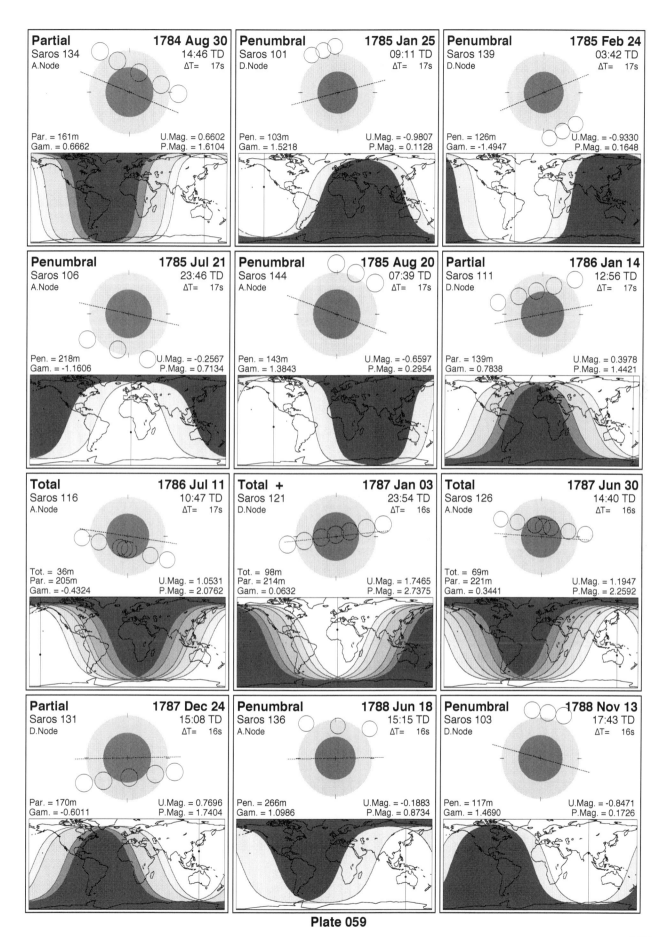

Partial	**1784 Aug 30**
Saros 134	14:46 TD
A.Node	ΔT= 17s
Par. = 161m	U.Mag. = 0.6602
Gam. = 0.6662	P.Mag. = 1.6104

Penumbral	**1785 Jan 25**
Saros 101	09:11 TD
D.Node	ΔT= 17s
Pen. = 103m	U.Mag. = -0.9807
Gam. = 1.5218	P.Mag. = 0.1128

Penumbral	**1785 Feb 24**
Saros 139	03:42 TD
D.Node	ΔT= 17s
Pen. = 126m	U.Mag. = -0.9330
Gam. = -1.4947	P.Mag. = 0.1648

Penumbral	**1785 Jul 21**
Saros 106	23:46 TD
A.Node	ΔT= 17s
Pen. = 218m	U.Mag. = -0.2567
Gam. = -1.1606	P.Mag. = 0.7134

Penumbral	**1785 Aug 20**
Saros 144	07:39 TD
A.Node	ΔT= 17s
Pen. = 143m	U.Mag. = -0.6597
Gam. = 1.3843	P.Mag. = 0.2954

Partial	**1786 Jan 14**
Saros 111	12:56 TD
D.Node	ΔT= 17s
Par. = 139m	U.Mag. = 0.3978
Gam. = 0.7838	P.Mag. = 1.4421

Total	**1786 Jul 11**
Saros 116	10:47 TD
A.Node	ΔT= 17s
Tot. = 36m	
Par. = 205m	U.Mag. = 1.0531
Gam. = -0.4324	P.Mag. = 2.0762

Total +	**1787 Jan 03**
Saros 121	23:54 TD
D.Node	ΔT= 16s
Tot. = 98m	
Par. = 214m	U.Mag. = 1.7465
Gam. = 0.0632	P.Mag. = 2.7375

Total	**1787 Jun 30**
Saros 126	14:40 TD
A.Node	ΔT= 16s
Tot. = 69m	
Par. = 221m	U.Mag. = 1.1947
Gam. = 0.3441	P.Mag. = 2.2592

Partial	**1787 Dec 24**
Saros 131	15:08 TD
D.Node	ΔT= 16s
Par. = 170m	U.Mag. = 0.7696
Gam. = -0.6011	P.Mag. = 1.7404

Penumbral	**1788 Jun 18**
Saros 136	15:15 TD
A.Node	ΔT= 16s
Pen. = 266m	U.Mag. = -0.1883
Gam. = 1.0986	P.Mag. = 0.8734

Penumbral	**1788 Nov 13**
Saros 103	17:43 TD
D.Node	ΔT= 16s
Pen. = 117m	U.Mag. = -0.8471
Gam. = 1.4690	P.Mag. = 0.1726

Plate 059

155

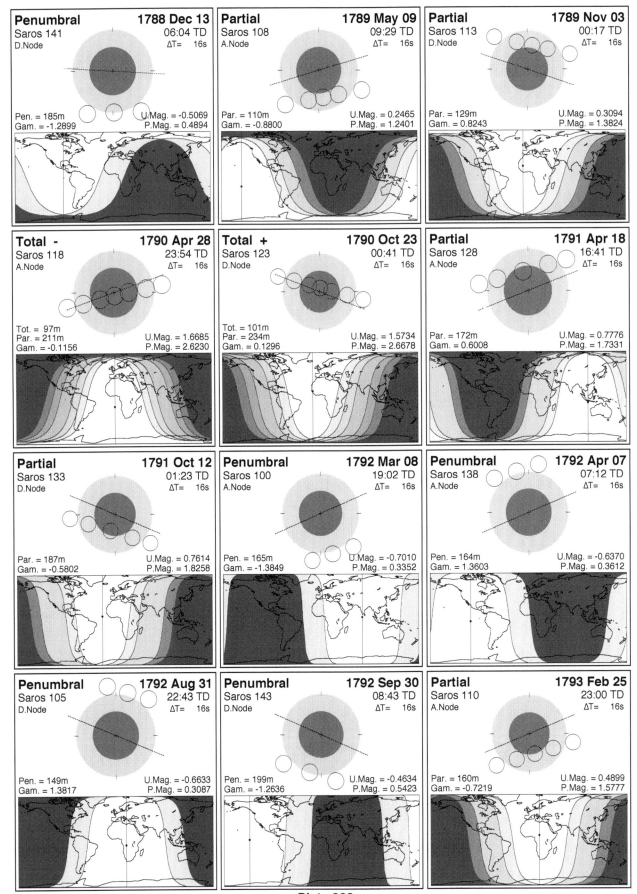

Penumbral — **1788 Dec 13**
Saros 141 — 06:04 TD
D.Node — ΔT= 16s
Pen. = 185m — U.Mag. = -0.5069
Gam. = -1.2899 — P.Mag. = 0.4894

Partial — **1789 May 09**
Saros 108 — 09:29 TD
A.Node — ΔT= 16s
Par. = 110m — U.Mag. = 0.2465
Gam. = -0.8800 — P.Mag. = 1.2401

Partial — **1789 Nov 03**
Saros 113 — 00:17 TD
D.Node — ΔT= 16s
Par. = 129m — U.Mag. = 0.3094
Gam. = 0.8243 — P.Mag. = 1.3824

Total - — **1790 Apr 28**
Saros 118 — 23:54 TD
A.Node — ΔT= 16s
Tot. = 97m
Par. = 211m — U.Mag. = 1.6685
Gam. = -0.1156 — P.Mag. = 2.6230

Total + — **1790 Oct 23**
Saros 123 — 00:41 TD
D.Node — ΔT= 16s
Tot. = 101m
Par. = 234m — U.Mag. = 1.5734
Gam. = 0.1296 — P.Mag. = 2.6678

Partial — **1791 Apr 18**
Saros 128 — 16:41 TD
A.Node — ΔT= 16s
Par. = 172m — U.Mag. = 0.7776
Gam. = 0.6008 — P.Mag. = 1.7331

Partial — **1791 Oct 12**
Saros 133 — 01:23 TD
D.Node — ΔT= 16s
Par. = 187m — U.Mag. = 0.7614
Gam. = -0.5802 — P.Mag. = 1.8258

Penumbral — **1792 Mar 08**
Saros 100 — 19:02 TD
A.Node — ΔT= 16s
Pen. = 165m — U.Mag. = -0.7010
Gam. = -1.3849 — P.Mag. = 0.3352

Penumbral — **1792 Apr 07**
Saros 138 — 07:12 TD
A.Node — ΔT= 16s
Pen. = 164m — U.Mag. = -0.6370
Gam. = 1.3603 — P.Mag. = 0.3612

Penumbral — **1792 Aug 31**
Saros 105 — 22:43 TD
D.Node — ΔT= 16s
Pen. = 149m — U.Mag. = -0.6633
Gam. = 1.3817 — P.Mag. = 0.3087

Penumbral — **1792 Sep 30**
Saros 143 — 08:43 TD
D.Node — ΔT= 16s
Pen. = 199m — U.Mag. = -0.4634
Gam. = -1.2636 — P.Mag. = 0.5423

Partial — **1793 Feb 25**
Saros 110 — 23:00 TD
A.Node — ΔT= 16s
Par. = 160m — U.Mag. = 0.4899
Gam. = -0.7219 — P.Mag. = 1.5777

Plate 060

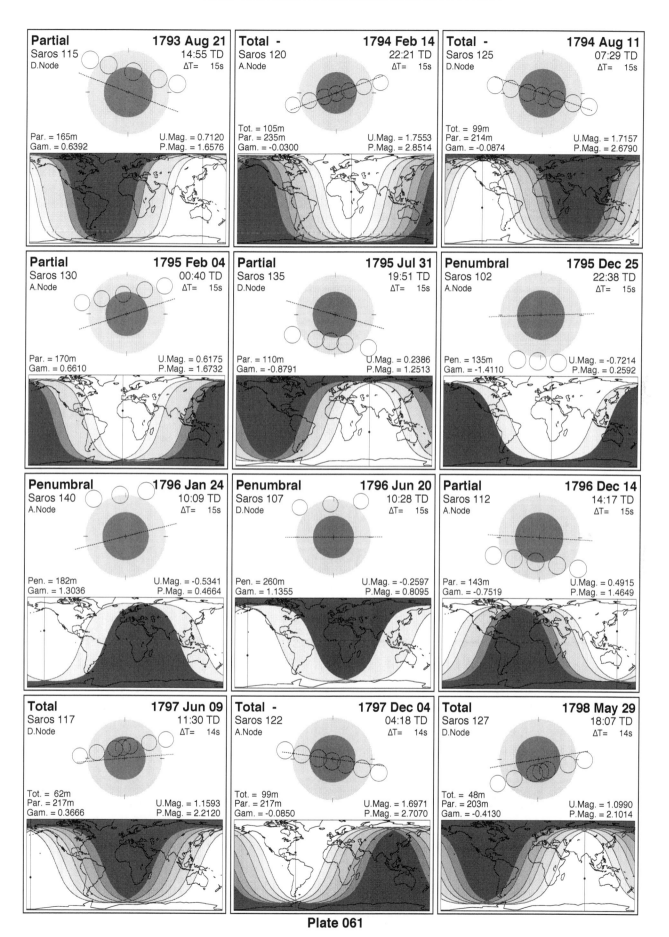

Partial   **1793 Aug 21**
Saros 115   14:55 TD
D.Node   ΔT= 15s
Par. = 165m   U.Mag. = 0.7120
Gam. = 0.6392   P.Mag. = 1.6576

Total -   **1794 Feb 14**
Saros 120   22:21 TD
A.Node   ΔT= 15s
Tot. = 105m
Par. = 235m   U.Mag. = 1.7553
Gam. = -0.0300   P.Mag. = 2.8514

Total -   **1794 Aug 11**
Saros 125   07:29 TD
D.Node   ΔT= 15s
Tot. = 99m
Par. = 214m   U.Mag. = 1.7157
Gam. = -0.0874   P.Mag. = 2.6790

Partial   **1795 Feb 04**
Saros 130   00:40 TD
A.Node   ΔT= 15s
Par. = 170m   U.Mag. = 0.6175
Gam. = 0.6610   P.Mag. = 1.6732

Partial   **1795 Jul 31**
Saros 135   19:51 TD
D.Node   ΔT= 15s
Par. = 110m   U.Mag. = 0.2386
Gam. = -0.8791   P.Mag. = 1.2513

Penumbral   **1795 Dec 25**
Saros 102   22:38 TD
A.Node   ΔT= 15s
Pen. = 135m   U.Mag. = -0.7214
Gam. = -1.4110   P.Mag. = 0.2592

Penumbral   **1796 Jan 24**
Saros 140   10:09 TD
A.Node   ΔT= 15s
Pen. = 182m   U.Mag. = -0.5341
Gam. = 1.3036   P.Mag. = 0.4664

Penumbral   **1796 Jun 20**
Saros 107   10:28 TD
D.Node   ΔT= 15s
Pen. = 260m   U.Mag. = -0.2597
Gam. = 1.1355   P.Mag. = 0.8095

Partial   **1796 Dec 14**
Saros 112   14:17 TD
A.Node   ΔT= 15s
Par. = 143m   U.Mag. = 0.4915
Gam. = -0.7519   P.Mag. = 1.4649

Total   **1797 Jun 09**
Saros 117   11:30 TD
D.Node   ΔT= 14s
Tot. = 62m
Par. = 217m   U.Mag. = 1.1593
Gam. = 0.3666   P.Mag. = 2.2120

Total -   **1797 Dec 04**
Saros 122   04:18 TD
A.Node   ΔT= 14s
Tot. = 99m
Par. = 217m   U.Mag. = 1.6971
Gam. = -0.0850   P.Mag. = 2.7070

Total   **1798 May 29**
Saros 127   18:07 TD
D.Node   ΔT= 14s
Tot. = 48m
Par. = 203m   U.Mag. = 1.0990
Gam. = -0.4130   P.Mag. = 2.1014

Plate 061

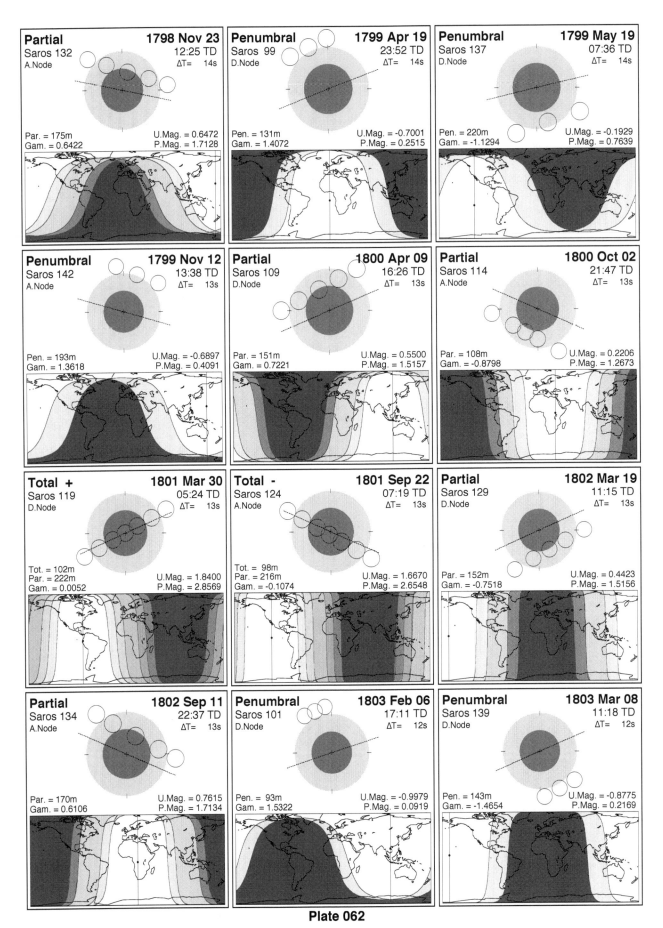

Partial   **1798 Nov 23**
Saros 132   12:25 TD
A.Node   ΔT= 14s
Par. = 175m   U.Mag. = 0.6472
Gam. = 0.6422   P.Mag. = 1.7128

Penumbral   **1799 Apr 19**
Saros 99   23:52 TD
D.Node   ΔT= 14s
Pen. = 131m   U.Mag. = -0.7001
Gam. = 1.4072   P.Mag. = 0.2515

Penumbral   **1799 May 19**
Saros 137   07:36 TD
D.Node   ΔT= 14s
Pen. = 220m   U.Mag. = -0.1929
Gam. = -1.1294   P.Mag. = 0.7639

Penumbral   **1799 Nov 12**
Saros 142   13:38 TD
A.Node   ΔT= 13s
Pen. = 193m   U.Mag. = -0.6897
Gam. = 1.3618   P.Mag. = 0.4091

Partial   **1800 Apr 09**
Saros 109   16:26 TD
D.Node   ΔT= 13s
Par. = 151m   U.Mag. = 0.5500
Gam. = 0.7221   P.Mag. = 1.5157

Partial   **1800 Oct 02**
Saros 114   21:47 TD
A.Node   ΔT= 13s
Par. = 108m   U.Mag. = 0.2206
Gam. = -0.8798   P.Mag. = 1.2673

Total +   **1801 Mar 30**
Saros 119   05:24 TD
D.Node   ΔT= 13s
Tot. = 102m
Par. = 222m   U.Mag. = 1.8400
Gam. = 0.0052   P.Mag. = 2.8569

Total -   **1801 Sep 22**
Saros 124   07:19 TD
A.Node   ΔT= 13s
Tot. = 98m
Par. = 216m   U.Mag. = 1.6670
Gam. = -0.1074   P.Mag. = 2.6548

Partial   **1802 Mar 19**
Saros 129   11:15 TD
D.Node   ΔT= 13s
Par. = 152m   U.Mag. = 0.4423
Gam. = -0.7518   P.Mag. = 1.5156

Partial   **1802 Sep 11**
Saros 134   22:37 TD
A.Node   ΔT= 13s
Par. = 170m   U.Mag. = 0.7615
Gam. = 0.6106   P.Mag. = 1.7134

Penumbral   **1803 Feb 06**
Saros 101   17:11 TD
D.Node   ΔT= 12s
Pen. = 93m   U.Mag. = -0.9979
Gam. = 1.5322   P.Mag. = 0.0919

Penumbral   **1803 Mar 08**
Saros 139   11:18 TD
D.Node   ΔT= 12s
Pen. = 143m   U.Mag. = -0.8775
Gam. = -1.4654   P.Mag. = 0.2169

Plate 062

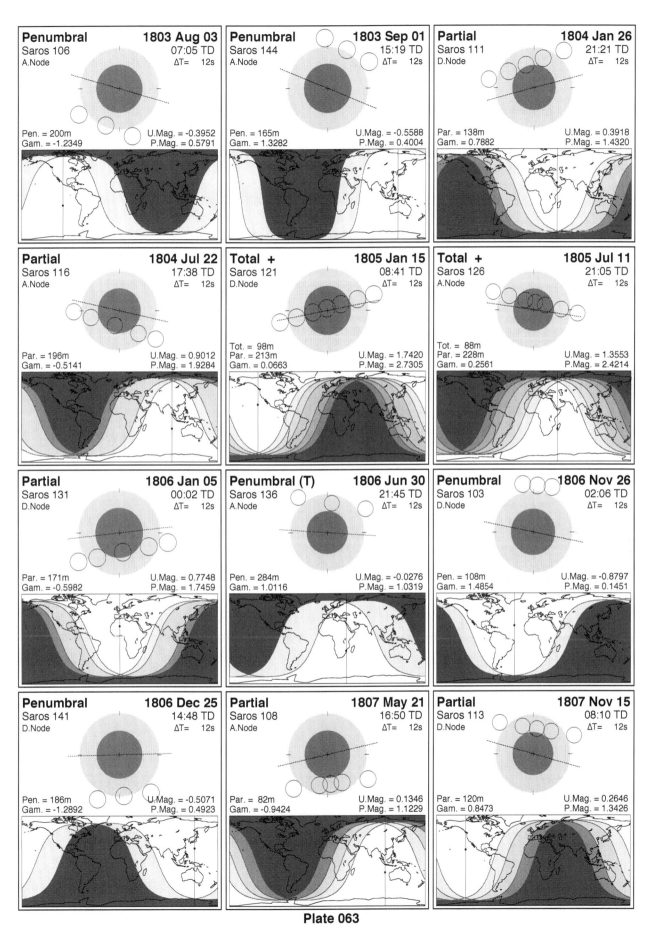

Penumbral	1803 Aug 03
Saros 106	07:05 TD
A.Node	ΔT= 12s
Pen. = 200m	U.Mag. = -0.3952
Gam. = -1.2349	P.Mag. = 0.5791

Penumbral	1803 Sep 01
Saros 144	15:19 TD
A.Node	ΔT= 12s
Pen. = 165m	U.Mag. = -0.5588
Gam. = 1.3282	P.Mag. = 0.4004

Partial	1804 Jan 26
Saros 111	21:21 TD
D.Node	ΔT= 12s
Par. = 138m	U.Mag. = 0.3918
Gam. = 0.7882	P.Mag. = 1.4320

Partial	1804 Jul 22
Saros 116	17:38 TD
A.Node	ΔT= 12s
Par. = 196m	U.Mag. = 0.9012
Gam. = -0.5141	P.Mag. = 1.9284

Total +	1805 Jan 15
Saros 121	08:41 TD
D.Node	ΔT= 12s
Tot. = 98m	
Par. = 213m	U.Mag. = 1.7420
Gam. = 0.0663	P.Mag. = 2.7305

Total +	1805 Jul 11
Saros 126	21:05 TD
A.Node	ΔT= 12s
Tot. = 88m	
Par. = 228m	U.Mag. = 1.3553
Gam. = 0.2561	P.Mag. = 2.4214

Partial	1806 Jan 05
Saros 131	00:02 TD
D.Node	ΔT= 12s
Par. = 171m	U.Mag. = 0.7748
Gam. = -0.5982	P.Mag. = 1.7459

Penumbral (T)	1806 Jun 30
Saros 136	21:45 TD
A.Node	ΔT= 12s
Pen. = 284m	U.Mag. = -0.0276
Gam. = 1.0116	P.Mag. = 1.0319

Penumbral	1806 Nov 26
Saros 103	02:06 TD
D.Node	ΔT= 12s
Pen. = 108m	U.Mag. = -0.8797
Gam. = 1.4854	P.Mag. = 0.1451

Penumbral	1806 Dec 25
Saros 141	14:48 TD
D.Node	ΔT= 12s
Pen. = 186m	U.Mag. = -0.5071
Gam. = -1.2892	P.Mag. = 0.4923

Partial	1807 May 21
Saros 108	16:50 TD
A.Node	ΔT= 12s
Par. = 82m	U.Mag. = 0.1346
Gam. = -0.9424	P.Mag. = 1.1229

Partial	1807 Nov 15
Saros 113	08:10 TD
D.Node	ΔT= 12s
Par. = 120m	U.Mag. = 0.2646
Gam. = 0.8473	P.Mag. = 1.3426

Plate 063

159

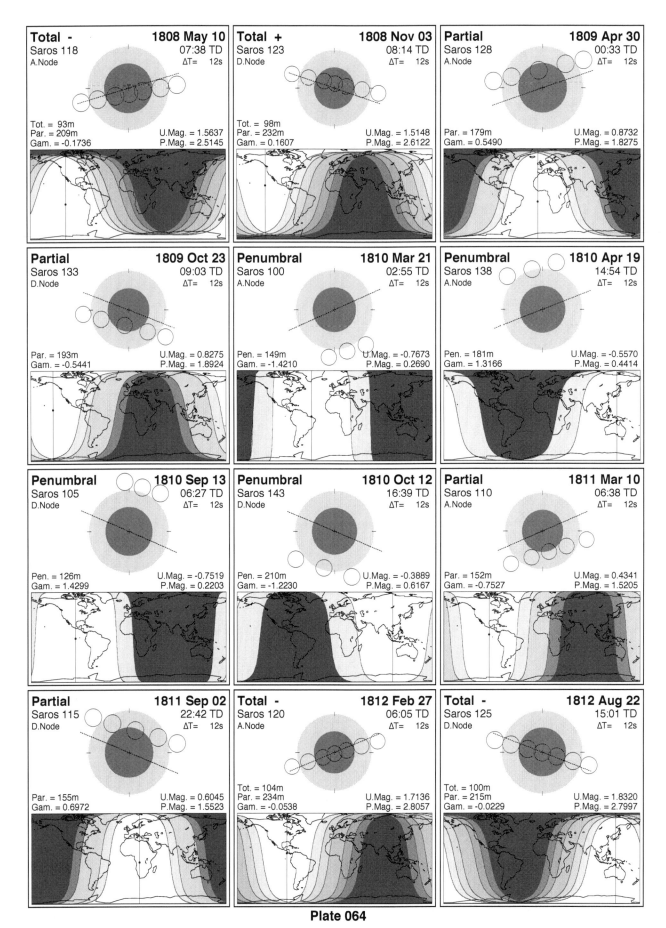

Total -   **1808 May 10**
Saros 118   07:38 TD
A.Node   ΔT= 12s
Tot. = 93m
Par. = 209m   U.Mag. = 1.5637
Gam. = -0.1736   P.Mag. = 2.5145

Total +   **1808 Nov 03**
Saros 123   08:14 TD
D.Node   ΔT= 12s
Tot. = 98m
Par. = 232m   U.Mag. = 1.5148
Gam. = 0.1607   P.Mag. = 2.6122

Partial   **1809 Apr 30**
Saros 128   00:33 TD
A.Node   ΔT= 12s
Par. = 179m   U.Mag. = 0.8732
Gam. = 0.5490   P.Mag. = 1.8275

Partial   **1809 Oct 23**
Saros 133   09:03 TD
D.Node   ΔT= 12s
Par. = 193m   U.Mag. = 0.8275
Gam. = -0.5441   P.Mag. = 1.8924

Penumbral   **1810 Mar 21**
Saros 100   02:55 TD
A.Node   ΔT= 12s
Pen. = 149m   U.Mag. = -0.7673
Gam. = -1.4210   P.Mag. = 0.2690

Penumbral   **1810 Apr 19**
Saros 138   14:54 TD
A.Node   ΔT= 12s
Pen. = 181m   U.Mag. = -0.5570
Gam. = 1.3166   P.Mag. = 0.4414

Penumbral   **1810 Sep 13**
Saros 105   06:27 TD
D.Node   ΔT= 12s
Pen. = 126m   U.Mag. = -0.7519
Gam. = 1.4299   P.Mag. = 0.2203

Penumbral   **1810 Oct 12**
Saros 143   16:39 TD
D.Node   ΔT= 12s
Pen. = 210m   U.Mag. = -0.3889
Gam. = -1.2230   P.Mag. = 0.6167

Partial   **1811 Mar 10**
Saros 110   06:38 TD
A.Node   ΔT= 12s
Par. = 152m   U.Mag. = 0.4341
Gam. = -0.7527   P.Mag. = 1.5205

Partial   **1811 Sep 02**
Saros 115   22:42 TD
D.Node   ΔT= 12s
Par. = 155m   U.Mag. = 0.6045
Gam. = 0.6972   P.Mag. = 1.5523

Total -   **1812 Feb 27**
Saros 120   06:05 TD
A.Node   ΔT= 12s
Tot. = 104m
Par. = 234m   U.Mag. = 1.7136
Gam. = -0.0538   P.Mag. = 2.8057

Total -   **1812 Aug 22**
Saros 125   15:01 TD
D.Node   ΔT= 12s
Tot. = 100m
Par. = 215m   U.Mag. = 1.8320
Gam. = -0.0229   P.Mag. = 2.7997

Plate 064

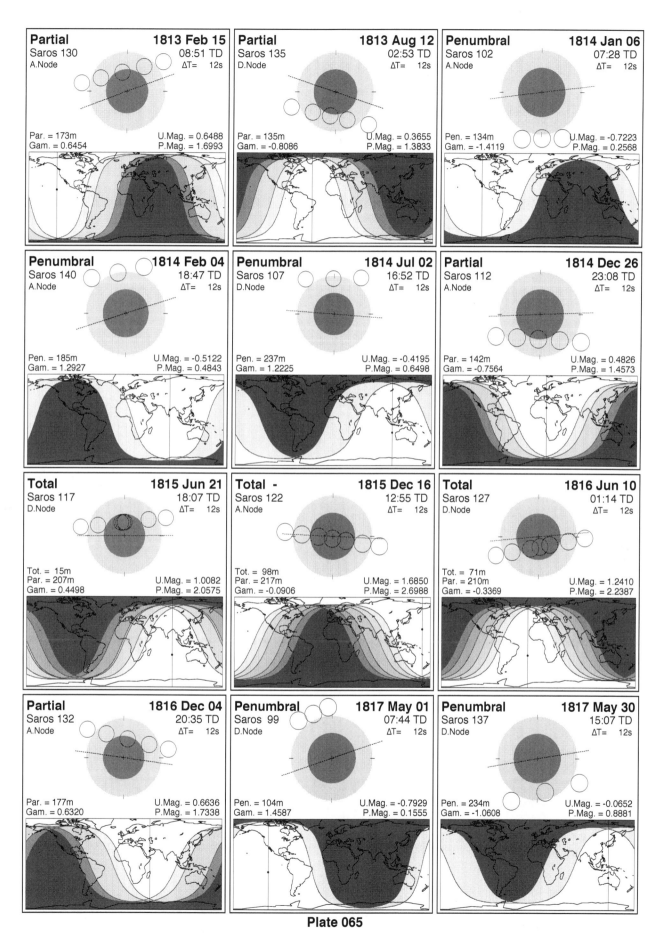

Partial	1813 Feb 15
Saros 130	08:51 TD
A.Node	ΔT= 12s
Par. = 173m	U.Mag. = 0.6488
Gam. = 0.6454	P.Mag. = 1.6993

Partial	1813 Aug 12
Saros 135	02:53 TD
D.Node	ΔT= 12s
Par. = 135m	U.Mag. = 0.3655
Gam. = -0.8086	P.Mag. = 1.3833

Penumbral	1814 Jan 06
Saros 102	07:28 TD
A.Node	ΔT= 12s
Pen. = 134m	U.Mag. = -0.7223
Gam. = -1.4119	P.Mag. = 0.2568

Penumbral	1814 Feb 04
Saros 140	18:47 TD
A.Node	ΔT= 12s
Pen. = 185m	U.Mag. = -0.5122
Gam. = 1.2927	P.Mag. = 0.4843

Penumbral	1814 Jul 02
Saros 107	16:52 TD
D.Node	ΔT= 12s
Pen. = 237m	U.Mag. = -0.4195
Gam. = 1.2225	P.Mag. = 0.6498

Partial	1814 Dec 26
Saros 112	23:08 TD
A.Node	ΔT= 12s
Par. = 142m	U.Mag. = 0.4826
Gam. = -0.7564	P.Mag. = 1.4573

Total	1815 Jun 21
Saros 117	18:07 TD
D.Node	ΔT= 12s
Tot. = 15m	
Par. = 207m	U.Mag. = 1.0082
Gam. = 0.4498	P.Mag. = 2.0575

Total -	1815 Dec 16
Saros 122	12:55 TD
A.Node	ΔT= 12s
Tot. = 98m	
Par. = 217m	U.Mag. = 1.6850
Gam. = -0.0906	P.Mag. = 2.6988

Total	1816 Jun 10
Saros 127	01:14 TD
D.Node	ΔT= 12s
Tot. = 71m	
Par. = 210m	U.Mag. = 1.2410
Gam. = -0.3369	P.Mag. = 2.2387

Partial	1816 Dec 04
Saros 132	20:35 TD
A.Node	ΔT= 12s
Par. = 177m	U.Mag. = 0.6636
Gam. = 0.6320	P.Mag. = 1.7338

Penumbral	1817 May 01
Saros 99	07:44 TD
D.Node	ΔT= 12s
Pen. = 104m	U.Mag. = -0.7929
Gam. = 1.4587	P.Mag. = 0.1555

Penumbral	1817 May 30
Saros 137	15:07 TD
D.Node	ΔT= 12s
Pen. = 234m	U.Mag. = -0.0652
Gam. = -1.0608	P.Mag. = 0.8881

Plate 065

161

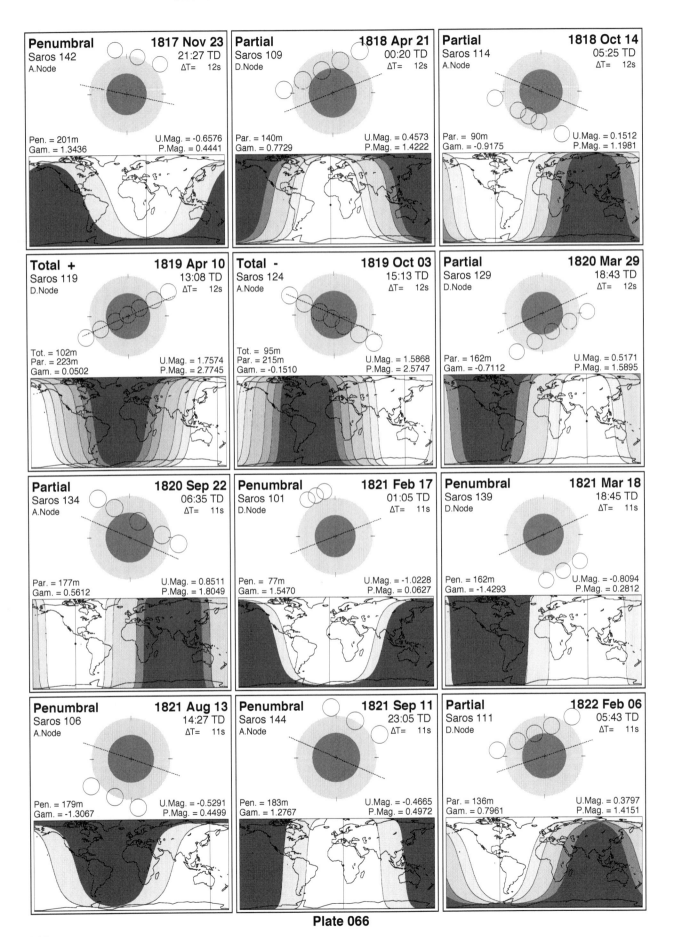

Penumbral   **1817 Nov 23**
Saros 142   21:27 TD
A.Node   ΔT= 12s
Pen. = 201m   U.Mag. = -0.6576
Gam. = 1.3436   P.Mag. = 0.4441

Partial   **1818 Apr 21**
Saros 109   00:20 TD
D.Node   ΔT= 12s
Par. = 140m   U.Mag. = 0.4573
Gam. = 0.7729   P.Mag. = 1.4222

Partial   **1818 Oct 14**
Saros 114   05:25 TD
A.Node   ΔT= 12s
Par. = 90m   U.Mag. = 0.1512
Gam. = -0.9175   P.Mag. = 1.1981

Total +   **1819 Apr 10**
Saros 119   13:08 TD
D.Node   ΔT= 12s
Tot. = 102m
Par. = 223m   U.Mag. = 1.7574
Gam. = 0.0502   P.Mag. = 2.7745

Total -   **1819 Oct 03**
Saros 124   15:13 TD
A.Node   ΔT= 12s
Tot. = 95m
Par. = 215m   U.Mag. = 1.5868
Gam. = -0.1510   P.Mag. = 2.5747

Partial   **1820 Mar 29**
Saros 129   18:43 TD
D.Node   ΔT= 12s
Par. = 162m   U.Mag. = 0.5171
Gam. = -0.7112   P.Mag. = 1.5895

Partial   **1820 Sep 22**
Saros 134   06:35 TD
A.Node   ΔT= 11s
Par. = 177m   U.Mag. = 0.8511
Gam. = 0.5612   P.Mag. = 1.8049

Penumbral   **1821 Feb 17**
Saros 101   01:05 TD
D.Node   ΔT= 11s
Pen. = 77m   U.Mag. = -1.0228
Gam. = 1.5470   P.Mag. = 0.0627

Penumbral   **1821 Mar 18**
Saros 139   18:45 TD
D.Node   ΔT= 11s
Pen. = 162m   U.Mag. = -0.8094
Gam. = -1.4293   P.Mag. = 0.2812

Penumbral   **1821 Aug 13**
Saros 106   14:27 TD
A.Node   ΔT= 11s
Pen. = 179m   U.Mag. = -0.5291
Gam. = -1.3067   P.Mag. = 0.4499

Penumbral   **1821 Sep 11**
Saros 144   23:05 TD
A.Node   ΔT= 11s
Pen. = 183m   U.Mag. = -0.4665
Gam. = 1.2767   P.Mag. = 0.4972

Partial   **1822 Feb 06**
Saros 111   05:43 TD
D.Node   ΔT= 11s
Par. = 136m   U.Mag. = 0.3797
Gam. = 0.7961   P.Mag. = 1.4151

Plate 066

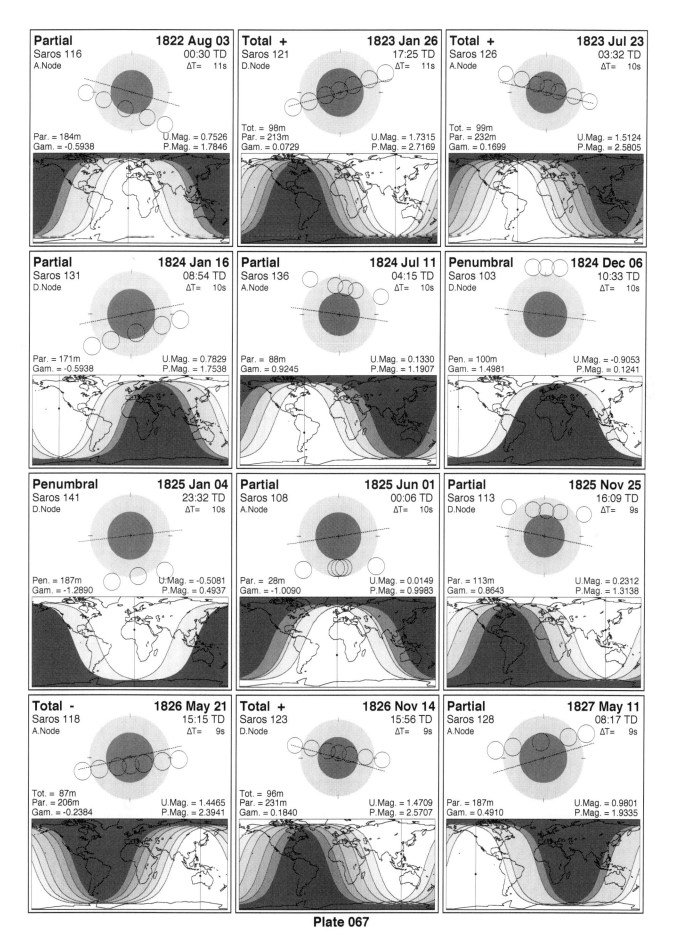

Partial	**1822 Aug 03**
Saros 116	00:30 TD
A.Node	ΔT = 11s
Par. = 184m	U.Mag. = 0.7526
Gam. = -0.5938	P.Mag. = 1.7846

Total +	**1823 Jan 26**
Saros 121	17:25 TD
D.Node	ΔT = 11s
Tot. = 98m	
Par. = 213m	U.Mag. = 1.7315
Gam. = 0.0729	P.Mag. = 2.7169

Total +	**1823 Jul 23**
Saros 126	03:32 TD
A.Node	ΔT = 10s
Tot. = 99m	
Par. = 232m	U.Mag. = 1.5124
Gam. = 0.1699	P.Mag. = 2.5805

Partial	**1824 Jan 16**
Saros 131	08:54 TD
D.Node	ΔT = 10s
Par. = 171m	U.Mag. = 0.7829
Gam. = -0.5938	P.Mag. = 1.7538

Partial	**1824 Jul 11**
Saros 136	04:15 TD
A.Node	ΔT = 10s
Par. = 88m	U.Mag. = 0.1330
Gam. = 0.9245	P.Mag. = 1.1907

Penumbral	**1824 Dec 06**
Saros 103	10:33 TD
D.Node	ΔT = 10s
Pen. = 100m	U.Mag. = -0.9053
Gam. = 1.4981	P.Mag. = 0.1241

Penumbral	**1825 Jan 04**
Saros 141	23:32 TD
D.Node	ΔT = 10s
Pen. = 187m	U.Mag. = -0.5081
Gam. = -1.2890	P.Mag. = 0.4937

Partial	**1825 Jun 01**
Saros 108	00:06 TD
A.Node	ΔT = 10s
Par. = 28m	U.Mag. = 0.0149
Gam. = -1.0090	P.Mag. = 0.9983

Partial	**1825 Nov 25**
Saros 113	16:09 TD
D.Node	ΔT = 9s
Par. = 113m	U.Mag. = 0.2312
Gam. = 0.8643	P.Mag. = 1.3138

Total -	**1826 May 21**
Saros 118	15:15 TD
A.Node	ΔT = 9s
Tot. = 87m	
Par. = 206m	U.Mag. = 1.4465
Gam. = -0.2384	P.Mag. = 2.3941

Total +	**1826 Nov 14**
Saros 123	15:56 TD
D.Node	ΔT = 9s
Tot. = 96m	
Par. = 231m	U.Mag. = 1.4709
Gam. = 0.1840	P.Mag. = 2.5707

Partial	**1827 May 11**
Saros 128	08:17 TD
A.Node	ΔT = 9s
Par. = 187m	U.Mag. = 0.9801
Gam. = 0.4910	P.Mag. = 1.9335

Plate 067

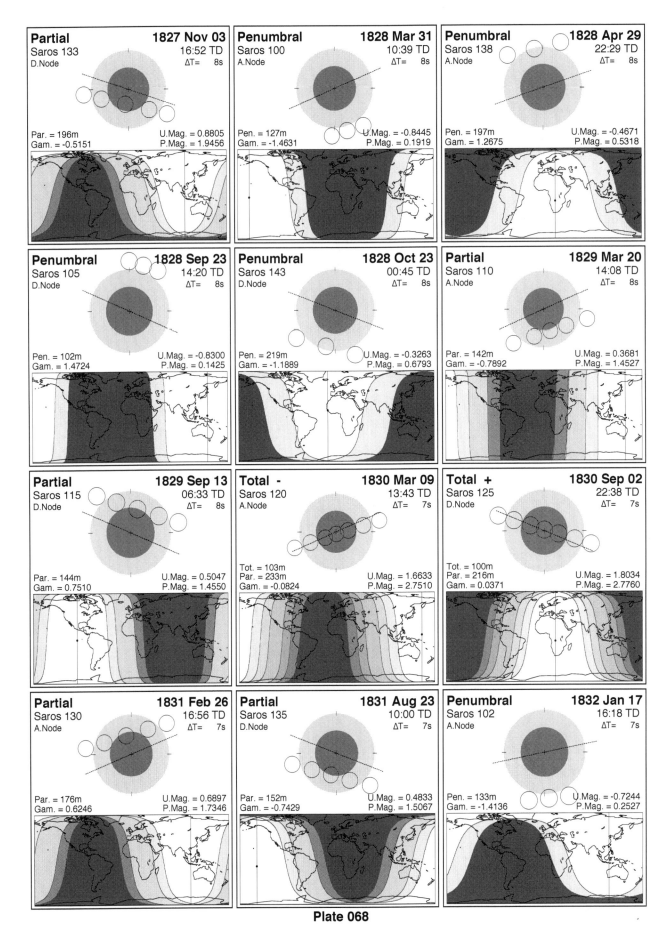

Partial   **1827 Nov 03**
Saros 133   16:52 TD
D.Node   ΔT= 8s

Par. = 196m   U.Mag. = 0.8805
Gam. = -0.5151   P.Mag. = 1.9456

Penumbral   **1828 Mar 31**
Saros 100   10:39 TD
A.Node   ΔT= 8s

Pen. = 127m   U.Mag. = -0.8445
Gam. = -1.4631   P.Mag. = 0.1919

Penumbral   **1828 Apr 29**
Saros 138   22:29 TD
A.Node   ΔT= 8s

Pen. = 197m   U.Mag. = -0.4671
Gam. = 1.2675   P.Mag. = 0.5318

Penumbral   **1828 Sep 23**
Saros 105   14:20 TD
D.Node   ΔT= 8s

Pen. = 102m   U.Mag. = -0.8300
Gam. = 1.4724   P.Mag. = 0.1425

Penumbral   **1828 Oct 23**
Saros 143   00:45 TD
D.Node   ΔT= 8s

Pen. = 219m   U.Mag. = -0.3263
Gam. = -1.1889   P.Mag. = 0.6793

Partial   **1829 Mar 20**
Saros 110   14:08 TD
A.Node   ΔT= 8s

Par. = 142m   U.Mag. = 0.3681
Gam. = -0.7892   P.Mag. = 1.4527

Partial   **1829 Sep 13**
Saros 115   06:33 TD
D.Node   ΔT= 8s

Par. = 144m   U.Mag. = 0.5047
Gam. = 0.7510   P.Mag. = 1.4550

Total -   **1830 Mar 09**
Saros 120   13:43 TD
A.Node   ΔT= 7s

Tot. = 103m
Par. = 233m   U.Mag. = 1.6633
Gam. = -0.0824   P.Mag. = 2.7510

Total +   **1830 Sep 02**
Saros 125   22:38 TD
D.Node   ΔT= 7s

Tot. = 100m
Par. = 216m   U.Mag. = 1.8034
Gam. = 0.0371   P.Mag. = 2.7760

Partial   **1831 Feb 26**
Saros 130   16:56 TD
A.Node   ΔT= 7s

Par. = 176m   U.Mag. = 0.6897
Gam. = 0.6246   P.Mag. = 1.7346

Partial   **1831 Aug 23**
Saros 135   10:00 TD
D.Node   ΔT= 7s

Par. = 152m   U.Mag. = 0.4833
Gam. = -0.7429   P.Mag. = 1.5067

Penumbral   **1832 Jan 17**
Saros 102   16:18 TD
A.Node   ΔT= 7s

Pen. = 133m   U.Mag. = -0.7244
Gam. = -1.4136   P.Mag. = 0.2527

Plate 068

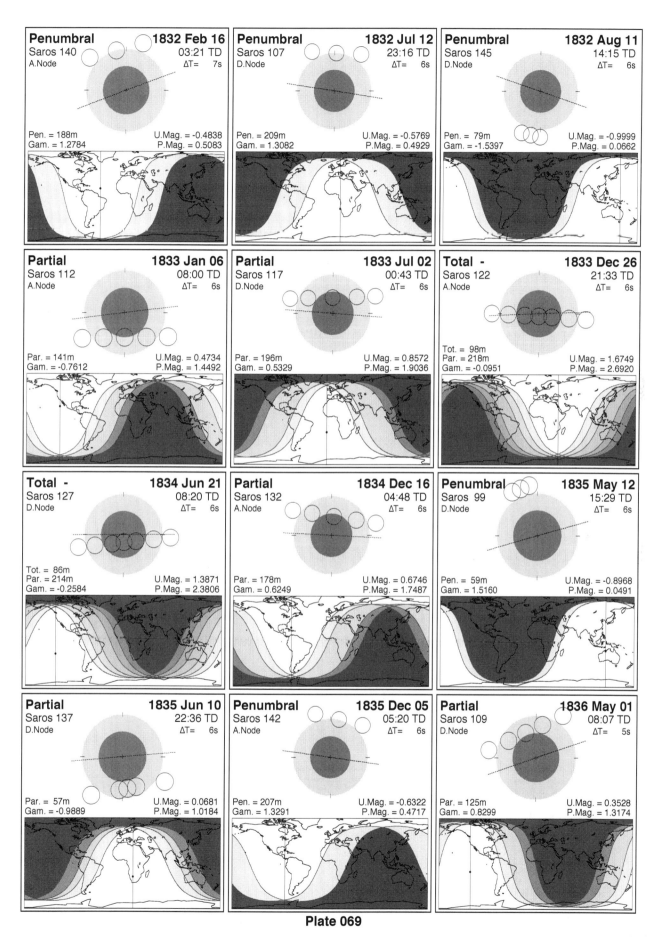

Penumbral	**1832 Feb 16**
Saros 140	03:21 TD
A.Node	ΔT= 7s
Pen. = 188m	U.Mag. = -0.4838
Gam. = 1.2784	P.Mag. = 0.5083

Penumbral	**1832 Jul 12**
Saros 107	23:16 TD
D.Node	ΔT= 6s
Pen. = 209m	U.Mag. = -0.5769
Gam. = 1.3082	P.Mag. = 0.4929

Penumbral	**1832 Aug 11**
Saros 145	14:15 TD
D.Node	ΔT= 6s
Pen. = 79m	U.Mag. = -0.9999
Gam. = -1.5397	P.Mag. = 0.0662

Partial	**1833 Jan 06**
Saros 112	08:00 TD
A.Node	ΔT= 6s
Par. = 141m	U.Mag. = 0.4734
Gam. = -0.7612	P.Mag. = 1.4492

Partial	**1833 Jul 02**
Saros 117	00:43 TD
D.Node	ΔT= 6s
Par. = 196m	U.Mag. = 0.8572
Gam. = 0.5329	P.Mag. = 1.9036

Total -	**1833 Dec 26**
Saros 122	21:33 TD
A.Node	ΔT= 6s
Tot. = 98m	U.Mag. = 1.6749
Par. = 218m	P.Mag. = 2.6920
Gam. = -0.0951	

Total -	**1834 Jun 21**
Saros 127	08:20 TD
D.Node	ΔT= 6s
Tot. = 86m	U.Mag. = 1.3871
Par. = 214m	P.Mag. = 2.3806
Gam. = -0.2584	

Partial	**1834 Dec 16**
Saros 132	04:48 TD
A.Node	ΔT= 6s
Par. = 178m	U.Mag. = 0.6746
Gam. = 0.6249	P.Mag. = 1.7487

Penumbral	**1835 May 12**
Saros 99	15:29 TD
D.Node	ΔT= 6s
Pen. = 59m	U.Mag. = -0.8968
Gam. = 1.5160	P.Mag. = 0.0491

Partial	**1835 Jun 10**
Saros 137	22:36 TD
D.Node	ΔT= 6s
Par. = 57m	U.Mag. = 0.0681
Gam. = -0.9889	P.Mag. = 1.0184

Penumbral	**1835 Dec 05**
Saros 142	05:20 TD
A.Node	ΔT= 6s
Pen. = 207m	U.Mag. = -0.6322
Gam. = 1.3291	P.Mag. = 0.4717

Partial	**1836 May 01**
Saros 109	08:07 TD
D.Node	ΔT= 5s
Par. = 125m	U.Mag. = 0.3528
Gam. = 0.8299	P.Mag. = 1.3174

Plate 069

165

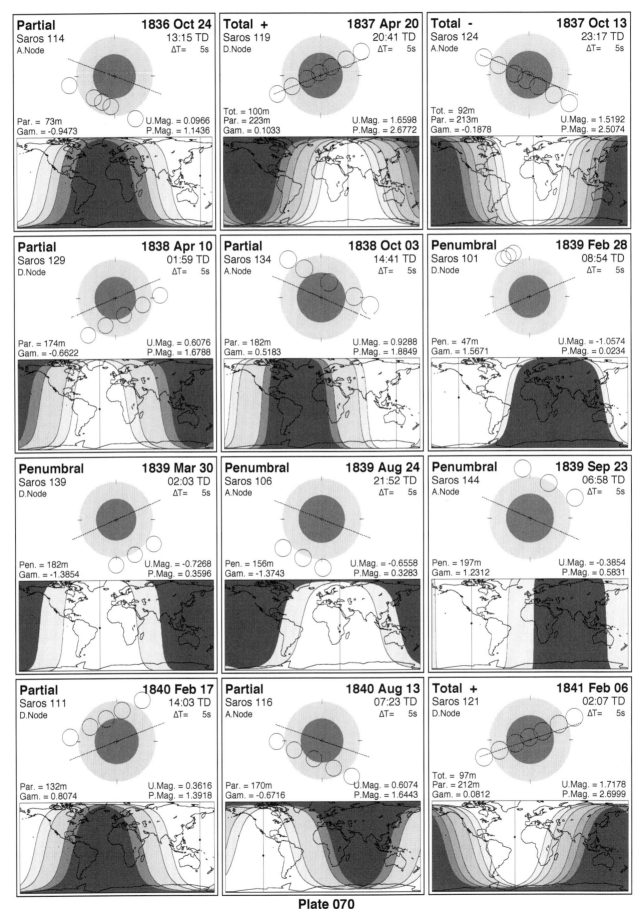

Partial	1836 Oct 24
Saros 114	13:15 TD
A.Node	ΔT= 5s

Par. = 73m   U.Mag. = 0.0966
Gam. = -0.9473   P.Mag. = 1.1436

Total +	1837 Apr 20
Saros 119	20:41 TD
D.Node	ΔT= 5s

Tot. = 100m
Par. = 223m   U.Mag. = 1.6598
Gam. = 0.1033   P.Mag. = 2.6772

Total -	1837 Oct 13
Saros 124	23:17 TD
A.Node	ΔT= 5s

Tot. = 92m
Par. = 213m   U.Mag. = 1.5192
Gam. = -0.1878   P.Mag. = 2.5074

Partial	1838 Apr 10
Saros 129	01:59 TD
D.Node	ΔT= 5s

Par. = 174m   U.Mag. = 0.6076
Gam. = -0.6622   P.Mag. = 1.6788

Partial	1838 Oct 03
Saros 134	14:41 TD
A.Node	ΔT= 5s

Par. = 182m   U.Mag. = 0.9288
Gam. = 0.5183   P.Mag. = 1.8849

Penumbral	1839 Feb 28
Saros 101	08:54 TD
D.Node	ΔT= 5s

Pen. = 47m   U.Mag. = -1.0574
Gam. = 1.5671   P.Mag. = 0.0234

Penumbral	1839 Mar 30
Saros 139	02:03 TD
D.Node	ΔT= 5s

Pen. = 182m   U.Mag. = -0.7268
Gam. = -1.3854   P.Mag. = 0.3596

Penumbral	1839 Aug 24
Saros 106	21:52 TD
A.Node	ΔT= 5s

Pen. = 156m   U.Mag. = -0.6558
Gam. = -1.3743   P.Mag. = 0.3283

Penumbral	1839 Sep 23
Saros 144	06:58 TD
A.Node	ΔT= 5s

Pen. = 197m   U.Mag. = -0.3854
Gam. = 1.2312   P.Mag. = 0.5831

Partial	1840 Feb 17
Saros 111	14:03 TD
D.Node	ΔT= 5s

Par. = 132m   U.Mag. = 0.3616
Gam. = 0.8074   P.Mag. = 1.3918

Partial	1840 Aug 13
Saros 116	07:23 TD
A.Node	ΔT= 5s

Par. = 170m   U.Mag. = 0.6074
Gam. = -0.6716   P.Mag. = 1.6443

Total +	1841 Feb 06
Saros 121	02:07 TD
D.Node	ΔT= 5s

Tot. = 97m
Par. = 212m   U.Mag. = 1.7178
Gam. = 0.0812   P.Mag. = 2.6999

Plate 070

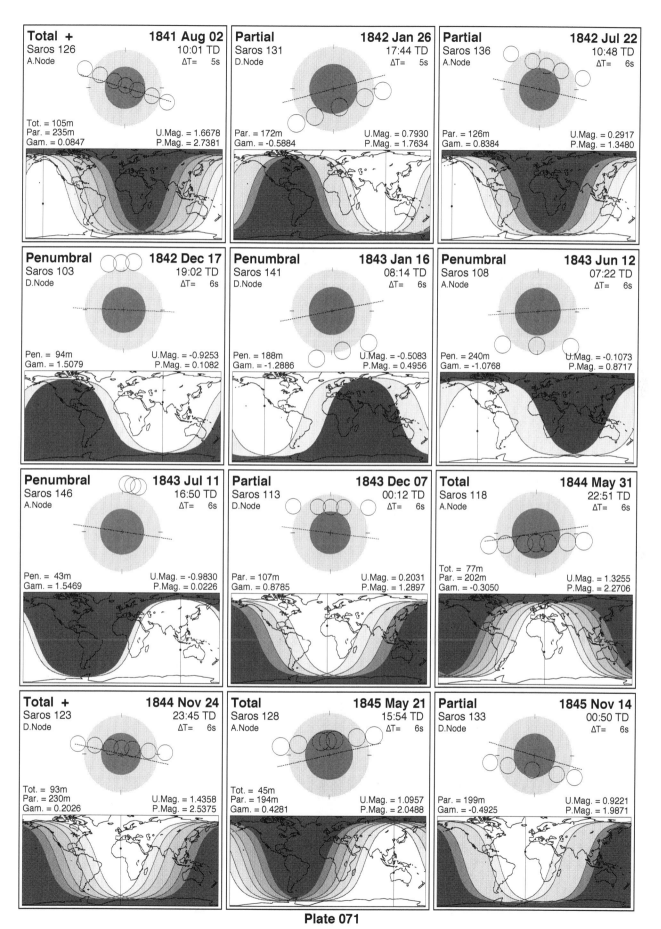

Total +   **1841 Aug 02**
Saros 126   10:01 TD
A.Node   ΔT= 5s
Tot. = 105m
Par. = 235m
Gam. = 0.0847   U.Mag. = 1.6678
P.Mag. = 2.7381

Partial   **1842 Jan 26**
Saros 131   17:44 TD
D.Node   ΔT= 5s
Par. = 172m
Gam. = -0.5884   U.Mag. = 0.7930
P.Mag. = 1.7634

Partial   **1842 Jul 22**
Saros 136   10:48 TD
A.Node   ΔT= 6s
Par. = 126m
Gam. = 0.8384   U.Mag. = 0.2917
P.Mag. = 1.3480

Penumbral   **1842 Dec 17**
Saros 103   19:02 TD
D.Node   ΔT= 6s
Pen. = 94m
Gam. = 1.5079   U.Mag. = -0.9253
P.Mag. = 0.1082

Penumbral   **1843 Jan 16**
Saros 141   08:14 TD
D.Node   ΔT= 6s
Pen. = 188m
Gam. = -1.2886   U.Mag. = -0.5083
P.Mag. = 0.4956

Penumbral   **1843 Jun 12**
Saros 108   07:22 TD
A.Node   ΔT= 6s
Pen. = 240m
Gam. = -1.0768   U.Mag. = -0.1073
P.Mag. = 0.8717

Penumbral   **1843 Jul 11**
Saros 146   16:50 TD
A.Node   ΔT= 6s
Pen. = 43m
Gam. = 1.5469   U.Mag. = -0.9830
P.Mag. = 0.0226

Partial   **1843 Dec 07**
Saros 113   00:12 TD
D.Node   ΔT= 6s
Par. = 107m
Gam. = 0.8785   U.Mag. = 0.2031
P.Mag. = 1.2897

Total   **1844 May 31**
Saros 118   22:51 TD
A.Node   ΔT= 6s
Tot. = 77m
Par. = 202m
Gam. = -0.3050   U.Mag. = 1.3255
P.Mag. = 2.2706

Total +   **1844 Nov 24**
Saros 123   23:45 TD
D.Node   ΔT= 6s
Tot. = 93m
Par. = 230m
Gam. = 0.2026   U.Mag. = 1.4358
P.Mag. = 2.5375

Total   **1845 May 21**
Saros 128   15:54 TD
A.Node   ΔT= 6s
Tot. = 45m
Par. = 194m
Gam. = 0.4281   U.Mag. = 1.0957
P.Mag. = 2.0488

Partial   **1845 Nov 14**
Saros 133   00:50 TD
D.Node   ΔT= 6s
Par. = 199m
Gam. = -0.4925   U.Mag. = 0.9221
P.Mag. = 1.9871

Plate 071

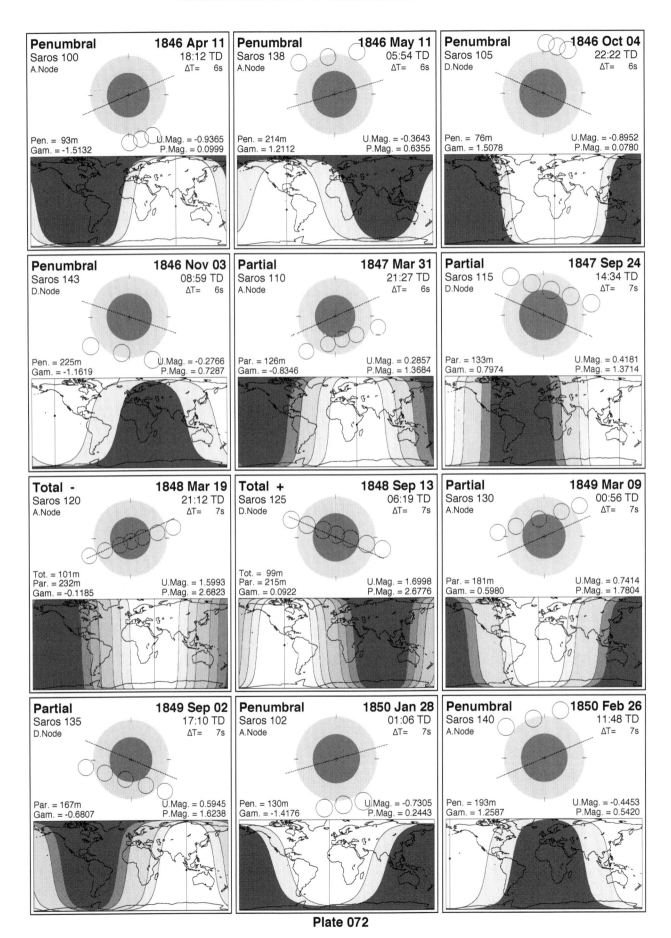

Penumbral   **1846 Apr 11**
Saros 100   18:12 TD
A.Node   ΔT= 6s
Pen. = 93m   U.Mag. = -0.9365
Gam. = -1.5132   P.Mag. = 0.0999

Penumbral   **1846 May 11**
Saros 138   05:54 TD
A.Node   ΔT= 6s
Pen. = 214m   U.Mag. = -0.3643
Gam. = 1.2112   P.Mag. = 0.6355

Penumbral   **1846 Oct 04**
Saros 105   22:22 TD
D.Node   ΔT= 6s
Pen. = 76m   U.Mag. = -0.8952
Gam. = 1.5078   P.Mag. = 0.0780

Penumbral   **1846 Nov 03**
Saros 143   08:59 TD
D.Node   ΔT= 6s
Pen. = 225m   U.Mag. = -0.2766
Gam. = -1.1619   P.Mag. = 0.7287

Partial   **1847 Mar 31**
Saros 110   21:27 TD
A.Node   ΔT= 6s
Par. = 126m   U.Mag. = 0.2857
Gam. = -0.8346   P.Mag. = 1.3684

Partial   **1847 Sep 24**
Saros 115   14:34 TD
D.Node   ΔT= 7s
Par. = 133m   U.Mag. = 0.4181
Gam. = 0.7974   P.Mag. = 1.3714

Total -   **1848 Mar 19**
Saros 120   21:12 TD
A.Node   ΔT= 7s
Tot. = 101m
Par. = 232m   U.Mag. = 1.5993
Gam. = -0.1185   P.Mag. = 2.6823

Total +   **1848 Sep 13**
Saros 125   06:19 TD
D.Node   ΔT= 7s
Tot. = 99m
Par. = 215m   U.Mag. = 1.6998
Gam. = 0.0922   P.Mag. = 2.6776

Partial   **1849 Mar 09**
Saros 130   00:56 TD
A.Node   ΔT= 7s
Par. = 181m   U.Mag. = 0.7414
Gam. = 0.5980   P.Mag. = 1.7804

Partial   **1849 Sep 02**
Saros 135   17:10 TD
D.Node   ΔT= 7s
Par. = 167m   U.Mag. = 0.5945
Gam. = -0.6807   P.Mag. = 1.6238

Penumbral   **1850 Jan 28**
Saros 102   01:06 TD
A.Node   ΔT= 7s
Pen. = 130m   U.Mag. = -0.7305
Gam. = -1.4176   P.Mag. = 0.2443

Penumbral   **1850 Feb 26**
Saros 140   11:48 TD
A.Node   ΔT= 7s
Pen. = 193m   U.Mag. = -0.4453
Gam. = 1.2587   P.Mag. = 0.5420

Plate 072

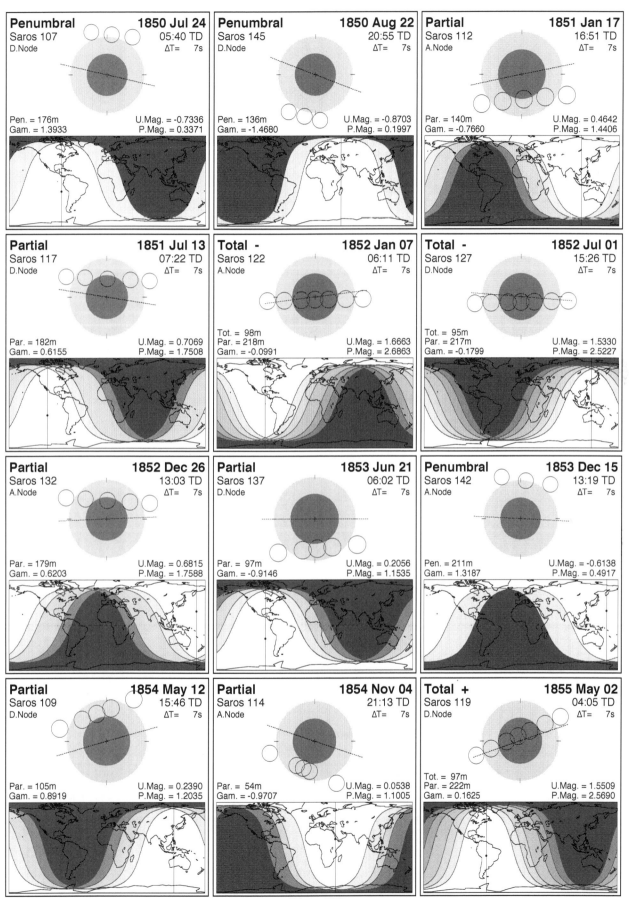

Penumbral	**1850 Jul 24**
Saros 107	05:40 TD
D.Node	ΔT= 7s
Pen. = 176m	U.Mag. = -0.7336
Gam. = 1.3933	P.Mag. = 0.3371

Penumbral	**1850 Aug 22**
Saros 145	20:55 TD
D.Node	ΔT= 7s
Pen. = 136m	U.Mag. = -0.8703
Gam. = -1.4680	P.Mag. = 0.1997

Partial	**1851 Jan 17**
Saros 112	16:51 TD
A.Node	ΔT= 7s
Par. = 140m	U.Mag. = 0.4642
Gam. = -0.7660	P.Mag. = 1.4406

Partial	**1851 Jul 13**
Saros 117	07:22 TD
D.Node	ΔT= 7s
Par. = 182m	U.Mag. = 0.7069
Gam. = 0.6155	P.Mag. = 1.7508

Total -	**1852 Jan 07**
Saros 122	06:11 TD
A.Node	ΔT= 7s
Tot. = 98m	
Par. = 218m	U.Mag. = 1.6663
Gam. = -0.0991	P.Mag. = 2.6863

Total -	**1852 Jul 01**
Saros 127	15:26 TD
D.Node	ΔT= 7s
Tot. = 95m	
Par. = 217m	U.Mag. = 1.5330
Gam. = -0.1799	P.Mag. = 2.5227

Partial	**1852 Dec 26**
Saros 132	13:03 TD
A.Node	ΔT= 7s
Par. = 179m	U.Mag. = 0.6815
Gam. = 0.6203	P.Mag. = 1.7588

Partial	**1853 Jun 21**
Saros 137	06:02 TD
D.Node	ΔT= 7s
Par. = 97m	U.Mag. = 0.2056
Gam. = -0.9146	P.Mag. = 1.1535

Penumbral	**1853 Dec 15**
Saros 142	13:19 TD
A.Node	ΔT= 7s
Pen. = 211m	U.Mag. = -0.6138
Gam. = 1.3187	P.Mag. = 0.4917

Partial	**1854 May 12**
Saros 109	15:46 TD
D.Node	ΔT= 7s
Par. = 105m	U.Mag. = 0.2390
Gam. = 0.8919	P.Mag. = 1.2035

Partial	**1854 Nov 04**
Saros 114	21:13 TD
A.Node	ΔT= 7s
Par. = 54m	U.Mag. = 0.0538
Gam. = -0.9707	P.Mag. = 1.1005

Total +	**1855 May 02**
Saros 119	04:05 TD
D.Node	ΔT= 7s
Tot. = 97m	
Par. = 222m	U.Mag. = 1.5509
Gam. = 0.1625	P.Mag. = 2.5690

Plate 073

169

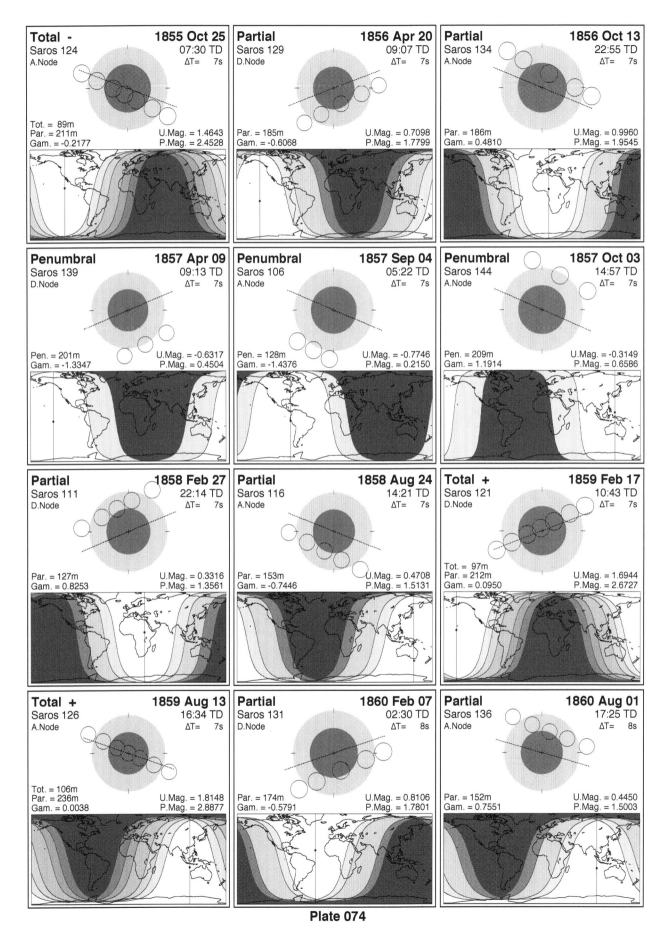

Total - **1855 Oct 25**	
Saros 124 07:30 TD	
A.Node ΔT= 7s	
Tot. = 89m	
Par. = 211m U.Mag. = 1.4643	
Gam. = -0.2177 P.Mag. = 2.4528	

Total -   **1855 Oct 25**
Saros 124   07:30 TD
A.Node   ΔT= 7s
Tot. = 89m
Par. = 211m   U.Mag. = 1.4643
Gam. = -0.2177   P.Mag. = 2.4528

Partial   **1856 Apr 20**
Saros 129   09:07 TD
D.Node   ΔT= 7s
Par. = 185m   U.Mag. = 0.7098
Gam. = -0.6068   P.Mag. = 1.7799

Partial   **1856 Oct 13**
Saros 134   22:55 TD
A.Node   ΔT= 7s
Par. = 186m   U.Mag. = 0.9960
Gam. = 0.4810   P.Mag. = 1.9545

Penumbral   **1857 Apr 09**
Saros 139   09:13 TD
D.Node   ΔT= 7s
Pen. = 201m   U.Mag. = -0.6317
Gam. = -1.3347   P.Mag. = 0.4504

Penumbral   **1857 Sep 04**
Saros 106   05:22 TD
A.Node   ΔT= 7s
Pen. = 128m   U.Mag. = -0.7746
Gam. = -1.4376   P.Mag. = 0.2150

Penumbral   **1857 Oct 03**
Saros 144   14:57 TD
A.Node   ΔT= 7s
Pen. = 209m   U.Mag. = -0.3149
Gam. = 1.1914   P.Mag. = 0.6586

Partial   **1858 Feb 27**
Saros 111   22:14 TD
D.Node   ΔT= 7s
Par. = 127m   U.Mag. = 0.3316
Gam. = 0.8253   P.Mag. = 1.3561

Partial   **1858 Aug 24**
Saros 116   14:21 TD
A.Node   ΔT= 7s
Par. = 153m   U.Mag. = 0.4708
Gam. = -0.7446   P.Mag. = 1.5131

Total +   **1859 Feb 17**
Saros 121   10:43 TD
D.Node   ΔT= 7s
Tot. = 97m
Par. = 212m   U.Mag. = 1.6944
Gam. = 0.0950   P.Mag. = 2.6727

Total +   **1859 Aug 13**
Saros 126   16:34 TD
A.Node   ΔT= 7s
Tot. = 106m
Par. = 236m   U.Mag. = 1.8148
Gam. = 0.0038   P.Mag. = 2.8877

Partial   **1860 Feb 07**
Saros 131   02:30 TD
D.Node   ΔT= 8s
Par. = 174m   U.Mag. = 0.8106
Gam. = -0.5791   P.Mag. = 1.7801

Partial   **1860 Aug 01**
Saros 136   17:25 TD
A.Node   ΔT= 8s
Par. = 152m   U.Mag. = 0.4450
Gam. = 0.7551   P.Mag. = 1.5003

Plate 074

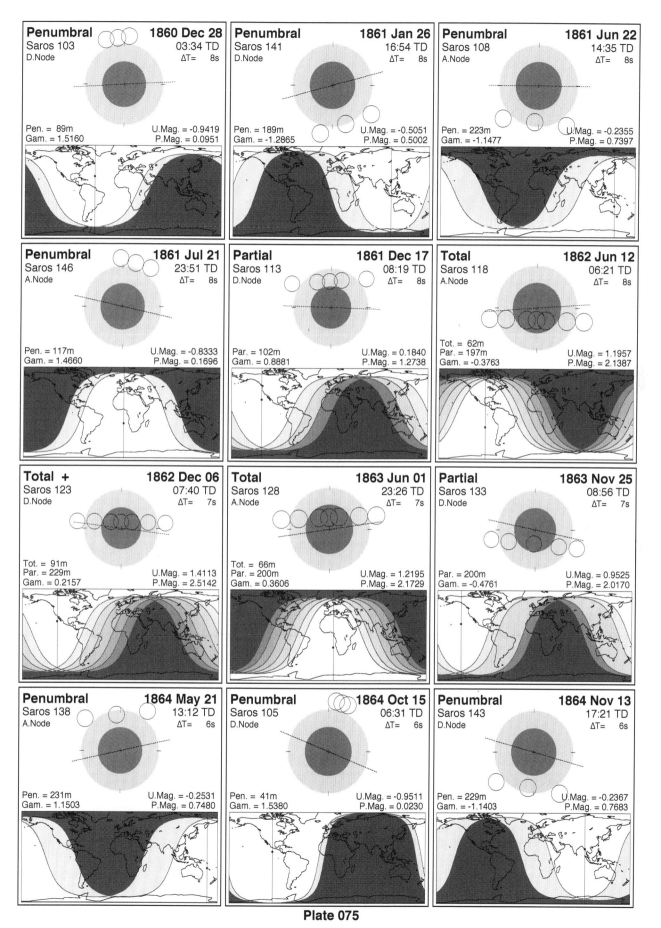

Penumbral   **1860 Dec 28**
Saros 103   03:34 TD
D.Node   ΔT= 8s
Pen. = 89m   U.Mag. = -0.9419
Gam. = 1.5160   P.Mag. = 0.0951

Penumbral   **1861 Jan 26**
Saros 141   16:54 TD
D.Node   ΔT= 8s
Pen. = 189m   U.Mag. = -0.5051
Gam. = -1.2865   P.Mag. = 0.5002

Penumbral   **1861 Jun 22**
Saros 108   14:35 TD
A.Node   ΔT= 8s
Pen. = 223m   U.Mag. = -0.2355
Gam. = -1.1477   P.Mag. = 0.7397

Penumbral   **1861 Jul 21**
Saros 146   23:51 TD
A.Node   ΔT= 8s
Pen. = 117m   U.Mag. = -0.8333
Gam. = 1.4660   P.Mag. = 0.1696

Partial   **1861 Dec 17**
Saros 113   08:19 TD
D.Node   ΔT= 8s
Par. = 102m   U.Mag. = 0.1840
Gam. = 0.8881   P.Mag. = 1.2738

Total   **1862 Jun 12**
Saros 118   06:21 TD
A.Node   ΔT= 8s
Tot. = 62m
Par. = 197m   U.Mag. = 1.1957
Gam. = -0.3763   P.Mag. = 2.1387

Total +   **1862 Dec 06**
Saros 123   07:40 TD
D.Node   ΔT= 7s
Tot. = 91m
Par. = 229m   U.Mag. = 1.4113
Gam. = 0.2157   P.Mag. = 2.5142

Total   **1863 Jun 01**
Saros 128   23:26 TD
A.Node   ΔT= 7s
Tot. = 66m
Par. = 200m   U.Mag. = 1.2195
Gam. = 0.3606   P.Mag. = 2.1729

Partial   **1863 Nov 25**
Saros 133   08:56 TD
D.Node   ΔT= 7s
Par. = 200m   U.Mag. = 0.9525
Gam. = -0.4761   P.Mag. = 2.0170

Penumbral   **1864 May 21**
Saros 138   13:12 TD
A.Node   ΔT= 6s
Pen. = 231m   U.Mag. = -0.2531
Gam. = 1.1503   P.Mag. = 0.7480

Penumbral   **1864 Oct 15**
Saros 105   06:31 TD
D.Node   ΔT= 6s
Pen. = 41m   U.Mag. = -0.9511
Gam. = 1.5380   P.Mag. = 0.0230

Penumbral   **1864 Nov 13**
Saros 143   17:21 TD
D.Node   ΔT= 6s
Pen. = 229m   U.Mag. = -0.2367
Gam. = -1.1403   P.Mag. = 0.7683

Plate 075

171

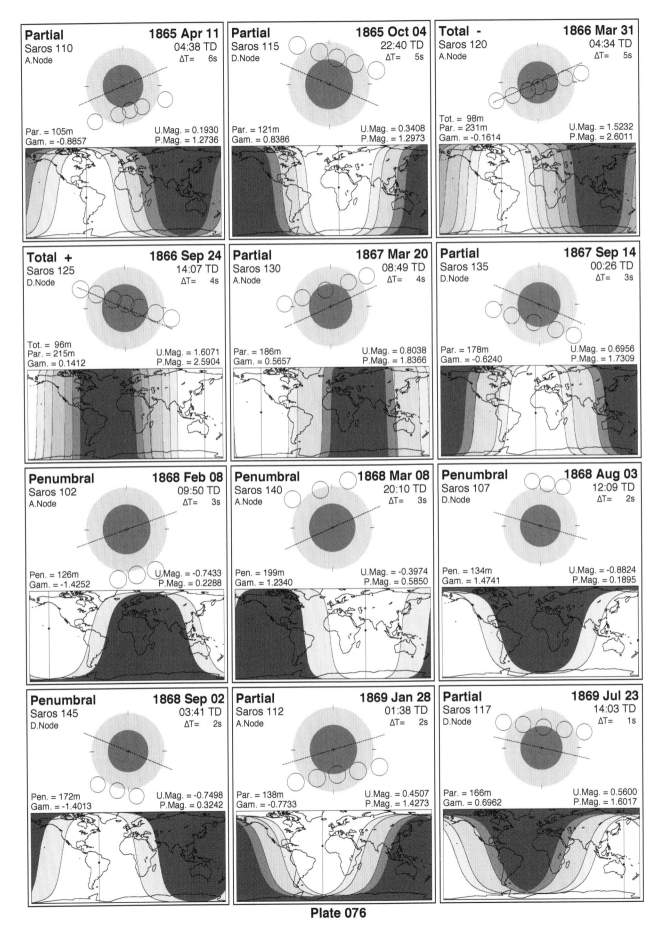

Partial	1865 Apr 11
Saros 110	04:38 TD
A.Node	ΔT= 6s
Par. = 105m	U.Mag. = 0.1930
Gam. = -0.8857	P.Mag. = 1.2736

Partial	1865 Oct 04
Saros 115	22:40 TD
D.Node	ΔT= 5s
Par. = 121m	U.Mag. = 0.3408
Gam. = 0.8386	P.Mag. = 1.2973

Total -	1866 Mar 31
Saros 120	04:34 TD
A.Node	ΔT= 5s
Tot. = 98m	
Par. = 231m	U.Mag. = 1.5232
Gam. = -0.1614	P.Mag. = 2.6011

Total +	1866 Sep 24
Saros 125	14:07 TD
D.Node	ΔT= 4s
Tot. = 96m	
Par. = 215m	U.Mag. = 1.6071
Gam. = 0.1412	P.Mag. = 2.5904

Partial	1867 Mar 20
Saros 130	08:49 TD
A.Node	ΔT= 4s
Par. = 186m	U.Mag. = 0.8038
Gam. = 0.5657	P.Mag. = 1.8366

Partial	1867 Sep 14
Saros 135	00:26 TD
D.Node	ΔT= 3s
Par. = 178m	U.Mag. = 0.6956
Gam. = -0.6240	P.Mag. = 1.7309

Penumbral	1868 Feb 08
Saros 102	09:50 TD
A.Node	ΔT= 3s
Pen. = 126m	U.Mag. = -0.7433
Gam. = -1.4252	P.Mag. = 0.2288

Penumbral	1868 Mar 08
Saros 140	20:10 TD
A.Node	ΔT= 3s
Pen. = 199m	U.Mag. = -0.3974
Gam. = 1.2340	P.Mag. = 0.5850

Penumbral	1868 Aug 03
Saros 107	12:09 TD
D.Node	ΔT= 2s
Pen. = 134m	U.Mag. = -0.8824
Gam. = 1.4741	P.Mag. = 0.1895

Penumbral	1868 Sep 02
Saros 145	03:41 TD
D.Node	ΔT= 2s
Pen. = 172m	U.Mag. = -0.7498
Gam. = -1.4013	P.Mag. = 0.3242

Partial	1869 Jan 28
Saros 112	01:38 TD
A.Node	ΔT= 2s
Par. = 138m	U.Mag. = 0.4507
Gam. = -0.7733	P.Mag. = 1.4273

Partial	1869 Jul 23
Saros 117	14:03 TD
D.Node	ΔT= 1s
Par. = 166m	U.Mag. = 0.5600
Gam. = 0.6962	P.Mag. = 1.6017

Plate 076

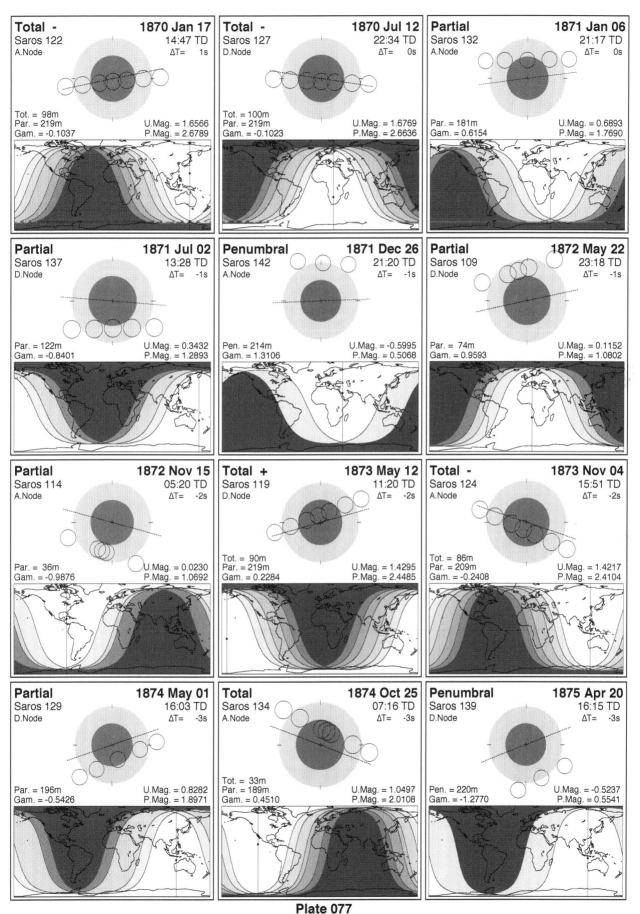

Total - **1870 Jan 17** Saros 122 14:47 TD A.Node ΔT= 1s Tot. = 98m Par. = 219m U.Mag. = 1.6566 Gam. = -0.1037 P.Mag. = 2.6789	**Total -** **1870 Jul 12** Saros 127 22:34 TD D.Node ΔT= 0s Tot. = 100m Par. = 219m U.Mag. = 1.6769 Gam. = -0.1023 P.Mag. = 2.6636	**Partial** **1871 Jan 06** Saros 132 21:17 TD A.Node ΔT= 0s Par. = 181m U.Mag. = 0.6893 Gam. = 0.6154 P.Mag. = 1.7690
Partial **1871 Jul 02** Saros 137 13:28 TD D.Node ΔT= -1s Par. = 122m U.Mag. = 0.3432 Gam. = -0.8401 P.Mag. = 1.2893	**Penumbral** **1871 Dec 26** Saros 142 21:20 TD A.Node ΔT= -1s Pen. = 214m U.Mag. = -0.5995 Gam. = 1.3106 P.Mag. = 0.5068	**Partial** **1872 May 22** Saros 109 23:18 TD D.Node ΔT= -1s Par. = 74m U.Mag. = 0.1152 Gam. = 0.9593 P.Mag. = 1.0802
Partial **1872 Nov 15** Saros 114 05:20 TD A.Node ΔT= -2s Par. = 36m U.Mag. = 0.0230 Gam. = -0.9876 P.Mag. = 1.0692	**Total +** **1873 May 12** Saros 119 11:20 TD D.Node ΔT= -2s Tot. = 90m Par. = 219m U.Mag. = 1.4295 Gam. = 0.2284 P.Mag. = 2.4485	**Total -** **1873 Nov 04** Saros 124 15:51 TD A.Node ΔT= -2s Tot. = 86m Par. = 209m U.Mag. = 1.4217 Gam. = -0.2408 P.Mag. = 2.4104
Partial **1874 May 01** Saros 129 16:03 TD D.Node ΔT= -3s Par. = 196m U.Mag. = 0.8282 Gam. = -0.5426 P.Mag. = 1.8971	**Total** **1874 Oct 25** Saros 134 07:16 TD A.Node ΔT= -3s Tot. = 33m Par. = 189m U.Mag. = 1.0497 Gam. = 0.4510 P.Mag. = 2.0108	**Penumbral** **1875 Apr 20** Saros 139 16:15 TD D.Node ΔT= -3s Pen. = 220m U.Mag. = -0.5237 Gam. = -1.2770 P.Mag. = 0.5541

Plate 077

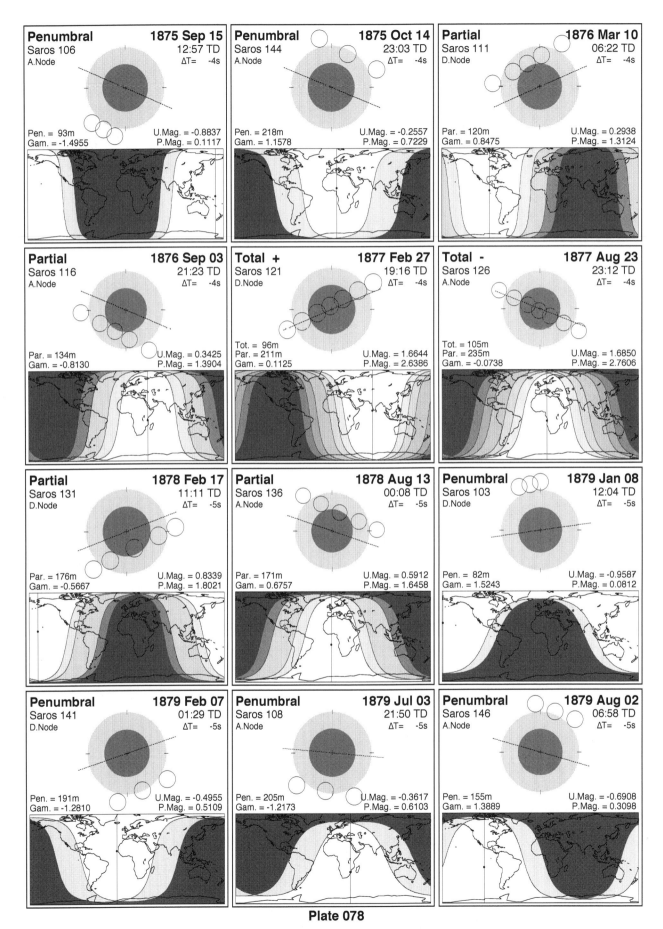

Penumbral   **1875 Sep 15**
Saros 106   12:57 TD
A.Node   ΔT= -4s
Pen. = 93m   U.Mag. = -0.8837
Gam. = -1.4955   P.Mag. = 0.1117

Penumbral   **1875 Oct 14**
Saros 144   23:03 TD
A.Node   ΔT= -4s
Pen. = 218m   U.Mag. = -0.2557
Gam. = 1.1578   P.Mag. = 0.7229

Partial   **1876 Mar 10**
Saros 111   06:22 TD
D.Node   ΔT= -4s
Par. = 120m   U.Mag. = 0.2938
Gam. = 0.8475   P.Mag. = 1.3124

Partial   **1876 Sep 03**
Saros 116   21:23 TD
A.Node   ΔT= -4s
Par. = 134m   U.Mag. = 0.3425
Gam. = -0.8130   P.Mag. = 1.3904

Total +   **1877 Feb 27**
Saros 121   19:16 TD
D.Node   ΔT= -4s
Tot. = 96m
Par. = 211m   U.Mag. = 1.6644
Gam. = 0.1125   P.Mag. = 2.6386

Total -   **1877 Aug 23**
Saros 126   23:12 TD
A.Node   ΔT= -4s
Tot. = 105m
Par. = 235m   U.Mag. = 1.6850
Gam. = -0.0738   P.Mag. = 2.7606

Partial   **1878 Feb 17**
Saros 131   11:11 TD
D.Node   ΔT= -5s
Par. = 176m   U.Mag. = 0.8339
Gam. = -0.5667   P.Mag. = 1.8021

Partial   **1878 Aug 13**
Saros 136   00:08 TD
A.Node   ΔT= -5s
Par. = 171m   U.Mag. = 0.5912
Gam. = 0.6757   P.Mag. = 1.6458

Penumbral   **1879 Jan 08**
Saros 103   12:04 TD
D.Node   ΔT= -5s
Pen. = 82m   U.Mag. = -0.9587
Gam. = 1.5243   P.Mag. = 0.0812

Penumbral   **1879 Feb 07**
Saros 141   01:29 TD
D.Node   ΔT= -5s
Pen. = 191m   U.Mag. = -0.4955
Gam. = -1.2810   P.Mag. = 0.5109

Penumbral   **1879 Jul 03**
Saros 108   21:50 TD
A.Node   ΔT= -5s
Pen. = 205m   U.Mag. = -0.3617
Gam. = -1.2173   P.Mag. = 0.6103

Penumbral   **1879 Aug 02**
Saros 146   06:58 TD
A.Node   ΔT= -5s
Pen. = 155m   U.Mag. = -0.6908
Gam. = 1.3889   P.Mag. = 0.3098

Plate 078

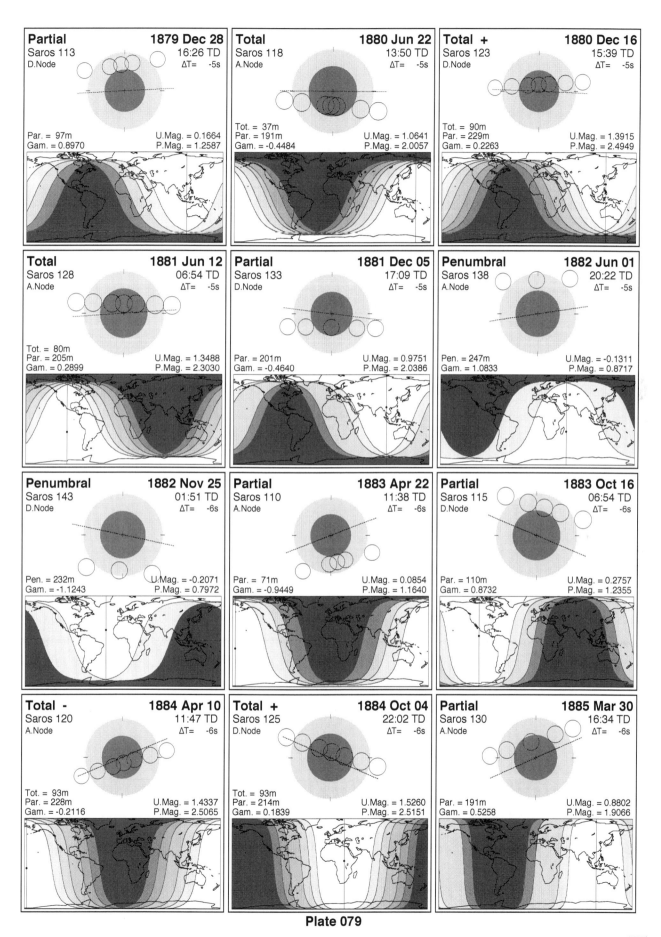

Partial   **1879 Dec 28**
Saros 113   16:26 TD
D.Node   ΔT= -5s

Par. = 97m   U.Mag. = 0.1664
Gam. = 0.8970   P.Mag. = 1.2587

Total   **1880 Jun 22**
Saros 118   13:50 TD
A.Node   ΔT= -5s

Tot. = 37m
Par. = 191m   U.Mag. = 1.0641
Gam. = -0.4484   P.Mag. = 2.0057

Total +   **1880 Dec 16**
Saros 123   15:39 TD
D.Node   ΔT= -5s

Tot. = 90m
Par. = 229m   U.Mag. = 1.3915
Gam. = 0.2263   P.Mag. = 2.4949

Total   **1881 Jun 12**
Saros 128   06:54 TD
A.Node   ΔT= -5s

Tot. = 80m
Par. = 205m   U.Mag. = 1.3488
Gam. = 0.2899   P.Mag. = 2.3030

Partial   **1881 Dec 05**
Saros 133   17:09 TD
D.Node   ΔT= -5s

Par. = 201m   U.Mag. = 0.9751
Gam. = -0.4640   P.Mag. = 2.0386

Penumbral   **1882 Jun 01**
Saros 138   20:22 TD
A.Node   ΔT= -5s

Pen. = 247m   U.Mag. = -0.1311
Gam. = 1.0833   P.Mag. = 0.8717

Penumbral   **1882 Nov 25**
Saros 143   01:51 TD
D.Node   ΔT= -6s

Pen. = 232m   U.Mag. = -0.2071
Gam. = -1.1243   P.Mag. = 0.7972

Partial   **1883 Apr 22**
Saros 110   11:38 TD
A.Node   ΔT= -6s

Par. = 71m   U.Mag. = 0.0854
Gam. = -0.9449   P.Mag. = 1.1640

Partial   **1883 Oct 16**
Saros 115   06:54 TD
D.Node   ΔT= -6s

Par. = 110m   U.Mag. = 0.2757
Gam. = 0.8732   P.Mag. = 1.2355

Total -   **1884 Apr 10**
Saros 120   11:47 TD
A.Node   ΔT= -6s

Tot. = 93m
Par. = 228m   U.Mag. = 1.4337
Gam. = -0.2116   P.Mag. = 2.5065

Total +   **1884 Oct 04**
Saros 125   22:02 TD
D.Node   ΔT= -6s

Tot. = 93m
Par. = 214m   U.Mag. = 1.5260
Gam. = 0.1839   P.Mag. = 2.5151

Partial   **1885 Mar 30**
Saros 130   16:34 TD
A.Node   ΔT= -6s

Par. = 191m   U.Mag. = 0.8802
Gam. = 0.5258   P.Mag. = 1.9066

Plate 079

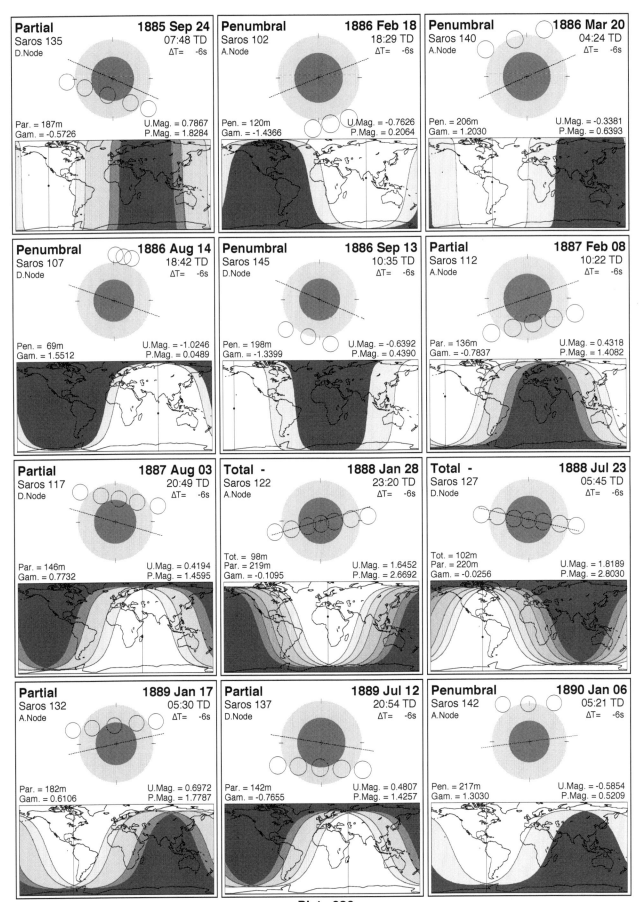

Partial   **1885 Sep 24**
Saros 135   07:48 TD
D.Node   ΔT= -6s
Par. = 187m   U.Mag. = 0.7867
Gam. = -0.5726   P.Mag. = 1.8284

Penumbral   **1886 Feb 18**
Saros 102   18:29 TD
A.Node   ΔT= -6s
Pen. = 120m   U.Mag. = -0.7626
Gam. = -1.4366   P.Mag. = 0.2064

Penumbral   **1886 Mar 20**
Saros 140   04:24 TD
A.Node   ΔT= -6s
Pen. = 206m   U.Mag. = -0.3381
Gam. = 1.2030   P.Mag. = 0.6393

Penumbral   **1886 Aug 14**
Saros 107   18:42 TD
D.Node   ΔT= -6s
Pen. = 69m   U.Mag. = -1.0246
Gam. = 1.5512   P.Mag. = 0.0489

Penumbral   **1886 Sep 13**
Saros 145   10:35 TD
D.Node   ΔT= -6s
Pen. = 198m   U.Mag. = -0.6392
Gam. = -1.3399   P.Mag. = 0.4390

Partial   **1887 Feb 08**
Saros 112   10:22 TD
A.Node   ΔT= -6s
Par. = 136m   U.Mag. = 0.4318
Gam. = -0.7837   P.Mag. = 1.4082

Partial   **1887 Aug 03**
Saros 117   20:49 TD
D.Node   ΔT= -6s
Par. = 146m   U.Mag. = 0.4194
Gam. = 0.7732   P.Mag. = 1.4595

Total -   **1888 Jan 28**
Saros 122   23:20 TD
A.Node   ΔT= -6s
Tot. = 98m
Par. = 219m   U.Mag. = 1.6452
Gam. = -0.1095   P.Mag. = 2.6692

Total -   **1888 Jul 23**
Saros 127   05:45 TD
D.Node   ΔT= -6s
Tot. = 102m
Par. = 220m   U.Mag. = 1.8189
Gam. = -0.0256   P.Mag. = 2.8030

Partial   **1889 Jan 17**
Saros 132   05:30 TD
A.Node   ΔT= -6s
Par. = 182m   U.Mag. = 0.6972
Gam. = 0.6106   P.Mag. = 1.7787

Partial   **1889 Jul 12**
Saros 137   20:54 TD
D.Node   ΔT= -6s
Par. = 142m   U.Mag. = 0.4807
Gam. = -0.7655   P.Mag. = 1.4257

Penumbral   **1890 Jan 06**
Saros 142   05:21 TD
A.Node   ΔT= -6s
Pen. = 217m   U.Mag. = -0.5854
Gam. = 1.3030   P.Mag. = 0.5209

Plate 080

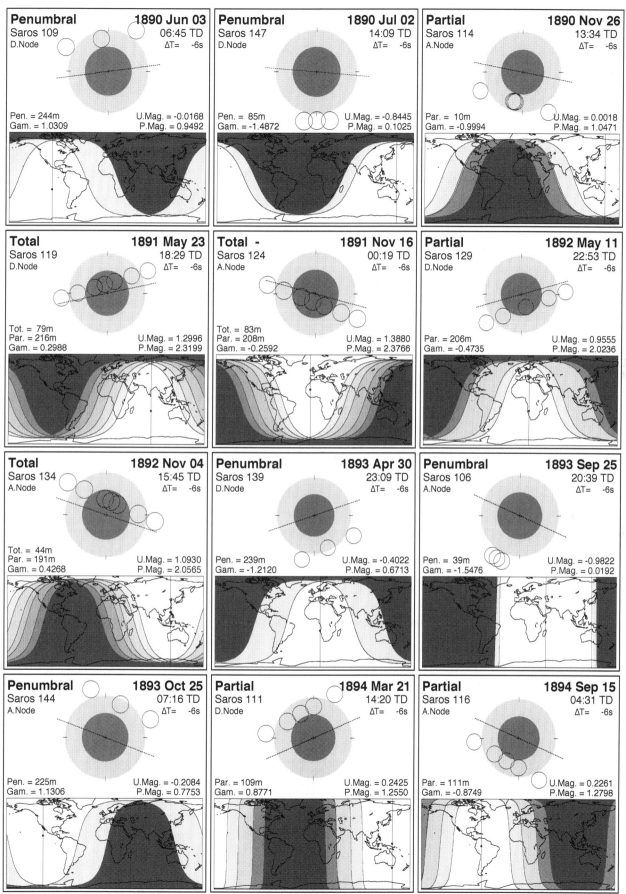

Penumbral	1890 Jun 03
Saros 109	06:45 TD
D.Node	ΔT= -6s

Pen. = 244m
Gam. = 1.0309
U.Mag. = -0.0168
P.Mag. = 0.9492

Penumbral	1890 Jul 02
Saros 147	14:09 TD
D.Node	ΔT= -6s

Pen. = 85m
Gam. = -1.4872
U.Mag. = -0.8445
P.Mag. = 0.1025

Partial	1890 Nov 26
Saros 114	13:34 TD
A.Node	ΔT= -6s

Par. = 10m
Gam. = -0.9994
U.Mag. = 0.0018
P.Mag. = 1.0471

Total	1891 May 23
Saros 119	18:29 TD
D.Node	ΔT= -6s

Tot. = 79m
Par. = 216m
Gam. = 0.2988
U.Mag. = 1.2996
P.Mag. = 2.3199

Total -	1891 Nov 16
Saros 124	00:19 TD
A.Node	ΔT= -6s

Tot. = 83m
Par. = 208m
Gam. = -0.2592
U.Mag. = 1.3880
P.Mag. = 2.3766

Partial	1892 May 11
Saros 129	22:53 TD
D.Node	ΔT= -6s

Par. = 206m
Gam. = -0.4735
U.Mag. = 0.9555
P.Mag. = 2.0236

Total	1892 Nov 04
Saros 134	15:45 TD
A.Node	ΔT= -6s

Tot. = 44m
Par. = 191m
Gam. = 0.4268
U.Mag. = 1.0930
P.Mag. = 2.0565

Penumbral	1893 Apr 30
Saros 139	23:09 TD
D.Node	ΔT= -6s

Pen. = 239m
Gam. = -1.2120
U.Mag. = -0.4022
P.Mag. = 0.6713

Penumbral	1893 Sep 25
Saros 106	20:39 TD
A.Node	ΔT= -6s

Pen. = 39m
Gam. = -1.5476
U.Mag. = -0.9822
P.Mag. = 0.0192

Penumbral	1893 Oct 25
Saros 144	07:16 TD
A.Node	ΔT= -6s

Pen. = 225m
Gam. = 1.1306
U.Mag. = -0.2084
P.Mag. = 0.7753

Partial	1894 Mar 21
Saros 111	14:20 TD
D.Node	ΔT= -6s

Par. = 109m
Gam. = 0.8771
U.Mag. = 0.2425
P.Mag. = 1.2550

Partial	1894 Sep 15
Saros 116	04:31 TD
A.Node	ΔT= -6s

Par. = 111m
Gam. = -0.8749
U.Mag. = 0.2261
P.Mag. = 1.2798

Plate 081

177

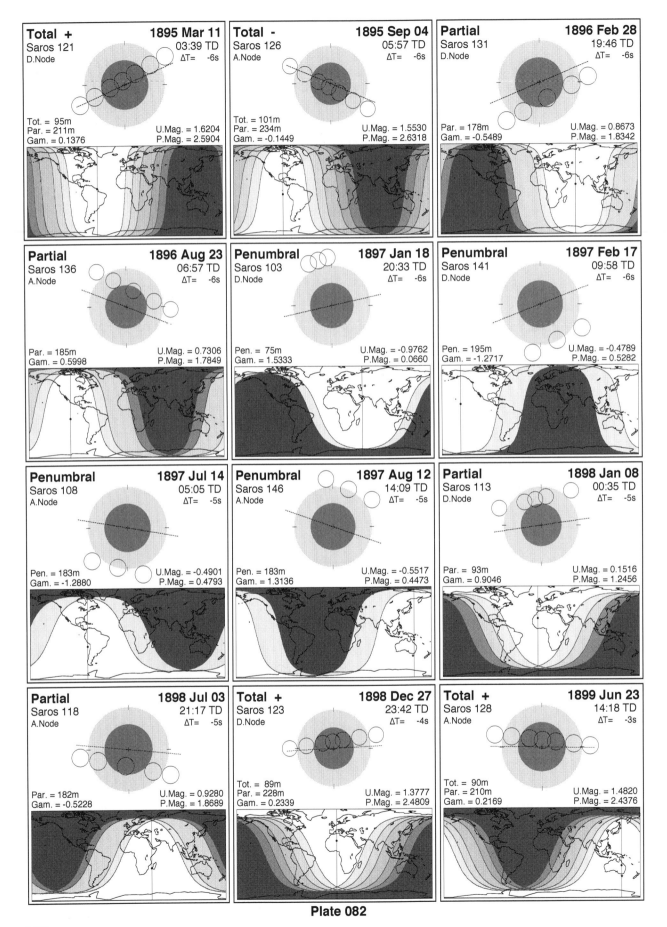

Total +   **1895 Mar 11**
Saros 121   03:39 TD
D.Node   ΔT= -6s

Tot. = 95m
Par. = 211m   U.Mag. = 1.6204
Gam. = 0.1376   P.Mag. = 2.5904

Total -   **1895 Sep 04**
Saros 126   05:57 TD
A.Node   ΔT= -6s

Tot. = 101m
Par. = 234m   U.Mag. = 1.5530
Gam. = -0.1449   P.Mag. = 2.6318

Partial   **1896 Feb 28**
Saros 131   19:46 TD
D.Node   ΔT= -6s

Par. = 178m   U.Mag. = 0.8673
Gam. = -0.5489   P.Mag. = 1.8342

Partial   **1896 Aug 23**
Saros 136   06:57 TD
A.Node   ΔT= -6s

Par. = 185m   U.Mag. = 0.7306
Gam. = 0.5998   P.Mag. = 1.7849

Penumbral   **1897 Jan 18**
Saros 103   20:33 TD
D.Node   ΔT= -6s

Pen. = 75m   U.Mag. = -0.9762
Gam. = 1.5333   P.Mag. = 0.0660

Penumbral   **1897 Feb 17**
Saros 141   09:58 TD
D.Node   ΔT= -6s

Pen. = 195m   U.Mag. = -0.4789
Gam. = -1.2717   P.Mag. = 0.5282

Penumbral   **1897 Jul 14**
Saros 108   05:05 TD
A.Node   ΔT= -5s

Pen. = 183m   U.Mag. = -0.4901
Gam. = -1.2880   P.Mag. = 0.4793

Penumbral   **1897 Aug 12**
Saros 146   14:09 TD
A.Node   ΔT= -5s

Pen. = 183m   U.Mag. = -0.5517
Gam. = 1.3136   P.Mag. = 0.4473

Partial   **1898 Jan 08**
Saros 113   00:35 TD
D.Node   ΔT= -5s

Par. = 93m   U.Mag. = 0.1516
Gam. = 0.9046   P.Mag. = 1.2456

Partial   **1898 Jul 03**
Saros 118   21:17 TD
A.Node   ΔT= -5s

Par. = 182m   U.Mag. = 0.9280
Gam. = -0.5228   P.Mag. = 1.8689

Total +   **1898 Dec 27**
Saros 123   23:42 TD
D.Node   ΔT= -4s

Tot. = 89m
Par. = 228m   U.Mag. = 1.3777
Gam. = 0.2339   P.Mag. = 2.4809

Total +   **1899 Jun 23**
Saros 128   14:18 TD
A.Node   ΔT= -3s

Tot. = 90m
Par. = 210m   U.Mag. = 1.4820
Gam. = 0.2169   P.Mag. = 2.4376

Plate 082

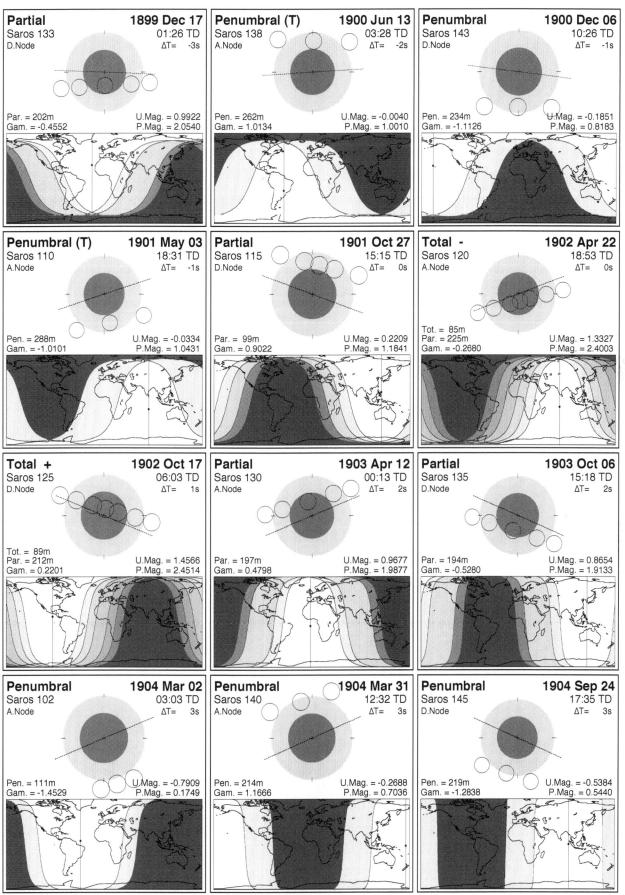

Partial	1899 Dec 17
Saros 133	01:26 TD
D.Node	ΔT= -3s
Par. = 202m	U.Mag. = 0.9922
Gam. = -0.4552	P.Mag. = 2.0540

Penumbral (T)	1900 Jun 13
Saros 138	03:28 TD
A.Node	ΔT= -2s
Pen. = 262m	U.Mag. = -0.0040
Gam. = 1.0134	P.Mag. = 1.0010

Penumbral	1900 Dec 06
Saros 143	10:26 TD
D.Node	ΔT= -1s
Pen. = 234m	U.Mag. = -0.1851
Gam. = -1.1126	P.Mag. = 0.8183

Penumbral (T)	1901 May 03
Saros 110	18:31 TD
A.Node	ΔT= -1s
Pen. = 288m	U.Mag. = -0.0334
Gam. = -1.0101	P.Mag. = 1.0431

Partial	1901 Oct 27
Saros 115	15:15 TD
D.Node	ΔT= 0s
Par. = 99m	U.Mag. = 0.2209
Gam. = 0.9022	P.Mag. = 1.1841

Total -	1902 Apr 22
Saros 120	18:53 TD
A.Node	ΔT= 0s
Tot. = 85m	
Par. = 225m	U.Mag. = 1.3327
Gam. = -0.2680	P.Mag. = 2.4003

Total +	1902 Oct 17
Saros 125	06:03 TD
D.Node	ΔT= 1s
Tot. = 89m	
Par. = 212m	U.Mag. = 1.4566
Gam. = 0.2201	P.Mag. = 2.4514

Partial	1903 Apr 12
Saros 130	00:13 TD
A.Node	ΔT= 2s
Par. = 197m	U.Mag. = 0.9677
Gam. = 0.4798	P.Mag. = 1.9877

Partial	1903 Oct 06
Saros 135	15:18 TD
D.Node	ΔT= 2s
Par. = 194m	U.Mag. = 0.8654
Gam. = -0.5280	P.Mag. = 1.9133

Penumbral	1904 Mar 02
Saros 102	03:03 TD
A.Node	ΔT= 3s
Pen. = 111m	U.Mag. = -0.7909
Gam. = -1.4529	P.Mag. = 0.1749

Penumbral	1904 Mar 31
Saros 140	12:32 TD
A.Node	ΔT= 3s
Pen. = 214m	U.Mag. = -0.2688
Gam. = 1.1666	P.Mag. = 0.7036

Penumbral	1904 Sep 24
Saros 145	17:35 TD
D.Node	ΔT= 3s
Pen. = 219m	U.Mag. = -0.5384
Gam. = -1.2838	P.Mag. = 0.5440

Plate 083

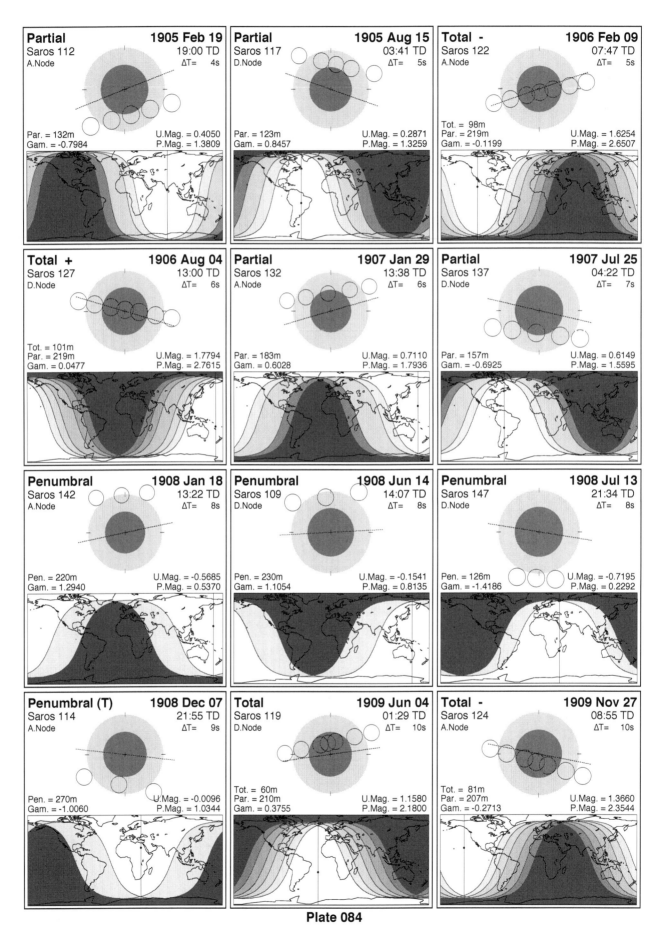

Partial   **1905 Feb 19**
Saros 112   19:00 TD
A.Node   ΔT= 4s

Par. = 132m   U.Mag. = 0.4050
Gam. = -0.7984   P.Mag. = 1.3809

Partial   **1905 Aug 15**
Saros 117   03:41 TD
D.Node   ΔT= 5s

Par. = 123m   U.Mag. = 0.2871
Gam. = 0.8457   P.Mag. = 1.3259

Total -   **1906 Feb 09**
Saros 122   07:47 TD
A.Node   ΔT= 5s

Tot. = 98m
Par. = 219m   U.Mag. = 1.6254
Gam. = -0.1199   P.Mag. = 2.6507

Total +   **1906 Aug 04**
Saros 127   13:00 TD
D.Node   ΔT= 6s

Tot. = 101m
Par. = 219m   U.Mag. = 1.7794
Gam. = 0.0477   P.Mag. = 2.7615

Partial   **1907 Jan 29**
Saros 132   13:38 TD
A.Node   ΔT= 6s

Par. = 183m   U.Mag. = 0.7110
Gam. = 0.6028   P.Mag. = 1.7936

Partial   **1907 Jul 25**
Saros 137   04:22 TD
D.Node   ΔT= 7s

Par. = 157m   U.Mag. = 0.6149
Gam. = -0.6925   P.Mag. = 1.5595

Penumbral   **1908 Jan 18**
Saros 142   13:22 TD
A.Node   ΔT= 8s

Pen. = 220m   U.Mag. = -0.5685
Gam. = 1.2940   P.Mag. = 0.5370

Penumbral   **1908 Jun 14**
Saros 109   14:07 TD
D.Node   ΔT= 8s

Pen. = 230m   U.Mag. = -0.1541
Gam. = 1.1054   P.Mag. = 0.8135

Penumbral   **1908 Jul 13**
Saros 147   21:34 TD
D.Node   ΔT= 8s

Pen. = 126m   U.Mag. = -0.7195
Gam. = -1.4186   P.Mag. = 0.2292

Penumbral (T)   **1908 Dec 07**
Saros 114   21:55 TD
A.Node   ΔT= 9s

Pen. = 270m   U.Mag. = -0.0096
Gam. = -1.0060   P.Mag. = 1.0344

Total   **1909 Jun 04**
Saros 119   01:29 TD
D.Node   ΔT= 10s

Tot. = 60m
Par. = 210m   U.Mag. = 1.1580
Gam. = 0.3755   P.Mag. = 2.1800

Total -   **1909 Nov 27**
Saros 124   08:55 TD
A.Node   ΔT= 10s

Tot. = 81m
Par. = 207m   U.Mag. = 1.3660
Gam. = -0.2713   P.Mag. = 2.3544

Plate 084

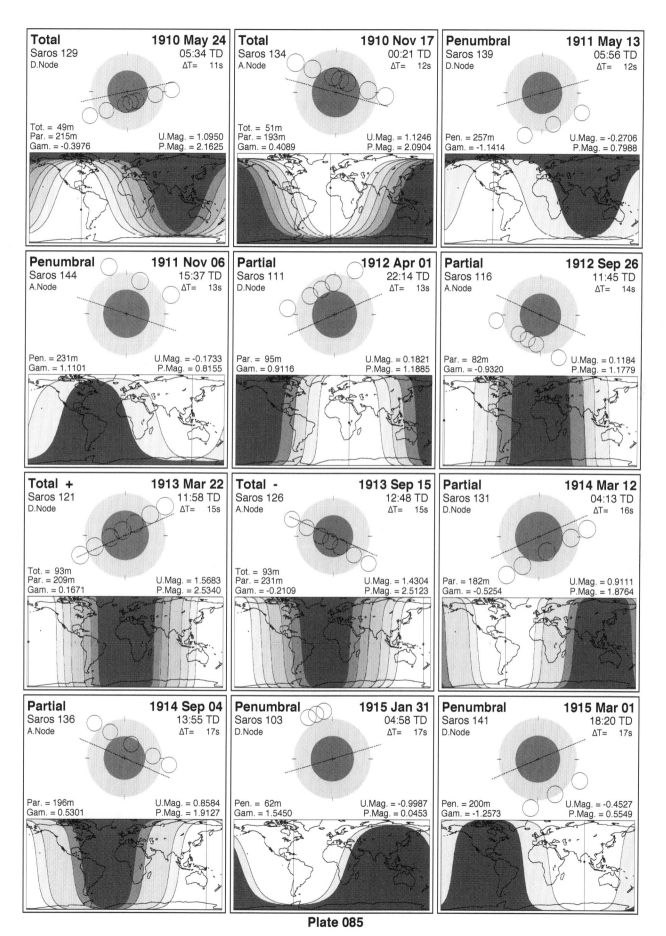

Plate 085

181

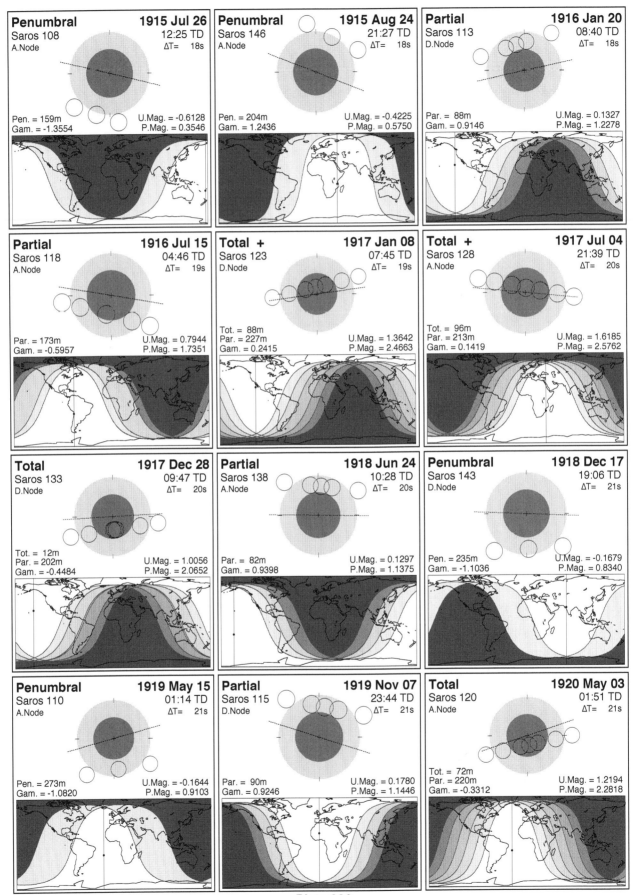

Penumbral   **1915 Jul 26**
Saros 108   12:25 TD
A.Node   ΔT= 18s
Pen. = 159m
Gam. = -1.3554   U.Mag. = -0.6128
   P.Mag. = 0.3546

Penumbral   **1915 Aug 24**
Saros 146   21:27 TD
A.Node   ΔT= 18s
Pen. = 204m
Gam. = 1.2436   U.Mag. = -0.4225
   P.Mag. = 0.5750

Partial   **1916 Jan 20**
Saros 113   08:40 TD
D.Node   ΔT= 18s
Par. = 88m
Gam. = 0.9146   U.Mag. = 0.1327
   P.Mag. = 1.2278

Partial   **1916 Jul 15**
Saros 118   04:46 TD
A.Node   ΔT= 19s
Par. = 173m
Gam. = -0.5957   U.Mag. = 0.7944
   P.Mag. = 1.7351

Total +   **1917 Jan 08**
Saros 123   07:45 TD
D.Node   ΔT= 19s
Tot. = 88m
Par. = 227m
Gam. = 0.2415   U.Mag. = 1.3642
   P.Mag. = 2.4663

Total +   **1917 Jul 04**
Saros 128   21:39 TD
A.Node   ΔT= 20s
Tot. = 96m
Par. = 213m
Gam. = 0.1419   U.Mag. = 1.6185
   P.Mag. = 2.5762

Total   **1917 Dec 28**
Saros 133   09:47 TD
D.Node   ΔT= 20s
Tot. = 12m
Par. = 202m
Gam. = -0.4484   U.Mag. = 1.0056
   P.Mag. = 2.0652

Partial   **1918 Jun 24**
Saros 138   10:28 TD
A.Node   ΔT= 20s
Par. = 82m
Gam. = 0.9398   U.Mag. = 0.1297
   P.Mag. = 1.1375

Penumbral   **1918 Dec 17**
Saros 143   19:06 TD
D.Node   ΔT= 21s
Pen. = 235m
Gam. = -1.1036   U.Mag. = -0.1679
   P.Mag. = 0.8340

Penumbral   **1919 May 15**
Saros 110   01:14 TD
A.Node   ΔT= 21s
Pen. = 273m
Gam. = -1.0820   U.Mag. = -0.1644
   P.Mag. = 0.9103

Partial   **1919 Nov 07**
Saros 115   23:44 TD
D.Node   ΔT= 21s
Par. = 90m
Gam. = 0.9246   U.Mag. = 0.1780
   P.Mag. = 1.1446

Total   **1920 May 03**
Saros 120   01:51 TD
A.Node   ΔT= 21s
Tot. = 72m
Par. = 220m
Gam. = -0.3312   U.Mag. = 1.2194
   P.Mag. = 2.2818

Plate 086

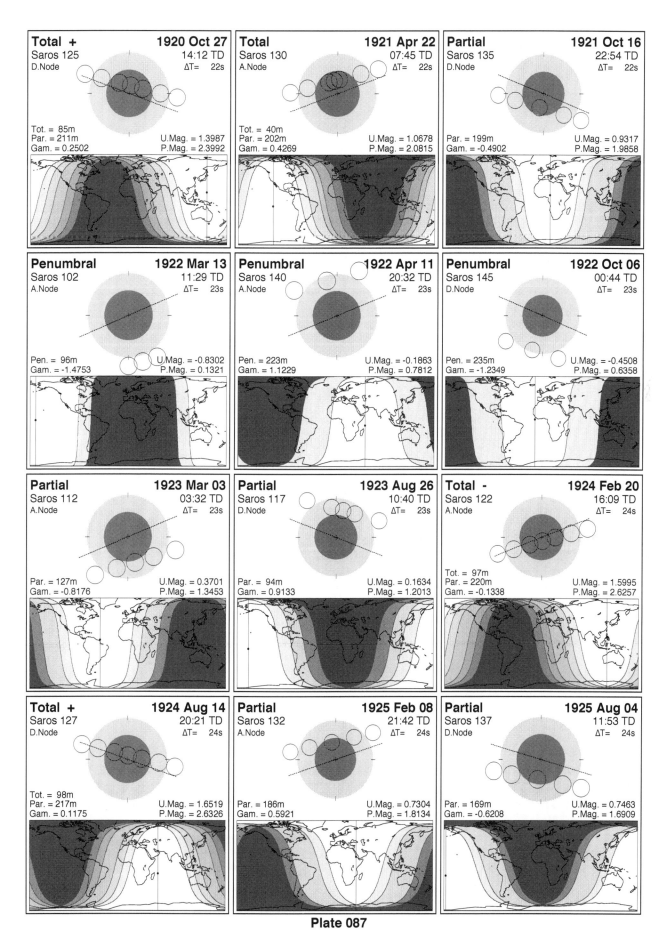

Total +   **1920 Oct 27**
Saros 125   14:12 TD
D.Node   ΔT= 22s
Tot. = 85m
Par. = 211m
Gam. = 0.2502   U.Mag. = 1.3987
    P.Mag. = 2.3992

Total   **1921 Apr 22**
Saros 130   07:45 TD
A.Node   ΔT= 22s
Tot. = 40m
Par. = 202m
Gam. = 0.4269   U.Mag. = 1.0678
    P.Mag. = 2.0815

Partial   **1921 Oct 16**
Saros 135   22:54 TD
D.Node   ΔT= 22s
Par. = 199m
    U.Mag. = 0.9317
    P.Mag. = 1.9858

Penumbral   **1922 Mar 13**
Saros 102   11:29 TD
A.Node   ΔT= 23s
Pen. = 96m
Gam. = -1.4753   U.Mag. = -0.8302
    P.Mag. = 0.1321

Penumbral   **1922 Apr 11**
Saros 140   20:32 TD
A.Node   ΔT= 23s
Pen. = 223m
Gam. = 1.1229   U.Mag. = -0.1863
    P.Mag. = 0.7812

Penumbral   **1922 Oct 06**
Saros 145   00:44 TD
D.Node   ΔT= 23s
Pen. = 235m
Gam. = -1.2349   U.Mag. = -0.4508
    P.Mag. = 0.6358

Partial   **1923 Mar 03**
Saros 112   03:32 TD
A.Node   ΔT= 23s
Par. = 127m
Gam. = -0.8176   U.Mag. = 0.3701
    P.Mag. = 1.3453

Partial   **1923 Aug 26**
Saros 117   10:40 TD
D.Node   ΔT= 23s
Par. = 94m
Gam. = 0.9133   U.Mag. = 0.1634
    P.Mag. = 1.2013

Total -   **1924 Feb 20**
Saros 122   16:09 TD
A.Node   ΔT= 24s
Tot. = 97m
Par. = 220m
Gam. = -0.1338   U.Mag. = 1.5995
    P.Mag. = 2.6257

Total +   **1924 Aug 14**
Saros 127   20:21 TD
D.Node   ΔT= 24s
Tot. = 98m
Par. = 217m
Gam. = 0.1175   U.Mag. = 1.6519
    P.Mag. = 2.6326

Partial   **1925 Feb 08**
Saros 132   21:42 TD
A.Node   ΔT= 24s
Par. = 186m
Gam. = 0.5921   U.Mag. = 0.7304
    P.Mag. = 1.8134

Partial   **1925 Aug 04**
Saros 137   11:53 TD
D.Node   ΔT= 24s
Par. = 169m
Gam. = -0.6208   U.Mag. = 0.7463
    P.Mag. = 1.6909

Plate 087

183

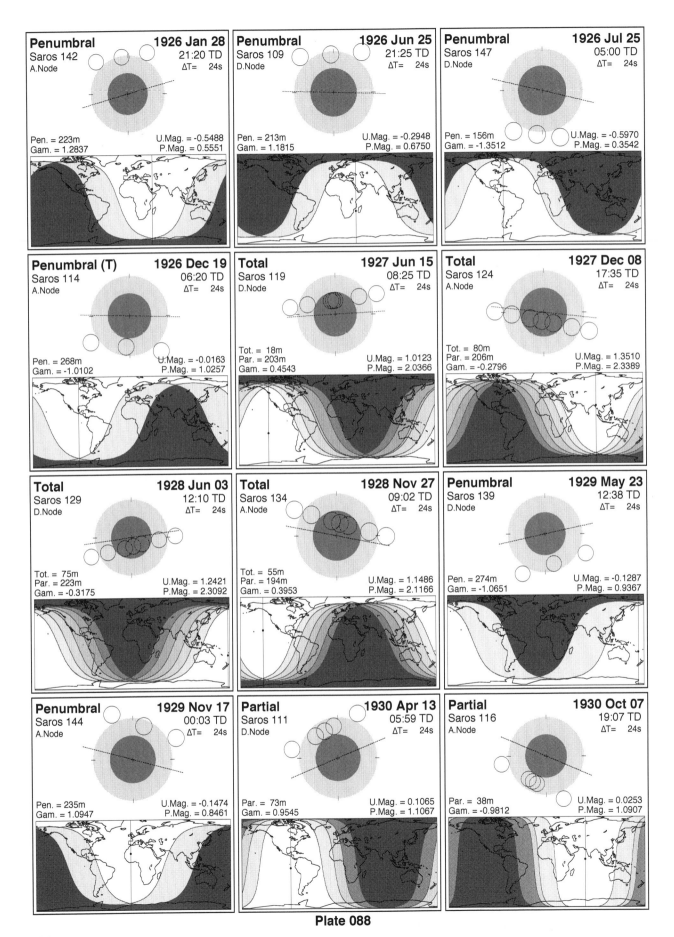

Penumbral **1926 Jan 28**	
Saros 142 21:20 TD	
A.Node ΔT= 24s	
Pen. = 223m U.Mag. = -0.5488	
Gam. = 1.2837 P.Mag. = 0.5551	

Penumbral   **1926 Jun 25**
Saros 109   21:25 TD
D.Node   ΔT= 24s
Pen. = 213m   U.Mag. = -0.2948
Gam. = 1.1815   P.Mag. = 0.6750

Penumbral   **1926 Jul 25**
Saros 147   05:00 TD
D.Node   ΔT= 24s
Pen. = 156m   U.Mag. = -0.5970
Gam. = -1.3512   P.Mag. = 0.3542

Penumbral (T)   **1926 Dec 19**
Saros 114   06:20 TD
A.Node   ΔT= 24s
Pen. = 268m   U.Mag. = -0.0163
Gam. = -1.0102   P.Mag. = 1.0257

Total   **1927 Jun 15**
Saros 119   08:25 TD
D.Node   ΔT= 24s
Tot. = 18m
Par. = 203m   U.Mag. = 1.0123
Gam. = 0.4543   P.Mag. = 2.0366

Total   **1927 Dec 08**
Saros 124   17:35 TD
A.Node   ΔT= 24s
Tot. = 80m
Par. = 206m   U.Mag. = 1.3510
Gam. = -0.2796   P.Mag. = 2.3389

Total   **1928 Jun 03**
Saros 129   12:10 TD
D.Node   ΔT= 24s
Tot. = 75m
Par. = 223m   U.Mag. = 1.2421
Gam. = -0.3175   P.Mag. = 2.3092

Total   **1928 Nov 27**
Saros 134   09:02 TD
A.Node   ΔT= 24s
Tot. = 55m
Par. = 194m   U.Mag. = 1.1486
Gam. = 0.3953   P.Mag. = 2.1166

Penumbral   **1929 May 23**
Saros 139   12:38 TD
D.Node   ΔT= 24s
Pen. = 274m   U.Mag. = -0.1287
Gam. = -1.0651   P.Mag. = 0.9367

Penumbral   **1929 Nov 17**
Saros 144   00:03 TD
A.Node   ΔT= 24s
Pen. = 235m   U.Mag. = -0.1474
Gam. = 1.0947   P.Mag. = 0.8461

Partial   **1930 Apr 13**
Saros 111   05:59 TD
D.Node   ΔT= 24s
Par. = 73m   U.Mag. = 0.1065
Gam. = 0.9545   P.Mag. = 1.1067

Partial   **1930 Oct 07**
Saros 116   19:07 TD
A.Node   ΔT= 24s
Par. = 38m   U.Mag. = 0.0253
Gam. = -0.9812   P.Mag. = 1.0907

Plate 088

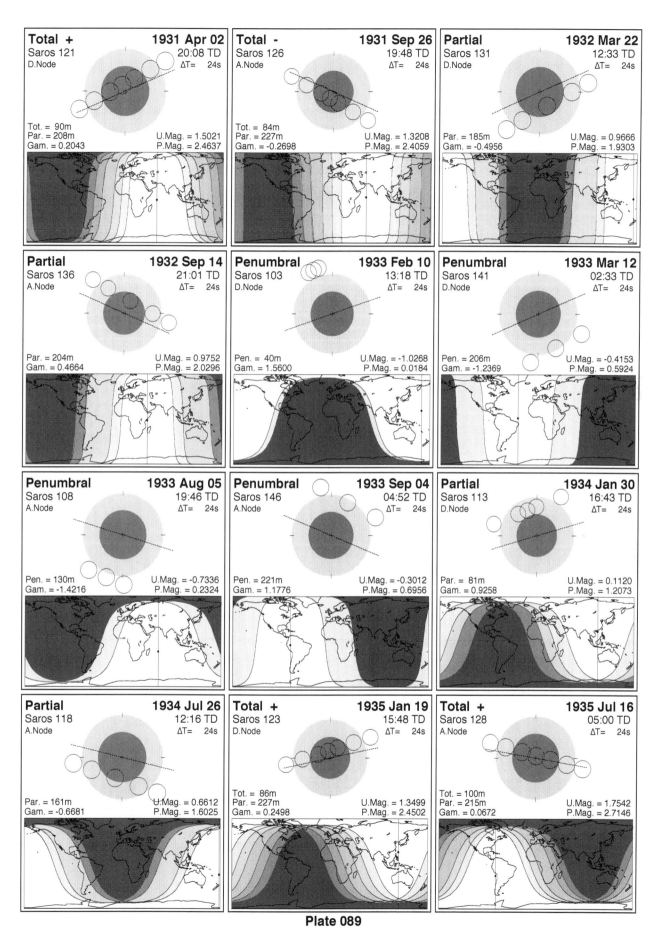

Total + **1931 Apr 02**	
Saros 121 20:08 TD	
D.Node ΔT= 24s	
Tot. = 90m	
Par. = 208m U.Mag. = 1.5021	
Gam. = 0.2043 P.Mag. = 2.4637	

Total +   **1931 Apr 02**
Saros 121   20:08 TD
D.Node   ΔT= 24s
Tot. = 90m
Par. = 208m   U.Mag. = 1.5021
Gam. = 0.2043   P.Mag. = 2.4637

Total −   **1931 Sep 26**
Saros 126   19:48 TD
A.Node   ΔT= 24s
Tot. = 84m
Par. = 227m   U.Mag. = 1.3208
Gam. = -0.2698   P.Mag. = 2.4059

Partial   **1932 Mar 22**
Saros 131   12:33 TD
D.Node   ΔT= 24s
Par. = 185m   U.Mag. = 0.9666
Gam. = -0.4956   P.Mag. = 1.9303

Partial   **1932 Sep 14**
Saros 136   21:01 TD
A.Node   ΔT= 24s
Par. = 204m   U.Mag. = 0.9752
Gam. = 0.4664   P.Mag. = 2.0296

Penumbral   **1933 Feb 10**
Saros 103   13:18 TD
D.Node   ΔT= 24s
Pen. = 40m   U.Mag. = -1.0268
Gam. = 1.5600   P.Mag. = 0.0184

Penumbral   **1933 Mar 12**
Saros 141   02:33 TD
D.Node   ΔT= 24s
Pen. = 206m   U.Mag. = -0.4153
Gam. = -1.2369   P.Mag. = 0.5924

Penumbral   **1933 Aug 05**
Saros 108   19:46 TD
A.Node   ΔT= 24s
Pen. = 130m   U.Mag. = -0.7336
Gam. = -1.4216   P.Mag. = 0.2324

Penumbral   **1933 Sep 04**
Saros 146   04:52 TD
A.Node   ΔT= 24s
Pen. = 221m   U.Mag. = -0.3012
Gam. = 1.1776   P.Mag. = 0.6956

Partial   **1934 Jan 30**
Saros 113   16:43 TD
D.Node   ΔT= 24s
Par. = 81m   U.Mag. = 0.1120
Gam. = 0.9258   P.Mag. = 1.2073

Partial   **1934 Jul 26**
Saros 118   12:16 TD
A.Node   ΔT= 24s
Par. = 161m   U.Mag. = 0.6612
Gam. = -0.6681   P.Mag. = 1.6025

Total +   **1935 Jan 19**
Saros 123   15:48 TD
D.Node   ΔT= 24s
Tot. = 86m
Par. = 227m   U.Mag. = 1.3499
Gam. = 0.2498   P.Mag. = 2.4502

Total +   **1935 Jul 16**
Saros 128   05:00 TD
A.Node   ΔT= 24s
Tot. = 100m
Par. = 215m   U.Mag. = 1.7542
Gam. = 0.0672   P.Mag. = 2.7146

Plate 089

185

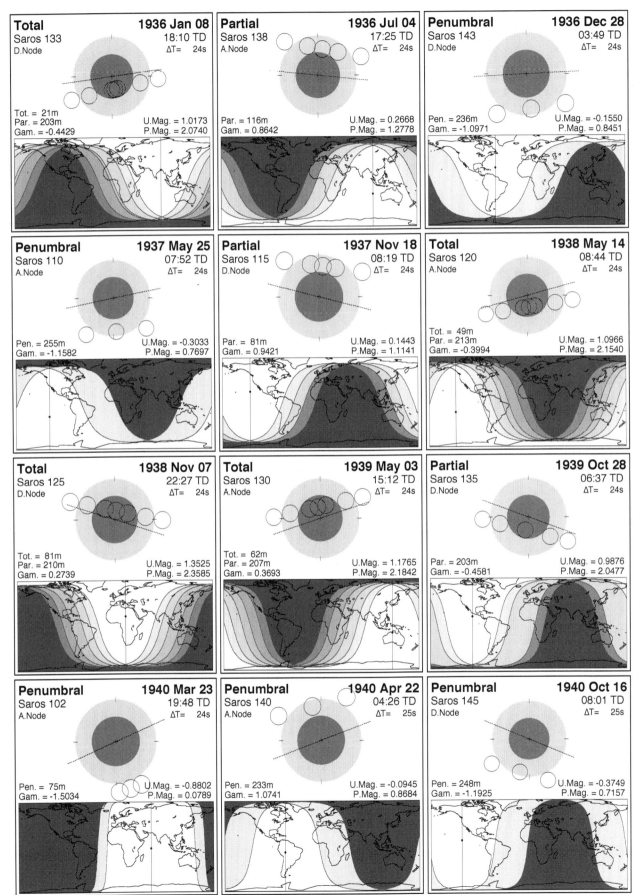

Total 1936 Jan 08	**Partial** 1936 Jul 04	**Penumbral** 1936 Dec 28
Saros 133 18:10 TD	Saros 138 17:25 TD	Saros 143 03:49 TD
D.Node ΔT= 24s	A.Node ΔT= 24s	D.Node ΔT= 24s
Tot. = 21m		
Par. = 203m U.Mag. = 1.0173	Par. = 116m U.Mag. = 0.2668	Pen. = 236m U.Mag. = -0.1550
Gam. = -0.4429 P.Mag. = 2.0740	Gam. = 0.8642 P.Mag. = 1.2778	Gam. = -1.0971 P.Mag. = 0.8451
Penumbral 1937 May 25	**Partial** 1937 Nov 18	**Total** 1938 May 14
Saros 110 07:52 TD	Saros 115 08:19 TD	Saros 120 08:44 TD
A.Node ΔT= 24s	D.Node ΔT= 24s	A.Node ΔT= 24s
		Tot. = 49m
Pen. = 255m U.Mag. = -0.3033	Par. = 81m U.Mag. = 0.1443	Par. = 213m U.Mag. = 1.0966
Gam. = -1.1582 P.Mag. = 0.7697	Gam. = 0.9421 P.Mag. = 1.1141	Gam. = -0.3994 P.Mag. = 2.1540
Total 1938 Nov 07	**Total** 1939 May 03	**Partial** 1939 Oct 28
Saros 125 22:27 TD	Saros 130 15:12 TD	Saros 135 06:37 TD
D.Node ΔT= 24s	A.Node ΔT= 24s	D.Node ΔT= 24s
Tot. = 81m	Tot. = 62m	
Par. = 210m U.Mag. = 1.3525	Par. = 207m U.Mag. = 1.1765	Par. = 203m U.Mag. = 0.9876
Gam. = 0.2739 P.Mag. = 2.3585	Gam. = 0.3693 P.Mag. = 2.1842	Gam. = -0.4581 P.Mag. = 2.0477
Penumbral 1940 Mar 23	**Penumbral** 1940 Apr 22	**Penumbral** 1940 Oct 16
Saros 102 19:48 TD	Saros 140 04:26 TD	Saros 145 08:01 TD
A.Node ΔT= 24s	A.Node ΔT= 25s	D.Node ΔT= 25s
Pen. = 75m U.Mag. = -0.8802	Pen. = 233m U.Mag. = -0.0945	Pen. = 248m U.Mag. = -0.3749
Gam. = -1.5034 P.Mag. = 0.0789	Gam. = 1.0741 P.Mag. = 0.8684	Gam. = -1.1925 P.Mag. = 0.7157

Plate 090

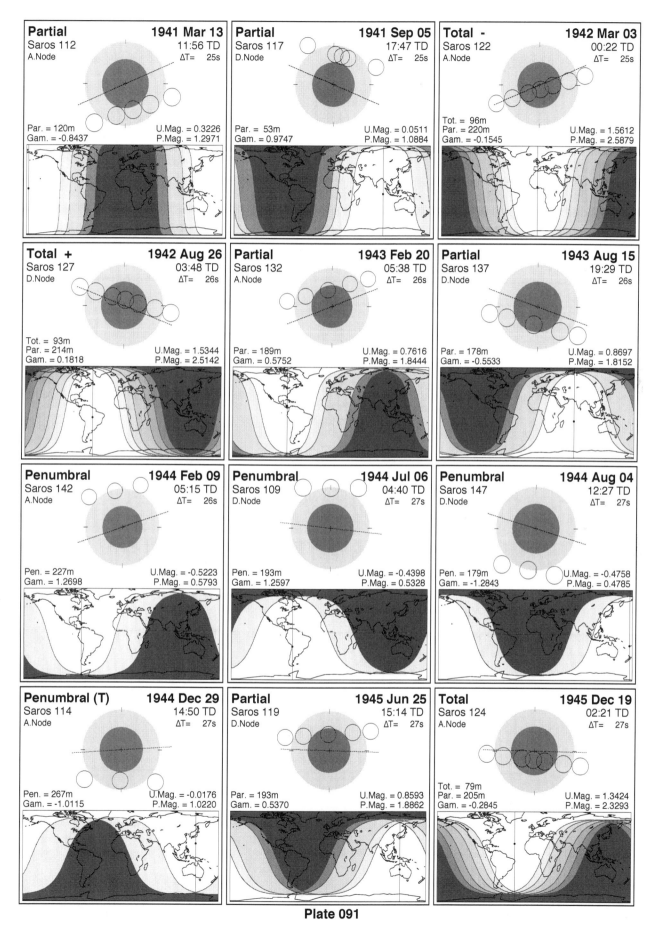

Partial 1941 Mar 13 Saros 112 11:56 TD A.Node ΔT= 25s Par. = 120m U.Mag. = 0.3226 Gam. = -0.8437 P.Mag. = 1.2971	**Partial** 1941 Sep 05 Saros 117 17:47 TD D.Node ΔT= 25s Par. = 53m U.Mag. = 0.0511 Gam. = 0.9747 P.Mag. = 1.0884	**Total -** 1942 Mar 03 Saros 122 00:22 TD A.Node ΔT= 25s Tot. = 96m Par. = 220m U.Mag. = 1.5612 Gam. = -0.1545 P.Mag. = 2.5879
Total + 1942 Aug 26 Saros 127 03:48 TD D.Node ΔT= 26s Tot. = 93m Par. = 214m U.Mag. = 1.5344 Gam. = 0.1818 P.Mag. = 2.5142	**Partial** 1943 Feb 20 Saros 132 05:38 TD A.Node ΔT= 26s Par. = 189m U.Mag. = 0.7616 Gam. = 0.5752 P.Mag. = 1.8444	**Partial** 1943 Aug 15 Saros 137 19:29 TD D.Node ΔT= 26s Par. = 178m U.Mag. = 0.8697 Gam. = -0.5533 P.Mag. = 1.8152
Penumbral 1944 Feb 09 Saros 142 05:15 TD A.Node ΔT= 26s Pen. = 227m U.Mag. = -0.5223 Gam. = 1.2698 P.Mag. = 0.5793	**Penumbral** 1944 Jul 06 Saros 109 04:40 TD D.Node ΔT= 27s Pen. = 193m U.Mag. = -0.4398 Gam. = 1.2597 P.Mag. = 0.5328	**Penumbral** 1944 Aug 04 Saros 147 12:27 TD D.Node ΔT= 27s Pen. = 179m U.Mag. = -0.4758 Gam. = -1.2843 P.Mag. = 0.4785
Penumbral (T) 1944 Dec 29 Saros 114 14:50 TD A.Node ΔT= 27s Pen. = 267m U.Mag. = -0.0176 Gam. = -1.0115 P.Mag. = 1.0220	**Partial** 1945 Jun 25 Saros 119 15:14 TD D.Node ΔT= 27s Par. = 193m U.Mag. = 0.8593 Gam. = 0.5370 P.Mag. = 1.8862	**Total** 1945 Dec 19 Saros 124 02:21 TD A.Node ΔT= 27s Tot. = 79m Par. = 205m U.Mag. = 1.3424 Gam. = -0.2845 P.Mag. = 2.3293

Plate 091

187

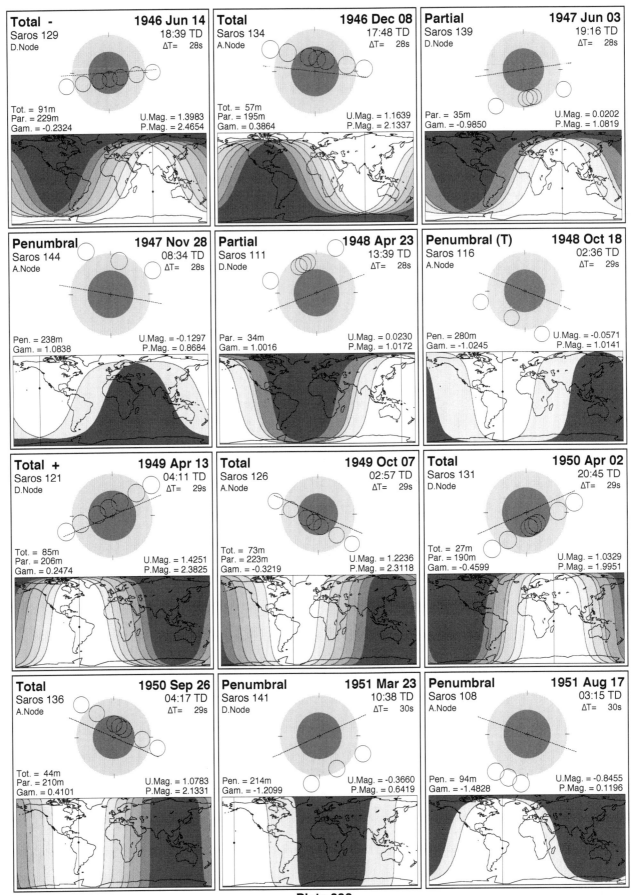

Total -	**1946 Jun 14**
Saros 129	18:39 TD
D.Node	ΔT= 28s

Tot. = 91m
Par. = 229m
Gam. = -0.2324
U.Mag. = 1.3983
P.Mag. = 2.4654

Total	**1946 Dec 08**
Saros 134	17:48 TD
A.Node	ΔT= 28s

Tot. = 57m
Par. = 195m
Gam. = 0.3864
U.Mag. = 1.1639
P.Mag. = 2.1337

Partial	**1947 Jun 03**
Saros 139	19:16 TD
D.Node	ΔT= 28s

Par. = 35m
Gam. = -0.9850
U.Mag. = 0.0202
P.Mag. = 1.0819

Penumbral	**1947 Nov 28**
Saros 144	08:34 TD
A.Node	ΔT= 28s

Pen. = 238m
Gam. = 1.0838
U.Mag. = -0.1297
P.Mag. = 0.8684

Partial	**1948 Apr 23**
Saros 111	13:39 TD
D.Node	ΔT= 28s

Par. = 34m
Gam. = 1.0016
U.Mag. = 0.0230
P.Mag. = 1.0172

Penumbral (T)	**1948 Oct 18**
Saros 116	02:36 TD
A.Node	ΔT= 29s

Pen. = 280m
Gam. = -1.0245
U.Mag. = -0.0571
P.Mag. = 1.0141

Total +	**1949 Apr 13**
Saros 121	04:11 TD
D.Node	ΔT= 29s

Tot. = 85m
Par. = 206m
Gam. = 0.2474
U.Mag. = 1.4251
P.Mag. = 2.3825

Total	**1949 Oct 07**
Saros 126	02:57 TD
A.Node	ΔT= 29s

Tot. = 73m
Par. = 223m
Gam. = -0.3219
U.Mag. = 1.2236
P.Mag. = 2.3118

Total	**1950 Apr 02**
Saros 131	20:45 TD
D.Node	ΔT= 29s

Tot. = 27m
Par. = 190m
Gam. = -0.4599
U.Mag. = 1.0329
P.Mag. = 1.9951

Total	**1950 Sep 26**
Saros 136	04:17 TD
A.Node	ΔT= 29s

Tot. = 44m
Par. = 210m
Gam. = 0.4101
U.Mag. = 1.0783
P.Mag. = 2.1331

Penumbral	**1951 Mar 23**
Saros 141	10:38 TD
D.Node	ΔT= 30s

Pen. = 214m
Gam. = -1.2099
U.Mag. = -0.3660
P.Mag. = 0.6419

Penumbral	**1951 Aug 17**
Saros 108	03:15 TD
A.Node	ΔT= 30s

Pen. = 94m
Gam. = -1.4828
U.Mag. = -0.8455
P.Mag. = 0.1196

Plate 092

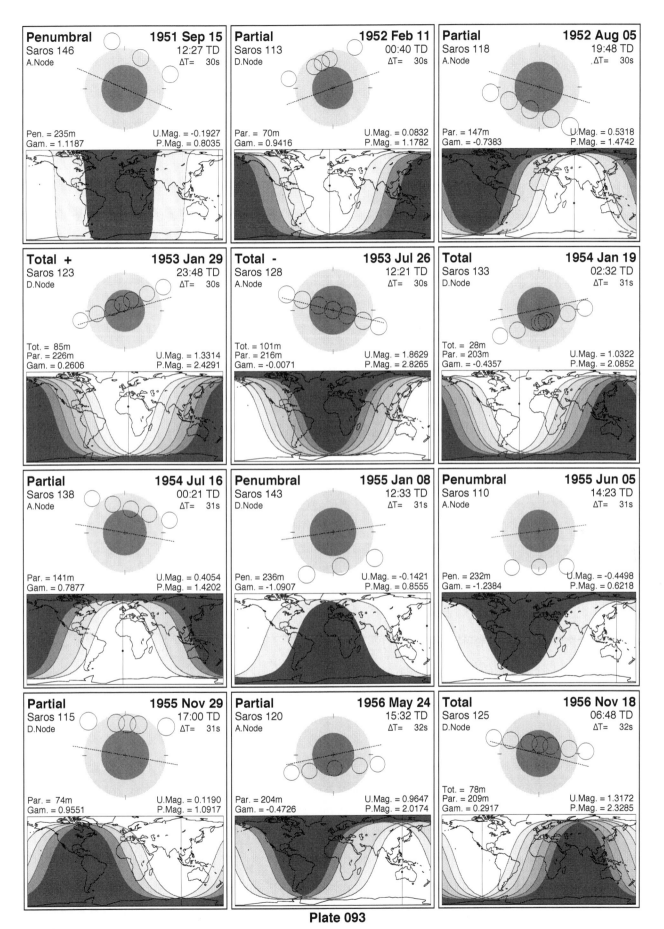

Penumbral — 1951 Sep 15
Saros 146 — 12:27 TD
A.Node — ΔT= 30s
Pen. = 235m — U.Mag. = -0.1927
Gam. = 1.1187 — P.Mag. = 0.8035

Partial — 1952 Feb 11
Saros 113 — 00:40 TD
D.Node — ΔT= 30s
Par. = 70m — U.Mag. = 0.0832
Gam. = 0.9416 — P.Mag. = 1.1782

Partial — 1952 Aug 05
Saros 118 — 19:48 TD
A.Node — ΔT= 30s
Par. = 147m — U.Mag. = 0.5318
Gam. = -0.7383 — P.Mag. = 1.4742

Total + — 1953 Jan 29
Saros 123 — 23:48 TD
D.Node — ΔT= 30s
Tot. = 85m
Par. = 226m — U.Mag. = 1.3314
Gam. = 0.2606 — P.Mag. = 2.4291

Total - — 1953 Jul 26
Saros 128 — 12:21 TD
A.Node — ΔT= 30s
Tot. = 101m
Par. = 216m — U.Mag. = 1.8629
Gam. = -0.0071 — P.Mag. = 2.8265

Total — 1954 Jan 19
Saros 133 — 02:32 TD
D.Node — ΔT= 31s
Tot. = 28m
Par. = 203m — U.Mag. = 1.0322
Gam. = -0.4357 — P.Mag. = 2.0852

Partial — 1954 Jul 16
Saros 138 — 00:21 TD
A.Node — ΔT= 31s
Par. = 141m — U.Mag. = 0.4054
Gam. = 0.7877 — P.Mag. = 1.4202

Penumbral — 1955 Jan 08
Saros 143 — 12:33 TD
D.Node — ΔT= 31s
Pen. = 236m — U.Mag. = -0.1421
Gam. = -1.0907 — P.Mag. = 0.8555

Penumbral — 1955 Jun 05
Saros 110 — 14:23 TD
A.Node — ΔT= 31s
Pen. = 232m — U.Mag. = -0.4498
Gam. = -1.2384 — P.Mag. = 0.6218

Partial — 1955 Nov 29
Saros 115 — 17:00 TD
D.Node — ΔT= 31s
Par. = 74m — U.Mag. = 0.1190
Gam. = 0.9551 — P.Mag. = 1.0917

Partial — 1956 May 24
Saros 120 — 15:32 TD
A.Node — ΔT= 32s
Par. = 204m — U.Mag. = 0.9647
Gam. = -0.4726 — P.Mag. = 2.0174

Total — 1956 Nov 18
Saros 125 — 06:48 TD
D.Node — ΔT= 32s
Tot. = 78m
Par. = 209m — U.Mag. = 1.3172
Gam. = 0.2917 — P.Mag. = 2.3285

Plate 093

189

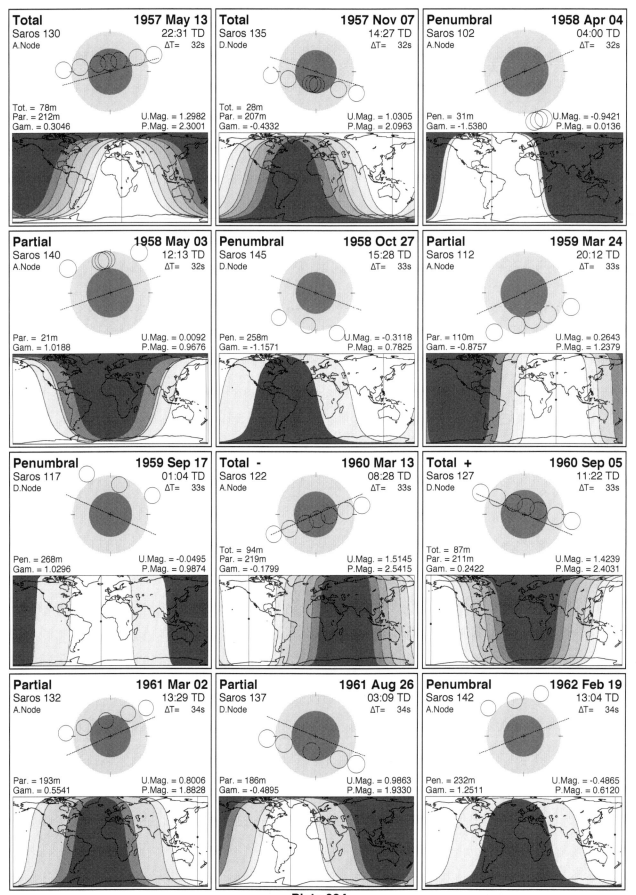

Total 1957 May 13	**Total** 1957 Nov 07	**Penumbral** 1958 Apr 04
Saros 130 22:31 TD	Saros 135 14:27 TD	Saros 102 04:00 TD
A.Node ΔT= 32s	D.Node ΔT= 32s	A.Node ΔT= 32s
Tot. = 78m	Tot. = 28m	Pen. = 31m
Par. = 212m U.Mag. = 1.2982	Par. = 207m U.Mag. = 1.0305	U.Mag. = -0.9421
Gam. = 0.3046 P.Mag. = 2.3001	Gam. = -0.4332 P.Mag. = 2.0963	Gam. = -1.5380 P.Mag. = 0.0136
Partial 1958 May 03	**Penumbral** 1958 Oct 27	**Partial** 1959 Mar 24
Saros 140 12:13 TD	Saros 145 15:28 TD	Saros 112 20:12 TD
A.Node ΔT= 32s	D.Node ΔT= 33s	A.Node ΔT= 33s
Par. = 21m U.Mag. = 0.0092	Pen. = 258m U.Mag. = -0.3118	Par. = 110m U.Mag. = 0.2643
Gam. = 1.0188 P.Mag. = 0.9676	Gam. = -1.1571 P.Mag. = 0.7825	Gam. = -0.8757 P.Mag. = 1.2379
Penumbral 1959 Sep 17	**Total -** 1960 Mar 13	**Total +** 1960 Sep 05
Saros 117 01:04 TD	Saros 122 08:28 TD	Saros 127 11:22 TD
D.Node ΔT= 33s	A.Node ΔT= 33s	D.Node ΔT= 33s
		Tot. = 87m
Pen. = 268m U.Mag. = -0.0495	Tot. = 94m	Par. = 211m U.Mag. = 1.4239
Gam. = 1.0296 P.Mag. = 0.9874	Par. = 219m U.Mag. = 1.5145	Gam. = 0.2422 P.Mag. = 2.4031
	Gam. = -0.1799 P.Mag. = 2.5415	
Partial 1961 Mar 02	**Partial** 1961 Aug 26	**Penumbral** 1962 Feb 19
Saros 132 13:29 TD	Saros 137 03:09 TD	Saros 142 13:04 TD
A.Node ΔT= 34s	D.Node ΔT= 34s	A.Node ΔT= 34s
Par. = 193m U.Mag. = 0.8006	Par. = 186m U.Mag. = 0.9863	Pen. = 232m U.Mag. = -0.4865
Gam. = 0.5541 P.Mag. = 1.8828	Gam. = -0.4895 P.Mag. = 1.9330	Gam. = 1.2511 P.Mag. = 0.6120

Plate 094

190

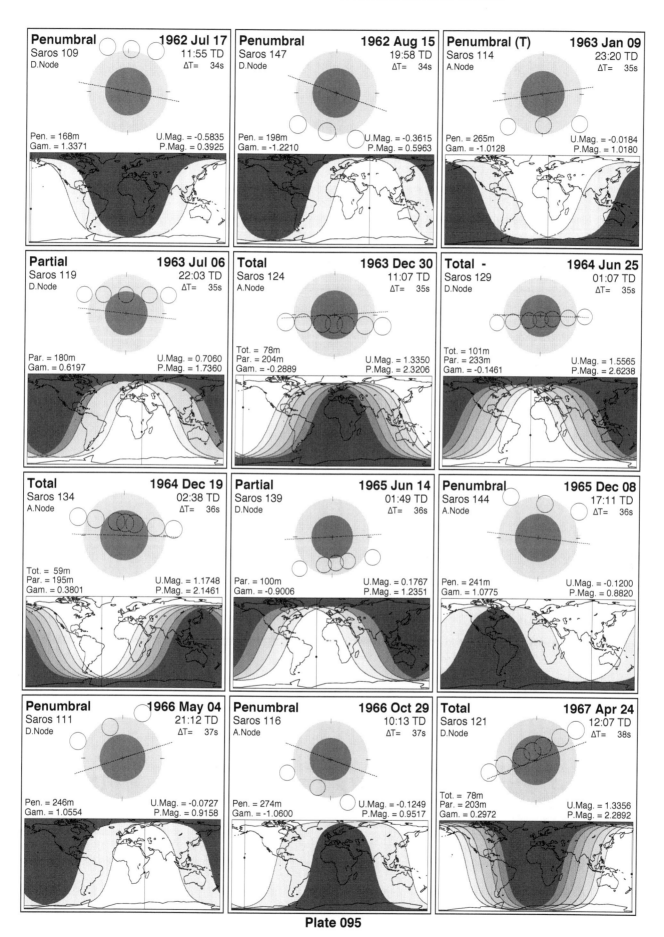

Penumbral　　　　**1962 Jul 17**
Saros 109　　　　　　11:55 TD
D.Node　　　　　　　ΔT=　34s
Pen. = 168m　　　　U.Mag. = -0.5835
Gam. = 1.3371　　　P.Mag. = 0.3925

Penumbral　　　　**1962 Aug 15**
Saros 147　　　　　　19:58 TD
D.Node　　　　　　　ΔT=　34s
Pen. = 198m　　　　U.Mag. = -0.3615
Gam. = -1.2210　　　P.Mag. = 0.5963

Penumbral (T)　　**1963 Jan 09**
Saros 114　　　　　　23:20 TD
A.Node　　　　　　　ΔT=　35s
Pen. = 265m　　　　U.Mag. = -0.0184
Gam. = -1.0128　　　P.Mag. = 1.0180

Partial　　　　　**1963 Jul 06**
Saros 119　　　　　　22:03 TD
D.Node　　　　　　　ΔT=　35s
Par. = 180m　　　　U.Mag. = 0.7060
Gam. = 0.6197　　　P.Mag. = 1.7360

Total　　　　　　**1963 Dec 30**
Saros 124　　　　　　11:07 TD
A.Node　　　　　　　ΔT=　35s
Tot. = 78m
Par. = 204m　　　　U.Mag. = 1.3350
Gam. = -0.2889　　　P.Mag. = 2.3206

Total -　　　　　**1964 Jun 25**
Saros 129　　　　　　01:07 TD
D.Node　　　　　　　ΔT=　35s
Tot. = 101m
Par. = 233m　　　　U.Mag. = 1.5565
Gam. = -0.1461　　　P.Mag. = 2.6238

Total　　　　　　**1964 Dec 19**
Saros 134　　　　　　02:38 TD
A.Node　　　　　　　ΔT=　36s
Tot. = 59m
Par. = 195m　　　　U.Mag. = 1.1748
Gam. = 0.3801　　　P.Mag. = 2.1461

Partial　　　　　**1965 Jun 14**
Saros 139　　　　　　01:49 TD
D.Node　　　　　　　ΔT=　36s
Par. = 100m　　　　U.Mag. = 0.1767
Gam. = -0.9006　　　P.Mag. = 1.2351

Penumbral　　　　**1965 Dec 08**
Saros 144　　　　　　17:11 TD
A.Node　　　　　　　ΔT=　36s
Pen. = 241m　　　　U.Mag. = -0.1200
Gam. = 1.0775　　　P.Mag. = 0.8820

Penumbral　　　　**1966 May 04**
Saros 111　　　　　　21:12 TD
D.Node　　　　　　　ΔT=　37s
Pen. = 246m　　　　U.Mag. = -0.0727
Gam. = 1.0554　　　P.Mag. = 0.9158

Penumbral　　　　**1966 Oct 29**
Saros 116　　　　　　10:13 TD
A.Node　　　　　　　ΔT=　37s
Pen. = 274m　　　　U.Mag. = -0.1249
Gam. = -1.0600　　　P.Mag. = 0.9517

Total　　　　　　**1967 Apr 24**
Saros 121　　　　　　12:07 TD
D.Node　　　　　　　ΔT=　38s
Tot. = 78m
Par. = 203m　　　　U.Mag. = 1.3356
Gam. = 0.2972　　　P.Mag. = 2.2892

Plate 095

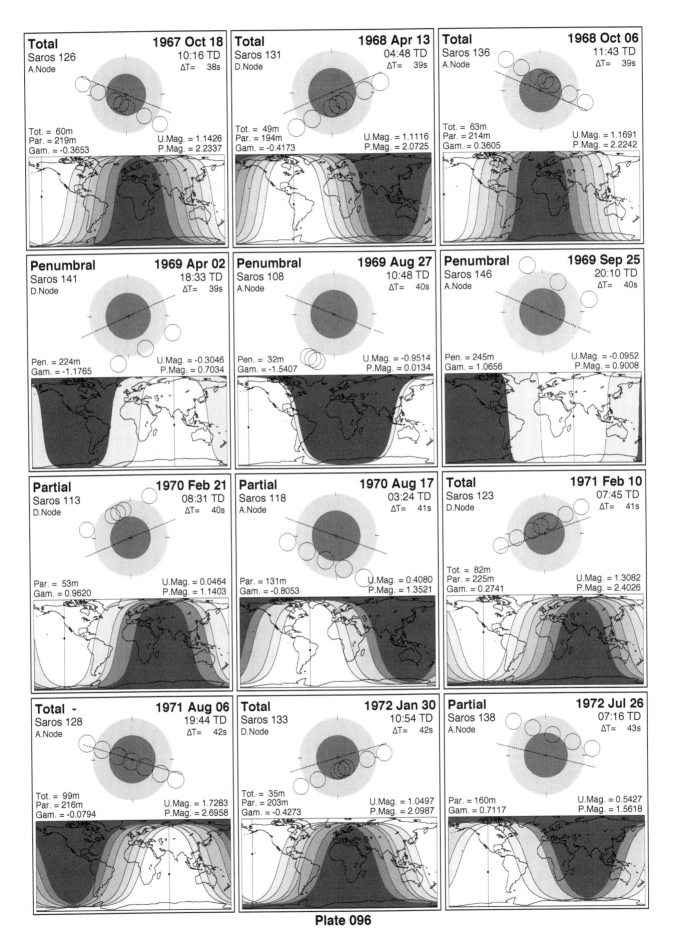

Total   **1967 Oct 18**
Saros 126   10:16 TD
A.Node   ΔT= 38s
Tot. = 60m
Par. = 219m
Gam. = -0.3653   U.Mag. = 1.1426   P.Mag. = 2.2337

Total   **1968 Apr 13**
Saros 131   04:48 TD
D.Node   ΔT= 39s
Tot. = 49m
Par. = 194m
Gam. = -0.4173   U.Mag. = 1.1116   P.Mag. = 2.0725

Total   **1968 Oct 06**
Saros 136   11:43 TD
A.Node   ΔT= 39s
Tot. = 63m
Par. = 214m
Gam. = 0.3605   U.Mag. = 1.1691   P.Mag. = 2.2242

Penumbral   **1969 Apr 02**
Saros 141   18:33 TD
D.Node   ΔT= 39s
Pen. = 224m
Gam. = -1.1765   U.Mag. = -0.3046   P.Mag. = 0.7034

Penumbral   **1969 Aug 27**
Saros 108   10:48 TD
A.Node   ΔT= 40s
Pen. = 32m
Gam. = -1.5407   U.Mag. = -0.9514   P.Mag. = 0.0134

Penumbral   **1969 Sep 25**
Saros 146   20:10 TD
A.Node   ΔT= 40s
Pen. = 245m
Gam. = 1.0656   U.Mag. = -0.0952   P.Mag. = 0.9008

Partial   **1970 Feb 21**
Saros 113   08:31 TD
D.Node   ΔT= 40s
Par. = 53m
Gam. = 0.9620   U.Mag. = 0.0464   P.Mag. = 1.1403

Partial   **1970 Aug 17**
Saros 118   03:24 TD
A.Node   ΔT= 41s
Par. = 131m
Gam. = -0.8053   U.Mag. = 0.4080   P.Mag. = 1.3521

Total   **1971 Feb 10**
Saros 123   07:45 TD
D.Node   ΔT= 41s
Tot. = 82m
Par. = 225m
Gam. = 0.2741   U.Mag. = 1.3082   P.Mag. = 2.4026

Total -   **1971 Aug 06**
Saros 128   19:44 TD
A.Node   ΔT= 42s
Tot. = 99m
Par. = 216m
Gam. = -0.0794   U.Mag. = 1.7283   P.Mag. = 2.6958

Total   **1972 Jan 30**
Saros 133   10:54 TD
D.Node   ΔT= 42s
Tot. = 35m
Par. = 203m
Gam. = -0.4273   U.Mag. = 1.0497   P.Mag. = 2.0987

Partial   **1972 Jul 26**
Saros 138   07:16 TD
A.Node   ΔT= 43s
Par. = 160m
Gam. = 0.7117   U.Mag. = 0.5427   P.Mag. = 1.5618

Plate 096

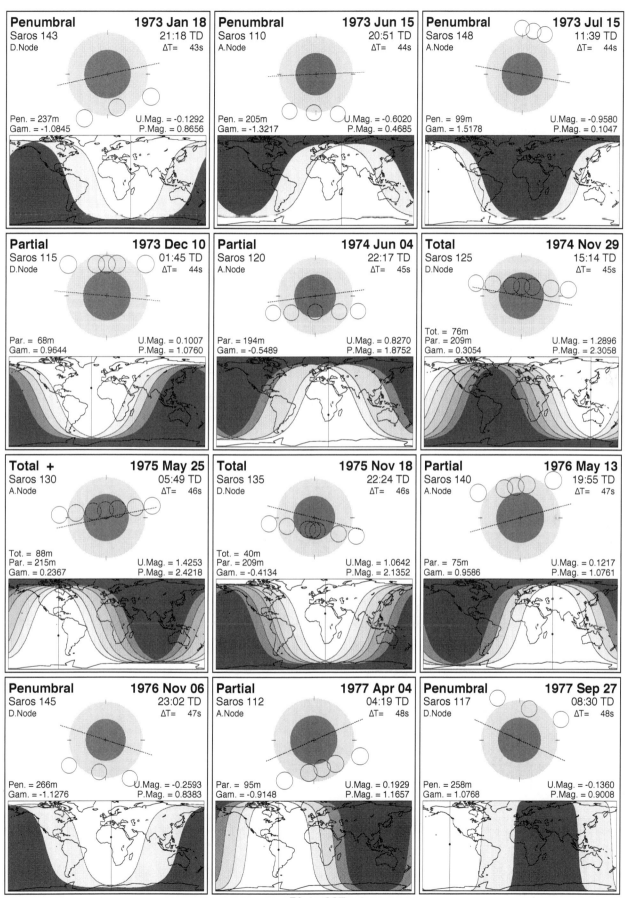

Penumbral **1973 Jan 18**	
Saros 143	21:18 TD
D.Node	ΔT= 43s
Pen. = 237m	U.Mag. = -0.1292
Gam. = -1.0845	P.Mag. = 0.8656

Penumbral **1973 Jun 15**	
Saros 110	20:51 TD
A.Node	ΔT= 44s
Pen. = 205m	U.Mag. = -0.6020
Gam. = -1.3217	P.Mag. = 0.4685

Penumbral **1973 Jul 15**	
Saros 148	11:39 TD
A.Node	ΔT= 44s
Pen. = 99m	U.Mag. = -0.9580
Gam. = 1.5178	P.Mag. = 0.1047

Partial **1973 Dec 10**	
Saros 115	01:45 TD
D.Node	ΔT= 44s
Par. = 68m	U.Mag. = 0.1007
Gam. = 0.9644	P.Mag. = 1.0760

Partial **1974 Jun 04**	
Saros 120	22:17 TD
A.Node	ΔT= 45s
Par. = 194m	U.Mag. = 0.8270
Gam. = -0.5489	P.Mag. = 1.8752

Total **1974 Nov 29**	
Saros 125	15:14 TD
D.Node	ΔT= 45s
Tot. = 76m	
Par. = 209m	U.Mag. = 1.2896
Gam. = 0.3054	P.Mag. = 2.3058

Total + **1975 May 25**	
Saros 130	05:49 TD
A.Node	ΔT= 46s
Tot. = 88m	
Par. = 215m	U.Mag. = 1.4253
Gam. = 0.2367	P.Mag. = 2.4218

Total **1975 Nov 18**	
Saros 135	22:24 TD
D.Node	ΔT= 46s
Tot. = 40m	
Par. = 209m	U.Mag. = 1.0642
Gam. = -0.4134	P.Mag. = 2.1352

Partial **1976 May 13**	
Saros 140	19:55 TD
A.Node	ΔT= 47s
Par. = 75m	U.Mag. = 0.1217
Gam. = 0.9586	P.Mag. = 1.0761

Penumbral **1976 Nov 06**	
Saros 145	23:02 TD
D.Node	ΔT= 47s
Pen. = 266m	U.Mag. = -0.2593
Gam. = -1.1276	P.Mag. = 0.8383

Partial **1977 Apr 04**	
Saros 112	04:19 TD
A.Node	ΔT= 48s
Par. = 95m	U.Mag. = 0.1929
Gam. = -0.9148	P.Mag. = 1.1657

Penumbral **1977 Sep 27**	
Saros 117	08:30 TD
D.Node	ΔT= 48s
Pen. = 258m	U.Mag. = -0.1360
Gam. = 1.0768	P.Mag. = 0.9008

Plate 097

193

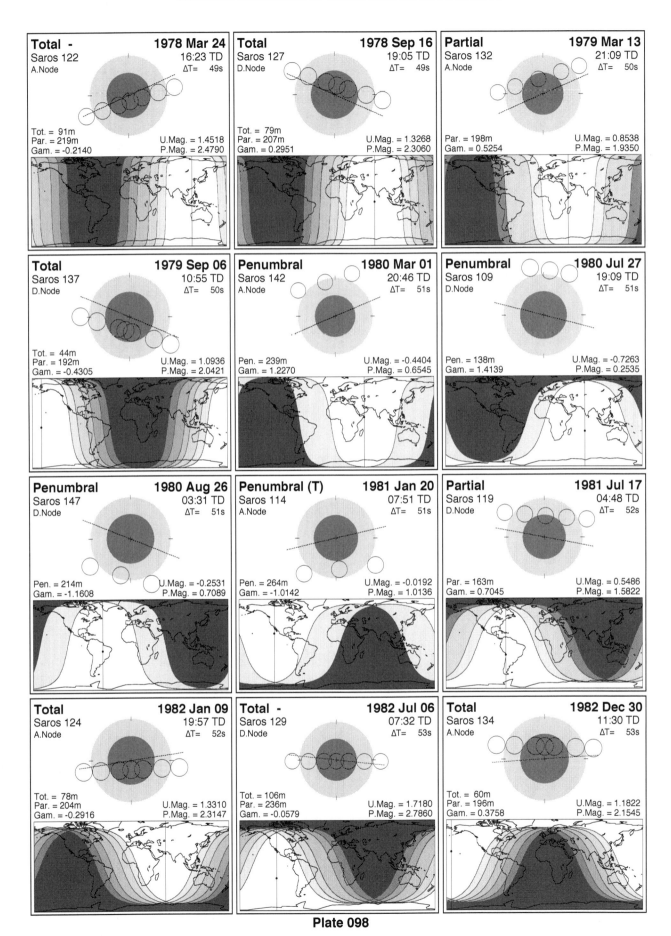

Total -	**1978 Mar 24**
Saros 122	16:23 TD
A.Node	ΔT= 49s
Tot. = 91m	
Par. = 219m	U.Mag. = 1.4518
Gam. = -0.2140	P.Mag. = 2.4790

Total	**1978 Sep 16**
Saros 127	19:05 TD
D.Node	ΔT= 49s
Tot. = 79m	
Par. = 207m	U.Mag. = 1.3268
Gam. = 0.2951	P.Mag. = 2.3060

Partial	**1979 Mar 13**
Saros 132	21:09 TD
A.Node	ΔT= 50s
Par. = 198m	U.Mag. = 0.8538
Gam. = 0.5254	P.Mag. = 1.9350

Total	**1979 Sep 06**
Saros 137	10:55 TD
D.Node	ΔT= 50s
Tot. = 44m	
Par. = 192m	U.Mag. = 1.0936
Gam. = -0.4305	P.Mag. = 2.0421

Penumbral	**1980 Mar 01**
Saros 142	20:46 TD
A.Node	ΔT= 51s
Pen. = 239m	U.Mag. = -0.4404
Gam. = 1.2270	P.Mag. = 0.6545

Penumbral	**1980 Jul 27**
Saros 109	19:09 TD
D.Node	ΔT= 51s
Pen. = 138m	U.Mag. = -0.7263
Gam. = 1.4139	P.Mag. = 0.2535

Penumbral	**1980 Aug 26**
Saros 147	03:31 TD
D.Node	ΔT= 51s
Pen. = 214m	U.Mag. = -0.2531
Gam. = -1.1608	P.Mag. = 0.7089

Penumbral (T)	**1981 Jan 20**
Saros 114	07:51 TD
A.Node	ΔT= 51s
Pen. = 264m	U.Mag. = -0.0192
Gam. = -1.0142	P.Mag. = 1.0136

Partial	**1981 Jul 17**
Saros 119	04:48 TD
D.Node	ΔT= 52s
Par. = 163m	U.Mag. = 0.5486
Gam. = 0.7045	P.Mag. = 1.5822

Total	**1982 Jan 09**
Saros 124	19:57 TD
A.Node	ΔT= 52s
Tot. = 78m	
Par. = 204m	U.Mag. = 1.3310
Gam. = -0.2916	P.Mag. = 2.3147

Total -	**1982 Jul 06**
Saros 129	07:32 TD
D.Node	ΔT= 53s
Tot. = 106m	
Par. = 236m	U.Mag. = 1.7180
Gam. = -0.0579	P.Mag. = 2.7860

Total	**1982 Dec 30**
Saros 134	11:30 TD
A.Node	ΔT= 53s
Tot. = 60m	
Par. = 196m	U.Mag. = 1.1822
Gam. = 0.3758	P.Mag. = 2.1545

Plate 098

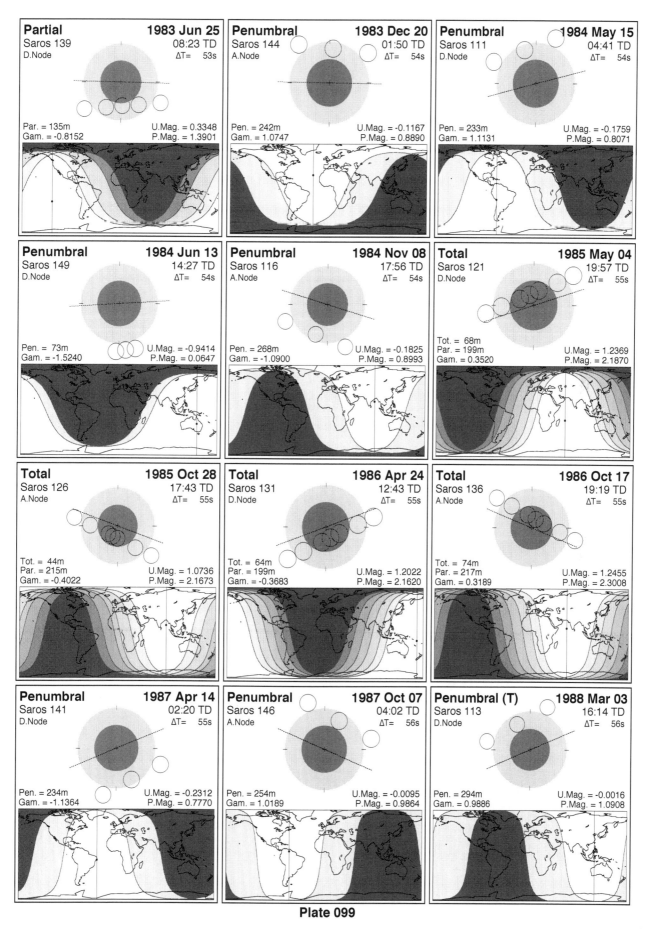

Partial   **1983 Jun 25**
Saros 139   08:23 TD
D.Node   ΔT= 53s
Par. = 135m   U.Mag. = 0.3348
Gam. = -0.8152   P.Mag. = 1.3901

Penumbral   **1983 Dec 20**
Saros 144   01:50 TD
A.Node   ΔT= 54s
Pen. = 242m   U.Mag. = -0.1167
Gam. = 1.0747   P.Mag. = 0.8890

Penumbral   **1984 May 15**
Saros 111   04:41 TD
D.Node   ΔT= 54s
Pen. = 233m   U.Mag. = -0.1759
Gam. = 1.1131   P.Mag. = 0.8071

Penumbral   **1984 Jun 13**
Saros 149   14:27 TD
D.Node   ΔT= 54s
Pen. = 73m   U.Mag. = -0.9414
Gam. = -1.5240   P.Mag. = 0.0647

Penumbral   **1984 Nov 08**
Saros 116   17:56 TD
A.Node   ΔT= 54s
Pen. = 268m   U.Mag. = -0.1825
Gam. = -1.0900   P.Mag. = 0.8993

Total   **1985 May 04**
Saros 121   19:57 TD
D.Node   ΔT= 55s
Tot. = 68m
Par. = 199m   U.Mag. = 1.2369
Gam. = 0.3520   P.Mag. = 2.1870

Total   **1985 Oct 28**
Saros 126   17:43 TD
A.Node   ΔT= 55s
Tot. = 44m
Par. = 215m   U.Mag. = 1.0736
Gam. = -0.4022   P.Mag. = 2.1673

Total   **1986 Apr 24**
Saros 131   12:43 TD
D.Node   ΔT= 55s
Tot. = 64m
Par. = 199m   U.Mag. = 1.2022
Gam. = -0.3683   P.Mag. = 2.1620

Total   **1986 Oct 17**
Saros 136   19:19 TD
A.Node   ΔT= 55s
Tot. = 74m
Par. = 217m   U.Mag. = 1.2455
Gam. = 0.3189   P.Mag. = 2.3008

Penumbral   **1987 Apr 14**
Saros 141   02:20 TD
D.Node   ΔT= 55s
Pen. = 234m   U.Mag. = -0.2312
Gam. = -1.1364   P.Mag. = 0.7770

Penumbral   **1987 Oct 07**
Saros 146   04:02 TD
A.Node   ΔT= 56s
Pen. = 254m   U.Mag. = -0.0095
Gam. = 1.0189   P.Mag. = 0.9864

Penumbral (T)   **1988 Mar 03**
Saros 113   16:14 TD
D.Node   ΔT= 56s
Pen. = 294m   U.Mag. = -0.0016
Gam. = 0.9886   P.Mag. = 1.0908

Plate 099

195

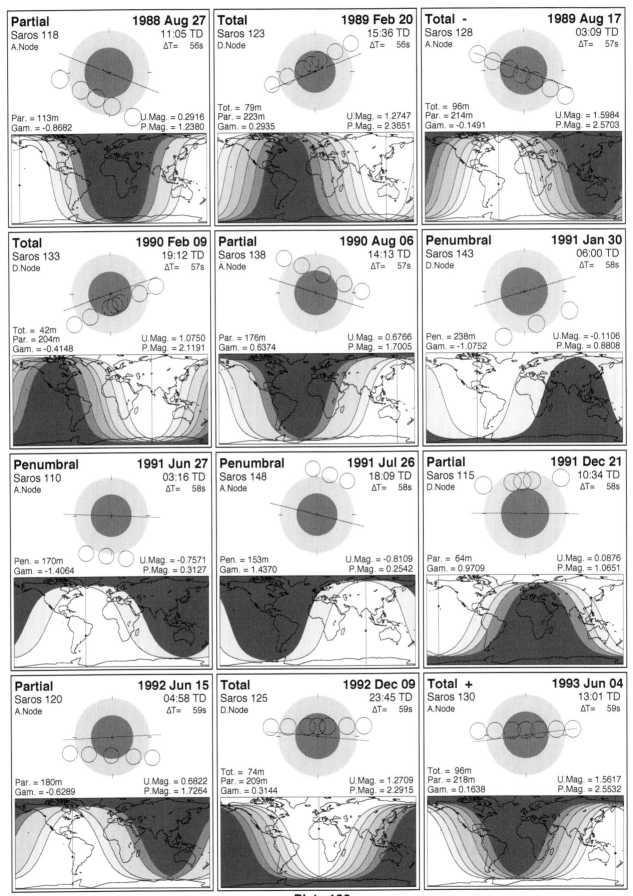

Partial **1988 Aug 27**	**Total** **1989 Feb 20**	**Total -** **1989 Aug 17**
Saros 118 11:05 TD	Saros 123 15:36 TD	Saros 128 03:09 TD
A.Node ΔT= 56s	D.Node ΔT= 56s	A.Node ΔT= 57s
Par. = 113m U.Mag. = 0.2916	Tot. = 79m U.Mag. = 1.2747	Tot. = 96m U.Mag. = 1.5984
Gam. = -0.8682 P.Mag. = 1.2380	Par. = 223m P.Mag. = 2.3651	Par. = 214m P.Mag. = 2.5703
	Gam. = 0.2935	Gam. = -0.1491
Total **1990 Feb 09**	**Partial** **1990 Aug 06**	**Penumbral** **1991 Jan 30**
Saros 133 19:12 TD	Saros 138 14:13 TD	Saros 143 06:00 TD
D.Node ΔT= 57s	A.Node ΔT= 57s	D.Node ΔT= 58s
Tot. = 42m U.Mag. = 1.0750	Par. = 176m U.Mag. = 0.6766	Pen. = 238m U.Mag. = -0.1106
Par. = 204m P.Mag. = 2.1191	Gam. = 0.6374 P.Mag. = 1.7005	Gam. = -1.0752 P.Mag. = 0.8808
Gam. = -0.4148		
Penumbral **1991 Jun 27**	**Penumbral** **1991 Jul 26**	**Partial** **1991 Dec 21**
Saros 110 03:16 TD	Saros 148 18:09 TD	Saros 115 10:34 TD
A.Node ΔT= 58s	A.Node ΔT= 58s	D.Node ΔT= 58s
Pen. = 170m U.Mag. = -0.7571	Pen. = 153m U.Mag. = -0.8109	Par. = 64m U.Mag. = 0.0876
Gam. = -1.4064 P.Mag. = 0.3127	Gam. = 1.4370 P.Mag. = 0.2542	Gam. = 0.9709 P.Mag. = 1.0651
Partial **1992 Jun 15**	**Total** **1992 Dec 09**	**Total +** **1993 Jun 04**
Saros 120 04:58 TD	Saros 125 23:45 TD	Saros 130 13:01 TD
A.Node ΔT= 59s	D.Node ΔT= 59s	A.Node ΔT= 59s
Par. = 180m U.Mag. = 0.6822	Tot. = 74m U.Mag. = 1.2709	Tot. = 96m U.Mag. = 1.5617
Gam. = -0.6289 P.Mag. = 1.7264	Par. = 209m P.Mag. = 2.2915	Par. = 218m P.Mag. = 2.5532
	Gam. = 0.3144	Gam. = 0.1638

Plate 100

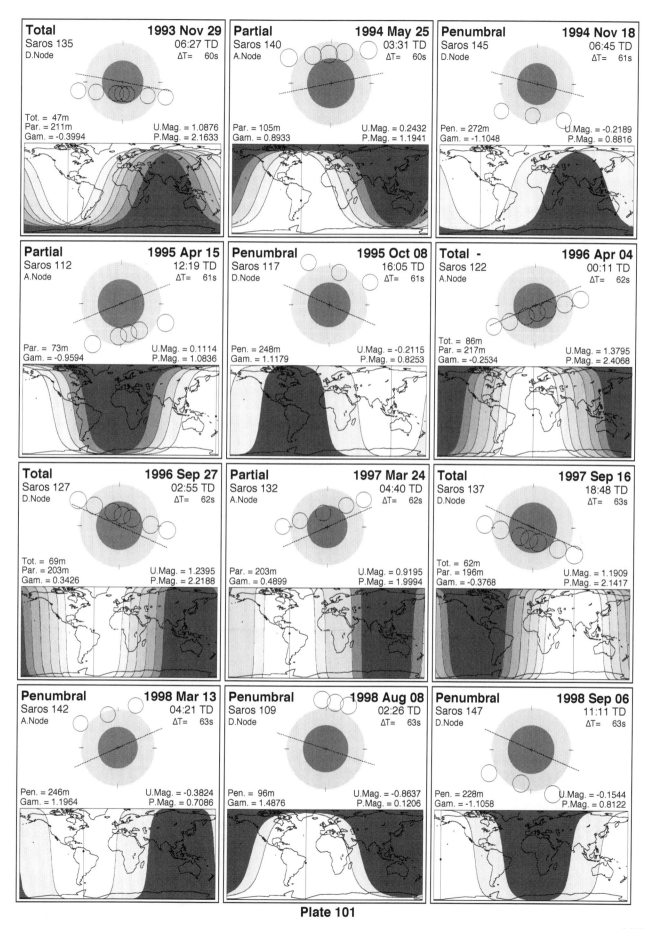

Total	**1993 Nov 29**
Saros 135	06:27 TD
D.Node	ΔT= 60s

Tot. = 47m
Par. = 211m
Gam. = -0.3994
U.Mag. = 1.0876
P.Mag. = 2.1633

Partial	**1994 May 25**
Saros 140	03:31 TD
A.Node	ΔT= 60s

Par. = 105m
Gam. = 0.8933
U.Mag. = 0.2432
P.Mag. = 1.1941

Penumbral	**1994 Nov 18**
Saros 145	06:45 TD
D.Node	ΔT= 61s

Pen. = 272m
Gam. = -1.1048
U.Mag. = -0.2189
P.Mag. = 0.8816

Partial	**1995 Apr 15**
Saros 112	12:19 TD
A.Node	ΔT= 61s

Par. = 73m
Gam. = -0.9594
U.Mag. = 0.1114
P.Mag. = 1.0836

Penumbral	**1995 Oct 08**
Saros 117	16:05 TD
D.Node	ΔT= 61s

Pen. = 248m
Gam. = 1.1179
U.Mag. = -0.2115
P.Mag. = 0.8253

Total -	**1996 Apr 04**
Saros 122	00:11 TD
A.Node	ΔT= 62s

Tot. = 86m
Par. = 217m
Gam. = -0.2534
U.Mag. = 1.3795
P.Mag. = 2.4068

Total	**1996 Sep 27**
Saros 127	02:55 TD
D.Node	ΔT= 62s

Tot. = 69m
Par. = 203m
Gam. = 0.3426
U.Mag. = 1.2395
P.Mag. = 2.2188

Partial	**1997 Mar 24**
Saros 132	04:40 TD
A.Node	ΔT= 62s

Par. = 203m
Gam. = 0.4899
U.Mag. = 0.9195
P.Mag. = 1.9994

Total	**1997 Sep 16**
Saros 137	18:48 TD
D.Node	ΔT= 63s

Tot. = 62m
Par. = 196m
Gam. = -0.3768
U.Mag. = 1.1909
P.Mag. = 2.1417

Penumbral	**1998 Mar 13**
Saros 142	04:21 TD
A.Node	ΔT= 63s

Pen. = 246m
Gam. = 1.1964
U.Mag. = -0.3824
P.Mag. = 0.7086

Penumbral	**1998 Aug 08**
Saros 109	02:26 TD
D.Node	ΔT= 63s

Pen. = 96m
Gam. = 1.4876
U.Mag. = -0.8637
P.Mag. = 0.1206

Penumbral	**1998 Sep 06**
Saros 147	11:11 TD
D.Node	ΔT= 63s

Pen. = 228m
Gam. = -1.1058
U.Mag. = -0.1544
P.Mag. = 0.8122

Plate 101

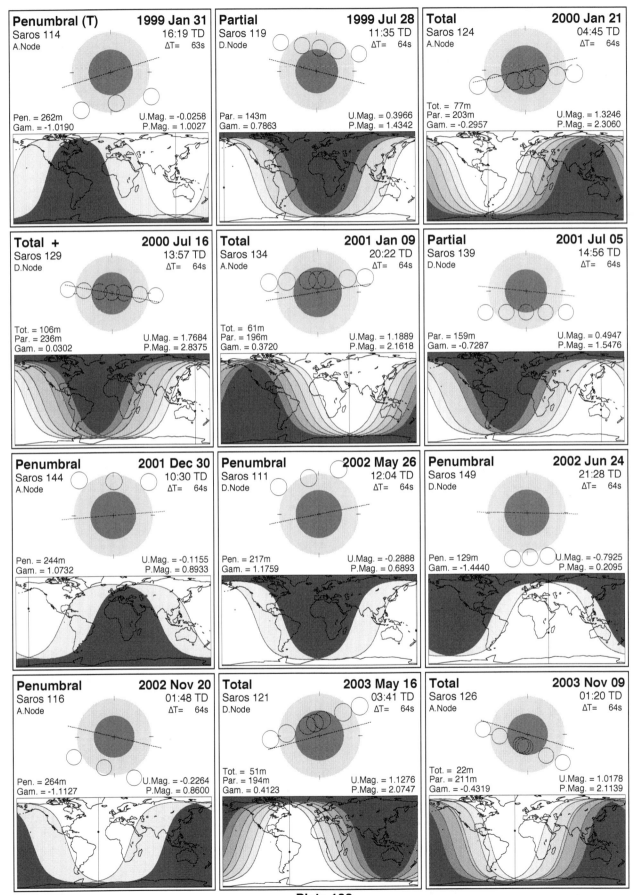

Penumbral (T)	1999 Jan 31
Saros 114	16:19 TD
A.Node	ΔT= 63s
Pen. = 262m	U.Mag. = -0.0258
Gam. = -1.0190	P.Mag. = 1.0027

Partial	1999 Jul 28
Saros 119	11:35 TD
D.Node	ΔT= 64s
Par. = 143m	U.Mag. = 0.3966
Gam. = 0.7863	P.Mag. = 1.4342

Total	2000 Jan 21
Saros 124	04:45 TD
A.Node	ΔT= 64s
Tot. = 77m	
Par. = 203m	U.Mag. = 1.3246
Gam. = -0.2957	P.Mag. = 2.3060

Total +	2000 Jul 16
Saros 129	13:57 TD
D.Node	ΔT= 64s
Tot. = 106m	
Par. = 236m	U.Mag. = 1.7684
Gam. = 0.0302	P.Mag. = 2.8375

Total	2001 Jan 09
Saros 134	20:22 TD
A.Node	ΔT= 64s
Tot. = 61m	
Par. = 196m	U.Mag. = 1.1889
Gam. = 0.3720	P.Mag. = 2.1618

Partial	2001 Jul 05
Saros 139	14:56 TD
D.Node	ΔT= 64s
Par. = 159m	U.Mag. = 0.4947
Gam. = -0.7287	P.Mag. = 1.5476

Penumbral	2001 Dec 30
Saros 144	10:30 TD
A.Node	ΔT= 64s
Pen. = 244m	U.Mag. = -0.1155
Gam. = 1.0732	P.Mag. = 0.8933

Penumbral	2002 May 26
Saros 111	12:04 TD
D.Node	ΔT= 64s
Pen. = 217m	U.Mag. = -0.2888
Gam. = 1.1759	P.Mag. = 0.6893

Penumbral	2002 Jun 24
Saros 149	21:28 TD
D.Node	ΔT= 64s
Pen. = 129m	U.Mag. = -0.7925
Gam. = -1.4440	P.Mag. = 0.2095

Penumbral	2002 Nov 20
Saros 116	01:48 TD
A.Node	ΔT= 64s
Pen. = 264m	U.Mag. = -0.2264
Gam. = -1.1127	P.Mag. = 0.8600

Total	2003 May 16
Saros 121	03:41 TD
D.Node	ΔT= 64s
Tot. = 51m	
Par. = 194m	U.Mag. = 1.1276
Gam. = 0.4123	P.Mag. = 2.0747

Total	2003 Nov 09
Saros 126	01:20 TD
A.Node	ΔT= 64s
Tot. = 22m	
Par. = 211m	U.Mag. = 1.0178
Gam. = -0.4319	P.Mag. = 2.1139

Plate 102

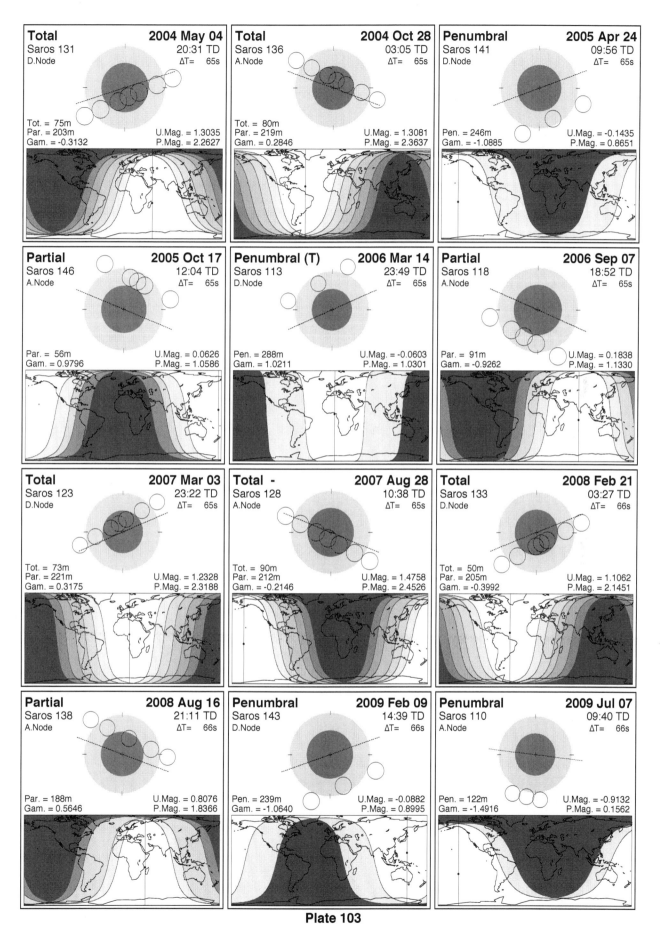

Total — **2004 May 04**
Saros 131 — 20:31 TD
D.Node — ΔT= 65s
Tot. = 75m
Par. = 203m — U.Mag. = 1.3035
Gam. = -0.3132 — P.Mag. = 2.2627

Total — **2004 Oct 28**
Saros 136 — 03:05 TD
A.Node — ΔT= 65s
Tot. = 80m
Par. = 219m — U.Mag. = 1.3081
Gam. = 0.2846 — P.Mag. = 2.3637

Penumbral — **2005 Apr 24**
Saros 141 — 09:56 TD
D.Node — ΔT= 65s
Pen. = 246m — U.Mag. = -0.1435
Gam. = -1.0885 — P.Mag. = 0.8651

Partial — **2005 Oct 17**
Saros 146 — 12:04 TD
A.Node — ΔT= 65s
Par. = 56m — U.Mag. = 0.0626
Gam. = 0.9796 — P.Mag. = 1.0586

Penumbral (T) — **2006 Mar 14**
Saros 113 — 23:49 TD
D.Node — ΔT= 65s
Pen. = 288m — U.Mag. = -0.0603
Gam. = 1.0211 — P.Mag. = 1.0301

Partial — **2006 Sep 07**
Saros 118 — 18:52 TD
A.Node — ΔT= 65s
Par. = 91m — U.Mag. = 0.1838
Gam. = -0.9262 — P.Mag. = 1.1330

Total — **2007 Mar 03**
Saros 123 — 23:22 TD
D.Node — ΔT= 65s
Tot. = 73m
Par. = 221m — U.Mag. = 1.2328
Gam. = 0.3175 — P.Mag. = 2.3188

Total - — **2007 Aug 28**
Saros 128 — 10:38 TD
A.Node — ΔT= 65s
Tot. = 90m
Par. = 212m — U.Mag. = 1.4758
Gam. = -0.2146 — P.Mag. = 2.4526

Total — **2008 Feb 21**
Saros 133 — 03:27 TD
D.Node — ΔT= 66s
Tot. = 50m
Par. = 205m — U.Mag. = 1.1062
Gam. = -0.3992 — P.Mag. = 2.1451

Partial — **2008 Aug 16**
Saros 138 — 21:11 TD
A.Node — ΔT= 66s
Par. = 188m — U.Mag. = 0.8076
Gam. = 0.5646 — P.Mag. = 1.8366

Penumbral — **2009 Feb 09**
Saros 143 — 14:39 TD
D.Node — ΔT= 66s
Pen. = 239m — U.Mag. = -0.0882
Gam. = -1.0640 — P.Mag. = 0.8995

Penumbral — **2009 Jul 07**
Saros 110 — 09:40 TD
A.Node — ΔT= 66s
Pen. = 122m — U.Mag. = -0.9132
Gam. = -1.4916 — P.Mag. = 0.1562

Plate 103

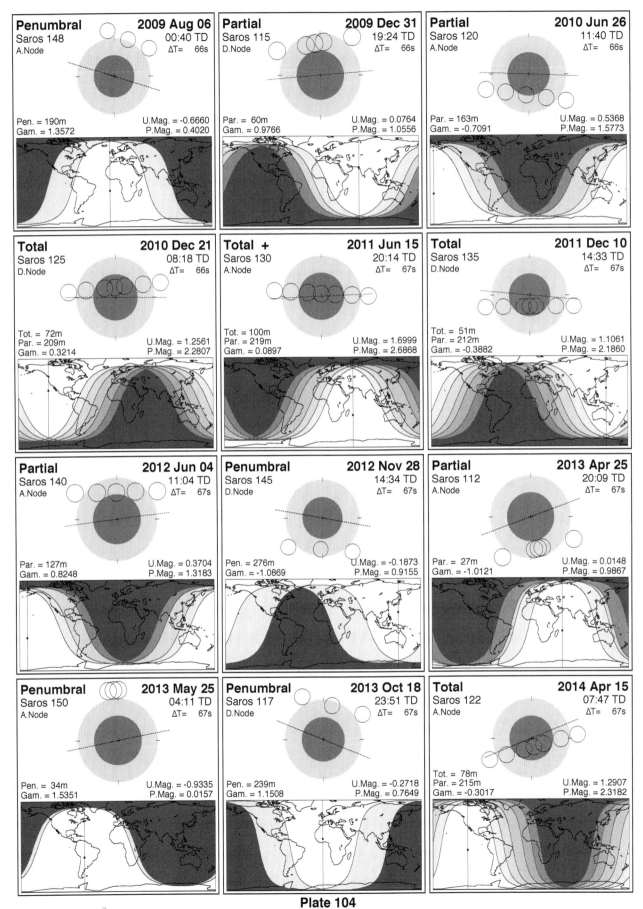

Penumbral **2009 Aug 06** Saros 148 00:40 TD A.Node ΔT= 66s Pen. = 190m U.Mag. = -0.6660 Gam. = 1.3572 P.Mag. = 0.4020	**Partial** **2009 Dec 31** Saros 115 19:24 TD D.Node ΔT= 66s Par. = 60m U.Mag. = 0.0764 Gam. = 0.9766 P.Mag. = 1.0556	**Partial** **2010 Jun 26** Saros 120 11:40 TD A.Node ΔT= 66s Par. = 163m U.Mag. = 0.5368 Gam. = -0.7091 P.Mag. = 1.5773
Total **2010 Dec 21** Saros 125 08:18 TD D.Node ΔT= 66s Tot. = 72m Par. = 209m U.Mag. = 1.2561 Gam. = 0.3214 P.Mag. = 2.2807	**Total +** **2011 Jun 15** Saros 130 20:14 TD A.Node ΔT= 67s Tot. = 100m Par. = 219m U.Mag. = 1.6999 Gam. = 0.0897 P.Mag. = 2.6868	**Total** **2011 Dec 10** Saros 135 14:33 TD D.Node ΔT= 67s Tot. = 51m Par. = 212m U.Mag. = 1.1061 Gam. = -0.3882 P.Mag. = 2.1860
Partial **2012 Jun 04** Saros 140 11:04 TD A.Node ΔT= 67s Par. = 127m U.Mag. = 0.3704 Gam. = 0.8248 P.Mag. = 1.3183	**Penumbral** **2012 Nov 28** Saros 145 14:34 TD D.Node ΔT= 67s Pen. = 276m U.Mag. = -0.1873 Gam. = -1.0869 P.Mag. = 0.9155	**Partial** **2013 Apr 25** Saros 112 20:09 TD A.Node ΔT= 67s Par. = 27m U.Mag. = 0.0148 Gam. = -1.0121 P.Mag. = 0.9867
Penumbral **2013 May 25** Saros 150 04:11 TD A.Node ΔT= 67s Pen. = 34m U.Mag. = -0.9335 Gam. = 1.5351 P.Mag. = 0.0157	**Penumbral** **2013 Oct 18** Saros 117 23:51 TD D.Node ΔT= 67s Pen. = 239m U.Mag. = -0.2718 Gam. = 1.1508 P.Mag. = 0.7649	**Total** **2014 Apr 15** Saros 122 07:47 TD A.Node ΔT= 67s Tot. = 78m Par. = 215m U.Mag. = 1.2907 Gam. = -0.3017 P.Mag. = 2.3182

Plate 104

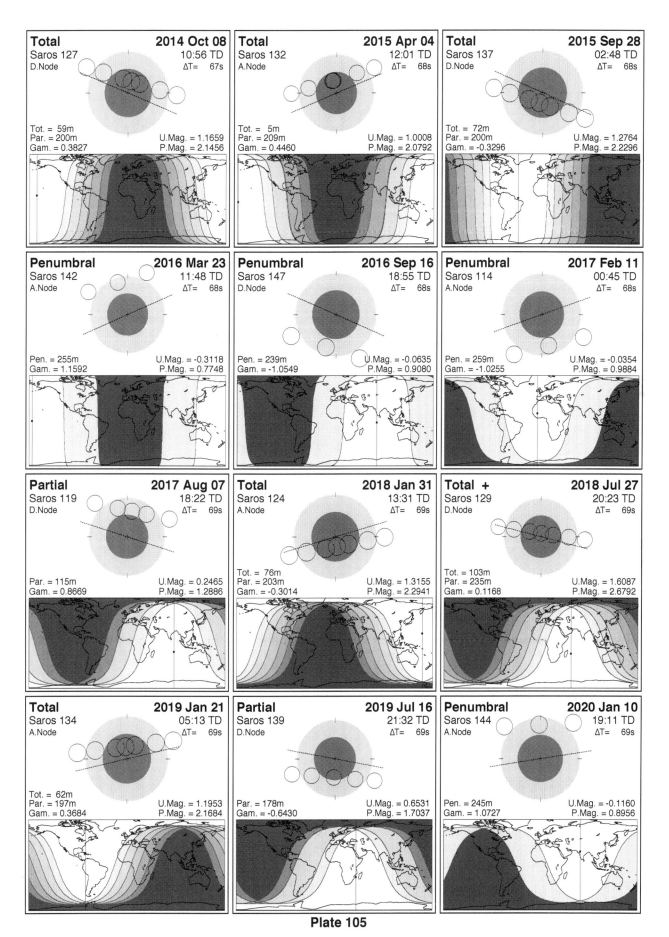

Plate 105

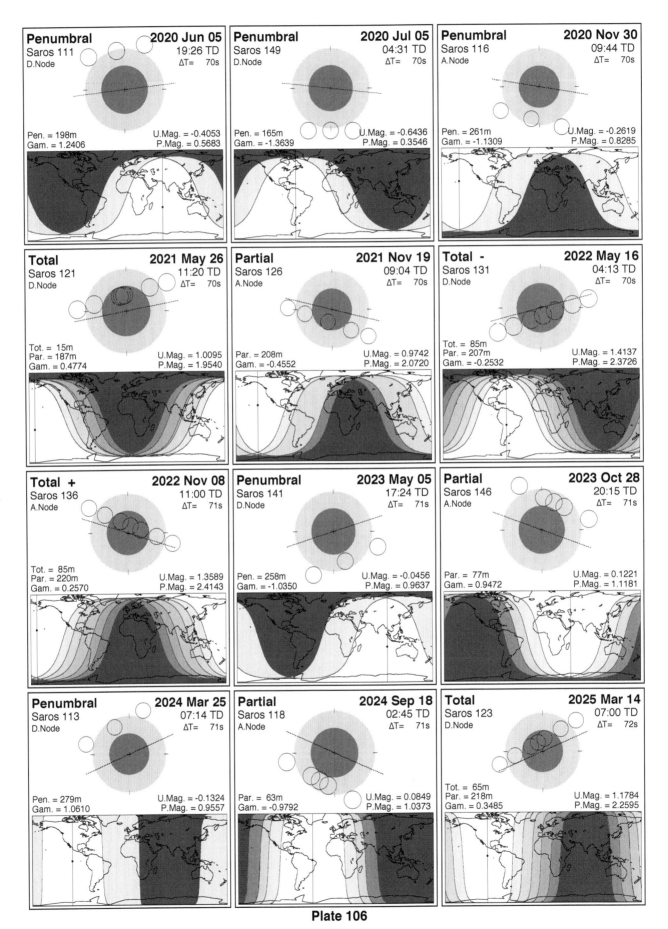

Penumbral — **2020 Jun 05**
Saros 111 — 19:26 TD
D.Node — ΔT= 70s
Pen. = 198m
Gam. = 1.2406 — U.Mag. = -0.4053 — P.Mag. = 0.5683

Penumbral — **2020 Jul 05**
Saros 149 — 04:31 TD
D.Node — ΔT= 70s
Pen. = 165m
Gam. = -1.3639 — U.Mag. = -0.6436 — P.Mag. = 0.3546

Penumbral — **2020 Nov 30**
Saros 116 — 09:44 TD
A.Node — ΔT= 70s
Pen. = 261m
Gam. = -1.1309 — U.Mag. = -0.2619 — P.Mag. = 0.8285

Total — **2021 May 26**
Saros 121 — 11:20 TD
D.Node — ΔT= 70s
Tot. = 15m
Par. = 187m — U.Mag. = 1.0095
Gam. = 0.4774 — P.Mag. = 1.9540

Partial — **2021 Nov 19**
Saros 126 — 09:04 TD
A.Node — ΔT= 70s
Par. = 208m — U.Mag. = 0.9742
Gam. = -0.4552 — P.Mag. = 2.0720

Total - — **2022 May 16**
Saros 131 — 04:13 TD
D.Node — ΔT= 70s
Tot. = 85m
Par. = 207m — U.Mag. = 1.4137
Gam. = -0.2532 — P.Mag. = 2.3726

Total + — **2022 Nov 08**
Saros 136 — 11:00 TD
A.Node — ΔT= 71s
Tot. = 85m
Par. = 220m — U.Mag. = 1.3589
Gam. = 0.2570 — P.Mag. = 2.4143

Penumbral — **2023 May 05**
Saros 141 — 17:24 TD
D.Node — ΔT= 71s
Pen. = 258m
Gam. = -1.0350 — U.Mag. = -0.0456 — P.Mag. = 0.9637

Partial — **2023 Oct 28**
Saros 146 — 20:15 TD
A.Node — ΔT= 71s
Par. = 77m — U.Mag. = 0.1221
Gam. = 0.9472 — P.Mag. = 1.1181

Penumbral — **2024 Mar 25**
Saros 113 — 07:14 TD
D.Node — ΔT= 71s
Pen. = 279m
Gam. = 1.0610 — U.Mag. = -0.1324 — P.Mag. = 0.9557

Partial — **2024 Sep 18**
Saros 118 — 02:45 TD
A.Node — ΔT= 71s
Par. = 63m — U.Mag. = 0.0849
Gam. = -0.9792 — P.Mag. = 1.0373

Total — **2025 Mar 14**
Saros 123 — 07:00 TD
D.Node — ΔT= 72s
Tot. = 65m
Par. = 218m — U.Mag. = 1.1784
Gam. = 0.3485 — P.Mag. = 2.2595

Plate 106

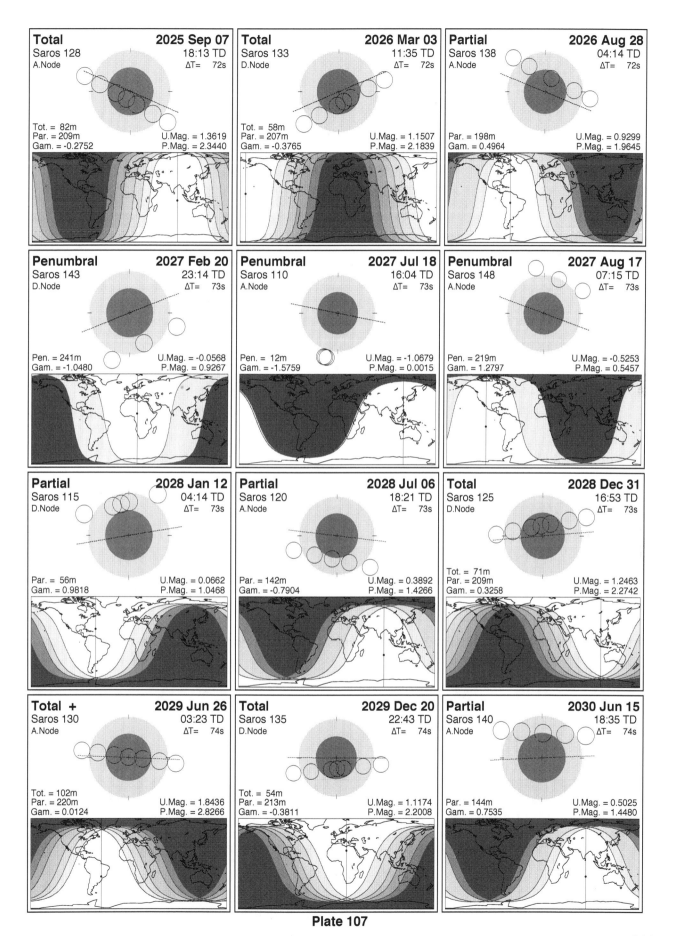

Total — **2025 Sep 07**
Saros 128 — 18:13 TD
A.Node — ΔT= 72s
Tot. = 82m
Par. = 209m — U.Mag. = 1.3619
Gam. = -0.2752 — P.Mag. = 2.3440

Total — **2026 Mar 03**
Saros 133 — 11:35 TD
D.Node — ΔT= 72s
Tot. = 58m
Par. = 207m — U.Mag. = 1.1507
Gam. = -0.3765 — P.Mag. = 2.1839

Partial — **2026 Aug 28**
Saros 138 — 04:14 TD
A.Node — ΔT= 72s
Par. = 198m — U.Mag. = 0.9299
Gam. = 0.4964 — P.Mag. = 1.9645

Penumbral — **2027 Feb 20**
Saros 143 — 23:14 TD
D.Node — ΔT= 73s
Pen. = 241m — U.Mag. = -0.0568
Gam. = -1.0480 — P.Mag. = 0.9267

Penumbral — **2027 Jul 18**
Saros 110 — 16:04 TD
A.Node — ΔT= 73s
Pen. = 12m — U.Mag. = -1.0679
Gam. = -1.5759 — P.Mag. = 0.0015

Penumbral — **2027 Aug 17**
Saros 148 — 07:15 TD
A.Node — ΔT= 73s
Pen. = 219m — U.Mag. = -0.5253
Gam. = 1.2797 — P.Mag. = 0.5457

Partial — **2028 Jan 12**
Saros 115 — 04:14 TD
D.Node — ΔT= 73s
Par. = 56m — U.Mag. = 0.0662
Gam. = 0.9818 — P.Mag. = 1.0468

Partial — **2028 Jul 06**
Saros 120 — 18:21 TD
A.Node — ΔT= 73s
Par. = 142m — U.Mag. = 0.3892
Gam. = -0.7904 — P.Mag. = 1.4266

Total — **2028 Dec 31**
Saros 125 — 16:53 TD
D.Node — ΔT= 73s
Tot. = 71m
Par. = 209m — U.Mag. = 1.2463
Gam. = 0.3258 — P.Mag. = 2.2742

Total + — **2029 Jun 26**
Saros 130 — 03:23 TD
A.Node — ΔT= 74s
Tot. = 102m
Par. = 220m — U.Mag. = 1.8436
Gam. = 0.0124 — P.Mag. = 2.8266

Total — **2029 Dec 20**
Saros 135 — 22:43 TD
D.Node — ΔT= 74s
Tot. = 54m
Par. = 213m — U.Mag. = 1.1174
Gam. = -0.3811 — P.Mag. = 2.2008

Partial — **2030 Jun 15**
Saros 140 — 18:35 TD
A.Node — ΔT= 74s
Par. = 144m — U.Mag. = 0.5025
Gam. = 0.7535 — P.Mag. = 1.4480

Plate 107

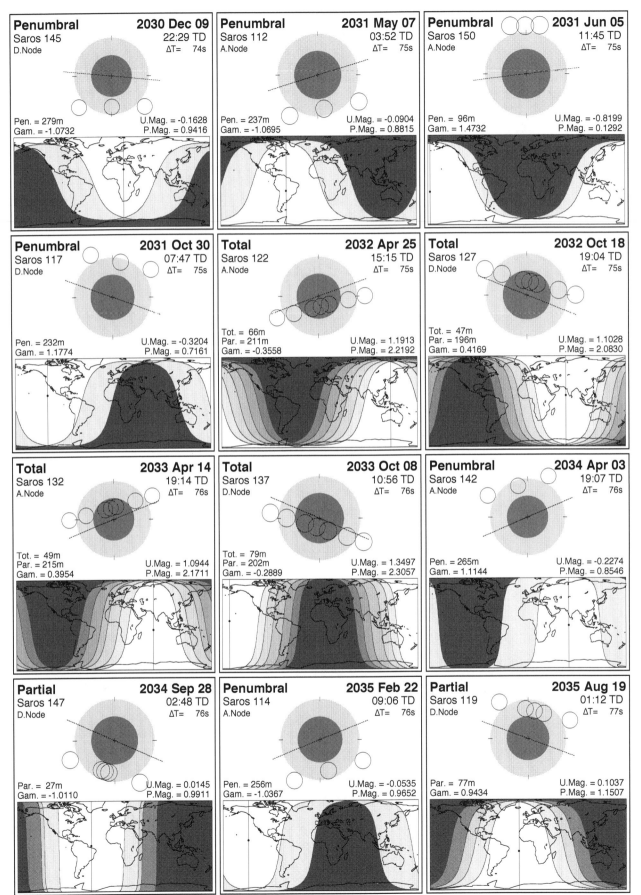

Penumbral   **2030 Dec 09**
Saros 145   22:29 TD
D.Node   ΔT= 74s
Pen. = 279m   U.Mag. = -0.1628
Gam. = -1.0732   P.Mag. = 0.9416

Penumbral   **2031 May 07**
Saros 112   03:52 TD
A.Node   ΔT= 75s
Pen. = 237m   U.Mag. = -0.0904
Gam. = -1.0695   P.Mag. = 0.8815

Penumbral   **2031 Jun 05**
Saros 150   11:45 TD
A.Node   ΔT= 75s
Pen. = 96m   U.Mag. = -0.8199
Gam. = 1.4732   P.Mag. = 0.1292

Penumbral   **2031 Oct 30**
Saros 117   07:47 TD
D.Node   ΔT= 75s
Pen. = 232m   U.Mag. = -0.3204
Gam. = 1.1774   P.Mag. = 0.7161

Total   **2032 Apr 25**
Saros 122   15:15 TD
A.Node   ΔT= 75s
Tot. = 66m
Par. = 211m   U.Mag. = 1.1913
Gam. = -0.3558   P.Mag. = 2.2192

Total   **2032 Oct 18**
Saros 127   19:04 TD
D.Node   ΔT= 75s
Tot. = 47m
Par. = 196m   U.Mag. = 1.1028
Gam. = 0.4169   P.Mag. = 2.0830

Total   **2033 Apr 14**
Saros 132   19:14 TD
A.Node   ΔT= 76s
Tot. = 49m
Par. = 215m   U.Mag. = 1.0944
Gam. = 0.3954   P.Mag. = 2.1711

Total   **2033 Oct 08**
Saros 137   10:56 TD
D.Node   ΔT= 76s
Tot. = 79m
Par. = 202m   U.Mag. = 1.3497
Gam. = -0.2889   P.Mag. = 2.3057

Penumbral   **2034 Apr 03**
Saros 142   19:07 TD
A.Node   ΔT= 76s
Pen. = 265m   U.Mag. = -0.2274
Gam. = 1.1144   P.Mag. = 0.8546

Partial   **2034 Sep 28**
Saros 147   02:48 TD
D.Node   ΔT= 76s
Par. = 27m   U.Mag. = 0.0145
Gam. = -1.0110   P.Mag. = 0.9911

Penumbral   **2035 Feb 22**
Saros 114   09:06 TD
A.Node   ΔT= 76s
Pen. = 256m   U.Mag. = -0.0535
Gam. = -1.0367   P.Mag. = 0.9652

Partial   **2035 Aug 19**
Saros 119   01:12 TD
D.Node   ΔT= 77s
Par. = 77m   U.Mag. = 0.1037
Gam. = 0.9434   P.Mag. = 1.1507

Plate 108

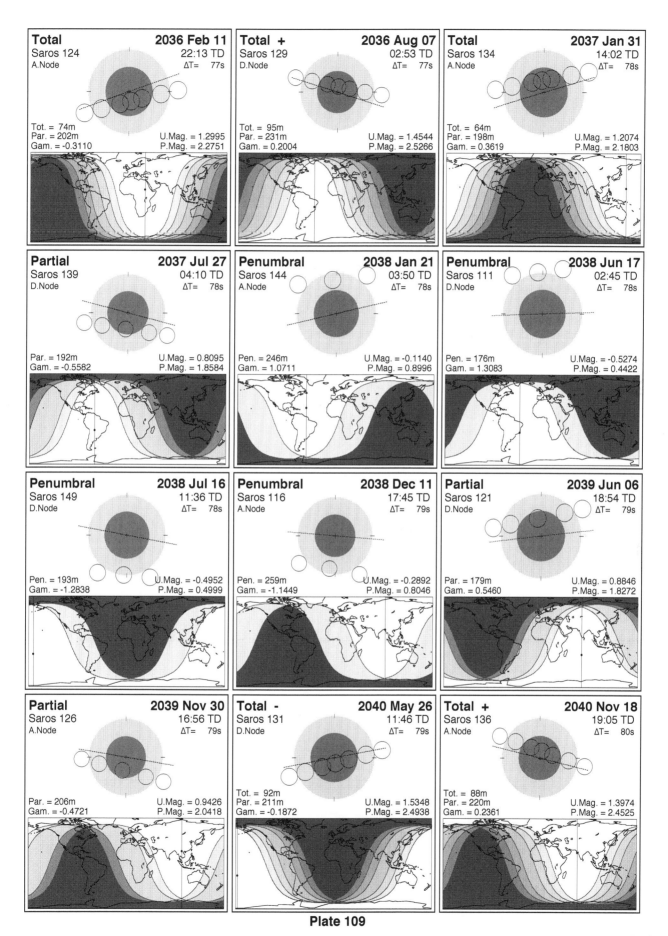

Total   **2036 Feb 11**
Saros 124   22:13 TD
A.Node   ΔT= 77s
Tot. = 74m
Par. = 202m
Gam. = -0.3110   U.Mag. = 1.2995
   P.Mag. = 2.2751

Total +   **2036 Aug 07**
Saros 129   02:53 TD
D.Node   ΔT= 77s
Tot. = 95m
Par. = 231m
Gam. = 0.2004   U.Mag. = 1.4544
   P.Mag. = 2.5266

Total   **2037 Jan 31**
Saros 134   14:02 TD
A.Node   ΔT= 78s
Tot. = 64m
Par. = 198m
Gam. = 0.3619   U.Mag. = 1.2074
   P.Mag. = 2.1803

Partial   **2037 Jul 27**
Saros 139   04:10 TD
D.Node   ΔT= 78s
Par. = 192m
Gam. = -0.5582   U.Mag. = 0.8095
   P.Mag. = 1.8584

Penumbral   **2038 Jan 21**
Saros 144   03:50 TD
A.Node   ΔT= 78s
Pen. = 246m
Gam. = 1.0711   U.Mag. = -0.1140
   P.Mag. = 0.8996

Penumbral   **2038 Jun 17**
Saros 111   02:45 TD
D.Node   ΔT= 78s
Pen. = 176m
Gam. = 1.3083   U.Mag. = -0.5274
   P.Mag. = 0.4422

Penumbral   **2038 Jul 16**
Saros 149   11:36 TD
D.Node   ΔT= 78s
Pen. = 193m
Gam. = -1.2838   U.Mag. = -0.4952
   P.Mag. = 0.4999

Penumbral   **2038 Dec 11**
Saros 116   17:45 TD
A.Node   ΔT= 79s
Pen. = 259m
Gam. = -1.1449   U.Mag. = -0.2892
   P.Mag. = 0.8046

Partial   **2039 Jun 06**
Saros 121   18:54 TD
D.Node   ΔT= 79s
Par. = 179m
Gam. = 0.5460   U.Mag. = 0.8846
   P.Mag. = 1.8272

Partial   **2039 Nov 30**
Saros 126   16:56 TD
A.Node   ΔT= 79s
Par. = 206m
Gam. = -0.4721   U.Mag. = 0.9426
   P.Mag. = 2.0418

Total -   **2040 May 26**
Saros 131   11:46 TD
D.Node   ΔT= 79s
Tot. = 92m
Par. = 211m
Gam. = -0.1872   U.Mag. = 1.5348
   P.Mag. = 2.4938

Total +   **2040 Nov 18**
Saros 136   19:05 TD
A.Node   ΔT= 80s
Tot. = 88m
Par. = 220m
Gam. = 0.2361   U.Mag. = 1.3974
   P.Mag. = 2.4525

Plate 109

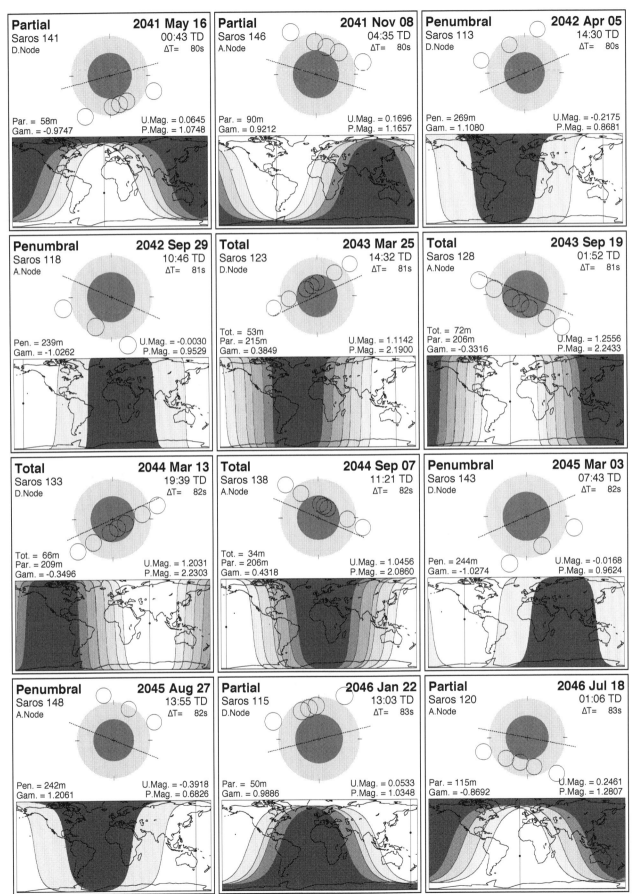

Partial 2041 May 16	**Partial** 2041 Nov 08
Saros 141	00:43 TD
D.Node	ΔT= 80s
Par. = 58m	U.Mag. = 0.0645
Gam. = -0.9747	P.Mag. = 1.0748

Partial   2041 May 16
Saros 141   00:43 TD
D.Node   ΔT= 80s
Par. = 58m   U.Mag. = 0.0645
Gam. = -0.9747   P.Mag. = 1.0748

Partial   2041 Nov 08
Saros 146   04:35 TD
A.Node   ΔT= 80s
Par. = 90m   U.Mag. = 0.1696
Gam. = 0.9212   P.Mag. = 1.1657

Penumbral   2042 Apr 05
Saros 113   14:30 TD
D.Node   ΔT= 80s
Pen. = 269m   U.Mag. = -0.2175
Gam. = 1.1080   P.Mag. = 0.8681

Penumbral   2042 Sep 29
Saros 118   10:46 TD
A.Node   ΔT= 81s
Pen. = 239m   U.Mag. = -0.0030
Gam. = -1.0262   P.Mag. = 0.9529

Total   2043 Mar 25
Saros 123   14:32 TD
D.Node   ΔT= 81s
Tot. = 53m
Par. = 215m   U.Mag. = 1.1142
Gam. = 0.3849   P.Mag. = 2.1900

Total   2043 Sep 19
Saros 128   01:52 TD
A.Node   ΔT= 81s
Tot. = 72m
Par. = 206m   U.Mag. = 1.2556
Gam. = -0.3316   P.Mag. = 2.2433

Total   2044 Mar 13
Saros 133   19:39 TD
D.Node   ΔT= 82s
Tot. = 66m
Par. = 209m   U.Mag. = 1.2031
Gam. = -0.3496   P.Mag. = 2.2303

Total   2044 Sep 07
Saros 138   11:21 TD
A.Node   ΔT= 82s
Tot. = 34m
Par. = 206m   U.Mag. = 1.0456
Gam. = 0.4318   P.Mag. = 2.0860

Penumbral   2045 Mar 03
Saros 143   07:43 TD
D.Node   ΔT= 82s
Pen. = 244m   U.Mag. = -0.0168
Gam. = -1.0274   P.Mag. = 0.9624

Penumbral   2045 Aug 27
Saros 148   13:55 TD
A.Node   ΔT= 82s
Pen. = 242m   U.Mag. = -0.3918
Gam. = 1.2061   P.Mag. = 0.6826

Partial   2046 Jan 22
Saros 115   13:03 TD
D.Node   ΔT= 83s
Par. = 50m   U.Mag. = 0.0533
Gam. = 0.9886   P.Mag. = 1.0348

Partial   2046 Jul 18
Saros 120   01:06 TD
A.Node   ΔT= 83s
Par. = 115m   U.Mag. = 0.2461
Gam. = -0.8692   P.Mag. = 1.2807

Plate 110

206

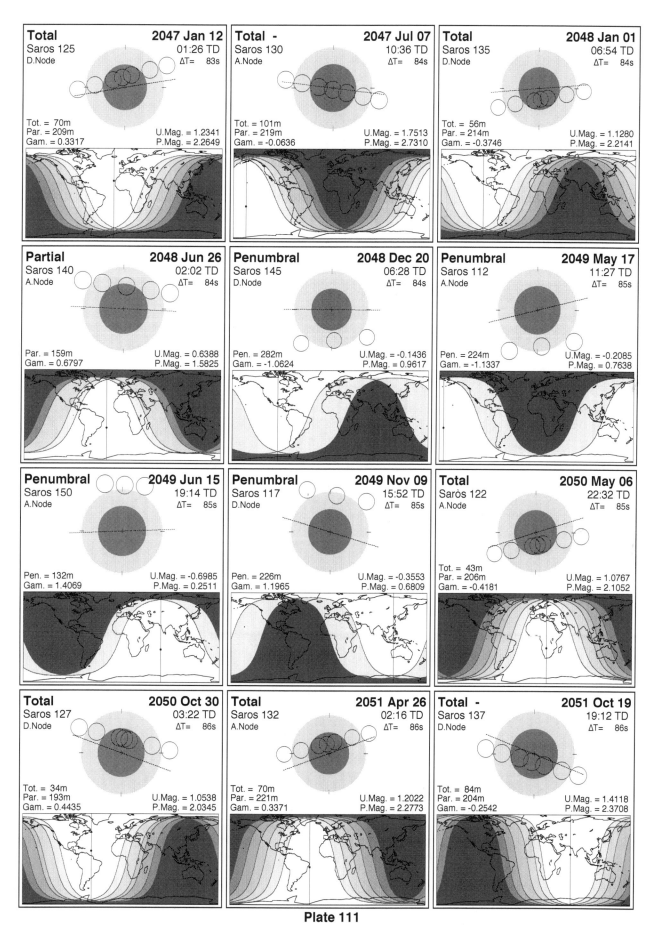

Total **2047 Jan 12**	
Saros 125 01:26 TD	
D.Node ΔT= 83s	
Tot. = 70m	
Par. = 209m U.Mag. = 1.2341	
Gam. = 0.3317 P.Mag. = 2.2649	

Total -   **2047 Jul 07**
Saros 130   10:36 TD
A.Node ΔT=   84s
Tot. = 101m
Par. = 219m   U.Mag. = 1.7513
Gam. = -0.0636   P.Mag. = 2.7310

Total   **2048 Jan 01**
Saros 135   06:54 TD
D.Node ΔT=   84s
Tot. = 56m
Par. = 214m   U.Mag. = 1.1280
Gam. = -0.3746   P.Mag. = 2.2141

Partial   **2048 Jun 26**
Saros 140   02:02 TD
A.Node ΔT=   84s
Par. = 159m   U.Mag. = 0.6388
Gam. = 0.6797   P.Mag. = 1.5825

Penumbral   **2048 Dec 20**
Saros 145   06:28 TD
D.Node ΔT=   84s
Pen. = 282m   U.Mag. = -0.1436
Gam. = -1.0624   P.Mag. = 0.9617

Penumbral   **2049 May 17**
Saros 112   11:27 TD
A.Node ΔT=   85s
Pen. = 224m   U.Mag. = -0.2085
Gam. = -1.1337   P.Mag. = 0.7638

Penumbral   **2049 Jun 15**
Saros 150   19:14 TD
A.Node ΔT=   85s
Pen. = 132m   U.Mag. = -0.6985
Gam. = 1.4069   P.Mag. = 0.2511

Penumbral   **2049 Nov 09**
Saros 117   15:52 TD
D.Node ΔT=   85s
Pen. = 226m   U.Mag. = -0.3553
Gam. = 1.1965   P.Mag. = 0.6809

Total   **2050 May 06**
Saros 122   22:32 TD
A.Node ΔT=   85s
Tot. = 43m
Par. = 206m   U.Mag. = 1.0767
Gam. = -0.4181   P.Mag. = 2.1052

Total   **2050 Oct 30**
Saros 127   03:22 TD
D.Node ΔT=   86s
Tot. = 34m
Par. = 193m   U.Mag. = 1.0538
Gam. = 0.4435   P.Mag. = 2.0345

Total   **2051 Apr 26**
Saros 132   02:16 TD
A.Node ΔT=   86s
Tot. = 70m
Par. = 221m   U.Mag. = 1.2022
Gam. = 0.3371   P.Mag. = 2.2773

Total -   **2051 Oct 19**
Saros 137   19:12 TD
D.Node ΔT=   86s
Tot. = 84m
Par. = 204m   U.Mag. = 1.4118
Gam. = -0.2542   P.Mag. = 2.3708

Plate 111

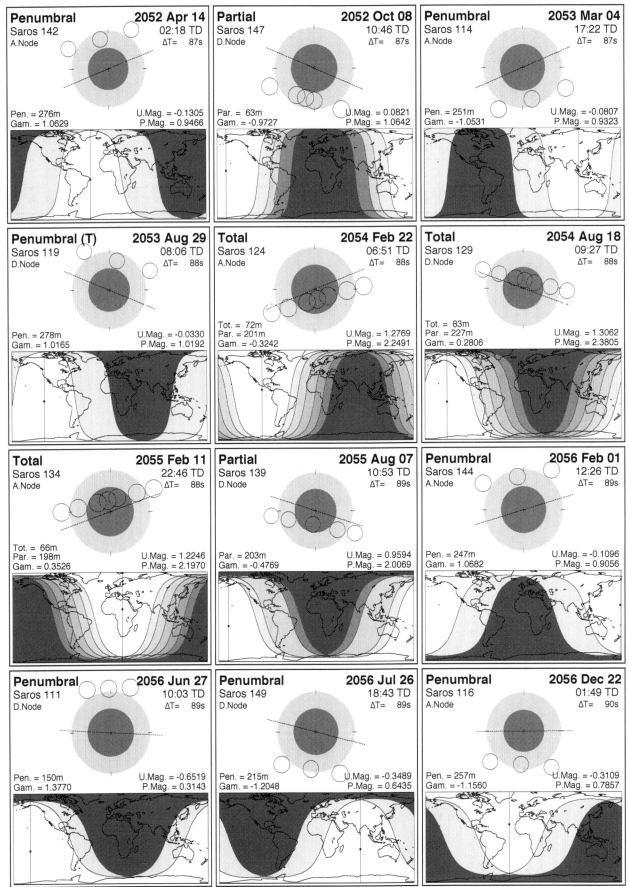

Penumbral   **2052 Apr 14**
Saros 142   02:18 TD
A.Node   ΔT= 87s

Pen. = 276m   U.Mag. = -0.1305
Gam. = 1.0629   P.Mag. = 0.9466

Partial   **2052 Oct 08**
Saros 147   10:46 TD
D.Node   ΔT= 87s

Par. = 63m   U.Mag. = 0.0821
Gam. = -0.9727   P.Mag. = 1.0642

Penumbral   **2053 Mar 04**
Saros 114   17:22 TD
A.Node   ΔT= 87s

Pen. = 251m   U.Mag. = -0.0807
Gam. = -1.0531   P.Mag. = 0.9323

Penumbral (T)   **2053 Aug 29**
Saros 119   08:06 TD
D.Node   ΔT= 88s

Pen. = 278m   U.Mag. = -0.0330
Gam. = 1.0165   P.Mag. = 1.0192

Total   **2054 Feb 22**
Saros 124   06:51 TD
A.Node   ΔT= 88s

Tot. = 72m
Par. = 201m   U.Mag. = 1.2769
Gam. = -0.3242   P.Mag. = 2.2491

Total   **2054 Aug 18**
Saros 129   09:27 TD
D.Node   ΔT= 88s

Tot. = 83m
Par. = 227m   U.Mag. = 1.3062
Gam. = 0.2806   P.Mag. = 2.3805

Total   **2055 Feb 11**
Saros 134   22:46 TD
A.Node   ΔT= 88s

Tot. = 66m
Par. = 198m   U.Mag. = 1.2246
Gam. = 0.3526   P.Mag. = 2.1970

Partial   **2055 Aug 07**
Saros 139   10:53 TD
D.Node   ΔT= 89s

Par. = 203m   U.Mag. = 0.9594
Gam. = -0.4769   P.Mag. = 2.0069

Penumbral   **2056 Feb 01**
Saros 144   12:26 TD
A.Node   ΔT= 89s

Pen. = 247m   U.Mag. = -0.1096
Gam. = 1.0682   P.Mag. = 0.9056

Penumbral   **2056 Jun 27**
Saros 111   10:03 TD
D.Node   ΔT= 89s

Pen. = 150m   U.Mag. = -0.6519
Gam. = 1.3770   P.Mag. = 0.3143

Penumbral   **2056 Jul 26**
Saros 149   18:43 TD
D.Node   ΔT= 89s

Pen. = 215m   U.Mag. = -0.3489
Gam. = -1.2048   P.Mag. = 0.6435

Penumbral   **2056 Dec 22**
Saros 116   01:49 TD
A.Node   ΔT= 90s

Pen. = 257m   U.Mag. = -0.3109
Gam. = -1.1560   P.Mag. = 0.7857

Plate 112

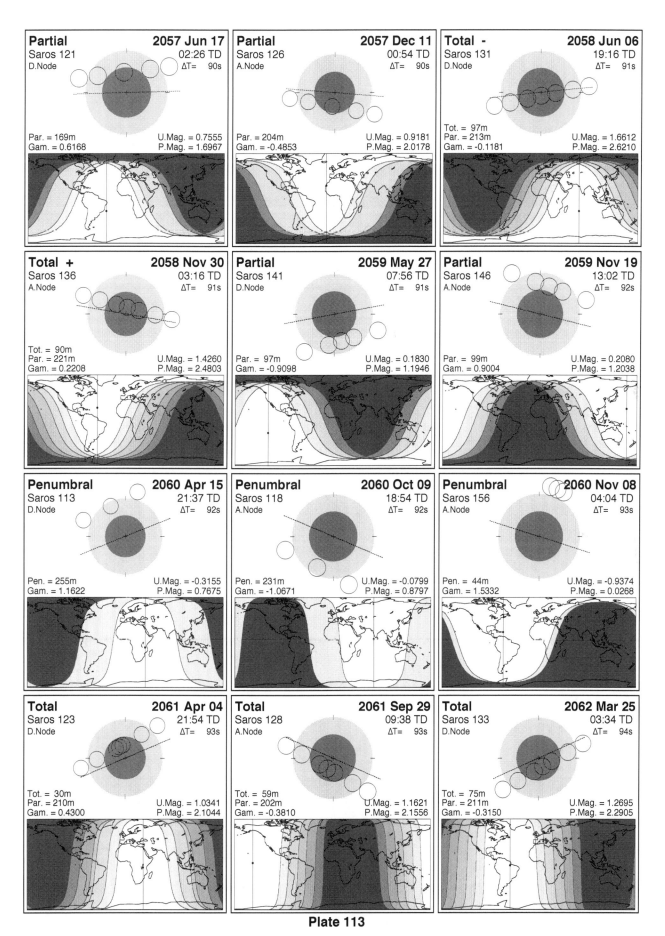

Partial **2057 Jun 17**	
Saros 121 02:26 TD	
D.Node ΔT= 90s	
Par. = 169m U.Mag. = 0.7555	
Gam. = 0.6168 P.Mag. = 1.6967	

| **Partial** **2057 Dec 11** |
| Saros 126 00:54 TD |
| A.Node ΔT= 90s |
| Par. = 204m U.Mag. = 0.9181 |
| Gam. = -0.4853 P.Mag. = 2.0178 |

| **Total -** **2058 Jun 06** |
| Saros 131 19:16 TD |
| D.Node ΔT= 91s |
| Tot. = 97m U.Mag. = 1.6612 |
| Par. = 213m |
| Gam. = -0.1181 P.Mag. = 2.6210 |

| **Total +** **2058 Nov 30** |
| Saros 136 03:16 TD |
| A.Node ΔT= 91s |
| Tot. = 90m |
| Par. = 221m U.Mag. = 1.4260 |
| Gam. = 0.2208 P.Mag. = 2.4803 |

| **Partial** **2059 May 27** |
| Saros 141 07:56 TD |
| D.Node ΔT= 91s |
| Par. = 97m U.Mag. = 0.1830 |
| Gam. = -0.9098 P.Mag. = 1.1946 |

| **Partial** **2059 Nov 19** |
| Saros 146 13:02 TD |
| A.Node ΔT= 92s |
| Par. = 99m U.Mag. = 0.2080 |
| Gam. = 0.9004 P.Mag. = 1.2038 |

| **Penumbral** **2060 Apr 15** |
| Saros 113 21:37 TD |
| D.Node ΔT= 92s |
| Pen. = 255m U.Mag. = -0.3155 |
| Gam. = 1.1622 P.Mag. = 0.7675 |

| **Penumbral** **2060 Oct 09** |
| Saros 118 18:54 TD |
| A.Node ΔT= 92s |
| Pen. = 231m U.Mag. = -0.0799 |
| Gam. = -1.0671 P.Mag. = 0.8797 |

| **Penumbral** **2060 Nov 08** |
| Saros 156 04:04 TD |
| A.Node ΔT= 93s |
| Pen. = 44m U.Mag. = -0.9374 |
| Gam. = 1.5332 P.Mag. = 0.0268 |

| **Total** **2061 Apr 04** |
| Saros 123 21:54 TD |
| D.Node ΔT= 93s |
| Tot. = 30m |
| Par. = 210m U.Mag. = 1.0341 |
| Gam. = 0.4300 P.Mag. = 2.1044 |

| **Total** **2061 Sep 29** |
| Saros 128 09:38 TD |
| A.Node ΔT= 93s |
| Tot. = 59m |
| Par. = 202m U.Mag. = 1.1621 |
| Gam. = -0.3810 P.Mag. = 2.1556 |

| **Total** **2062 Mar 25** |
| Saros 133 03:34 TD |
| D.Node ΔT= 94s |
| Tot. = 75m |
| Par. = 211m U.Mag. = 1.2695 |
| Gam. = -0.3150 P.Mag. = 2.2905 |

Plate 113

209

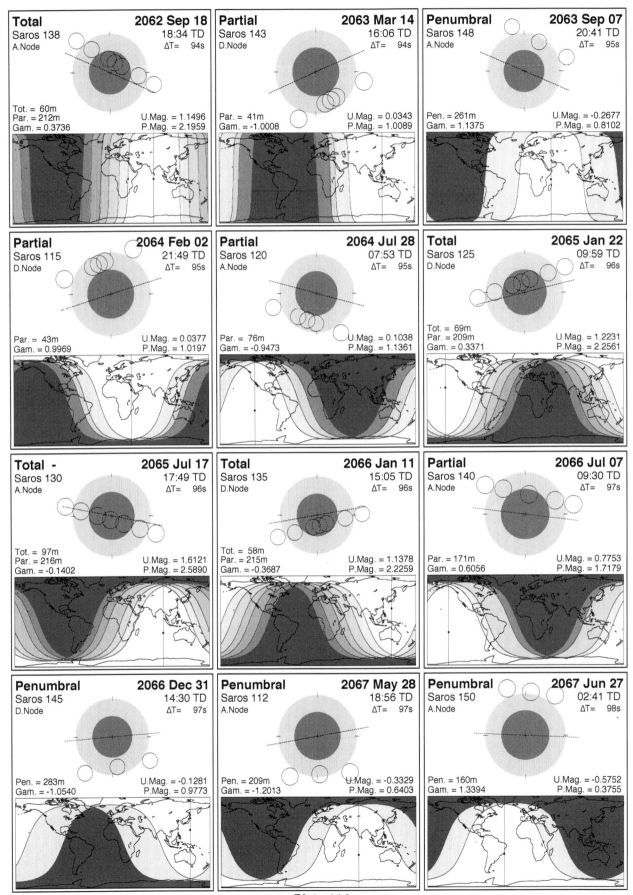

Total **2062 Sep 18** Saros 138 18:34 TD A.Node ΔT= 94s Tot. = 60m Par. = 212m U.Mag. = 1.1496 Gam. = 0.3736 P.Mag. = 2.1959	**Partial** **2063 Mar 14** Saros 143 16:06 TD D.Node ΔT= 94s Par. = 41m U.Mag. = 0.0343 Gam. = -1.0008 P.Mag. = 1.0089	**Penumbral** **2063 Sep 07** Saros 148 20:41 TD A.Node ΔT= 95s Pen. = 261m U.Mag. = -0.2677 Gam. = 1.1375 P.Mag. = 0.8102
Partial **2064 Feb 02** Saros 115 21:49 TD D.Node ΔT= 95s Par. = 43m U.Mag. = 0.0377 Gam. = 0.9969 P.Mag. = 1.0197	**Partial** **2064 Jul 28** Saros 120 07:53 TD A.Node ΔT= 95s Par. = 76m U.Mag. = 0.1038 Gam. = -0.9473 P.Mag. = 1.1361	**Total** **2065 Jan 22** Saros 125 09:59 TD D.Node ΔT= 96s Tot. = 69m Par. = 209m U.Mag. = 1.2231 Gam. = 0.3371 P.Mag. = 2.2561
Total - **2065 Jul 17** Saros 130 17:49 TD A.Node ΔT= 96s Tot. = 97m Par. = 216m U.Mag. = 1.6121 Gam. = -0.1402 P.Mag. = 2.5890	**Total** **2066 Jan 11** Saros 135 15:05 TD D.Node ΔT= 96s Tot. = 58m Par. = 215m U.Mag. = 1.1378 Gam. = -0.3687 P.Mag. = 2.2259	**Partial** **2066 Jul 07** Saros 140 09:30 TD A.Node ΔT= 97s Par. = 171m U.Mag. = 0.7753 Gam. = 0.6056 P.Mag. = 1.7179
Penumbral **2066 Dec 31** Saros 145 14:30 TD D.Node ΔT= 97s Pen. = 283m U.Mag. = -0.1281 Gam. = -1.0540 P.Mag. = 0.9773	**Penumbral** **2067 May 28** Saros 112 18:56 TD A.Node ΔT= 97s Pen. = 209m U.Mag. = -0.3329 Gam. = -1.2013 P.Mag. = 0.6403	**Penumbral** **2067 Jun 27** Saros 150 02:41 TD A.Node ΔT= 98s Pen. = 160m U.Mag. = -0.5752 Gam. = 1.3394 P.Mag. = 0.3755

Plate 114

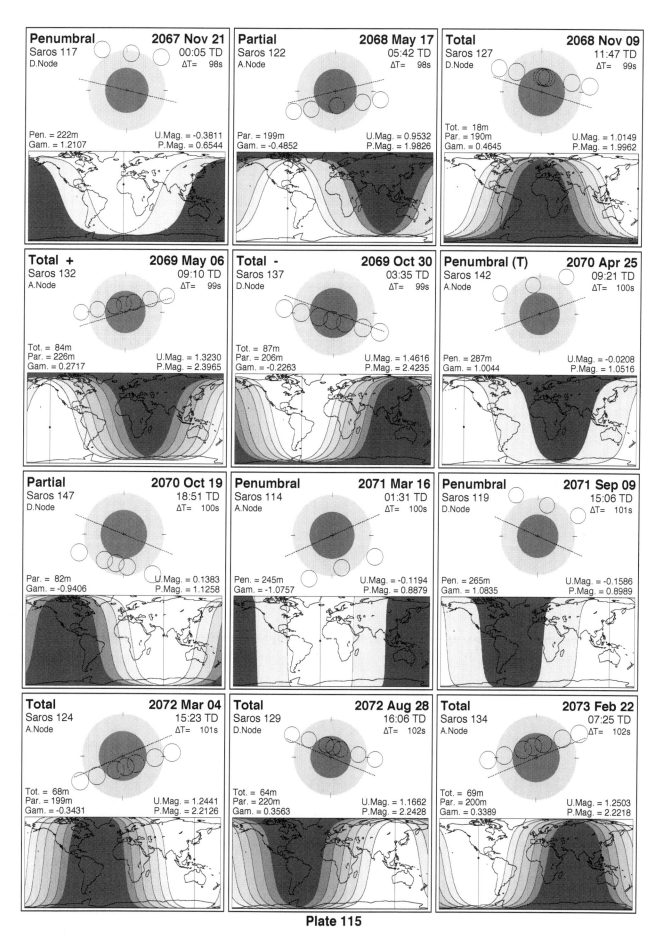

Penumbral   **2067 Nov 21**
Saros 117   00:05 TD
D.Node   ΔT= 98s

Pen. = 222m   U.Mag. = -0.3811
Gam. = 1.2107   P.Mag. = 0.6544

Partial   **2068 May 17**
Saros 122   05:42 TD
A.Node   ΔT= 98s

Par. = 199m   U.Mag. = 0.9532
Gam. = -0.4852   P.Mag. = 1.9826

Total   **2068 Nov 09**
Saros 127   11:47 TD
D.Node   ΔT= 99s

Tot. = 18m
Par. = 190m   U.Mag. = 1.0149
Gam. = 0.4645   P.Mag. = 1.9962

Total +   **2069 May 06**
Saros 132   09:10 TD
A.Node   ΔT= 99s

Tot. = 84m
Par. = 226m   U.Mag. = 1.3230
Gam. = 0.2717   P.Mag. = 2.3965

Total -   **2069 Oct 30**
Saros 137   03:35 TD
D.Node   ΔT= 99s

Tot. = 87m
Par. = 206m   U.Mag. = 1.4616
Gam. = -0.2263   P.Mag. = 2.4235

Penumbral (T)   **2070 Apr 25**
Saros 142   09:21 TD
A.Node   ΔT= 100s

Pen. = 287m   U.Mag. = -0.0208
Gam. = 1.0044   P.Mag. = 1.0516

Partial   **2070 Oct 19**
Saros 147   18:51 TD
D.Node   ΔT= 100s

Par. = 82m   U.Mag. = 0.1383
Gam. = -0.9406   P.Mag. = 1.1258

Penumbral   **2071 Mar 16**
Saros 114   01:31 TD
A.Node   ΔT= 100s

Pen. = 245m   U.Mag. = -0.1194
Gam. = -1.0757   P.Mag. = 0.8879

Penumbral   **2071 Sep 09**
Saros 119   15:06 TD
D.Node   ΔT= 101s

Pen. = 265m   U.Mag. = -0.1586
Gam. = 1.0835   P.Mag. = 0.8989

Total   **2072 Mar 04**
Saros 124   15:23 TD
A.Node   ΔT= 101s

Tot. = 68m
Par. = 199m   U.Mag. = 1.2441
Gam. = -0.3431   P.Mag. = 2.2126

Total   **2072 Aug 28**
Saros 129   16:06 TD
D.Node   ΔT= 102s

Tot. = 64m
Par. = 220m   U.Mag. = 1.1662
Gam. = 0.3563   P.Mag. = 2.2428

Total   **2073 Feb 22**
Saros 134   07:25 TD
A.Node   ΔT= 102s

Tot. = 69m
Par. = 200m   U.Mag. = 1.2503
Gam. = 0.3389   P.Mag. = 2.2218

Plate 115

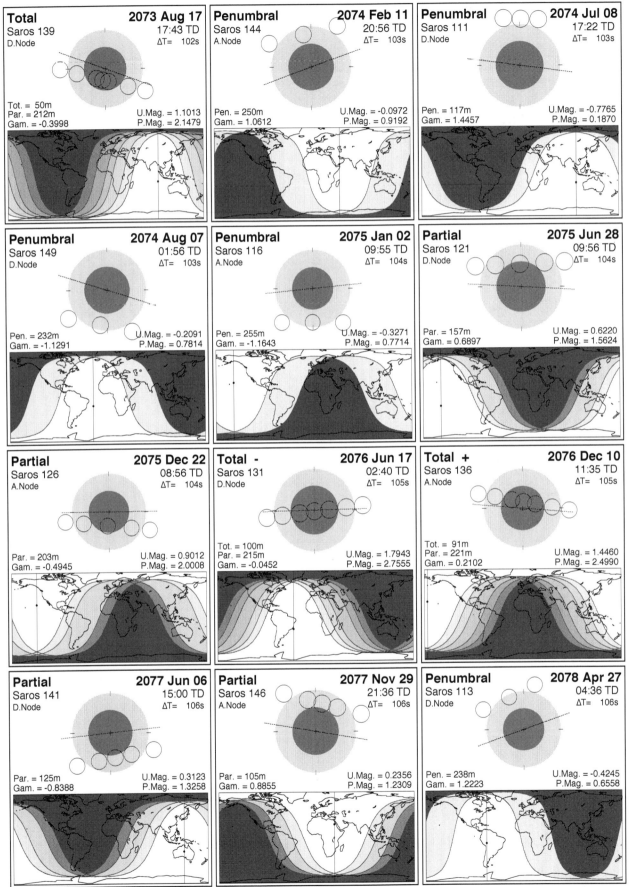

Total	2073 Aug 17
Saros 139	17:43 TD
D.Node	ΔT= 102s

Tot. = 50m
Par. = 212m
Gam. = -0.3998
U.Mag. = 1.1013
P.Mag. = 2.1479

Penumbral	2074 Feb 11
Saros 144	20:56 TD
A.Node	ΔT= 103s

Pen. = 250m
Gam. = 1.0612
U.Mag. = -0.0972
P.Mag. = 0.9192

Penumbral	2074 Jul 08
Saros 111	17:22 TD
D.Node	ΔT= 103s

Pen. = 117m
Gam. = 1.4457
U.Mag. = -0.7765
P.Mag. = 0.1870

Penumbral	2074 Aug 07
Saros 149	01:56 TD
D.Node	ΔT= 103s

Pen. = 232m
Gam. = -1.1291
U.Mag. = -0.2091
P.Mag. = 0.7814

Penumbral	2075 Jan 02
Saros 116	09:55 TD
A.Node	ΔT= 104s

Pen. = 255m
Gam. = -1.1643
U.Mag. = -0.3271
P.Mag. = 0.7714

Partial	2075 Jun 28
Saros 121	09:56 TD
D.Node	ΔT= 104s

Par. = 157m
Gam. = 0.6897
U.Mag. = 0.6220
P.Mag. = 1.5624

Partial	2075 Dec 22
Saros 126	08:56 TD
A.Node	ΔT= 104s

Par. = 203m
Gam. = -0.4945
U.Mag. = 0.9012
P.Mag. = 2.0008

Total -	2076 Jun 17
Saros 131	02:40 TD
D.Node	ΔT= 105s

Tot. = 100m
Par. = 215m
Gam. = -0.0452
U.Mag. = 1.7943
P.Mag. = 2.7555

Total +	2076 Dec 10
Saros 136	11:35 TD
A.Node	ΔT= 105s

Tot. = 91m
Par. = 221m
Gam. = 0.2102
U.Mag. = 1.4460
P.Mag. = 2.4990

Partial	2077 Jun 06
Saros 141	15:00 TD
D.Node	ΔT= 106s

Par. = 125m
Gam. = -0.8388
U.Mag. = 0.3123
P.Mag. = 1.3258

Partial	2077 Nov 29
Saros 146	21:36 TD
A.Node	ΔT= 106s

Par. = 105m
Gam. = 0.8855
U.Mag. = 0.2356
P.Mag. = 1.2309

Penumbral	2078 Apr 27
Saros 113	04:36 TD
D.Node	ΔT= 106s

Pen. = 238m
Gam. = 1.2223
U.Mag. = -0.4245
P.Mag. = 0.6558

Plate 116

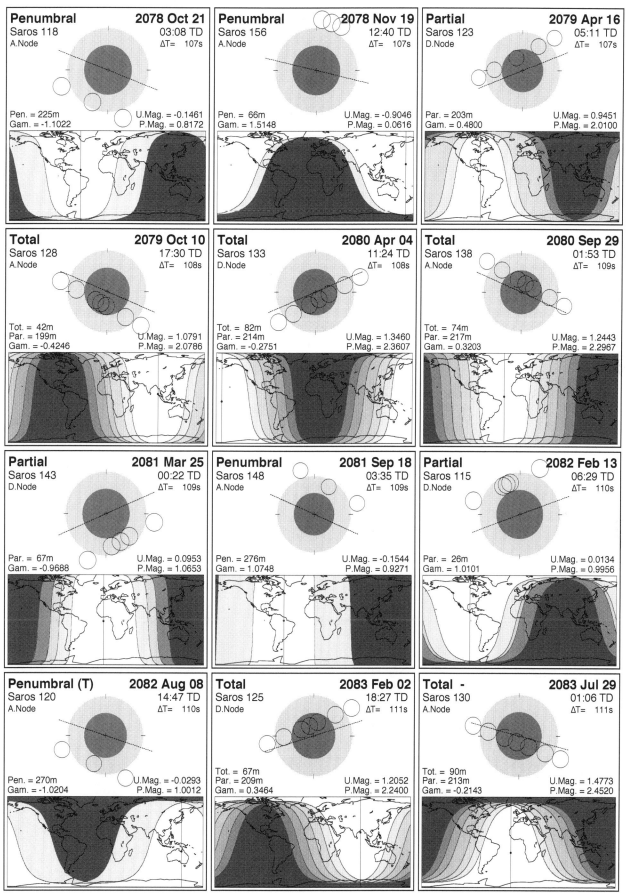

Penumbral **2078 Oct 21**	
Saros 118 03:08 TD	
A.Node ΔT= 107s	
Pen. = 225m U.Mag. = -0.1461	
Gam. = -1.1022 P.Mag. = 0.8172	

Penumbral   **2078 Nov 19**
Saros 156   12:40 TD
A.Node   ΔT= 107s
Pen. = 66m   U.Mag. = -0.9046
Gam. = 1.5148   P.Mag. = 0.0616

Partial   **2079 Apr 16**
Saros 123   05:11 TD
D.Node   ΔT= 107s
Par. = 203m   U.Mag. = 0.9451
Gam. = 0.4800   P.Mag. = 2.0100

Total   **2079 Oct 10**
Saros 128   17:30 TD
A.Node   ΔT= 108s
Tot. = 42m
Par. = 199m   U.Mag. = 1.0791
Gam. = -0.4246   P.Mag. = 2.0786

Total   **2080 Apr 04**
Saros 133   11:24 TD
D.Node   ΔT= 108s
Tot. = 82m
Par. = 214m   U.Mag. = 1.3460
Gam. = -0.2751   P.Mag. = 2.3607

Total   **2080 Sep 29**
Saros 138   01:53 TD
A.Node   ΔT= 109s
Tot. = 74m
Par. = 217m   U.Mag. = 1.2443
Gam. = 0.3203   P.Mag. = 2.2967

Partial   **2081 Mar 25**
Saros 143   00:22 TD
D.Node   ΔT= 109s
Par. = 67m   U.Mag. = 0.0953
Gam. = -0.9688   P.Mag. = 1.0653

Penumbral   **2081 Sep 18**
Saros 148   03:35 TD
A.Node   ΔT= 109s
Pen. = 276m   U.Mag. = -0.1544
Gam. = 1.0748   P.Mag. = 0.9271

Partial   **2082 Feb 13**
Saros 115   06:29 TD
D.Node   ΔT= 110s
Par. = 26m   U.Mag. = 0.0134
Gam. = 1.0101   P.Mag. = 0.9956

Penumbral (T)   **2082 Aug 08**
Saros 120   14:47 TD
A.Node   ΔT= 110s
Pen. = 270m   U.Mag. = -0.0293
Gam. = -1.0204   P.Mag. = 1.0012

Total   **2083 Feb 02**
Saros 125   18:27 TD
D.Node   ΔT= 111s
Tot. = 67m
Par. = 209m   U.Mag. = 1.2052
Gam. = 0.3464   P.Mag. = 2.2400

Total -   **2083 Jul 29**
Saros 130   01:06 TD
A.Node   ΔT= 111s
Tot. = 90m
Par. = 213m   U.Mag. = 1.4773
Gam. = -0.2143   P.Mag. = 2.4520

Plate 117

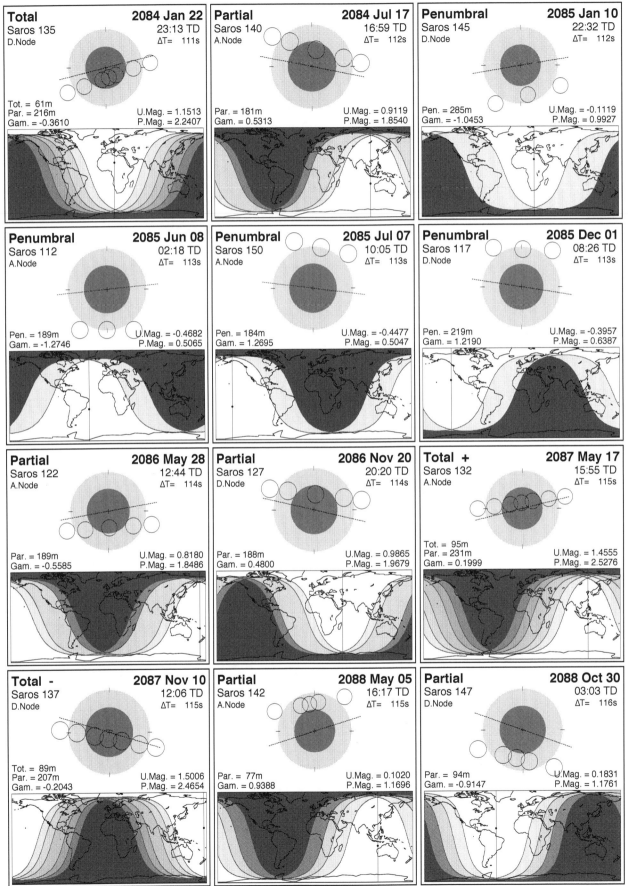

Total   **2084 Jan 22**
Saros 135   23:13 TD
D.Node   ΔT= 111s
Tot. = 61m
Par. = 216m   U.Mag. = 1.1513
Gam. = -0.3610   P.Mag. = 2.2407

Partial   **2084 Jul 17**
Saros 140   16:59 TD
A.Node   ΔT= 112s
Par. = 181m   U.Mag. = 0.9119
Gam. = 0.5313   P.Mag. = 1.8540

Penumbral   **2085 Jan 10**
Saros 145   22:32 TD
D.Node   ΔT= 112s
Pen. = 285m   U.Mag. = -0.1119
Gam. = -1.0453   P.Mag. = 0.9927

Penumbral   **2085 Jun 08**
Saros 112   02:18 TD
A.Node   ΔT= 113s
Pen. = 189m   U.Mag. = -0.4682
Gam. = -1.2746   P.Mag. = 0.5065

Penumbral   **2085 Jul 07**
Saros 150   10:05 TD
A.Node   ΔT= 113s
Pen. = 184m   U.Mag. = -0.4477
Gam. = 1.2695   P.Mag. = 0.5047

Penumbral   **2085 Dec 01**
Saros 117   08:26 TD
D.Node   ΔT= 113s
Pen. = 219m   U.Mag. = -0.3957
Gam. = 1.2190   P.Mag. = 0.6387

Partial   **2086 May 28**
Saros 122   12:44 TD
A.Node   ΔT= 114s
Par. = 189m   U.Mag. = 0.8180
Gam. = -0.5585   P.Mag. = 1.8486

Partial   **2086 Nov 20**
Saros 127   20:20 TD
D.Node   ΔT= 114s
Par. = 188m   U.Mag. = 0.9865
Gam. = 0.4800   P.Mag. = 1.9679

Total +   **2087 May 17**
Saros 132   15:55 TD
A.Node   ΔT= 115s
Tot. = 95m
Par. = 231m   U.Mag. = 1.4555
Gam. = 0.1999   P.Mag. = 2.5276

Total -   **2087 Nov 10**
Saros 137   12:06 TD
D.Node   ΔT= 115s
Tot. = 89m
Par. = 207m   U.Mag. = 1.5006
Gam. = -0.2043   P.Mag. = 2.4654

Partial   **2088 May 05**
Saros 142   16:17 TD
A.Node   ΔT= 115s
Par. = 77m   U.Mag. = 0.1020
Gam. = 0.9388   P.Mag. = 1.1696

Partial   **2088 Oct 30**
Saros 147   03:03 TD
D.Node   ΔT= 116s
Par. = 94m   U.Mag. = 0.1831
Gam. = -0.9147   P.Mag. = 1.1761

Plate 118

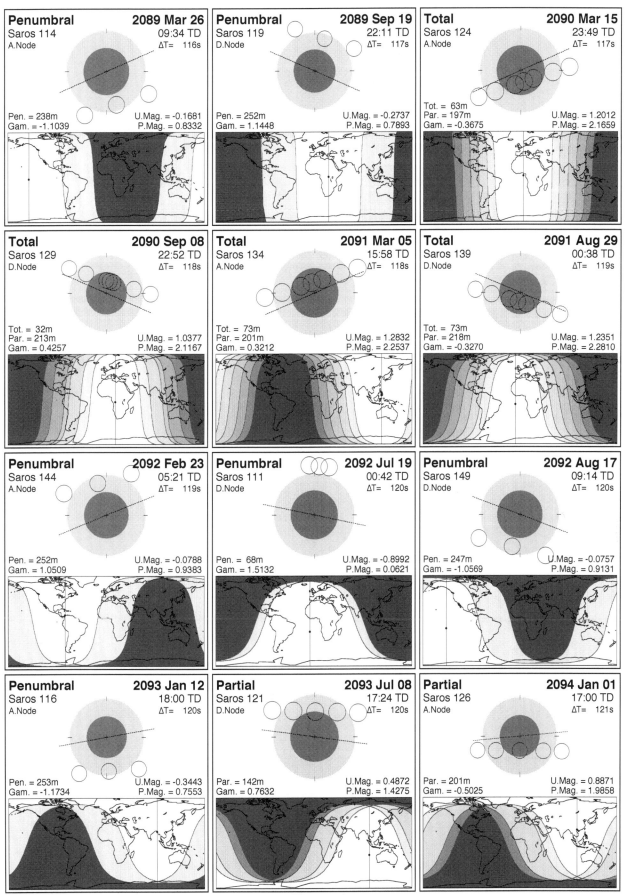

Penumbral **2089 Mar 26**	**Penumbral** **2089 Sep 19**
Saros 114 09:34 TD	Saros 119 22:11 TD
A.Node ΔT= 116s	D.Node ΔT= 117s
Pen. = 238m U.Mag. = -0.1681	Pen. = 252m U.Mag. = -0.2737
Gam. = -1.1039 P.Mag. = 0.8332	Gam. = 1.1448 P.Mag. = 0.7893

Total   **2090 Mar 15**
Saros 124   23:49 TD
A.Node   ΔT= 117s
Tot. = 63m
Par. = 197m   U.Mag. = 1.2012
Gam. = -0.3675   P.Mag. = 2.1659

Total   **2090 Sep 08**
Saros 129   22:52 TD
D.Node   ΔT= 118s
Tot. = 32m
Par. = 213m   U.Mag. = 1.0377
Gam. = 0.4257   P.Mag. = 2.1167

Total   **2091 Mar 05**
Saros 134   15:58 TD
A.Node   ΔT= 118s
Tot. = 73m
Par. = 201m   U.Mag. = 1.2832
Gam. = 0.3212   P.Mag. = 2.2537

Total   **2091 Aug 29**
Saros 139   00:38 TD
D.Node   ΔT= 119s
Tot. = 73m
Par. = 218m   U.Mag. = 1.2351
Gam. = -0.3270   P.Mag. = 2.2810

Penumbral   **2092 Feb 23**
Saros 144   05:21 TD
A.Node   ΔT= 119s
Pen. = 252m   U.Mag. = -0.0788
Gam. = 1.0509   P.Mag. = 0.9383

Penumbral   **2092 Jul 19**
Saros 111   00:42 TD
D.Node   ΔT= 120s
Pen. = 68m   U.Mag. = -0.8992
Gam. = 1.5132   P.Mag. = 0.0621

Penumbral   **2092 Aug 17**
Saros 149   09:14 TD
D.Node   ΔT= 120s
Pen. = 247m   U.Mag. = -0.0757
Gam. = -1.0569   P.Mag. = 0.9131

Penumbral   **2093 Jan 12**
Saros 116   18:00 TD
A.Node   ΔT= 120s
Pen. = 253m   U.Mag. = -0.3443
Gam. = -1.1734   P.Mag. = 0.7553

Partial   **2093 Jul 08**
Saros 121   17:24 TD
D.Node   ΔT= 120s
Par. = 142m   U.Mag. = 0.4872
Gam. = 0.7632   P.Mag. = 1.4275

Partial   **2094 Jan 01**
Saros 126   17:00 TD
A.Node   ΔT= 121s
Par. = 201m   U.Mag. = 0.8871
Gam. = -0.5025   P.Mag. = 1.9858

Plate 119

215

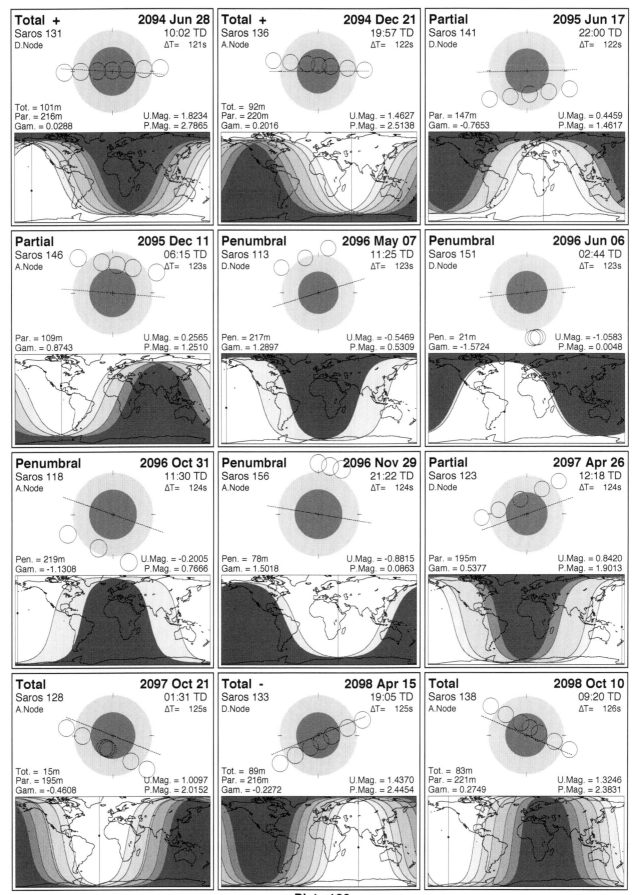

Total + **2094 Jun 28** Saros 131 10:02 TD D.Node ΔT= 121s Tot. = 101m Par. = 216m U.Mag. = 1.8234 Gam. = 0.0288 P.Mag. = 2.7865	**Total +** **2094 Dec 21** Saros 136 19:57 TD A.Node ΔT= 122s Tot. = 92m Par. = 220m U.Mag. = 1.4627 Gam. = 0.2016 P.Mag. = 2.5138	**Partial** **2095 Jun 17** Saros 141 22:00 TD D.Node ΔT= 122s Par. = 147m U.Mag. = 0.4459 Gam. = -0.7653 P.Mag. = 1.4617
Partial **2095 Dec 11** Saros 146 06:15 TD A.Node ΔT= 123s Par. = 109m U.Mag. = 0.2565 Gam. = 0.8743 P.Mag. = 1.2510	**Penumbral** **2096 May 07** Saros 113 11:25 TD D.Node ΔT= 123s Pen. = 217m U.Mag. = -0.5469 Gam. = 1.2897 P.Mag. = 0.5309	**Penumbral** **2096 Jun 06** Saros 151 02:44 TD D.Node ΔT= 123s Pen. = 21m U.Mag. = -1.0583 Gam. = -1.5724 P.Mag. = 0.0048
Penumbral **2096 Oct 31** Saros 118 11:30 TD A.Node ΔT= 124s Pen. = 219m U.Mag. = -0.2005 Gam. = -1.1308 P.Mag. = 0.7666	**Penumbral** **2096 Nov 29** Saros 156 21:22 TD A.Node ΔT= 124s Pen. = 78m U.Mag. = -0.8815 Gam. = 1.5018 P.Mag. = 0.0863	**Partial** **2097 Apr 26** Saros 123 12:18 TD D.Node ΔT= 124s Par. = 195m U.Mag. = 0.8420 Gam. = 0.5377 P.Mag. = 1.9013
Total **2097 Oct 21** Saros 128 01:31 TD A.Node ΔT= 125s Tot. = 15m Par. = 195m U.Mag. = 1.0097 Gam. = -0.4608 P.Mag. = 2.0152	**Total -** **2098 Apr 15** Saros 133 19:05 TD D.Node ΔT= 125s Tot. = 89m Par. = 216m U.Mag. = 1.4370 Gam. = -0.2272 P.Mag. = 2.4454	**Total** **2098 Oct 10** Saros 138 09:20 TD A.Node ΔT= 126s Tot. = 83m Par. = 221m U.Mag. = 1.3246 Gam. = 0.2749 P.Mag. = 2.3831

Plate 120

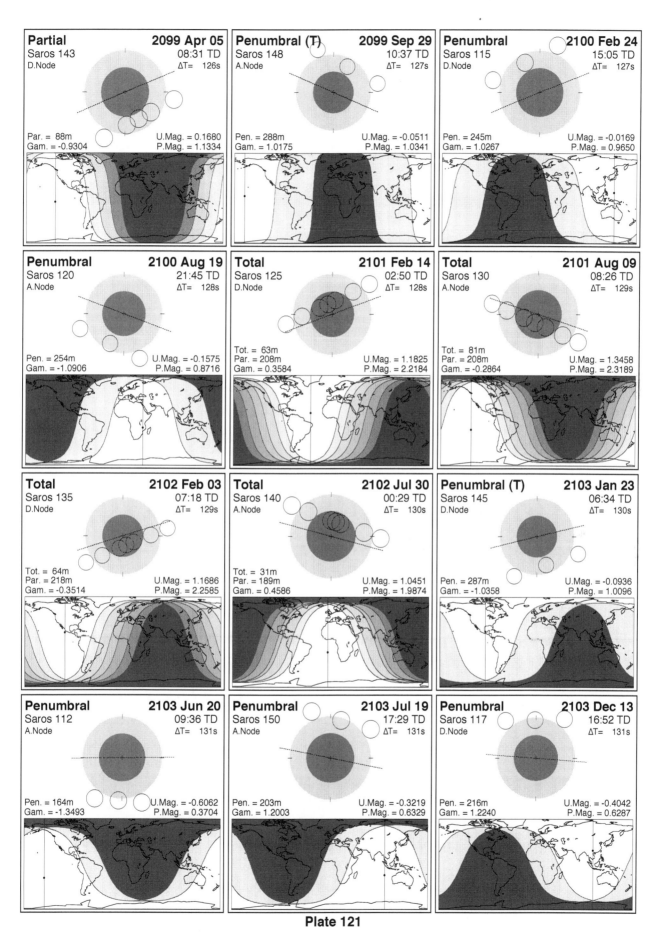

Partial   **2099 Apr 05**
Saros 143   08:31 TD
D.Node   ΔT= 126s
Par. = 88m   U.Mag. = 0.1680
Gam. = -0.9304   P.Mag. = 1.1334

Penumbral (T)   **2099 Sep 29**
Saros 148   10:37 TD
A.Node   ΔT= 127s
Pen. = 288m   U.Mag. = -0.0511
Gam. = 1.0175   P.Mag. = 1.0341

Penumbral   **2100 Feb 24**
Saros 115   15:05 TD
D.Node   ΔT= 127s
Pen. = 245m   U.Mag. = -0.0169
Gam. = 1.0267   P.Mag. = 0.9650

Penumbral   **2100 Aug 19**
Saros 120   21:45 TD
A.Node   ΔT= 128s
Pen. = 254m   U.Mag. = -0.1575
Gam. = -1.0906   P.Mag. = 0.8716

Total   **2101 Feb 14**
Saros 125   02:50 TD
D.Node   ΔT= 128s
Tot. = 63m
Par. = 208m   U.Mag. = 1.1825
Gam. = 0.3584   P.Mag. = 2.2184

Total   **2101 Aug 09**
Saros 130   08:26 TD
A.Node   ΔT= 129s
Tot. = 81m
Par. = 208m   U.Mag. = 1.3458
Gam. = -0.2864   P.Mag. = 2.3189

Total   **2102 Feb 03**
Saros 135   07:18 TD
D.Node   ΔT= 129s
Tot. = 64m
Par. = 218m   U.Mag. = 1.1686
Gam. = -0.3514   P.Mag. = 2.2585

Total   **2102 Jul 30**
Saros 140   00:29 TD
A.Node   ΔT= 130s
Tot. = 31m
Par. = 189m   U.Mag. = 1.0451
Gam. = 0.4586   P.Mag. = 1.9874

Penumbral (T)   **2103 Jan 23**
Saros 145   06:34 TD
D.Node   ΔT= 130s
Pen. = 287m   U.Mag. = -0.0936
Gam. = -1.0358   P.Mag. = 1.0096

Penumbral   **2103 Jun 20**
Saros 112   09:36 TD
A.Node   ΔT= 131s
Pen. = 164m   U.Mag. = -0.6062
Gam. = -1.3493   P.Mag. = 0.3704

Penumbral   **2103 Jul 19**
Saros 150   17:29 TD
A.Node   ΔT= 131s
Pen. = 203m   U.Mag. = -0.3219
Gam. = 1.2003   P.Mag. = 0.6329

Penumbral   **2103 Dec 13**
Saros 117   16:52 TD
D.Node   ΔT= 131s
Pen. = 216m   U.Mag. = -0.4042
Gam. = 1.2240   P.Mag. = 0.6287

Plate 121

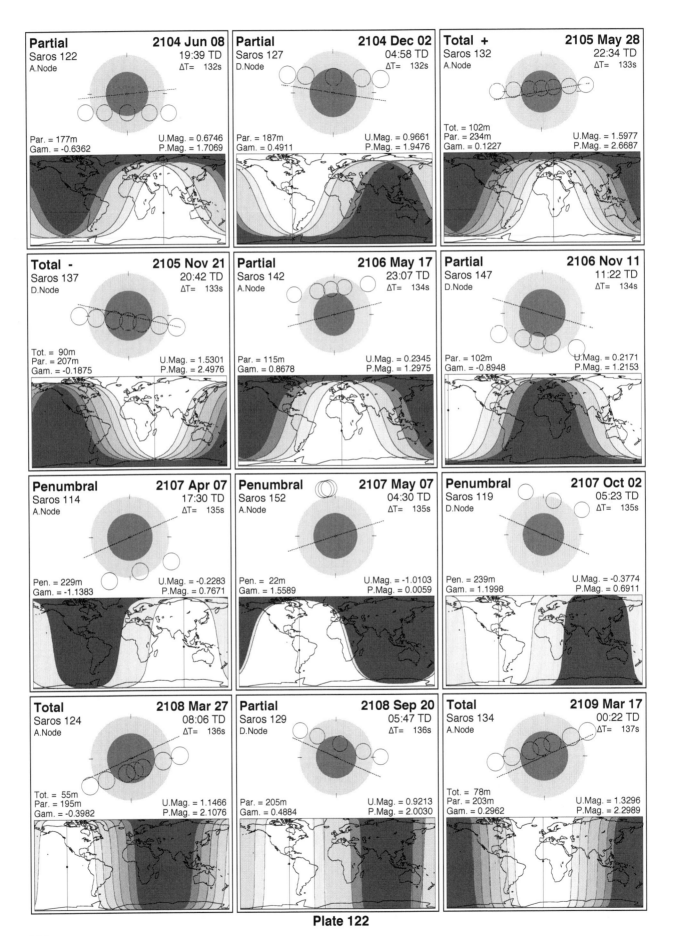

Partial — 2104 Jun 08
Saros 122 — 19:39 TD
A.Node — ΔT= 132s
Par. = 177m — U.Mag. = 0.6746
Gam. = -0.6362 — P.Mag. = 1.7069

Partial — 2104 Dec 02
Saros 127 — 04:58 TD
D.Node — ΔT= 132s
Par. = 187m — U.Mag. = 0.9661
Gam. = 0.4911 — P.Mag. = 1.9476

Total + — 2105 May 28
Saros 132 — 22:34 TD
A.Node — ΔT= 133s
Tot. = 102m
Par. = 234m — U.Mag. = 1.5977
Gam. = 0.1227 — P.Mag. = 2.6687

Total - — 2105 Nov 21
Saros 137 — 20:42 TD
D.Node — ΔT= 133s
Tot. = 90m
Par. = 207m — U.Mag. = 1.5301
Gam. = -0.1875 — P.Mag. = 2.4976

Partial — 2106 May 17
Saros 142 — 23:07 TD
A.Node — ΔT= 134s
Par. = 115m — U.Mag. = 0.2345
Gam. = 0.8678 — P.Mag. = 1.2975

Partial — 2106 Nov 11
Saros 147 — 11:22 TD
D.Node — ΔT= 134s
Par. = 102m — U.Mag. = 0.2171
Gam. = -0.8948 — P.Mag. = 1.2153

Penumbral — 2107 Apr 07
Saros 114 — 17:30 TD
A.Node — ΔT= 135s
Pen. = 229m — U.Mag. = -0.2283
Gam. = -1.1383 — P.Mag. = 0.7671

Penumbral — 2107 May 07
Saros 152 — 04:30 TD
A.Node — ΔT= 135s
Pen. = 22m — U.Mag. = -1.0103
Gam. = 1.5589 — P.Mag. = 0.0059

Penumbral — 2107 Oct 02
Saros 119 — 05:23 TD
D.Node — ΔT= 135s
Pen. = 239m — U.Mag. = -0.3774
Gam. = 1.1998 — P.Mag. = 0.6911

Total — 2108 Mar 27
Saros 124 — 08:06 TD
A.Node — ΔT= 136s
Tot. = 55m
Par. = 195m — U.Mag. = 1.1466
Gam. = -0.3982 — P.Mag. = 2.1076

Partial — 2108 Sep 20
Saros 129 — 05:47 TD
D.Node — ΔT= 136s
Par. = 205m — U.Mag. = 0.9213
Gam. = 0.4884 — P.Mag. = 2.0030

Total — 2109 Mar 17
Saros 134 — 00:22 TD
A.Node — ΔT= 137s
Tot. = 78m
Par. = 203m — U.Mag. = 1.3296
Gam. = 0.2962 — P.Mag. = 2.2989

Plate 122

218

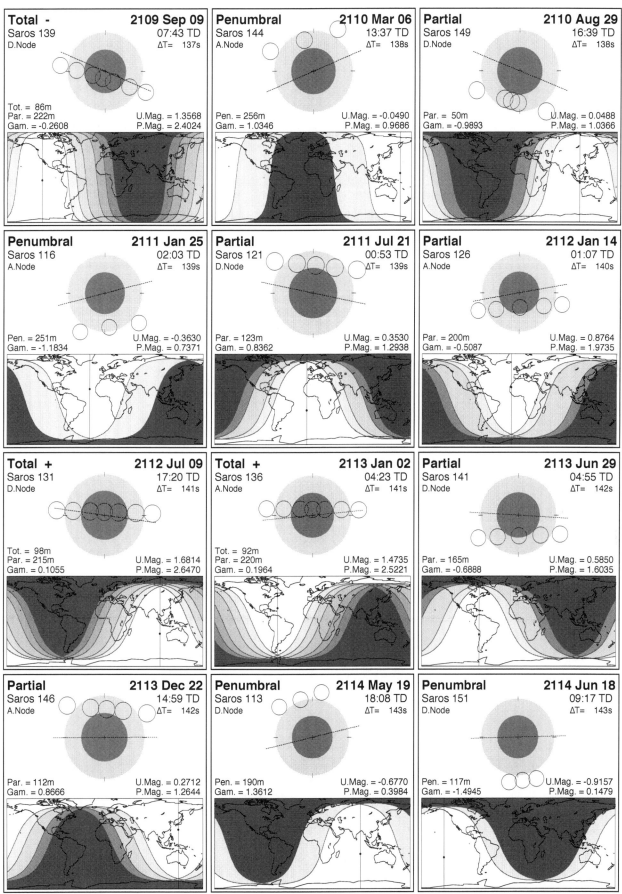

Total -   **2109 Sep 09**
Saros 139   07:43 TD
D.Node   ΔT= 137s

Tot. = 86m
Par. = 222m   U.Mag. = 1.3568
Gam. = -0.2608   P.Mag. = 2.4024

Penumbral   **2110 Mar 06**
Saros 144   13:37 TD
A.Node   ΔT= 138s

Pen. = 256m   U.Mag. = -0.0490
Gam. = 1.0346   P.Mag. = 0.9686

Partial   **2110 Aug 29**
Saros 149   16:39 TD
D.Node   ΔT= 138s

Par. = 50m   U.Mag. = 0.0488
Gam. = -0.9893   P.Mag. = 1.0366

Penumbral   **2111 Jan 25**
Saros 116   02:03 TD
A.Node   ΔT= 139s

Pen. = 251m   U.Mag. = -0.3630
Gam. = -1.1834   P.Mag. = 0.7371

Partial   **2111 Jul 21**
Saros 121   00:53 TD
D.Node   ΔT= 139s

Par. = 123m   U.Mag. = 0.3530
Gam. = 0.8362   P.Mag. = 1.2938

Partial   **2112 Jan 14**
Saros 126   01:07 TD
A.Node   ΔT= 140s

Par. = 200m   U.Mag. = 0.8764
Gam. = -0.5087   P.Mag. = 1.9735

Total +   **2112 Jul 09**
Saros 131   17:20 TD
D.Node   ΔT= 141s

Tot. = 98m
Par. = 215m   U.Mag. = 1.6814
Gam. = 0.1055   P.Mag. = 2.6470

Total +   **2113 Jan 02**
Saros 136   04:23 TD
A.Node   ΔT= 141s

Tot. = 92m
Par. = 220m   U.Mag. = 1.4735
Gam. = 0.1964   P.Mag. = 2.5221

Partial   **2113 Jun 29**
Saros 141   04:55 TD
D.Node   ΔT= 142s

Par. = 165m   U.Mag. = 0.5850
Gam. = -0.6888   P.Mag. = 1.6035

Partial   **2113 Dec 22**
Saros 146   14:59 TD
A.Node   ΔT= 142s

Par. = 112m   U.Mag. = 0.2712
Gam. = 0.8666   P.Mag. = 1.2644

Penumbral   **2114 May 19**
Saros 113   18:08 TD
D.Node   ΔT= 143s

Pen. = 190m   U.Mag. = -0.6770
Gam. = 1.3612   P.Mag. = 0.3984

Penumbral   **2114 Jun 18**
Saros 151   09:17 TD
D.Node   ΔT= 143s

Pen. = 117m   U.Mag. = -0.9157
Gam. = -1.4945   P.Mag. = 0.1479

Plate 123

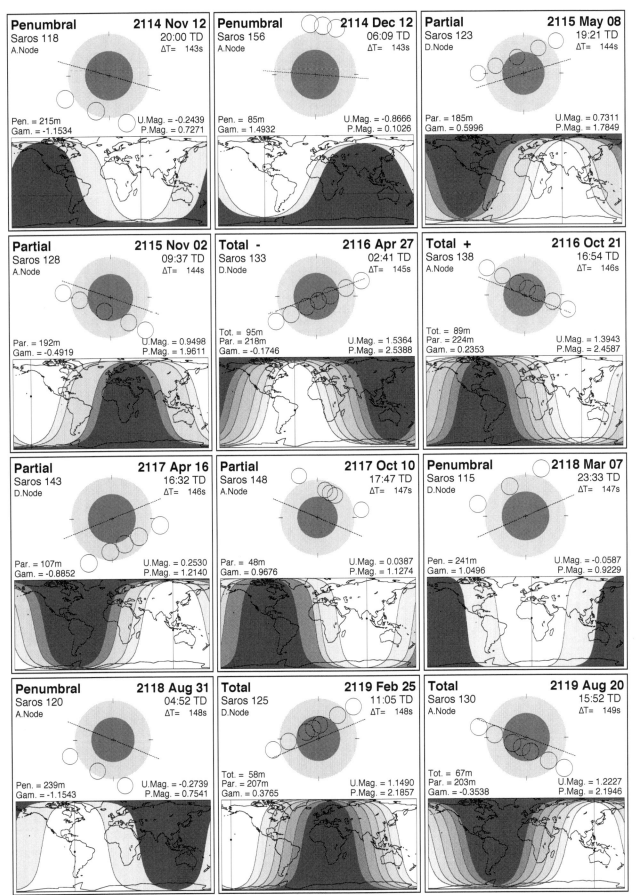

Penumbral	**2114 Nov 12**
Saros 118	20:00 TD
A.Node	ΔT= 143s
Pen. = 215m	U.Mag. = -0.2439
Gam. = -1.1534	P.Mag. = 0.7271

Penumbral	**2114 Dec 12**
Saros 156	06:09 TD
A.Node	ΔT= 143s
Pen. = 85m	U.Mag. = -0.8666
Gam. = 1.4932	P.Mag. = 0.1026

Partial	**2115 May 08**
Saros 123	19:21 TD
D.Node	ΔT= 144s
Par. = 185m	U.Mag. = 0.7311
Gam. = 0.5996	P.Mag. = 1.7849

Partial	**2115 Nov 02**
Saros 128	09:37 TD
A.Node	ΔT= 144s
Par. = 192m	U.Mag. = 0.9498
Gam. = -0.4919	P.Mag. = 1.9611

Total -	**2116 Apr 27**
Saros 133	02:41 TD
D.Node	ΔT= 145s
Tot. = 95m	
Par. = 218m	U.Mag. = 1.5364
Gam. = -0.1746	P.Mag. = 2.5388

Total +	**2116 Oct 21**
Saros 138	16:54 TD
A.Node	ΔT= 146s
Tot. = 89m	
Par. = 224m	U.Mag. = 1.3943
Gam. = 0.2353	P.Mag. = 2.4587

Partial	**2117 Apr 16**
Saros 143	16:32 TD
D.Node	ΔT= 146s
Par. = 107m	U.Mag. = 0.2530
Gam. = -0.8852	P.Mag. = 1.2140

Partial	**2117 Oct 10**
Saros 148	17:47 TD
A.Node	ΔT= 147s
Par. = 48m	U.Mag. = 0.0387
Gam. = 0.9676	P.Mag. = 1.1274

Penumbral	**2118 Mar 07**
Saros 115	23:33 TD
D.Node	ΔT= 147s
Pen. = 241m	U.Mag. = -0.0587
Gam. = 1.0496	P.Mag. = 0.9229

Penumbral	**2118 Aug 31**
Saros 120	04:52 TD
A.Node	ΔT= 148s
Pen. = 239m	U.Mag. = -0.2739
Gam. = -1.1543	P.Mag. = 0.7541

Total	**2119 Feb 25**
Saros 125	11:05 TD
D.Node	ΔT= 148s
Tot. = 58m	
Par. = 207m	U.Mag. = 1.1490
Gam. = 0.3765	P.Mag. = 2.1857

Total	**2119 Aug 20**
Saros 130	15:52 TD
A.Node	ΔT= 149s
Tot. = 67m	
Par. = 203m	U.Mag. = 1.2227
Gam. = -0.3538	P.Mag. = 2.1946

Plate 124

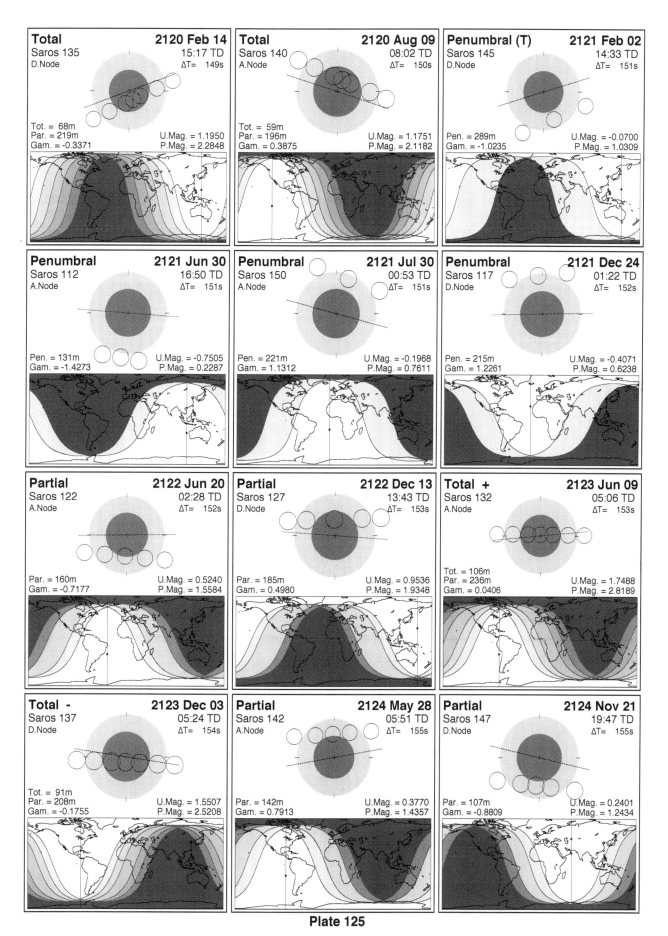

Total 2120 Feb 14	**Total** 2120 Aug 09	**Penumbral (T)** 2121 Feb 02
Saros 135 15:17 TD	Saros 140 08:02 TD	Saros 145 14:33 TD
D.Node ΔT= 149s	A.Node ΔT= 150s	D.Node ΔT= 151s
Tot. = 68m	Tot. = 59m	
Par. = 219m U.Mag. = 1.1950	Par. = 196m U.Mag. = 1.1751	Pen. = 289m U.Mag. = -0.0700
Gam. = -0.3371 P.Mag. = 2.2848	Gam. = 0.3875 P.Mag. = 2.1182	Gam. = -1.0235 P.Mag. = 1.0309
Penumbral 2121 Jun 30	**Penumbral** 2121 Jul 30	**Penumbral** 2121 Dec 24
Saros 112 16:50 TD	Saros 150 00:53 TD	Saros 117 01:22 TD
A.Node ΔT= 151s	A.Node ΔT= 151s	D.Node ΔT= 152s
Pen. = 131m U.Mag. = -0.7505	Pen. = 221m U.Mag. = -0.1968	Pen. = 215m U.Mag. = -0.4071
Gam. = -1.4273 P.Mag. = 0.2287	Gam. = 1.1312 P.Mag. = 0.7611	Gam. = 1.2261 P.Mag. = 0.6238
Partial 2122 Jun 20	**Partial** 2122 Dec 13	**Total +** 2123 Jun 09
Saros 122 02:28 TD	Saros 127 13:43 TD	Saros 132 05:06 TD
A.Node ΔT= 152s	D.Node ΔT= 153s	A.Node ΔT= 153s
		Tot. = 106m
Par. = 160m U.Mag. = 0.5240	Par. = 185m U.Mag. = 0.9536	Par. = 236m U.Mag. = 1.7488
Gam. = -0.7177 P.Mag. = 1.5584	Gam. = 0.4980 P.Mag. = 1.9348	Gam. = 0.0406 P.Mag. = 2.8189
Total - 2123 Dec 03	**Partial** 2124 May 28	**Partial** 2124 Nov 21
Saros 137 05:24 TD	Saros 142 05:51 TD	Saros 147 19:47 TD
D.Node ΔT= 154s	A.Node ΔT= 155s	D.Node ΔT= 155s
Tot. = 91m		
Par. = 208m U.Mag. = 1.5507	Par. = 142m U.Mag. = 0.3770	Par. = 107m U.Mag. = 0.2401
Gam. = -0.1755 P.Mag. = 2.5208	Gam. = 0.7913 P.Mag. = 1.4357	Gam. = -0.8809 P.Mag. = 1.2434

Plate 125

221

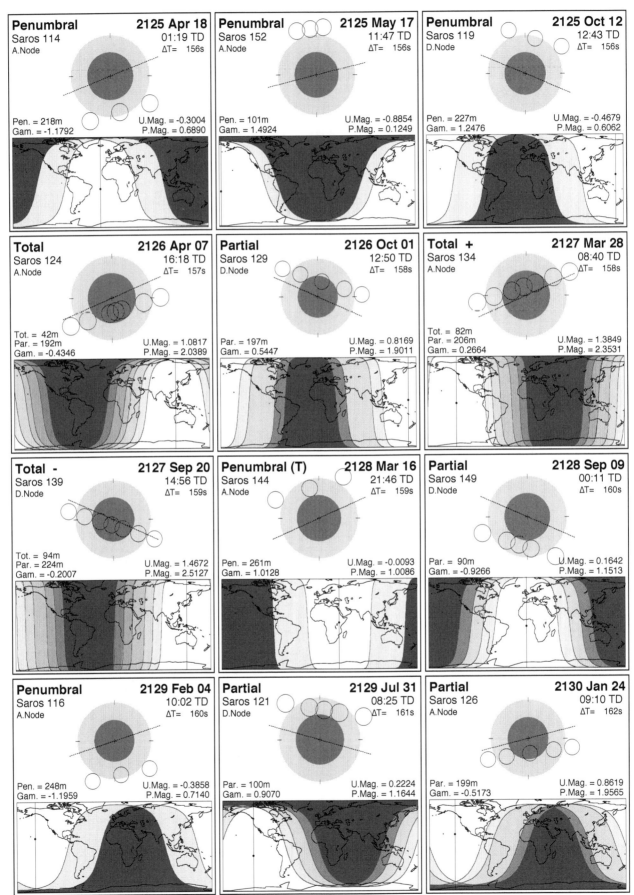

Penumbral   2125 Apr 18
Saros 114   01:19 TD
A.Node   ΔT= 156s
Pen. = 218m   U.Mag. = -0.3004
Gam. = -1.1792   P.Mag. = 0.6890

Penumbral   2125 May 17
Saros 152   11:47 TD
A.Node   ΔT= 156s
Pen. = 101m   U.Mag. = -0.8854
Gam. = 1.4924   P.Mag. = 0.1249

Penumbral   2125 Oct 12
Saros 119   12:43 TD
D.Node   ΔT= 156s
Pen. = 227m   U.Mag. = -0.4679
Gam. = 1.2476   P.Mag. = 0.6062

Total   2126 Apr 07
Saros 124   16:18 TD
A.Node   ΔT= 157s
Tot. = 42m
Par. = 192m   U.Mag. = 1.0817
Gam. = -0.4346   P.Mag. = 2.0389

Partial   2126 Oct 01
Saros 129   12:50 TD
D.Node   ΔT= 158s
Par. = 197m   U.Mag. = 0.8169
Gam. = 0.5447   P.Mag. = 1.9011

Total +   2127 Mar 28
Saros 134   08:40 TD
A.Node   ΔT= 158s
Tot. = 82m
Par. = 206m   U.Mag. = 1.3849
Gam. = 0.2664   P.Mag. = 2.3531

Total -   2127 Sep 20
Saros 139   14:56 TD
D.Node   ΔT= 159s
Tot. = 94m
Par. = 224m   U.Mag. = 1.4672
Gam. = -0.2007   P.Mag. = 2.5127

Penumbral (T)   2128 Mar 16
Saros 144   21:46 TD
A.Node   ΔT= 159s
Pen. = 261m   U.Mag. = -0.0093
Gam. = 1.0128   P.Mag. = 1.0086

Partial   2128 Sep 09
Saros 149   00:11 TD
D.Node   ΔT= 160s
Par. = 90m   U.Mag. = 0.1642
Gam. = -0.9266   P.Mag. = 1.1513

Penumbral   2129 Feb 04
Saros 116   10:02 TD
A.Node   ΔT= 160s
Pen. = 248m   U.Mag. = -0.3858
Gam. = -1.1959   P.Mag. = 0.7140

Partial   2129 Jul 31
Saros 121   08:25 TD
D.Node   ΔT= 161s
Par. = 100m   U.Mag. = 0.2224
Gam. = 0.9070   P.Mag. = 1.1644

Partial   2130 Jan 24
Saros 126   09:10 TD
A.Node   ΔT= 162s
Par. = 199m   U.Mag. = 0.8619
Gam. = -0.5173   P.Mag. = 1.9565

Plate 126

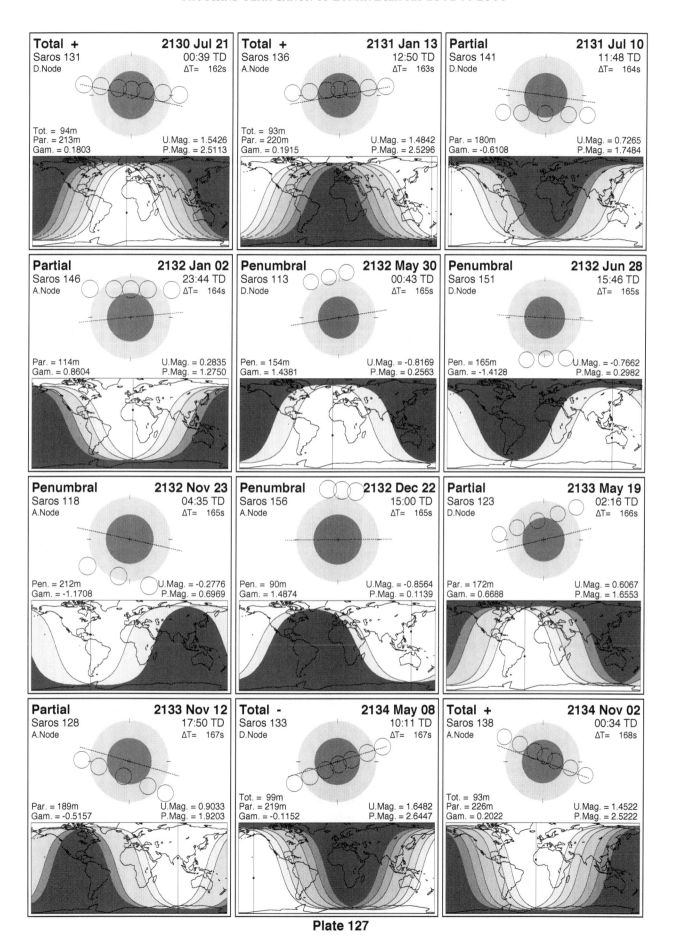

Total +   **2130 Jul 21**
Saros 131   00:39 TD
D.Node   ΔT= 162s
Tot. = 94m
Par. = 213m   U.Mag. = 1.5426
Gam. = 0.1803   P.Mag. = 2.5113

Total +   **2131 Jan 13**
Saros 136   12:50 TD
A.Node   ΔT= 163s
Tot. = 93m
Par. = 220m   U.Mag. = 1.4842
Gam. = 0.1915   P.Mag. = 2.5296

Partial   **2131 Jul 10**
Saros 141   11:48 TD
D.Node   ΔT= 164s
Par. = 180m   U.Mag. = 0.7265
Gam. = -0.6108   P.Mag. = 1.7484

Partial   **2132 Jan 02**
Saros 146   23:44 TD
A.Node   ΔT= 164s
Par. = 114m   U.Mag. = 0.2835
Gam. = 0.8604   P.Mag. = 1.2750

Penumbral   **2132 May 30**
Saros 113   00:43 TD
D.Node   ΔT= 165s
Pen. = 154m   U.Mag. = -0.8169
Gam. = 1.4381   P.Mag. = 0.2563

Penumbral   **2132 Jun 28**
Saros 151   15:46 TD
D.Node   ΔT= 165s
Pen. = 165m   U.Mag. = -0.7662
Gam. = -1.4128   P.Mag. = 0.2982

Penumbral   **2132 Nov 23**
Saros 118   04:35 TD
A.Node   ΔT= 165s
Pen. = 212m   U.Mag. = -0.2776
Gam. = -1.1708   P.Mag. = 0.6969

Penumbral   **2132 Dec 22**
Saros 156   15:00 TD
A.Node   ΔT= 165s
Pen. = 90m   U.Mag. = -0.8564
Gam. = 1.4874   P.Mag. = 0.1139

Partial   **2133 May 19**
Saros 123   02:16 TD
D.Node   ΔT= 166s
Par. = 172m   U.Mag. = 0.6067
Gam. = 0.6688   P.Mag. = 1.6553

Partial   **2133 Nov 12**
Saros 128   17:50 TD
A.Node   ΔT= 167s
Par. = 189m   U.Mag. = 0.9033
Gam. = -0.5157   P.Mag. = 1.9203

Total -   **2134 May 08**
Saros 133   10:11 TD
D.Node   ΔT= 167s
Tot. = 99m
Par. = 219m   U.Mag. = 1.6482
Gam. = -0.1152   P.Mag. = 2.6447

Total +   **2134 Nov 02**
Saros 138   00:34 TD
A.Node   ΔT= 168s
Tot. = 93m
Par. = 226m   U.Mag. = 1.4522
Gam. = 0.2022   P.Mag. = 2.5222

Plate 127

223

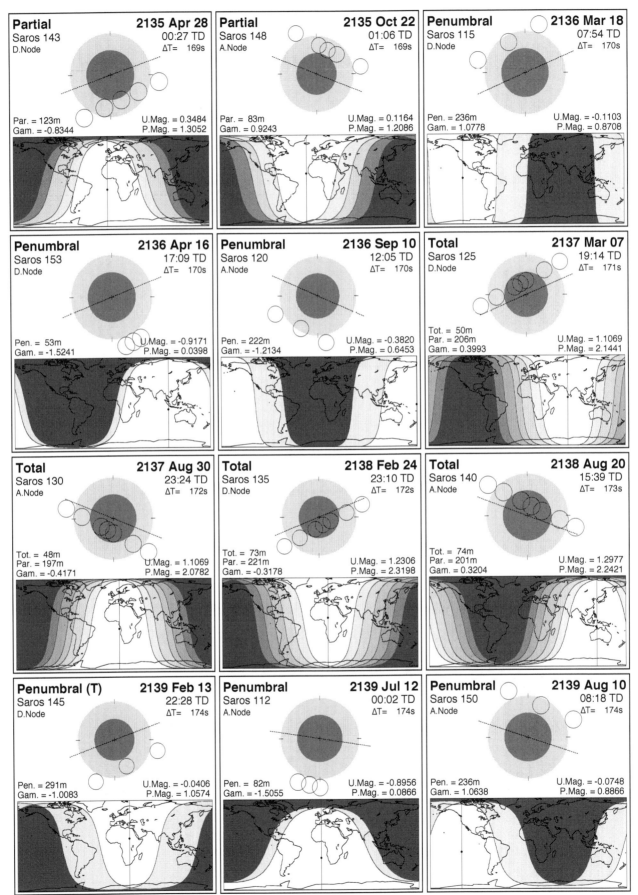

Partial   **2135 Apr 28**
Saros 143   00:27 TD
D.Node   ΔT= 169s
Par. = 123m   U.Mag. = 0.3484
Gam. = -0.8344   P.Mag. = 1.3052

Partial   **2135 Oct 22**
Saros 148   01:06 TD
A.Node   ΔT= 169s
Par. = 83m   U.Mag. = 0.1164
Gam. = 0.9243   P.Mag. = 1.2086

Penumbral   **2136 Mar 18**
Saros 115   07:54 TD
D.Node   ΔT= 170s
Pen. = 236m   U.Mag. = -0.1103
Gam. = 1.0778   P.Mag. = 0.8708

Penumbral   **2136 Apr 16**
Saros 153   17:09 TD
D.Node   ΔT= 170s
Pen. = 53m   U.Mag. = -0.9171
Gam. = -1.5241   P.Mag. = 0.0398

Penumbral   **2136 Sep 10**
Saros 120   12:05 TD
A.Node   ΔT= 170s
Pen. = 222m   U.Mag. = -0.3820
Gam. = -1.2134   P.Mag. = 0.6453

Total   **2137 Mar 07**
Saros 125   19:14 TD
D.Node   ΔT= 171s
Tot. = 50m
Par. = 206m   U.Mag. = 1.1069
Gam. = 0.3993   P.Mag. = 2.1441

Total   **2137 Aug 30**
Saros 130   23:24 TD
A.Node   ΔT= 172s
Tot. = 48m
Par. = 197m   U.Mag. = 1.1069
Gam. = -0.4171   P.Mag. = 2.0782

Total   **2138 Feb 24**
Saros 135   23:10 TD
D.Node   ΔT= 172s
Tot. = 73m
Par. = 221m   U.Mag. = 1.2306
Gam. = -0.3178   P.Mag. = 2.3198

Total   **2138 Aug 20**
Saros 140   15:39 TD
A.Node   ΔT= 173s
Tot. = 74m
Par. = 201m   U.Mag. = 1.2977
Gam. = 0.3204   P.Mag. = 2.2421

Penumbral (T)   **2139 Feb 13**
Saros 145   22:28 TD
D.Node   ΔT= 174s
Pen. = 291m   U.Mag. = -0.0406
Gam. = -1.0083   P.Mag. = 1.0574

Penumbral   **2139 Jul 12**
Saros 112   00:02 TD
A.Node   ΔT= 174s
Pen. = 82m   U.Mag. = -0.8956
Gam. = -1.5055   P.Mag. = 0.0866

Penumbral   **2139 Aug 10**
Saros 150   08:18 TD
A.Node   ΔT= 174s
Pen. = 236m   U.Mag. = -0.0748
Gam. = 1.0638   P.Mag. = 0.8866

Plate 128

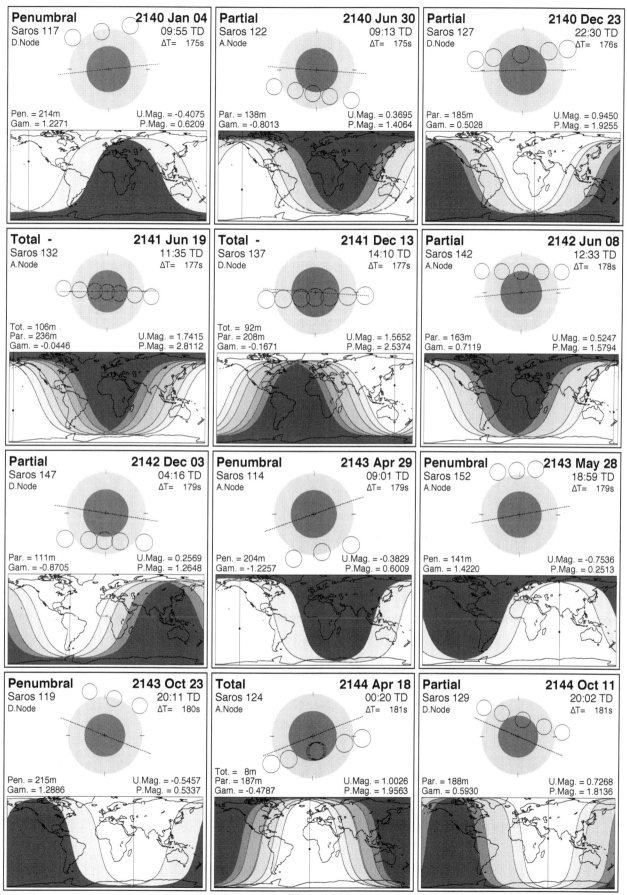

Penumbral   **2140 Jan 04**
Saros 117   09:55 TD
D.Node   ΔT= 175s

Pen. = 214m   U.Mag. = -0.4075
Gam. = 1.2271   P.Mag. = 0.6209

Partial   **2140 Jun 30**
Saros 122   09:13 TD
A.Node   ΔT= 175s

Par. = 138m   U.Mag. = 0.3695
Gam. = -0.8013   P.Mag. = 1.4064

Partial   **2140 Dec 23**
Saros 127   22:30 TD
D.Node   ΔT= 176s

Par. = 185m   U.Mag. = 0.9450
Gam. = 0.5028   P.Mag. = 1.9255

Total -   **2141 Jun 19**
Saros 132   11:35 TD
A.Node   ΔT= 177s

Tot. = 106m
Par. = 236m   U.Mag. = 1.7415
Gam. = -0.0446   P.Mag. = 2.8112

Total -   **2141 Dec 13**
Saros 137   14:10 TD
D.Node   ΔT= 177s

Tot. = 92m
Par. = 208m   U.Mag. = 1.5652
Gam. = -0.1671   P.Mag. = 2.5374

Partial   **2142 Jun 08**
Saros 142   12:33 TD
A.Node   ΔT= 178s

Par. = 163m   U.Mag. = 0.5247
Gam. = 0.7119   P.Mag. = 1.5794

Partial   **2142 Dec 03**
Saros 147   04:16 TD
D.Node   ΔT= 179s

Par. = 111m   U.Mag. = 0.2569
Gam. = -0.8705   P.Mag. = 1.2648

Penumbral   **2143 Apr 29**
Saros 114   09:01 TD
A.Node   ΔT= 179s

Pen. = 204m   U.Mag. = -0.3829
Gam. = -1.2257   P.Mag. = 0.6009

Penumbral   **2143 May 28**
Saros 152   18:59 TD
A.Node   ΔT= 179s

Pen. = 141m   U.Mag. = -0.7536
Gam. = 1.4220   P.Mag. = 0.2513

Penumbral   **2143 Oct 23**
Saros 119   20:11 TD
D.Node   ΔT= 180s

Pen. = 215m   U.Mag. = -0.5457
Gam. = 1.2886   P.Mag. = 0.5337

Total   **2144 Apr 18**
Saros 124   00:20 TD
A.Node   ΔT= 181s

Tot. = 8m
Par. = 187m   U.Mag. = 1.0026
Gam. = -0.4787   P.Mag. = 1.9563

Partial   **2144 Oct 11**
Saros 129   20:02 TD
D.Node   ΔT= 181s

Par. = 188m   U.Mag. = 0.7268
Gam. = 0.5930   P.Mag. = 1.8136

Plate 129

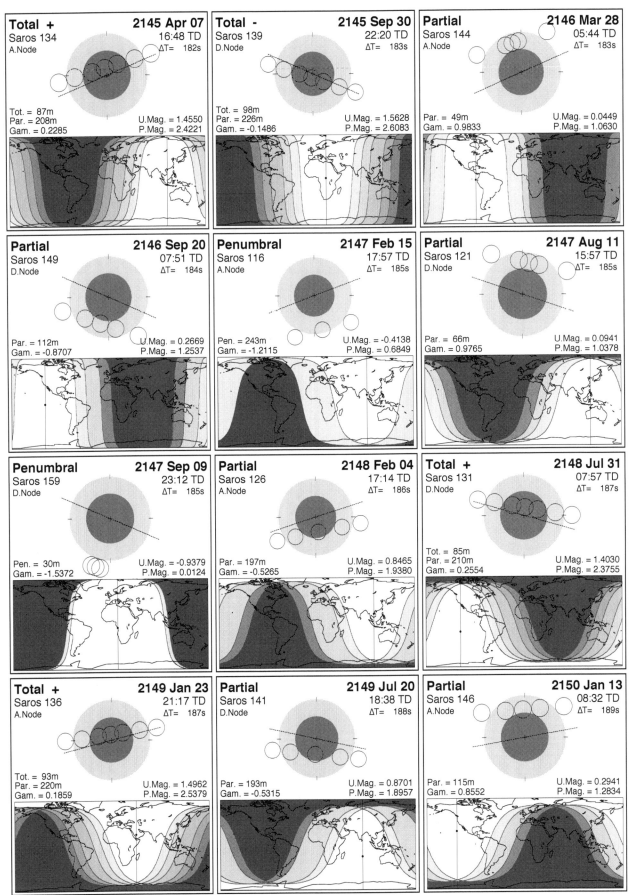

Total +   **2145 Apr 07**
Saros 134   16:48 TD
A.Node   ΔT= 182s
Tot. = 87m
Par. = 208m
Gam. = 0.2285   U.Mag. = 1.4550
     P.Mag. = 2.4221

Total -   **2145 Sep 30**
Saros 139   22:20 TD
D.Node   ΔT= 183s
Tot. = 98m
Par. = 226m
Gam. = -0.1486   U.Mag. = 1.5628
     P.Mag. = 2.6083

Partial   **2146 Mar 28**
Saros 144   05:44 TD
A.Node   ΔT= 183s
Par. = 49m
Gam. = 0.9833   U.Mag. = 0.0449
     P.Mag. = 1.0630

Partial   **2146 Sep 20**
Saros 149   07:51 TD
D.Node   ΔT= 184s
Par. = 112m
Gam. = -0.8707   U.Mag. = 0.2669
     P.Mag. = 1.2537

Penumbral   **2147 Feb 15**
Saros 116   17:57 TD
A.Node   ΔT= 185s
Pen. = 243m
Gam. = -1.2115   U.Mag. = -0.4138
     P.Mag. = 0.6849

Partial   **2147 Aug 11**
Saros 121   15:57 TD
D.Node   ΔT= 185s
Par. = 66m
Gam. = 0.9765   U.Mag. = 0.0941
     P.Mag. = 1.0378

Penumbral   **2147 Sep 09**
Saros 159   23:12 TD
D.Node   ΔT= 185s
Pen. = 30m
Gam. = -1.5372   U.Mag. = -0.9379
     P.Mag. = 0.0124

Partial   **2148 Feb 04**
Saros 126   17:14 TD
A.Node   ΔT= 186s
Par. = 197m
Gam. = -0.5265   U.Mag. = 0.8465
     P.Mag. = 1.9380

Total +   **2148 Jul 31**
Saros 131   07:57 TD
D.Node   ΔT= 187s
Tot. = 85m
Par. = 210m
Gam. = 0.2554   U.Mag. = 1.4030
     P.Mag. = 2.3755

Total +   **2149 Jan 23**
Saros 136   21:17 TD
A.Node   ΔT= 187s
Tot. = 93m
Par. = 220m
Gam. = 0.1859   U.Mag. = 1.4962
     P.Mag. = 2.5379

Partial   **2149 Jul 20**
Saros 141   18:38 TD
D.Node   ΔT= 188s
Par. = 193m
Gam. = -0.5315   U.Mag. = 0.8701
     P.Mag. = 1.8957

Partial   **2150 Jan 13**
Saros 146   08:32 TD
A.Node   ΔT= 189s
Par. = 115m
Gam. = 0.8552   U.Mag. = 0.2941
     P.Mag. = 1.2834

Plate 130

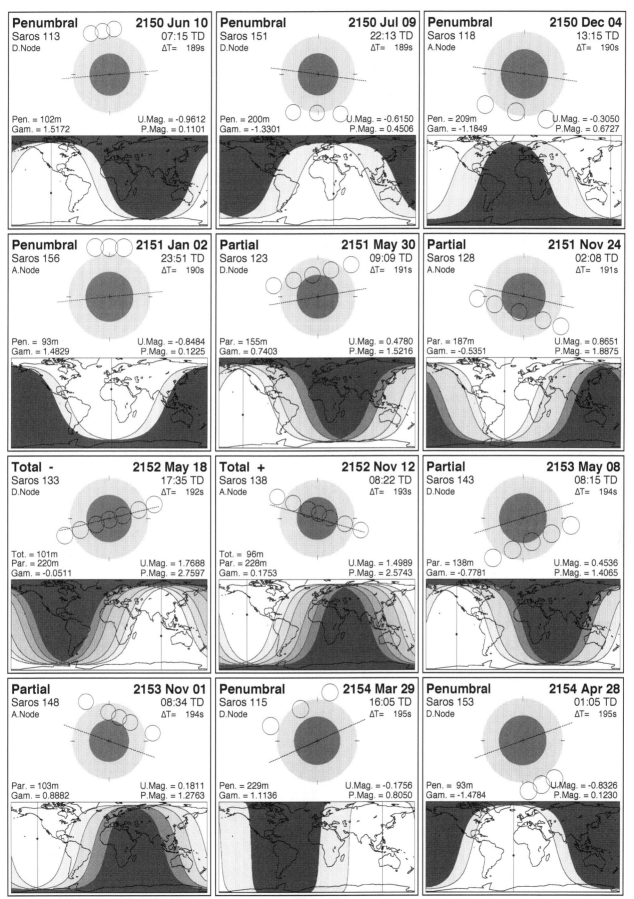

Penumbral	2150 Jun 10
Saros 113	07:15 TD
D.Node	ΔT= 189s
Pen. = 102m	U.Mag. = -0.9612
Gam. = 1.5172	P.Mag. = 0.1101

Penumbral	2150 Jul 09
Saros 151	22:13 TD
D.Node	ΔT= 189s
Pen. = 200m	U.Mag. = -0.6150
Gam. = -1.3301	P.Mag. = 0.4506

Penumbral	2150 Dec 04
Saros 118	13:15 TD
A.Node	ΔT= 190s
Pen. = 209m	U.Mag. = -0.3050
Gam. = -1.1849	P.Mag. = 0.6727

Penumbral	2151 Jan 02
Saros 156	23:51 TD
A.Node	ΔT= 190s
Pen. = 93m	U.Mag. = -0.8484
Gam. = 1.4829	P.Mag. = 0.1225

Partial	2151 May 30
Saros 123	09:09 TD
D.Node	ΔT= 191s
Par. = 155m	U.Mag. = 0.4780
Gam. = 0.7403	P.Mag. = 1.5216

Partial	2151 Nov 24
Saros 128	02:08 TD
A.Node	ΔT= 191s
Par. = 187m	U.Mag. = 0.8651
Gam. = -0.5351	P.Mag. = 1.8875

Total -	2152 May 18
Saros 133	17:35 TD
D.Node	ΔT= 192s
Tot. = 101m	
Par. = 220m	U.Mag. = 1.7688
Gam. = -0.0511	P.Mag. = 2.7597

Total +	2152 Nov 12
Saros 138	08:22 TD
A.Node	ΔT= 193s
Tot. = 96m	
Par. = 228m	U.Mag. = 1.4989
Gam. = 0.1753	P.Mag. = 2.5743

Partial	2153 May 08
Saros 143	08:15 TD
D.Node	ΔT= 194s
Par. = 138m	U.Mag. = 0.4536
Gam. = -0.7781	P.Mag. = 1.4065

Partial	2153 Nov 01
Saros 148	08:34 TD
A.Node	ΔT= 194s
Par. = 103m	U.Mag. = 0.1811
Gam. = 0.8882	P.Mag. = 1.2763

Penumbral	2154 Mar 29
Saros 115	16:05 TD
D.Node	ΔT= 195s
Pen. = 229m	U.Mag. = -0.1756
Gam. = 1.1136	P.Mag. = 0.8050

Penumbral	2154 Apr 28
Saros 153	01:05 TD
D.Node	ΔT= 195s
Pen. = 93m	U.Mag. = -0.8326
Gam. = -1.4784	P.Mag. = 0.1230

Plate 131

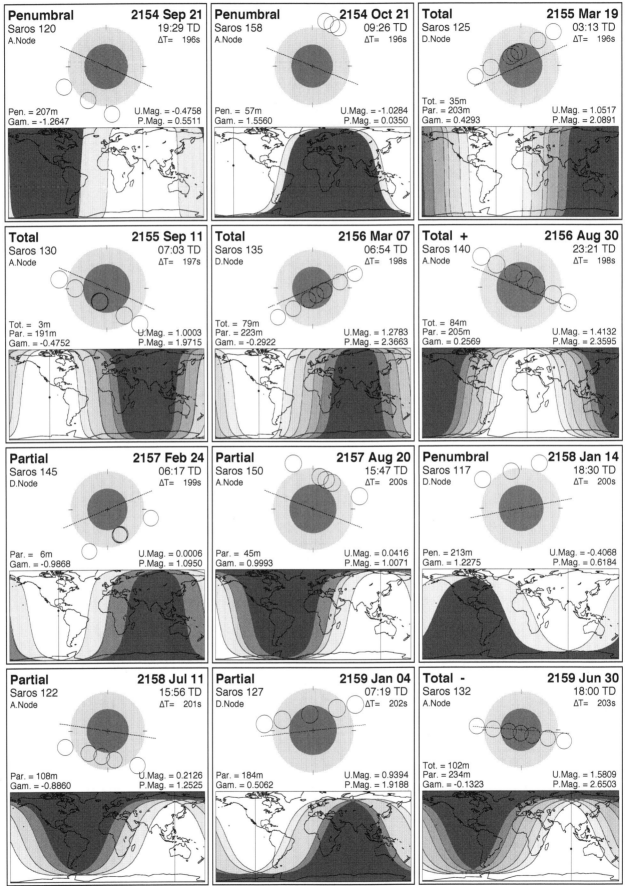

Penumbral   **2154 Sep 21**
Saros 120   19:29 TD
A.Node   ΔT= 196s
Pen. = 207m   U.Mag. = -0.4758
Gam. = -1.2647   P.Mag. = 0.5511

Penumbral   **2154 Oct 21**
Saros 158   09:26 TD
A.Node   ΔT= 196s
Pen. = 57m   U.Mag. = -1.0284
Gam. = 1.5560   P.Mag. = 0.0350

Total   **2155 Mar 19**
Saros 125   03:13 TD
D.Node   ΔT= 196s
Tot. = 35m   U.Mag. = 1.0517
Par. = 203m
Gam. = 0.4293   P.Mag. = 2.0891

Total   **2155 Sep 11**
Saros 130   07:03 TD
A.Node   ΔT= 197s
Tot. = 3m   U.Mag. = 1.0003
Par. = 191m
Gam. = -0.4752   P.Mag. = 1.9715

Total   **2156 Mar 07**
Saros 135   06:54 TD
D.Node   ΔT= 198s
Tot. = 79m   U.Mag. = 1.2783
Par. = 223m
Gam. = -0.2922   P.Mag. = 2.3663

Total +   **2156 Aug 30**
Saros 140   23:21 TD
A.Node   ΔT= 198s
Tot. = 84m   U.Mag. = 1.4132
Par. = 205m
Gam. = 0.2569   P.Mag. = 2.3595

Partial   **2157 Feb 24**
Saros 145   06:17 TD
D.Node   ΔT= 199s
Par. = 6m   U.Mag. = 0.0006
Gam. = -0.9868   P.Mag. = 1.0950

Partial   **2157 Aug 20**
Saros 150   15:47 TD
A.Node   ΔT= 200s
Par. = 45m   U.Mag. = 0.0416
Gam. = 0.9993   P.Mag. = 1.0071

Penumbral   **2158 Jan 14**
Saros 117   18:30 TD
D.Node   ΔT= 200s
Pen. = 213m   U.Mag. = -0.4068
Gam. = 1.2275   P.Mag. = 0.6184

Partial   **2158 Jul 11**
Saros 122   15:56 TD
A.Node   ΔT= 201s
Par. = 108m   U.Mag. = 0.2126
Gam. = -0.8860   P.Mag. = 1.2525

Partial   **2159 Jan 04**
Saros 127   07:19 TD
D.Node   ΔT= 202s
Par. = 184m   U.Mag. = 0.9394
Gam. = 0.5062   P.Mag. = 1.9188

Total -   **2159 Jun 30**
Saros 132   18:00 TD
A.Node   ΔT= 203s
Tot. = 102m   U.Mag. = 1.5809
Par. = 234m
Gam. = -0.1323   P.Mag. = 2.6503

Plate 132

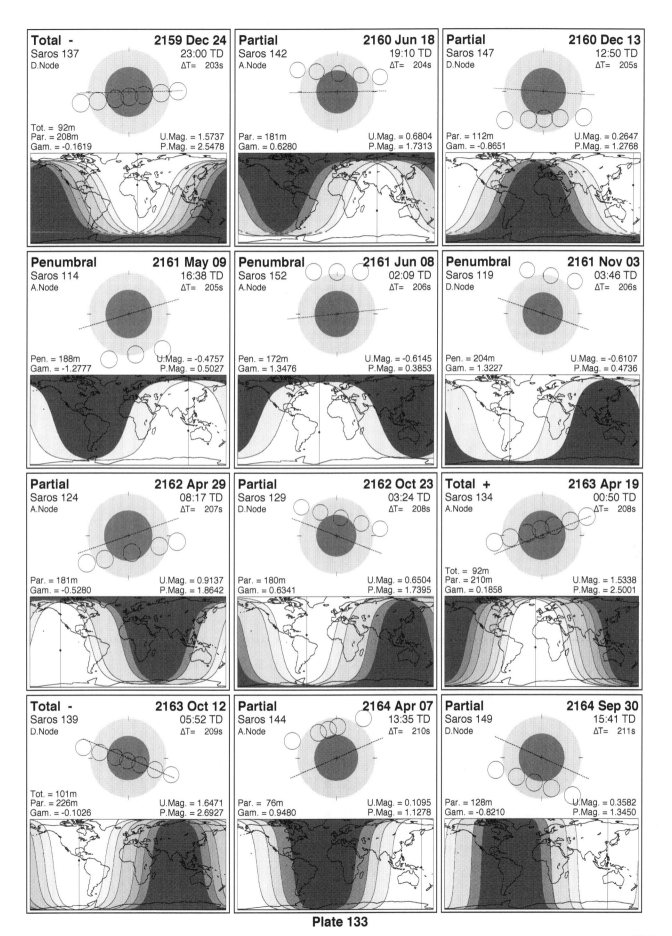

Total − **2159 Dec 24**	**Partial** **2160 Jun 18**	**Partial** **2160 Dec 13**
Saros 137 23:00 TD	Saros 142 19:10 TD	Saros 147 12:50 TD
D.Node ΔT= 203s	A.Node ΔT= 204s	D.Node ΔT= 205s
Tot. = 92m		
Par. = 208m U.Mag. = 1.5737	Par. = 181m U.Mag. = 0.6804	Par. = 112m U.Mag. = 0.2647
Gam. = −0.1619 P.Mag. = 2.5478	Gam. = 0.6280 P.Mag. = 1.7313	Gam. = −0.8651 P.Mag. = 1.2768
Penumbral **2161 May 09**	**Penumbral** **2161 Jun 08**	**Penumbral** **2161 Nov 03**
Saros 114 16:38 TD	Saros 152 02:09 TD	Saros 119 03:46 TD
A.Node ΔT= 205s	A.Node ΔT= 206s	D.Node ΔT= 206s
Pen. = 188m U.Mag. = −0.4757	Pen. = 172m U.Mag. = −0.6145	Pen. = 204m U.Mag. = −0.6107
Gam. = −1.2777 P.Mag. = 0.5027	Gam. = 1.3476 P.Mag. = 0.3853	Gam. = 1.3227 P.Mag. = 0.4736
Partial **2162 Apr 29**	**Partial** **2162 Oct 23**	**Total +** **2163 Apr 19**
Saros 124 08:17 TD	Saros 129 03:24 TD	Saros 134 00:50 TD
A.Node ΔT= 207s	D.Node ΔT= 208s	A.Node ΔT= 208s
		Tot. = 92m
Par. = 181m U.Mag. = 0.9137	Par. = 180m U.Mag. = 0.6504	Par. = 210m U.Mag. = 1.5338
Gam. = −0.5280 P.Mag. = 1.8642	Gam. = 0.6341 P.Mag. = 1.7395	Gam. = 0.1858 P.Mag. = 2.5001
Total − **2163 Oct 12**	**Partial** **2164 Apr 07**	**Partial** **2164 Sep 30**
Saros 139 05:52 TD	Saros 144 13:35 TD	Saros 149 15:41 TD
D.Node ΔT= 209s	A.Node ΔT= 210s	D.Node ΔT= 211s
Tot. = 101m		
Par. = 226m U.Mag. = 1.6471	Par. = 76m U.Mag. = 0.1095	Par. = 128m U.Mag. = 0.3582
Gam. = −0.1026 P.Mag. = 2.6927	Gam. = 0.9480 P.Mag. = 1.1278	Gam. = −0.8210 P.Mag. = 1.3450

Plate 133

229

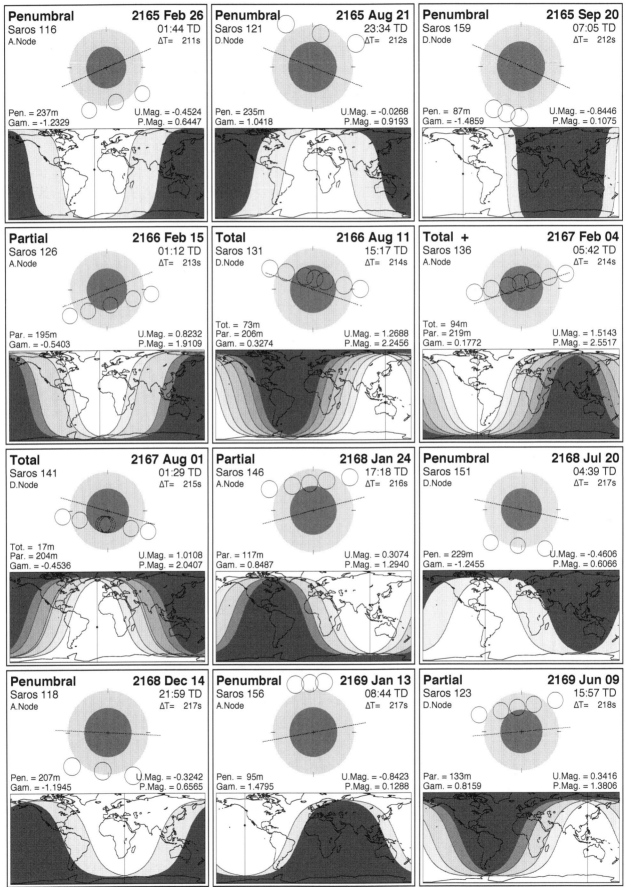

Penumbral   **2165 Feb 26**
Saros 116   01:44 TD
A.Node   ΔT= 211s
Pen. = 237m   U.Mag. = -0.4524
Gam. = -1.2329   P.Mag. = 0.6447

Penumbral   **2165 Aug 21**
Saros 121   23:34 TD
D.Node   ΔT= 212s
Pen. = 235m   U.Mag. = -0.0268
Gam. = 1.0418   P.Mag. = 0.9193

Penumbral   **2165 Sep 20**
Saros 159   07:05 TD
D.Node   ΔT= 212s
Pen. = 87m   U.Mag. = -0.8446
Gam. = -1.4859   P.Mag. = 0.1075

Partial   **2166 Feb 15**
Saros 126   01:12 TD
A.Node   ΔT= 213s
Par. = 195m   U.Mag. = 0.8232
Gam. = -0.5403   P.Mag. = 1.9109

Total   **2166 Aug 11**
Saros 131   15:17 TD
D.Node   ΔT= 214s
Tot. = 73m
Par. = 206m   U.Mag. = 1.2688
Gam. = 0.3274   P.Mag. = 2.2456

Total +   **2167 Feb 04**
Saros 136   05:42 TD
A.Node   ΔT= 214s
Tot. = 94m
Par. = 219m   U.Mag. = 1.5143
Gam. = 0.1772   P.Mag. = 2.5517

Total   **2167 Aug 01**
Saros 141   01:29 TD
D.Node   ΔT= 215s
Tot. = 17m
Par. = 204m   U.Mag. = 1.0108
Gam. = -0.4536   P.Mag. = 2.0407

Partial   **2168 Jan 24**
Saros 146   17:18 TD
A.Node   ΔT= 216s
Par. = 117m   U.Mag. = 0.3074
Gam. = 0.8487   P.Mag. = 1.2940

Penumbral   **2168 Jul 20**
Saros 151   04:39 TD
D.Node   ΔT= 217s
Pen. = 229m   U.Mag. = -0.4606
Gam. = -1.2455   P.Mag. = 0.6066

Penumbral   **2168 Dec 14**
Saros 118   21:59 TD
A.Node   ΔT= 217s
Pen. = 207m   U.Mag. = -0.3242
Gam. = -1.1945   P.Mag. = 0.6565

Penumbral   **2169 Jan 13**
Saros 156   08:44 TD
A.Node   ΔT= 217s
Pen. = 95m   U.Mag. = -0.8423
Gam. = 1.4795   P.Mag. = 0.1288

Partial   **2169 Jun 09**
Saros 123   15:57 TD
D.Node   ΔT= 218s
Par. = 133m   U.Mag. = 0.3416
Gam. = 0.8159   P.Mag. = 1.3806

Plate 134

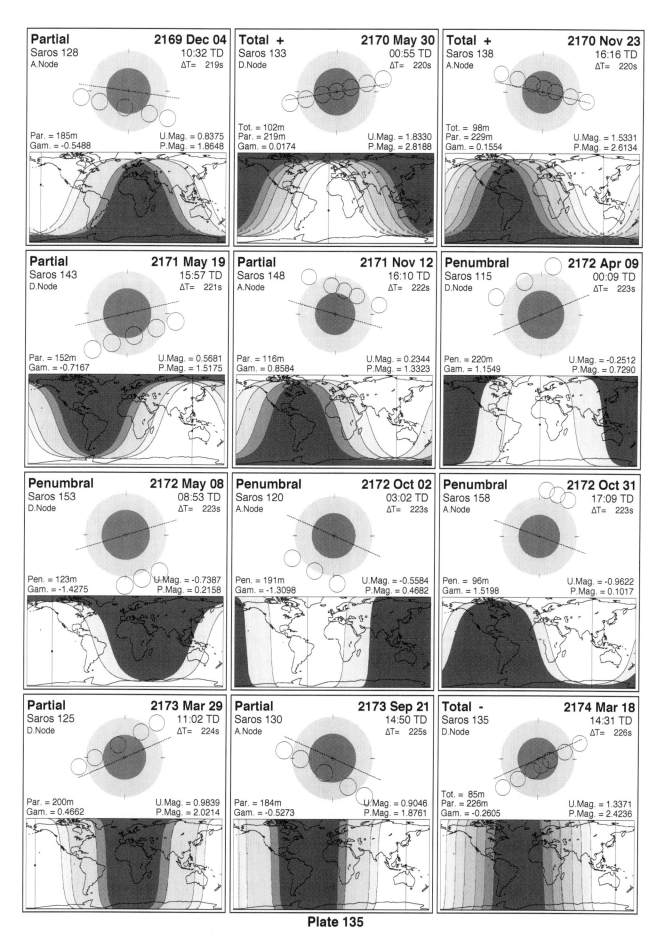

Partial   **2169 Dec 04**
Saros 128   10:32 TD
A.Node   ΔT= 219s
Par. = 185m   U.Mag. = 0.8375
Gam. = -0.5488   P.Mag. = 1.8648

Total +   **2170 May 30**
Saros 133   00:55 TD
D.Node   ΔT= 220s
Tot. = 102m
Par. = 219m   U.Mag. = 1.8330
Gam. = 0.0174   P.Mag. = 2.8188

Total +   **2170 Nov 23**
Saros 138   16:16 TD
A.Node   ΔT= 220s
Tot. = 98m
Par. = 229m   U.Mag. = 1.5331
Gam. = 0.1554   P.Mag. = 2.6134

Partial   **2171 May 19**
Saros 143   15:57 TD
D.Node   ΔT= 221s
Par. = 152m   U.Mag. = 0.5681
Gam. = -0.7167   P.Mag. = 1.5175

Partial   **2171 Nov 12**
Saros 148   16:10 TD
A.Node   ΔT= 222s
Par. = 116m   U.Mag. = 0.2344
Gam. = 0.8584   P.Mag. = 1.3323

Penumbral   **2172 Apr 09**
Saros 115   00:09 TD
D.Node   ΔT= 223s
Pen. = 220m   U.Mag. = -0.2512
Gam. = 1.1549   P.Mag. = 0.7290

Penumbral   **2172 May 08**
Saros 153   08:53 TD
D.Node   ΔT= 223s
Pen. = 123m   U.Mag. = -0.7387
Gam. = -1.4275   P.Mag. = 0.2158

Penumbral   **2172 Oct 02**
Saros 120   03:02 TD
A.Node   ΔT= 223s
Pen. = 191m   U.Mag. = -0.5584
Gam. = -1.3098   P.Mag. = 0.4682

Penumbral   **2172 Oct 31**
Saros 158   17:09 TD
A.Node   ΔT= 223s
Pen. = 96m   U.Mag. = -0.9622
Gam. = 1.5198   P.Mag. = 0.1017

Partial   **2173 Mar 29**
Saros 125   11:02 TD
D.Node   ΔT= 224s
Par. = 200m   U.Mag. = 0.9839
Gam. = 0.4662   P.Mag. = 2.0214

Partial   **2173 Sep 21**
Saros 130   14:50 TD
A.Node   ΔT= 225s
Par. = 184m   U.Mag. = 0.9046
Gam. = -0.5273   P.Mag. = 1.8761

Total -   **2174 Mar 18**
Saros 135   14:31 TD
D.Node   ΔT= 226s
Tot. = 85m
Par. = 226m   U.Mag. = 1.3371
Gam. = -0.2605   P.Mag. = 2.4236

Plate 135

231

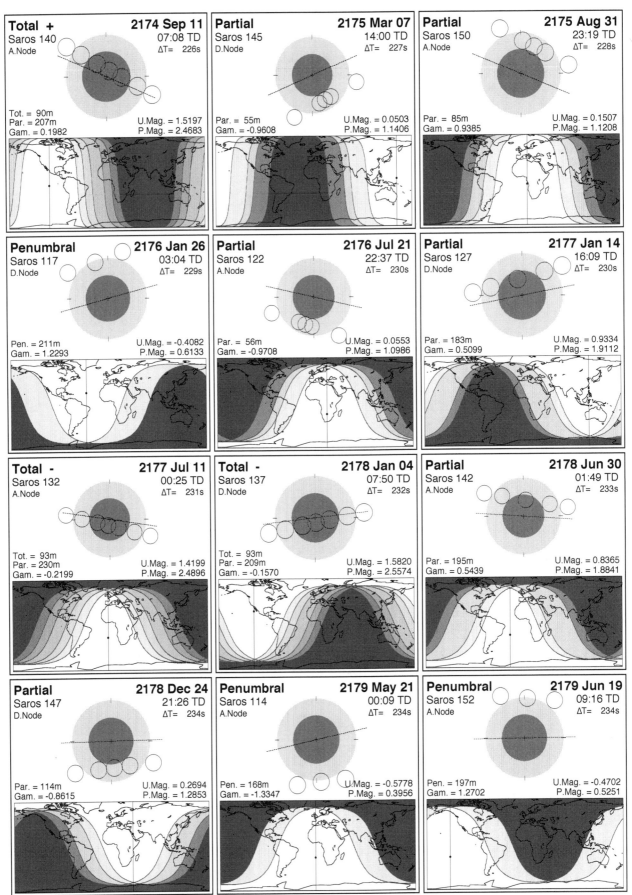

Total +   **2174 Sep 11**
Saros 140   07:08 TD
A.Node   ΔT= 226s
Tot. = 90m
Par. = 207m   U.Mag. = 1.5197
Gam. = 0.1982   P.Mag. = 2.4683

Partial   **2175 Mar 07**
Saros 145   14:00 TD
D.Node   ΔT= 227s
Par. = 55m   U.Mag. = 0.0503
Gam. = -0.9608   P.Mag. = 1.1406

Partial   **2175 Aug 31**
Saros 150   23:19 TD
A.Node   ΔT= 228s
Par. = 85m   U.Mag. = 0.1507
Gam. = 0.9385   P.Mag. = 1.1208

Penumbral   **2176 Jan 26**
Saros 117   03:04 TD
D.Node   ΔT= 229s
Pen. = 211m   U.Mag. = -0.4082
Gam. = 1.2293   P.Mag. = 0.6133

Partial   **2176 Jul 21**
Saros 122   22:37 TD
A.Node   ΔT= 230s
Par. = 56m   U.Mag. = 0.0553
Gam. = -0.9708   P.Mag. = 1.0986

Partial   **2177 Jan 14**
Saros 127   16:09 TD
D.Node   ΔT= 230s
Par. = 183m   U.Mag. = 0.9334
Gam. = 0.5099   P.Mag. = 1.9112

Total -   **2177 Jul 11**
Saros 132   00:25 TD
A.Node   ΔT= 231s
Tot. = 93m
Par. = 230m   U.Mag. = 1.4199
Gam. = -0.2199   P.Mag. = 2.4896

Total -   **2178 Jan 04**
Saros 137   07:50 TD
D.Node   ΔT= 232s
Tot. = 93m
Par. = 209m   U.Mag. = 1.5820
Gam. = -0.1570   P.Mag. = 2.5574

Partial   **2178 Jun 30**
Saros 142   01:49 TD
A.Node   ΔT= 233s
Par. = 195m   U.Mag. = 0.8365
Gam. = 0.5439   P.Mag. = 1.8841

Partial   **2178 Dec 24**
Saros 147   21:26 TD
D.Node   ΔT= 234s
Par. = 114m   U.Mag. = 0.2694
Gam. = -0.8615   P.Mag. = 1.2853

Penumbral   **2179 May 21**
Saros 114   00:09 TD
A.Node   ΔT= 234s
Pen. = 168m   U.Mag. = -0.5778
Gam. = -1.3347   P.Mag. = 0.3956

Penumbral   **2179 Jun 19**
Saros 152   09:16 TD
A.Node   ΔT= 234s
Pen. = 197m   U.Mag. = -0.4702
Gam. = 1.2702   P.Mag. = 0.5251

Plate 136

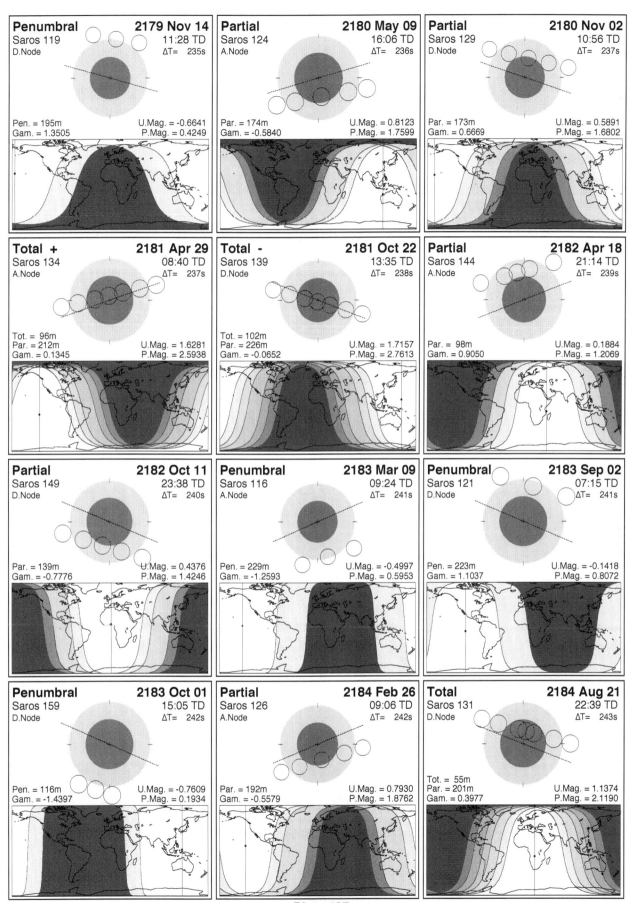

Plate 137

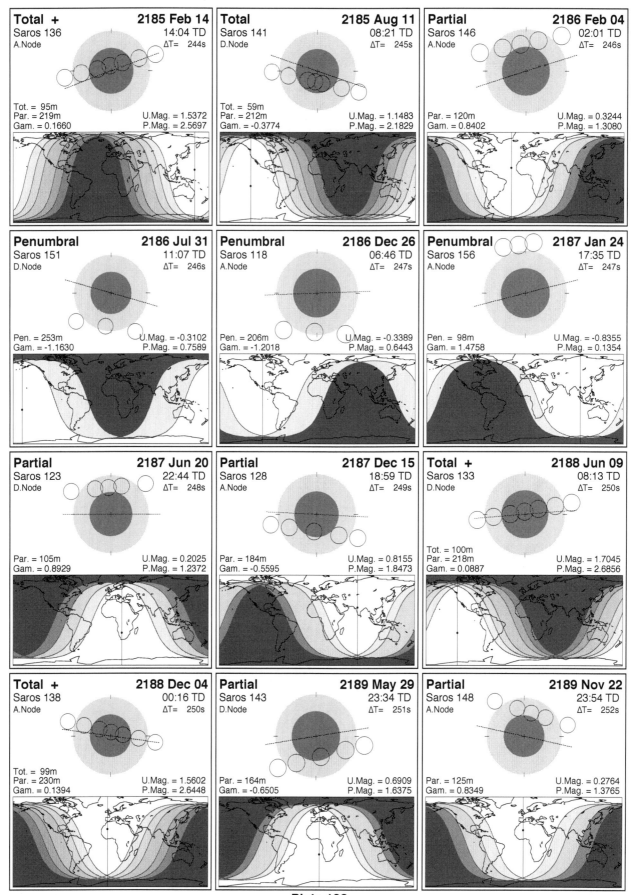

Total + **2185 Feb 14** Saros 136 14:04 TD A.Node ΔT= 244s Tot. = 95m Par. = 219m U.Mag. = 1.5372 Gam. = 0.1660 P.Mag. = 2.5697	**Total** **2185 Aug 11** Saros 141 08:21 TD D.Node ΔT= 245s Tot. = 59m Par. = 212m U.Mag. = 1.1483 Gam. = -0.3774 P.Mag. = 2.1829	**Partial** **2186 Feb 04** Saros 146 02:01 TD A.Node ΔT= 246s Par. = 120m U.Mag. = 0.3244 Gam. = 0.8402 P.Mag. = 1.3080
Penumbral **2186 Jul 31** Saros 151 11:07 TD D.Node ΔT= 246s Pen. = 253m U.Mag. = -0.3102 Gam. = -1.1630 P.Mag. = 0.7589	**Penumbral** **2186 Dec 26** Saros 118 06:46 TD A.Node ΔT= 247s Pen. = 206m U.Mag. = -0.3389 Gam. = -1.2018 P.Mag. = 0.6443	**Penumbral** **2187 Jan 24** Saros 156 17:35 TD A.Node ΔT= 247s Pen. = 98m U.Mag. = -0.8355 Gam. = 1.4758 P.Mag. = 0.1354
Partial **2187 Jun 20** Saros 123 22:44 TD D.Node ΔT= 248s Par. = 105m U.Mag. = 0.2025 Gam. = 0.8929 P.Mag. = 1.2372	**Partial** **2187 Dec 15** Saros 128 18:59 TD A.Node ΔT= 249s Par. = 184m U.Mag. = 0.8155 Gam. = -0.5595 P.Mag. = 1.8473	**Total +** **2188 Jun 09** Saros 133 08:13 TD D.Node ΔT= 250s Tot. = 100m Par. = 218m U.Mag. = 1.7045 Gam. = 0.0887 P.Mag. = 2.6856
Total + **2188 Dec 04** Saros 138 00:16 TD A.Node ΔT= 250s Tot. = 99m Par. = 230m U.Mag. = 1.5602 Gam. = 0.1394 P.Mag. = 2.6448	**Partial** **2189 May 29** Saros 143 23:34 TD D.Node ΔT= 251s Par. = 164m U.Mag. = 0.6909 Gam. = -0.6505 P.Mag. = 1.6375	**Partial** **2189 Nov 22** Saros 148 23:54 TD A.Node ΔT= 252s Par. = 125m U.Mag. = 0.2764 Gam. = 0.8349 P.Mag. = 1.3765

Plate 138

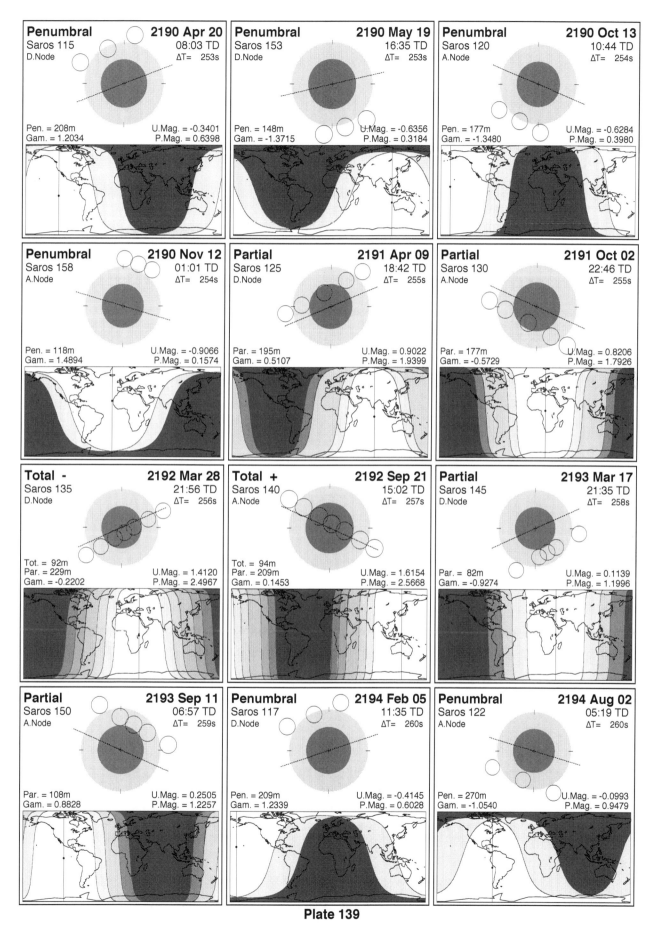

Penumbral   **2190 Apr 20**
Saros 115   08:03 TD
D.Node   ΔT= 253s

Pen. = 208m   U.Mag. = -0.3401
Gam. = 1.2034   P.Mag. = 0.6398

Penumbral   **2190 May 19**
Saros 153   16:35 TD
D.Node   ΔT= 253s

Pen. = 148m   U.Mag. = -0.6356
Gam. = -1.3715   P.Mag. = 0.3184

Penumbral   **2190 Oct 13**
Saros 120   10:44 TD
A.Node   ΔT= 254s

Pen. = 177m   U.Mag. = -0.6284
Gam. = -1.3480   P.Mag. = 0.3980

Penumbral   **2190 Nov 12**
Saros 158   01:01 TD
A.Node   ΔT= 254s

Pen. = 118m   U.Mag. = -0.9066
Gam. = 1.4894   P.Mag. = 0.1574

Partial   **2191 Apr 09**
Saros 125   18:42 TD
D.Node   ΔT= 255s

Par. = 195m   U.Mag. = 0.9022
Gam. = 0.5107   P.Mag. = 1.9399

Partial   **2191 Oct 02**
Saros 130   22:46 TD
A.Node   ΔT= 255s

Par. = 177m   U.Mag. = 0.8206
Gam. = -0.5729   P.Mag. = 1.7926

Total -   **2192 Mar 28**
Saros 135   21:56 TD
D.Node   ΔT= 256s

Tot. = 92m
Par. = 229m   U.Mag. = 1.4120
Gam. = -0.2202   P.Mag. = 2.4967

Total +   **2192 Sep 21**
Saros 140   15:02 TD
A.Node   ΔT= 257s

Tot. = 94m
Par. = 209m   U.Mag. = 1.6154
Gam. = 0.1453   P.Mag. = 2.5668

Partial   **2193 Mar 17**
Saros 145   21:35 TD
D.Node   ΔT= 258s

Par. = 82m   U.Mag. = 0.1139
Gam. = -0.9274   P.Mag. = 1.1996

Partial   **2193 Sep 11**
Saros 150   06:57 TD
A.Node   ΔT= 259s

Par. = 108m   U.Mag. = 0.2505
Gam. = 0.8828   P.Mag. = 1.2257

Penumbral   **2194 Feb 05**
Saros 117   11:35 TD
D.Node   ΔT= 260s

Pen. = 209m   U.Mag. = -0.4145
Gam. = 1.2339   P.Mag. = 0.6028

Penumbral   **2194 Aug 02**
Saros 122   05:19 TD
A.Node   ΔT= 260s

Pen. = 270m   U.Mag. = -0.0993
Gam. = -1.0540   P.Mag. = 0.9479

Plate 139

235

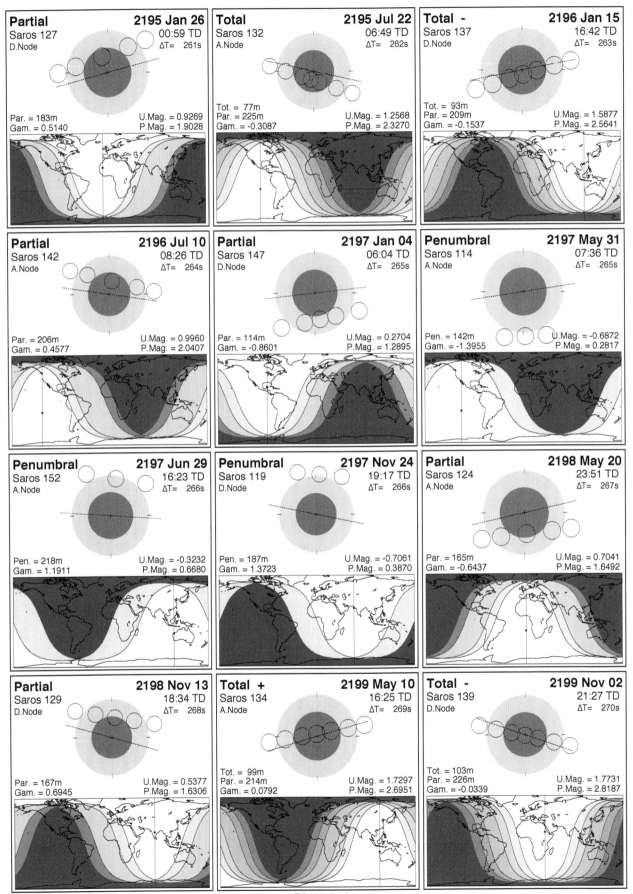

Partial   **2195 Jan 26**
Saros 127   00:59 TD
D.Node   ΔT= 261s

Par. = 183m   U.Mag. = 0.9269
Gam. = 0.5140   P.Mag. = 1.9028

Total   **2195 Jul 22**
Saros 132   06:49 TD
A.Node   ΔT= 262s

Tot. = 77m
Par. = 225m   U.Mag. = 1.2568
Gam. = -0.3087   P.Mag. = 2.3270

Total -   **2196 Jan 15**
Saros 137   16:42 TD
D.Node   ΔT= 263s

Tot. = 93m
Par. = 209m   U.Mag. = 1.5877
Gam. = -0.1537   P.Mag. = 2.5641

Partial   **2196 Jul 10**
Saros 142   08:26 TD
A.Node   ΔT= 264s

Par. = 206m   U.Mag. = 0.9960
Gam. = 0.4577   P.Mag. = 2.0407

Partial   **2197 Jan 04**
Saros 147   06:04 TD
D.Node   ΔT= 265s

Par. = 114m   U.Mag. = 0.2704
Gam. = -0.8601   P.Mag. = 1.2895

Penumbral   **2197 May 31**
Saros 114   07:36 TD
A.Node   ΔT= 265s

Pen. = 142m   U.Mag. = -0.6872
Gam. = -1.3955   P.Mag. = 0.2817

Penumbral   **2197 Jun 29**
Saros 152   16:23 TD
A.Node   ΔT= 266s

Pen. = 218m   U.Mag. = -0.3232
Gam. = 1.1911   P.Mag. = 0.6680

Penumbral   **2197 Nov 24**
Saros 119   19:17 TD
D.Node   ΔT= 266s

Pen. = 187m   U.Mag. = -0.7061
Gam. = 1.3723   P.Mag. = 0.3870

Partial   **2198 May 20**
Saros 124   23:51 TD
A.Node   ΔT= 267s

Par. = 165m   U.Mag. = 0.7041
Gam. = -0.6437   P.Mag. = 1.6492

Partial   **2198 Nov 13**
Saros 129   18:34 TD
D.Node   ΔT= 268s

Par. = 167m   U.Mag. = 0.5377
Gam. = 0.6945   P.Mag. = 1.6306

Total +   **2199 May 10**
Saros 134   16:25 TD
A.Node   ΔT= 269s

Tot. = 99m
Par. = 214m   U.Mag. = 1.7297
Gam. = 0.0792   P.Mag. = 2.6951

Total -   **2199 Nov 02**
Saros 139   21:27 TD
D.Node   ΔT= 270s

Tot. = 103m
Par. = 226m   U.Mag. = 1.7731
Gam. = -0.0339   P.Mag. = 2.8187

Plate 140

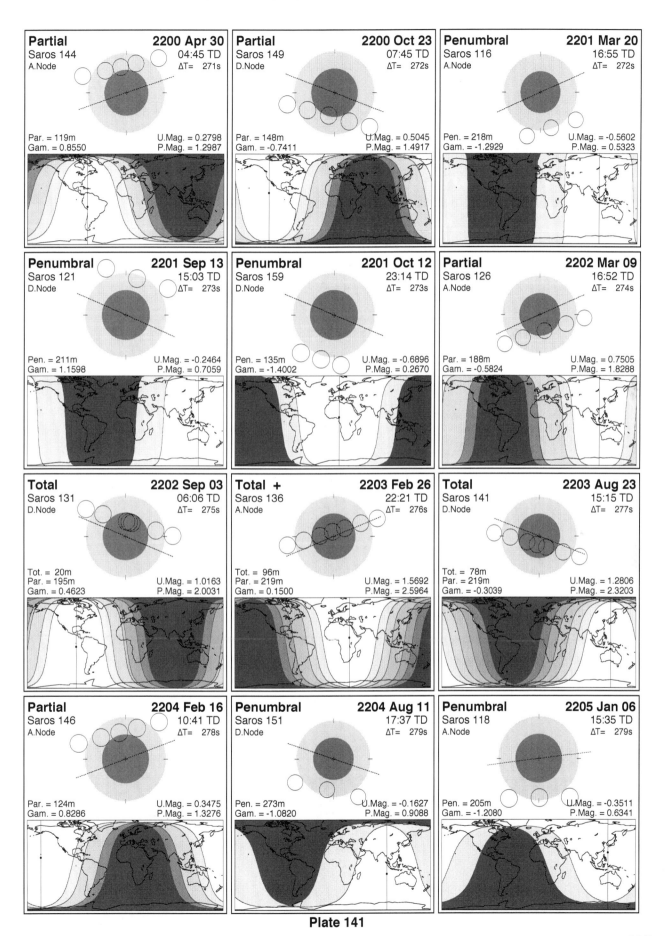

Partial	2200 Apr 30
Saros 144	04:45 TD
A.Node	ΔT= 271s
Par. = 119m	U.Mag. = 0.2798
Gam. = 0.8550	P.Mag. = 1.2987

Partial	2200 Oct 23
Saros 149	07:45 TD
D.Node	ΔT= 272s
Par. = 148m	U.Mag. = 0.5045
Gam. = -0.7411	P.Mag. = 1.4917

Penumbral	2201 Mar 20
Saros 116	16:55 TD
A.Node	ΔT= 272s
Pen. = 218m	U.Mag. = -0.5602
Gam. = -1.2929	P.Mag. = 0.5323

Penumbral	2201 Sep 13
Saros 121	15:03 TD
D.Node	ΔT= 273s
Pen. = 211m	U.Mag. = -0.2464
Gam. = 1.1598	P.Mag. = 0.7059

Penumbral	2201 Oct 12
Saros 159	23:14 TD
D.Node	ΔT= 273s
Pen. = 135m	U.Mag. = -0.6896
Gam. = -1.4002	P.Mag. = 0.2670

Partial	2202 Mar 09
Saros 126	16:52 TD
A.Node	ΔT= 274s
Par. = 188m	U.Mag. = 0.7505
Gam. = -0.5824	P.Mag. = 1.8288

Total	2202 Sep 03
Saros 131	06:06 TD
D.Node	ΔT= 275s
Tot. = 20m	
Par. = 195m	U.Mag. = 1.0163
Gam. = 0.4623	P.Mag. = 2.0031

Total +	2203 Feb 26
Saros 136	22:21 TD
A.Node	ΔT= 276s
Tot. = 96m	
Par. = 219m	U.Mag. = 1.5692
Gam. = 0.1500	P.Mag. = 2.5964

Total	2203 Aug 23
Saros 141	15:15 TD
D.Node	ΔT= 277s
Tot. = 78m	
Par. = 219m	U.Mag. = 1.2806
Gam. = -0.3039	P.Mag. = 2.3203

Partial	2204 Feb 16
Saros 146	10:41 TD
A.Node	ΔT= 278s
Par. = 124m	U.Mag. = 0.3475
Gam. = 0.8286	P.Mag. = 1.3276

Penumbral	2204 Aug 11
Saros 151	17:37 TD
D.Node	ΔT= 279s
Pen. = 273m	U.Mag. = -0.1627
Gam. = -1.0820	P.Mag. = 0.9088

Penumbral	2205 Jan 06
Saros 118	15:35 TD
A.Node	ΔT= 279s
Pen. = 205m	U.Mag. = -0.3511
Gam. = -1.2080	P.Mag. = 0.6341

Plate 141

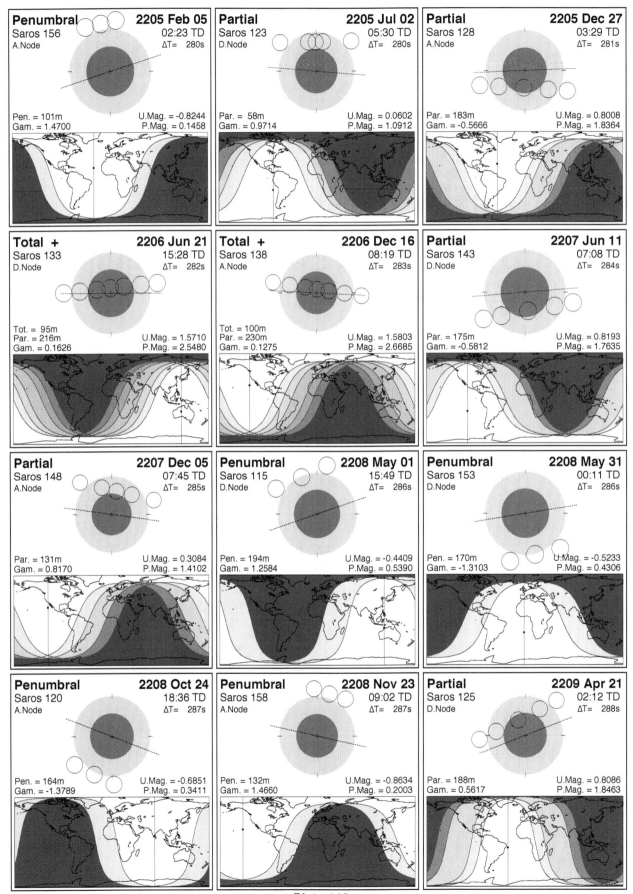

Penumbral   **2205 Feb 05**
Saros 156   02:23 TD
A.Node   ΔT= 280s

Pen. = 101m   U.Mag. = -0.8244
Gam. = 1.4700   P.Mag. = 0.1458

Partial   **2205 Jul 02**
Saros 123   05:30 TD
D.Node   ΔT= 280s

Par. = 58m   U.Mag. = 0.0602
Gam. = 0.9714   P.Mag. = 1.0912

Partial   **2205 Dec 27**
Saros 128   03:29 TD
A.Node   ΔT= 281s

Par. = 183m   U.Mag. = 0.8008
Gam. = -0.5666   P.Mag. = 1.8364

Total +   **2206 Jun 21**
Saros 133   15:28 TD
D.Node   ΔT= 282s

Tot. = 95m
Par. = 216m   U.Mag. = 1.5710
Gam. = 0.1626   P.Mag. = 2.5480

Total +   **2206 Dec 16**
Saros 138   08:19 TD
A.Node   ΔT= 283s

Tot. = 100m
Par. = 230m   U.Mag. = 1.5803
Gam. = 0.1275   P.Mag. = 2.6685

Partial   **2207 Jun 11**
Saros 143   07:08 TD
D.Node   ΔT= 284s

Par. = 175m   U.Mag. = 0.8193
Gam. = -0.5812   P.Mag. = 1.7635

Partial   **2207 Dec 05**
Saros 148   07:45 TD
A.Node   ΔT= 285s

Par. = 131m   U.Mag. = 0.3084
Gam. = 0.8170   P.Mag. = 1.4102

Penumbral   **2208 May 01**
Saros 115   15:49 TD
D.Node   ΔT= 286s

Pen. = 194m   U.Mag. = -0.4409
Gam. = 1.2584   P.Mag. = 0.5390

Penumbral   **2208 May 31**
Saros 153   00:11 TD
D.Node   ΔT= 286s

Pen. = 170m   U.Mag. = -0.5233
Gam. = -1.3103   P.Mag. = 0.4306

Penumbral   **2208 Oct 24**
Saros 120   18:36 TD
A.Node   ΔT= 287s

Pen. = 164m   U.Mag. = -0.6851
Gam. = -1.3789   P.Mag. = 0.3411

Penumbral   **2208 Nov 23**
Saros 158   09:02 TD
A.Node   ΔT= 287s

Pen. = 132m   U.Mag. = -0.8634
Gam. = 1.4660   P.Mag. = 0.2003

Partial   **2209 Apr 21**
Saros 125   02:12 TD
D.Node   ΔT= 288s

Par. = 188m   U.Mag. = 0.8086
Gam. = 0.5617   P.Mag. = 1.8463

Plate 142

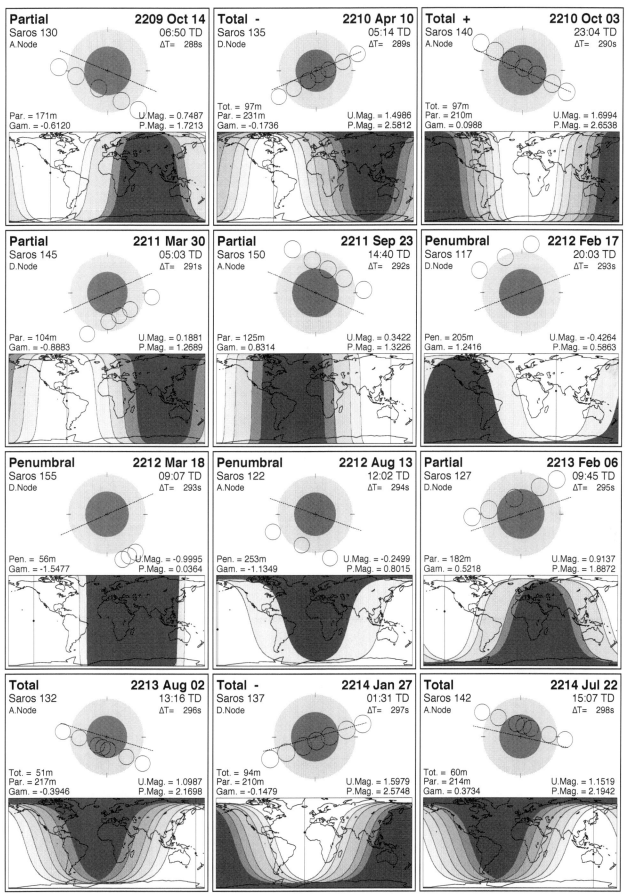

Partial	2209 Oct 14
Saros 130	06:50 TD
A.Node	ΔT= 288s
Par. = 171m	U.Mag. = 0.7487
Gam. = -0.6120	P.Mag. = 1.7213

Total -	2210 Apr 10
Saros 135	05:14 TD
D.Node	ΔT= 289s
Tot. = 97m	
Par. = 231m	U.Mag. = 1.4986
Gam. = -0.1736	P.Mag. = 2.5812

Total +	2210 Oct 03
Saros 140	23:04 TD
A.Node	ΔT= 290s
Tot. = 97m	
Par. = 210m	U.Mag. = 1.6994
Gam. = 0.0988	P.Mag. = 2.6538

Partial	2211 Mar 30
Saros 145	05:03 TD
D.Node	ΔT= 291s
Par. = 104m	U.Mag. = 0.1881
Gam. = -0.8883	P.Mag. = 1.2689

Partial	2211 Sep 23
Saros 150	14:40 TD
A.Node	ΔT= 292s
Par. = 125m	U.Mag. = 0.3422
Gam. = 0.8314	P.Mag. = 1.3226

Penumbral	2212 Feb 17
Saros 117	20:03 TD
D.Node	ΔT= 293s
Pen. = 205m	U.Mag. = -0.4264
Gam. = 1.2416	P.Mag. = 0.5863

Penumbral	2212 Mar 18
Saros 155	09:07 TD
D.Node	ΔT= 293s
Pen. = 56m	U.Mag. = -0.9995
Gam. = -1.5477	P.Mag. = 0.0364

Penumbral	2212 Aug 13
Saros 122	12:02 TD
A.Node	ΔT= 294s
Pen. = 253m	U.Mag. = -0.2499
Gam. = -1.1349	P.Mag. = 0.8015

Partial	2213 Feb 06
Saros 127	09:45 TD
D.Node	ΔT= 295s
Par. = 182m	U.Mag. = 0.9137
Gam. = 0.5218	P.Mag. = 1.8872

Total	2213 Aug 02
Saros 132	13:16 TD
A.Node	ΔT= 296s
Tot. = 51m	
Par. = 217m	U.Mag. = 1.0987
Gam. = -0.3946	P.Mag. = 2.1698

Total -	2214 Jan 27
Saros 137	01:31 TD
D.Node	ΔT= 297s
Tot. = 94m	
Par. = 210m	U.Mag. = 1.5979
Gam. = -0.1479	P.Mag. = 2.5748

Total	2214 Jul 22
Saros 142	15:07 TD
A.Node	ΔT= 298s
Tot. = 60m	
Par. = 214m	U.Mag. = 1.1519
Gam. = 0.3734	P.Mag. = 2.1942

Plate 143

239

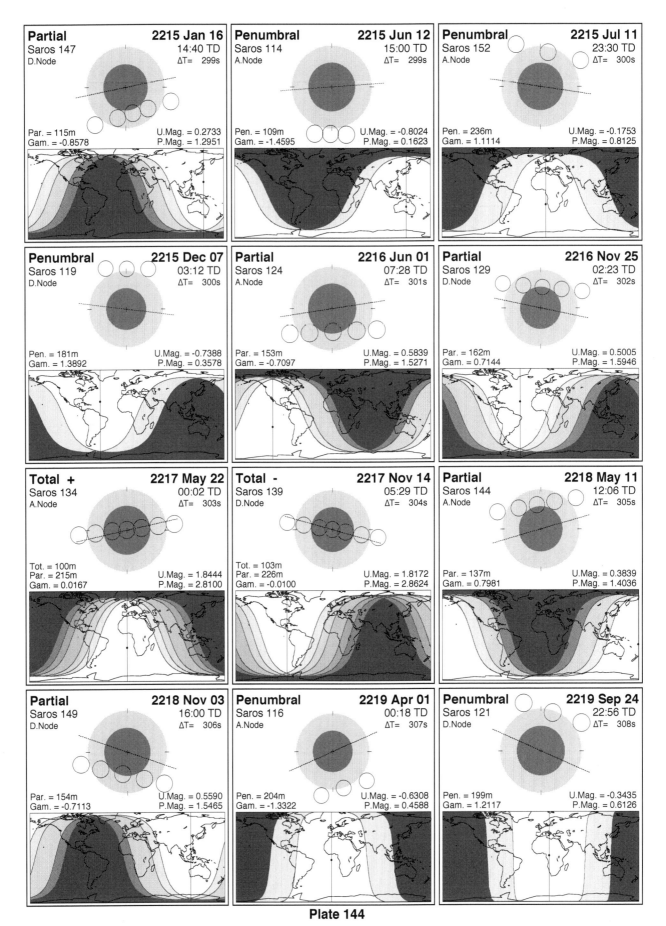

Partial   **2215 Jan 16**
Saros 147   14:40 TD
D.Node   ΔT= 299s
Par. = 115m   U.Mag. = 0.2733
Gam. = -0.8578   P.Mag. = 1.2951

Penumbral   **2215 Jun 12**
Saros 114   15:00 TD
A.Node   ΔT= 299s
Pen. = 109m   U.Mag. = -0.8024
Gam. = -1.4595   P.Mag. = 0.1623

Penumbral   **2215 Jul 11**
Saros 152   23:30 TD
A.Node   ΔT= 300s
Pen. = 236m   U.Mag. = -0.1753
Gam. = 1.1114   P.Mag. = 0.8125

Penumbral   **2215 Dec 07**
Saros 119   03:12 TD
D.Node   ΔT= 300s
Pen. = 181m   U.Mag. = -0.7388
Gam. = 1.3892   P.Mag. = 0.3578

Partial   **2216 Jun 01**
Saros 124   07:28 TD
A.Node   ΔT= 301s
Par. = 153m   U.Mag. = 0.5839
Gam. = -0.7097   P.Mag. = 1.5271

Partial   **2216 Nov 25**
Saros 129   02:23 TD
D.Node   ΔT= 302s
Par. = 162m   U.Mag. = 0.5005
Gam. = 0.7144   P.Mag. = 1.5946

Total +   **2217 May 22**
Saros 134   00:02 TD
A.Node   ΔT= 303s
Tot. = 100m
Par. = 215m   U.Mag. = 1.8444
Gam. = 0.0167   P.Mag. = 2.8100

Total -   **2217 Nov 14**
Saros 139   05:29 TD
D.Node   ΔT= 304s
Tot. = 103m
Par. = 226m   U.Mag. = 1.8172
Gam. = -0.0100   P.Mag. = 2.8624

Partial   **2218 May 11**
Saros 144   12:06 TD
A.Node   ΔT= 305s
Par. = 137m   U.Mag. = 0.3839
Gam. = 0.7981   P.Mag. = 1.4036

Partial   **2218 Nov 03**
Saros 149   16:00 TD
D.Node   ΔT= 306s
Par. = 154m   U.Mag. = 0.5590
Gam. = -0.7113   P.Mag. = 1.5465

Penumbral   **2219 Apr 01**
Saros 116   00:18 TD
A.Node   ΔT= 307s
Pen. = 204m   U.Mag. = -0.6308
Gam. = -1.3322   P.Mag. = 0.4588

Penumbral   **2219 Sep 24**
Saros 121   22:56 TD
D.Node   ΔT= 308s
Pen. = 199m   U.Mag. = -0.3435
Gam. = 1.2117   P.Mag. = 0.6126

Plate 144

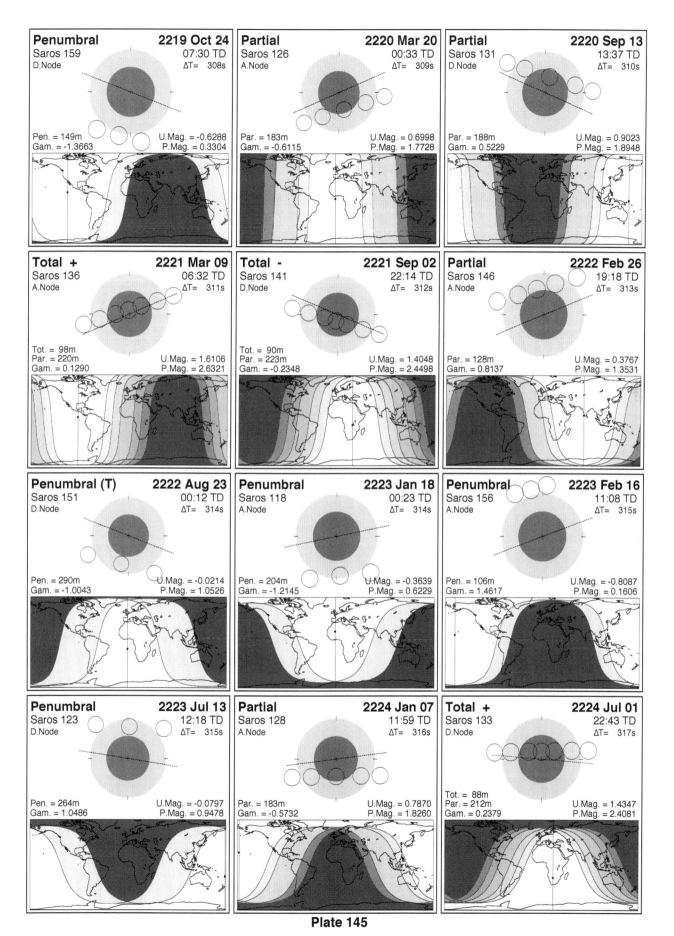

Penumbral 2219 Oct 24	**Partial** 2220 Mar 20	**Partial** 2220 Sep 13
Saros 159 07:30 TD	Saros 126 00:33 TD	Saros 131 13:37 TD
D.Node ΔT= 308s	A.Node ΔT= 309s	D.Node ΔT= 310s
Pen. = 149m U.Mag. = -0.6288	Par. = 183m U.Mag. = 0.6998	Par. = 188m U.Mag. = 0.9023
Gam. = -1.3663 P.Mag. = 0.3304	Gam. = -0.6115 P.Mag. = 1.7728	Gam. = 0.5229 P.Mag. = 1.8948
Total + 2221 Mar 09	**Total -** 2221 Sep 02	**Partial** 2222 Feb 26
Saros 136 06:32 TD	Saros 141 22:14 TD	Saros 146 19:18 TD
A.Node ΔT= 311s	D.Node ΔT= 312s	A.Node ΔT= 313s
Tot. = 98m	Tot. = 90m	
Par. = 220m U.Mag. = 1.6106	Par. = 223m U.Mag. = 1.4048	Par. = 128m U.Mag. = 0.3767
Gam. = 0.1290 P.Mag. = 2.6321	Gam. = -0.2348 P.Mag. = 2.4498	Gam. = 0.8137 P.Mag. = 1.3531
Penumbral (T) 2222 Aug 23	**Penumbral** 2223 Jan 18	**Penumbral** 2223 Feb 16
Saros 151 00:12 TD	Saros 118 00:23 TD	Saros 156 11:08 TD
D.Node ΔT= 314s	A.Node ΔT= 314s	A.Node ΔT= 315s
Pen. = 290m U.Mag. = -0.0214	Pen. = 204m U.Mag. = -0.3639	Pen. = 106m U.Mag. = -0.8087
Gam. = -1.0043 P.Mag. = 1.0526	Gam. = -1.2145 P.Mag. = 0.6229	Gam. = 1.4617 P.Mag. = 0.1606
Penumbral 2223 Jul 13	**Partial** 2224 Jan 07	**Total +** 2224 Jul 01
Saros 123 12:18 TD	Saros 128 11:59 TD	Saros 133 22:43 TD
D.Node ΔT= 315s	A.Node ΔT= 316s	D.Node ΔT= 317s
		Tot. = 88m
Pen. = 264m U.Mag. = -0.0797	Par. = 183m U.Mag. = 0.7870	Par. = 212m U.Mag. = 1.4347
Gam. = 1.0486 P.Mag. = 0.9478	Gam. = -0.5732 P.Mag. = 1.8260	Gam. = 0.2379 P.Mag. = 2.4081

Plate 145

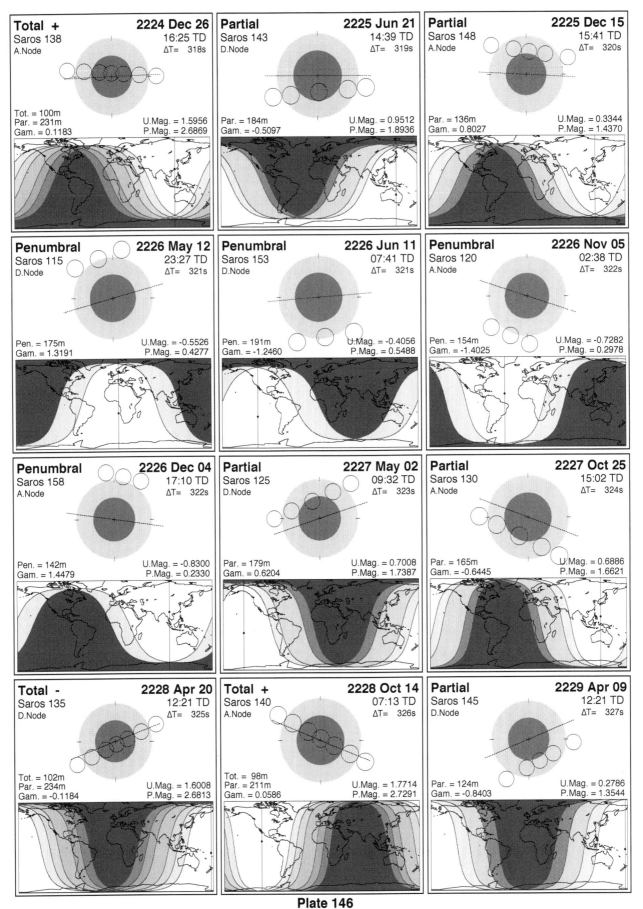

Total +   **2224 Dec 26**
Saros 138   16:25 TD
A.Node   ΔT= 318s
Tot. = 100m
Par. = 231m
Gam. = 0.1183   U.Mag. = 1.5956
     P.Mag. = 2.6869

Partial   **2225 Jun 21**
Saros 143   14:39 TD
D.Node   ΔT= 319s
Par. = 184m
Gam. = -0.5097   U.Mag. = 0.9512
     P.Mag. = 1.8936

Partial   **2225 Dec 15**
Saros 148   15:41 TD
A.Node   ΔT= 320s
Par. = 136m
Gam. = 0.8027   U.Mag. = 0.3344
     P.Mag. = 1.4370

Penumbral   **2226 May 12**
Saros 115   23:27 TD
D.Node   ΔT= 321s
Pen. = 175m
Gam. = 1.3191   U.Mag. = -0.5526
     P.Mag. = 0.4277

Penumbral   **2226 Jun 11**
Saros 153   07:41 TD
D.Node   ΔT= 321s
Pen. = 191m
Gam. = -1.2460   U.Mag. = -0.4056
     P.Mag. = 0.5488

Penumbral   **2226 Nov 05**
Saros 120   02:38 TD
A.Node   ΔT= 322s
Pen. = 154m
Gam. = -1.4025   U.Mag. = -0.7282
     P.Mag. = 0.2978

Penumbral   **2226 Dec 04**
Saros 158   17:10 TD
A.Node   ΔT= 322s
Pen. = 142m
Gam. = 1.4479   U.Mag. = -0.8300
     P.Mag. = 0.2330

Partial   **2227 May 02**
Saros 125   09:32 TD
D.Node   ΔT= 323s
Par. = 179m
Gam. = 0.6204   U.Mag. = 0.7008
     P.Mag. = 1.7387

Partial   **2227 Oct 25**
Saros 130   15:02 TD
A.Node   ΔT= 324s
Par. = 165m
Gam. = -0.6445   U.Mag. = 0.6886
     P.Mag. = 1.6621

Total -   **2228 Apr 20**
Saros 135   12:21 TD
D.Node   ΔT= 325s
Tot. = 102m
Par. = 234m
Gam. = -0.1184   U.Mag. = 1.6008
     P.Mag. = 2.6813

Total +   **2228 Oct 14**
Saros 140   07:13 TD
A.Node   ΔT= 326s
Tot. = 98m
Par. = 211m
Gam. = 0.0586   U.Mag. = 1.7714
     P.Mag. = 2.7291

Partial   **2229 Apr 09**
Saros 145   12:21 TD
D.Node   ΔT= 327s
Par. = 124m
Gam. = -0.8403   U.Mag. = 0.2786
     P.Mag. = 1.3544

Plate 146

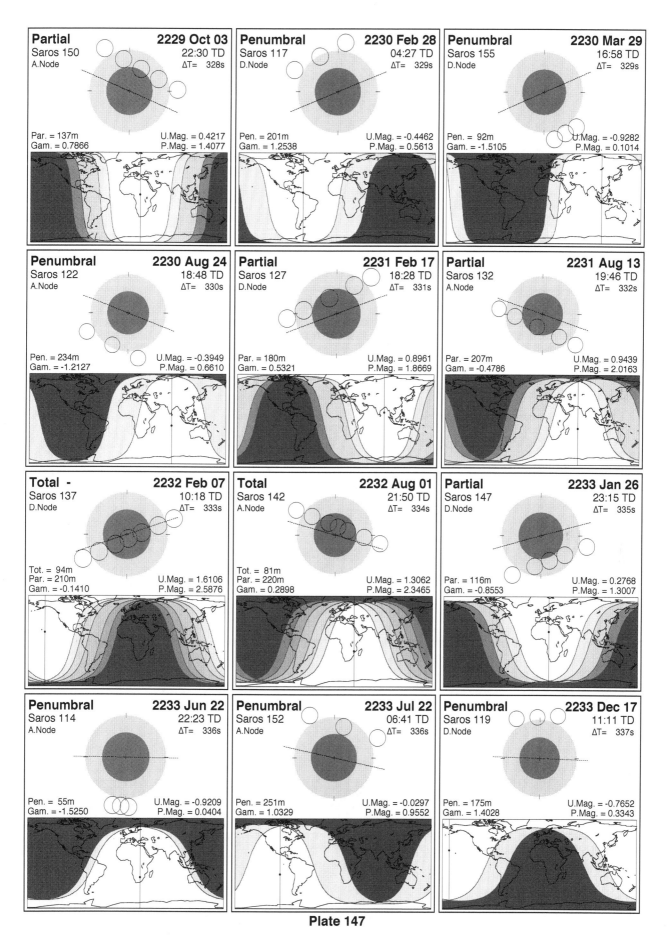

Partial   **2229 Oct 03**
Saros 150   22:30 TD
A.Node   ΔT= 328s
Par. = 137m   U.Mag. = 0.4217
Gam. = 0.7866   P.Mag. = 1.4077

Penumbral   **2230 Feb 28**
Saros 117   04:27 TD
D.Node   ΔT= 329s
Pen. = 201m   U.Mag. = -0.4462
Gam. = 1.2538   P.Mag. = 0.5613

Penumbral   **2230 Mar 29**
Saros 155   16:58 TD
D.Node   ΔT= 329s
Pen. = 92m   U.Mag. = -0.9282
Gam. = -1.5105   P.Mag. = 0.1014

Penumbral   **2230 Aug 24**
Saros 122   18:48 TD
A.Node   ΔT= 330s
Pen. = 234m   U.Mag. = -0.3949
Gam. = -1.2127   P.Mag. = 0.6610

Partial   **2231 Feb 17**
Saros 127   18:28 TD
D.Node   ΔT= 331s
Par. = 180m   U.Mag. = 0.8961
Gam. = 0.5321   P.Mag. = 1.8669

Partial   **2231 Aug 13**
Saros 132   19:46 TD
A.Node   ΔT= 332s
Par. = 207m   U.Mag. = 0.9439
Gam. = -0.4786   P.Mag. = 2.0163

Total -   **2232 Feb 07**
Saros 137   10:18 TD
D.Node   ΔT= 333s
Tot. = 94m
Par. = 210m   U.Mag. = 1.6106
Gam. = -0.1410   P.Mag. = 2.5876

Total   **2232 Aug 01**
Saros 142   21:50 TD
A.Node   ΔT= 334s
Tot. = 81m
Par. = 220m   U.Mag. = 1.3062
Gam. = 0.2898   P.Mag. = 2.3465

Partial   **2233 Jan 26**
Saros 147   23:15 TD
D.Node   ΔT= 335s
Par. = 116m   U.Mag. = 0.2768
Gam. = -0.8553   P.Mag. = 1.3007

Penumbral   **2233 Jun 22**
Saros 114   22:23 TD
A.Node   ΔT= 336s
Pen. = 55m   U.Mag. = -0.9209
Gam. = -1.5250   P.Mag. = 0.0404

Penumbral   **2233 Jul 22**
Saros 152   06:41 TD
A.Node   ΔT= 336s
Pen. = 251m   U.Mag. = -0.0297
Gam. = 1.0329   P.Mag. = 0.9552

Penumbral   **2233 Dec 17**
Saros 119   11:11 TD
D.Node   ΔT= 337s
Pen. = 175m   U.Mag. = -0.7652
Gam. = 1.4028   P.Mag. = 0.3343

Plate 147

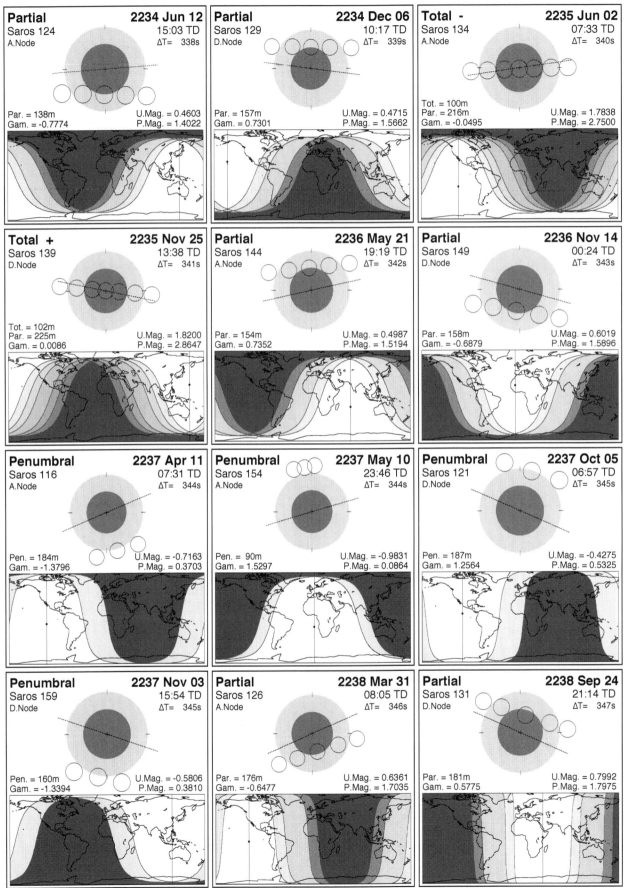

Partial **2234 Jun 12**	**Partial** **2234 Dec 06**	**Total -** **2235 Jun 02**
Saros 124 15:03 TD	Saros 129 10:17 TD	Saros 134 07:33 TD
A.Node ΔT= 338s	D.Node ΔT= 339s	A.Node ΔT= 340s
Par. = 138m U.Mag. = 0.4603	Par. = 157m U.Mag. = 0.4715	Tot. = 100m U.Mag. = 1.7838
Gam. = -0.7774 P.Mag. = 1.4022	Gam. = 0.7301 P.Mag. = 1.5662	Par. = 216m Gam. = -0.0495 P.Mag. = 2.7500
Total + **2235 Nov 25**	**Partial** **2236 May 21**	**Partial** **2236 Nov 14**
Saros 139 13:38 TD	Saros 144 19:19 TD	Saros 149 00:24 TD
D.Node ΔT= 341s	A.Node ΔT= 342s	D.Node ΔT= 343s
Tot. = 102m Par. = 225m U.Mag. = 1.8200	Par. = 154m U.Mag. = 0.4987	Par. = 158m U.Mag. = 0.6019
Gam. = 0.0086 P.Mag. = 2.8647	Gam. = 0.7352 P.Mag. = 1.5194	Gam. = -0.6879 P.Mag. = 1.5896
Penumbral **2237 Apr 11**	**Penumbral** **2237 May 10**	**Penumbral** **2237 Oct 05**
Saros 116 07:31 TD	Saros 154 23:46 TD	Saros 121 06:57 TD
A.Node ΔT= 344s	A.Node ΔT= 344s	D.Node ΔT= 345s
Pen. = 184m U.Mag. = -0.7163	Pen. = 90m U.Mag. = -0.9831	Pen. = 187m U.Mag. = -0.4275
Gam. = -1.3796 P.Mag. = 0.3703	Gam. = 1.5297 P.Mag. = 0.0864	Gam. = 1.2564 P.Mag. = 0.5325
Penumbral **2237 Nov 03**	**Partial** **2238 Mar 31**	**Partial** **2238 Sep 24**
Saros 159 15:54 TD	Saros 126 08:05 TD	Saros 131 21:14 TD
D.Node ΔT= 345s	A.Node ΔT= 346s	D.Node ΔT= 347s
Pen. = 160m U.Mag. = -0.5806	Par. = 176m U.Mag. = 0.6361	Par. = 181m U.Mag. = 0.7992
Gam. = -1.3394 P.Mag. = 0.3810	Gam. = -0.6477 P.Mag. = 1.7035	Gam. = 0.5775 P.Mag. = 1.7975

Plate 148

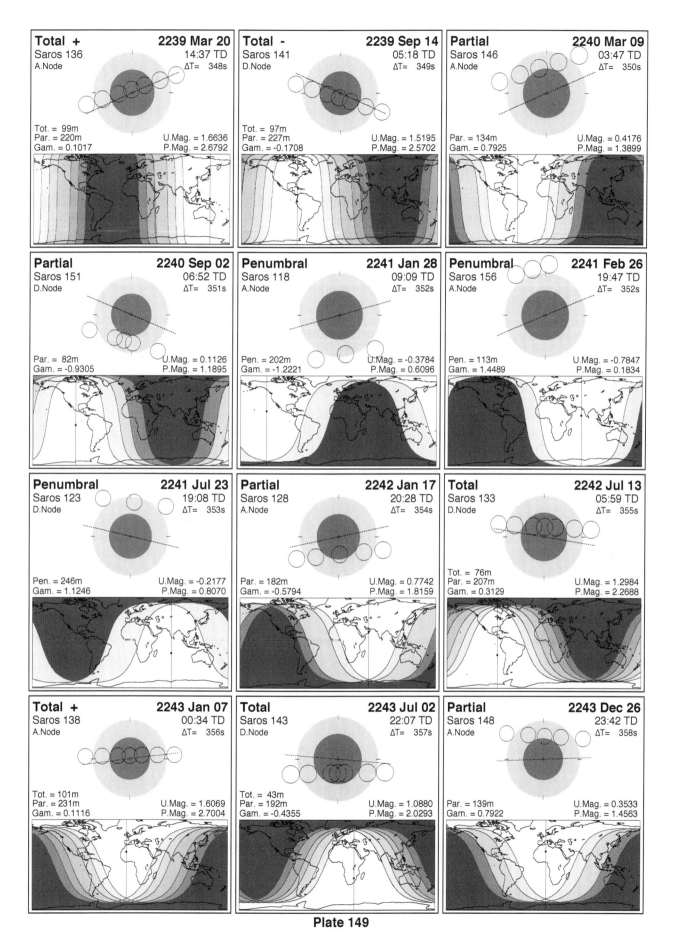

Total +	2239 Mar 20
Saros 136	14:37 TD
A.Node	ΔT= 348s
Tot. = 99m	
Par. = 220m	U.Mag. = 1.6636
Gam. = 0.1017	P.Mag. = 2.6792

Total -	2239 Sep 14
Saros 141	05:18 TD
D.Node	ΔT= 349s
Tot. = 97m	
Par. = 227m	U.Mag. = 1.5195
Gam. = -0.1708	P.Mag. = 2.5702

Partial	2240 Mar 09
Saros 146	03:47 TD
A.Node	ΔT= 350s
Par. = 134m	U.Mag. = 0.4176
Gam. = 0.7925	P.Mag. = 1.3899

Partial	2240 Sep 02
Saros 151	06:52 TD
D.Node	ΔT= 351s
Par. = 82m	U.Mag. = 0.1126
Gam. = -0.9305	P.Mag. = 1.1895

Penumbral	2241 Jan 28
Saros 118	09:09 TD
A.Node	ΔT= 352s
Pen. = 202m	U.Mag. = -0.3784
Gam. = -1.2221	P.Mag. = 0.6096

Penumbral	2241 Feb 26
Saros 156	19:47 TD
A.Node	ΔT= 352s
Pen. = 113m	U.Mag. = -0.7847
Gam. = 1.4489	P.Mag. = 0.1834

Penumbral	2241 Jul 23
Saros 123	19:08 TD
D.Node	ΔT= 353s
Pen. = 246m	U.Mag. = -0.2177
Gam. = 1.1246	P.Mag. = 0.8070

Partial	2242 Jan 17
Saros 128	20:28 TD
A.Node	ΔT= 354s
Par. = 182m	U.Mag. = 0.7742
Gam. = -0.5794	P.Mag. = 1.8159

Total	2242 Jul 13
Saros 133	05:59 TD
D.Node	ΔT= 355s
Tot. = 76m	
Par. = 207m	U.Mag. = 1.2984
Gam. = 0.3129	P.Mag. = 2.2688

Total +	2243 Jan 07
Saros 138	00:34 TD
A.Node	ΔT= 356s
Tot. = 101m	
Par. = 231m	U.Mag. = 1.6069
Gam. = 0.1116	P.Mag. = 2.7004

Total	2243 Jul 02
Saros 143	22:07 TD
D.Node	ΔT= 357s
Tot. = 43m	
Par. = 192m	U.Mag. = 1.0880
Gam. = -0.4355	P.Mag. = 2.0293

Partial	2243 Dec 26
Saros 148	23:42 TD
A.Node	ΔT= 358s
Par. = 139m	U.Mag. = 0.3533
Gam. = 0.7922	P.Mag. = 1.4563

Plate 149

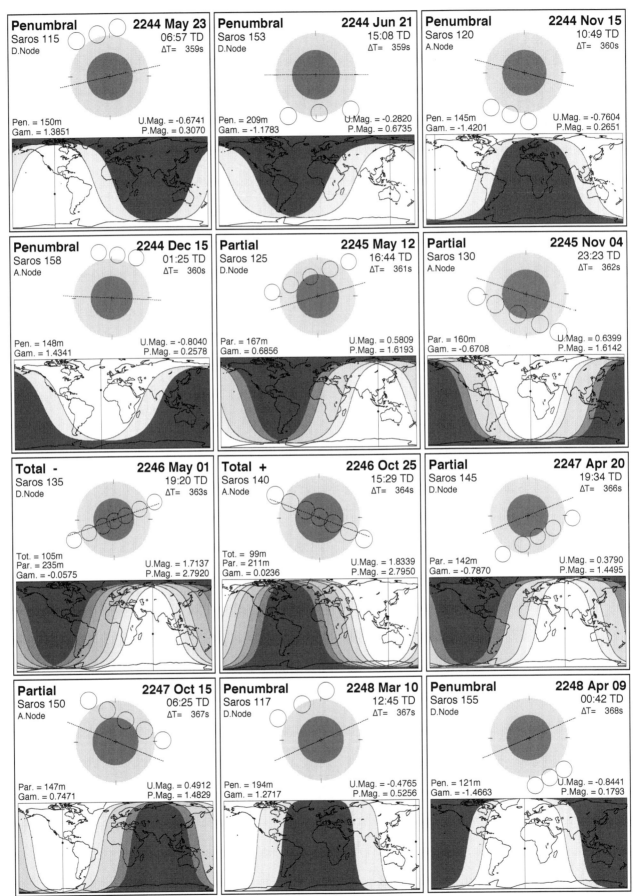

Penumbral   **2244 May 23**
Saros 115   06:57 TD
D.Node   ΔT= 359s
Pen. = 150m   U.Mag. = -0.6741
Gam. = 1.3851   P.Mag. = 0.3070

Penumbral   **2244 Jun 21**
Saros 153   15:08 TD
D.Node   ΔT= 359s
Pen. = 209m   U.Mag. = -0.2820
Gam. = -1.1783   P.Mag. = 0.6735

Penumbral   **2244 Nov 15**
Saros 120   10:49 TD
A.Node   ΔT= 360s
Pen. = 145m   U.Mag. = -0.7604
Gam. = -1.4201   P.Mag. = 0.2651

Penumbral   **2244 Dec 15**
Saros 158   01:25 TD
A.Node   ΔT= 360s
Pen. = 148m   U.Mag. = -0.8040
Gam. = 1.4341   P.Mag. = 0.2578

Partial   **2245 May 12**
Saros 125   16:44 TD
D.Node   ΔT= 361s
Par. = 167m   U.Mag. = 0.5809
Gam. = 0.6856   P.Mag. = 1.6193

Partial   **2245 Nov 04**
Saros 130   23:23 TD
A.Node   ΔT= 362s
Par. = 160m   U.Mag. = 0.6399
Gam. = -0.6708   P.Mag. = 1.6142

Total -   **2246 May 01**
Saros 135   19:20 TD
D.Node   ΔT= 363s
Tot. = 105m
Par. = 235m   U.Mag. = 1.7137
Gam. = -0.0575   P.Mag. = 2.7920

Total +   **2246 Oct 25**
Saros 140   15:29 TD
A.Node   ΔT= 364s
Tot. = 99m
Par. = 211m   U.Mag. = 1.8339
Gam. = 0.0236   P.Mag. = 2.7950

Partial   **2247 Apr 20**
Saros 145   19:34 TD
D.Node   ΔT= 366s
Par. = 142m   U.Mag. = 0.3790
Gam. = -0.7870   P.Mag. = 1.4495

Partial   **2247 Oct 15**
Saros 150   06:25 TD
A.Node   ΔT= 367s
Par. = 147m   U.Mag. = 0.4912
Gam. = 0.7471   P.Mag. = 1.4829

Penumbral   **2248 Mar 10**
Saros 117   12:45 TD
D.Node   ΔT= 367s
Pen. = 194m   U.Mag. = -0.4765
Gam. = 1.2717   P.Mag. = 0.5256

Penumbral   **2248 Apr 09**
Saros 155   00:42 TD
D.Node   ΔT= 368s
Pen. = 121m   U.Mag. = -0.8441
Gam. = -1.4663   P.Mag. = 0.1793

Plate 150

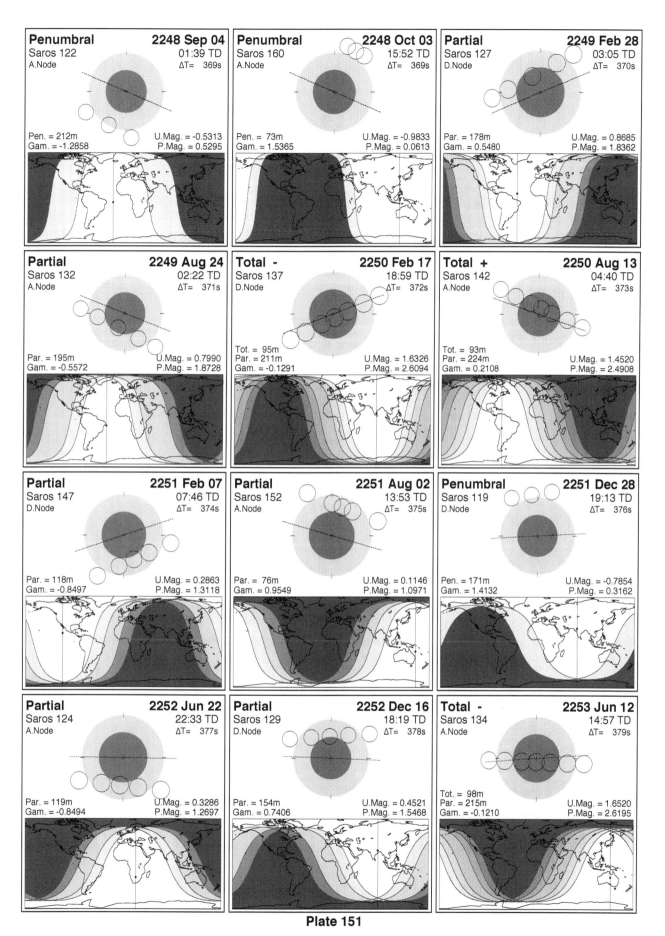

Penumbral **2248 Sep 04** Saros 122 01:39 TD A.Node ΔT= 369s Pen. = 212m U.Mag. = -0.5313 Gam. = -1.2858 P.Mag. = 0.5295	**Penumbral** **2248 Oct 03** Saros 160 15:52 TD A.Node ΔT= 369s Pen. = 73m U.Mag. = -0.9833 Gam. = 1.5365 P.Mag. = 0.0613	**Partial** **2249 Feb 28** Saros 127 03:05 TD D.Node ΔT= 370s Par. = 178m U.Mag. = 0.8685 Gam. = 0.5480 P.Mag. = 1.8362
Partial **2249 Aug 24** Saros 132 02:22 TD A.Node ΔT= 371s Par. = 195m U.Mag. = 0.7990 Gam. = -0.5572 P.Mag. = 1.8728	**Total -** **2250 Feb 17** Saros 137 18:59 TD D.Node ΔT= 372s Tot. = 95m Par. = 211m U.Mag. = 1.6326 Gam. = -0.1291 P.Mag. = 2.6094	**Total +** **2250 Aug 13** Saros 142 04:40 TD A.Node ΔT= 373s Tot. = 93m Par. = 224m U.Mag. = 1.4520 Gam. = 0.2108 P.Mag. = 2.4908
Partial **2251 Feb 07** Saros 147 07:46 TD D.Node ΔT= 374s Par. = 118m U.Mag. = 0.2863 Gam. = -0.8497 P.Mag. = 1.3118	**Partial** **2251 Aug 02** Saros 152 13:53 TD A.Node ΔT= 375s Par. = 76m U.Mag. = 0.1146 Gam. = 0.9549 P.Mag. = 1.0971	**Penumbral** **2251 Dec 28** Saros 119 19:13 TD D.Node ΔT= 376s Pen. = 171m U.Mag. = -0.7854 Gam. = 1.4132 P.Mag. = 0.3162
Partial **2252 Jun 22** Saros 124 22:33 TD A.Node ΔT= 377s Par. = 119m U.Mag. = 0.3286 Gam. = -0.8494 P.Mag. = 1.2697	**Partial** **2252 Dec 16** Saros 129 18:19 TD D.Node ΔT= 378s Par. = 154m U.Mag. = 0.4521 Gam. = 0.7406 P.Mag. = 1.5468	**Total -** **2253 Jun 12** Saros 134 14:57 TD A.Node ΔT= 379s Tot. = 98m Par. = 215m U.Mag. = 1.6520 Gam. = -0.1210 P.Mag. = 2.6195

Plate 151

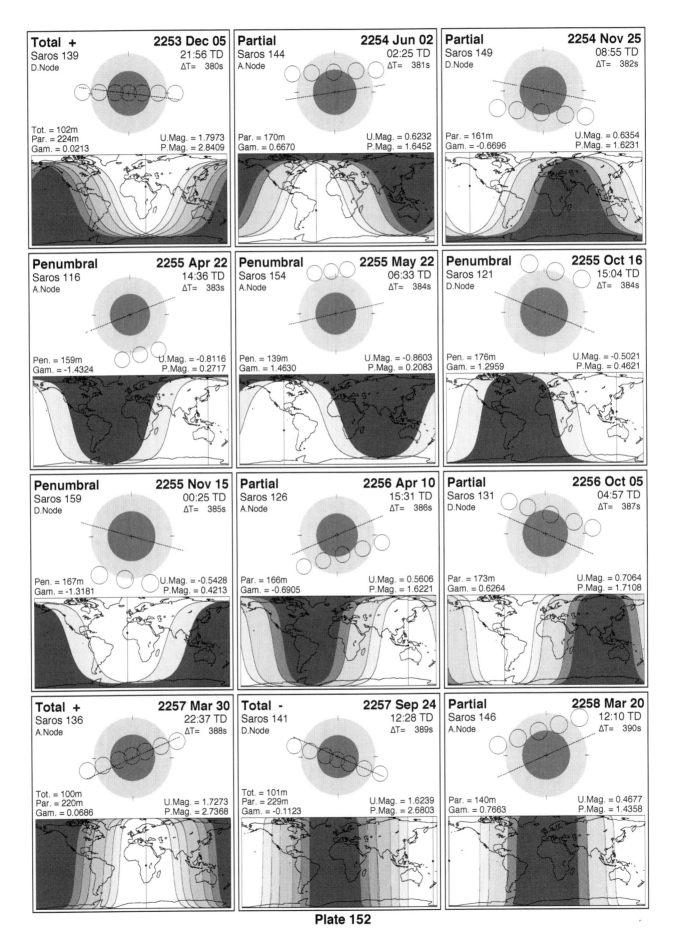

Total +   **2253 Dec 05**
Saros 139   21:56 TD
D.Node   ΔT= 380s
Tot. = 102m
Par. = 224m   U.Mag. = 1.7973
Gam. = 0.0213   P.Mag. = 2.8409

Partial   **2254 Jun 02**
Saros 144   02:25 TD
A.Node   ΔT= 381s
Par. = 170m   U.Mag. = 0.6232
Gam. = 0.6670   P.Mag. = 1.6452

Partial   **2254 Nov 25**
Saros 149   08:55 TD
D.Node   ΔT= 382s
Par. = 161m   U.Mag. = 0.6354
Gam. = -0.6696   P.Mag. = 1.6231

Penumbral   **2255 Apr 22**
Saros 116   14:36 TD
A.Node   ΔT= 383s
Pen. = 159m   U.Mag. = -0.8116
Gam. = -1.4324   P.Mag. = 0.2717

Penumbral   **2255 May 22**
Saros 154   06:33 TD
A.Node   ΔT= 384s
Pen. = 139m   U.Mag. = -0.8603
Gam. = 1.4630   P.Mag. = 0.2083

Penumbral   **2255 Oct 16**
Saros 121   15:04 TD
D.Node   ΔT= 384s
Pen. = 176m   U.Mag. = -0.5021
Gam. = 1.2959   P.Mag. = 0.4621

Penumbral   **2255 Nov 15**
Saros 159   00:25 TD
D.Node   ΔT= 385s
Pen. = 167m   U.Mag. = -0.5428
Gam. = -1.3181   P.Mag. = 0.4213

Partial   **2256 Apr 10**
Saros 126   15:31 TD
A.Node   ΔT= 386s
Par. = 166m   U.Mag. = 0.5606
Gam. = -0.6905   P.Mag. = 1.6221

Partial   **2256 Oct 05**
Saros 131   04:57 TD
D.Node   ΔT= 387s
Par. = 173m   U.Mag. = 0.7064
Gam. = 0.6264   P.Mag. = 1.7108

Total +   **2257 Mar 30**
Saros 136   22:37 TD
A.Node   ΔT= 388s
Tot. = 100m
Par. = 220m   U.Mag. = 1.7273
Gam. = 0.0686   P.Mag. = 2.7368

Total -   **2257 Sep 24**
Saros 141   12:28 TD
D.Node   ΔT= 389s
Tot. = 101m
Par. = 229m   U.Mag. = 1.6239
Gam. = -0.1123   P.Mag. = 2.6803

Partial   **2258 Mar 20**
Saros 146   12:10 TD
A.Node   ΔT= 390s
Par. = 140m   U.Mag. = 0.4677
Gam. = 0.7663   P.Mag. = 1.4358

Plate 152

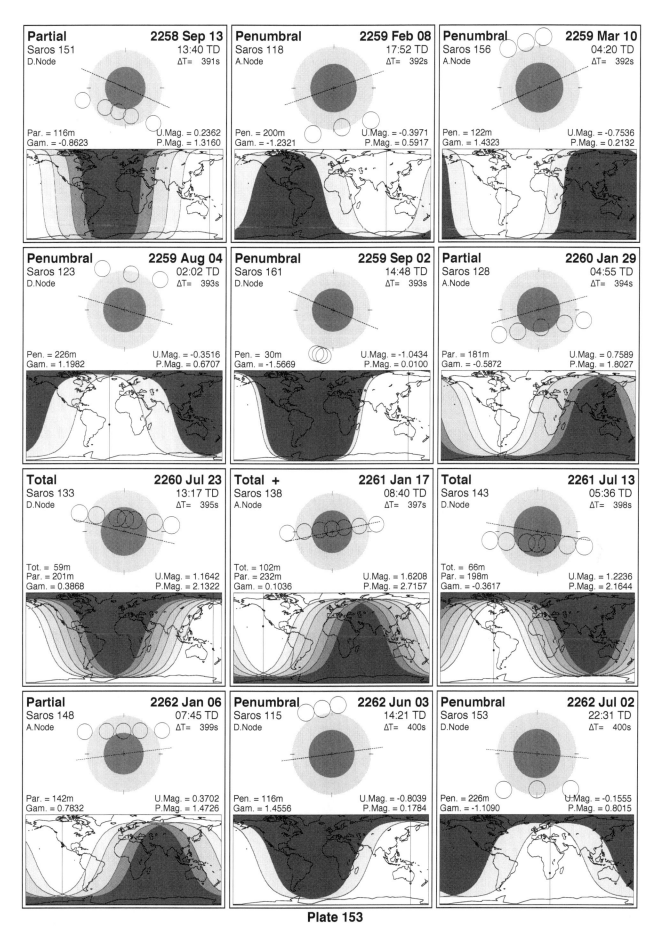

Partial	2258 Sep 13
Saros 151	13:40 TD
D.Node	ΔT= 391s
Par. = 116m	U.Mag. = 0.2362
Gam. = -0.8623	P.Mag. = 1.3160

Penumbral	2259 Feb 08
Saros 118	17:52 TD
A.Node	ΔT= 392s
Pen. = 200m	U.Mag. = -0.3971
Gam. = -1.2321	P.Mag. = 0.5917

Penumbral	2259 Mar 10
Saros 156	04:20 TD
A.Node	ΔT= 392s
Pen. = 122m	U.Mag. = -0.7536
Gam. = 1.4323	P.Mag. = 0.2132

Penumbral	2259 Aug 04
Saros 123	02:02 TD
D.Node	ΔT= 393s
Pen. = 226m	U.Mag. = -0.3516
Gam. = 1.1982	P.Mag. = 0.6707

Penumbral	2259 Sep 02
Saros 161	14:48 TD
D.Node	ΔT= 393s
Pen. = 30m	U.Mag. = -1.0434
Gam. = -1.5669	P.Mag. = 0.0100

Partial	2260 Jan 29
Saros 128	04:55 TD
A.Node	ΔT= 394s
Par. = 181m	U.Mag. = 0.7589
Gam. = -0.5872	P.Mag. = 1.8027

Total	2260 Jul 23
Saros 133	13:17 TD
D.Node	ΔT= 395s
Tot. = 59m	
Par. = 201m	U.Mag. = 1.1642
Gam. = 0.3868	P.Mag. = 2.1322

Total +	2261 Jan 17
Saros 138	08:40 TD
A.Node	ΔT= 397s
Tot. = 102m	
Par. = 232m	U.Mag. = 1.6208
Gam. = 0.1036	P.Mag. = 2.7157

Total	2261 Jul 13
Saros 143	05:36 TD
D.Node	ΔT= 398s
Tot. = 66m	
Par. = 198m	U.Mag. = 1.2236
Gam. = -0.3617	P.Mag. = 2.1644

Partial	2262 Jan 06
Saros 148	07:45 TD
A.Node	ΔT= 399s
Par. = 142m	U.Mag. = 0.3702
Gam. = 0.7832	P.Mag. = 1.4726

Penumbral	2262 Jun 03
Saros 115	14:21 TD
D.Node	ΔT= 400s
Pen. = 116m	U.Mag. = -0.8039
Gam. = 1.4556	P.Mag. = 0.1784

Penumbral	2262 Jul 02
Saros 153	22:31 TD
D.Node	ΔT= 400s
Pen. = 226m	U.Mag. = -0.1555
Gam. = -1.1090	P.Mag. = 0.8015

Plate 153

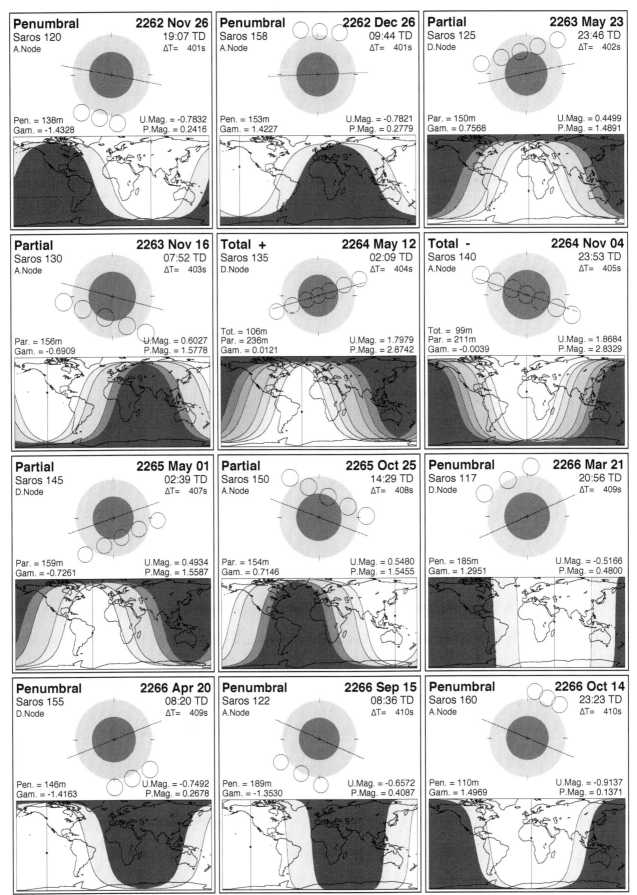

Penumbral   **2262 Nov 26**
Saros 120   19:07 TD
A.Node   ΔT= 401s
Pen. = 138m   U.Mag. = -0.7832
Gam. = -1.4328   P.Mag. = 0.2416

Penumbral   **2262 Dec 26**
Saros 158   09:44 TD
A.Node   ΔT= 401s
Pen. = 153m   U.Mag. = -0.7821
Gam. = 1.4227   P.Mag. = 0.2779

Partial   **2263 May 23**
Saros 125   23:46 TD
D.Node   ΔT= 402s
Par. = 150m   U.Mag. = 0.4499
Gam. = 0.7568   P.Mag. = 1.4891

Partial   **2263 Nov 16**
Saros 130   07:52 TD
A.Node   ΔT= 403s
Par. = 156m   U.Mag. = 0.6027
Gam. = -0.6909   P.Mag. = 1.5778

Total +   **2264 May 12**
Saros 135   02:09 TD
D.Node   ΔT= 404s
Tot. = 106m
Par. = 236m   U.Mag. = 1.7979
Gam. = 0.0121   P.Mag. = 2.8742

Total -   **2264 Nov 04**
Saros 140   23:53 TD
A.Node   ΔT= 405s
Tot. = 99m
Par. = 211m   U.Mag. = 1.8684
Gam. = -0.0039   P.Mag. = 2.8329

Partial   **2265 May 01**
Saros 145   02:39 TD
D.Node   ΔT= 407s
Par. = 159m   U.Mag. = 0.4934
Gam. = -0.7261   P.Mag. = 1.5587

Partial   **2265 Oct 25**
Saros 150   14:29 TD
A.Node   ΔT= 408s
Par. = 154m   U.Mag. = 0.5480
Gam. = 0.7146   P.Mag. = 1.5455

Penumbral   **2266 Mar 21**
Saros 117   20:56 TD
D.Node   ΔT= 409s
Pen. = 185m   U.Mag. = -0.5166
Gam. = 1.2951   P.Mag. = 0.4800

Penumbral   **2266 Apr 20**
Saros 155   08:20 TD
D.Node   ΔT= 409s
Pen. = 146m   U.Mag. = -0.7492
Gam. = -1.4163   P.Mag. = 0.2678

Penumbral   **2266 Sep 15**
Saros 122   08:36 TD
A.Node   ΔT= 410s
Pen. = 189m   U.Mag. = -0.6572
Gam. = -1.3530   P.Mag. = 0.4087

Penumbral   **2266 Oct 14**
Saros 160   23:23 TD
A.Node   ΔT= 410s
Pen. = 110m   U.Mag. = -0.9137
Gam. = 1.4969   P.Mag. = 0.1371

Plate 154

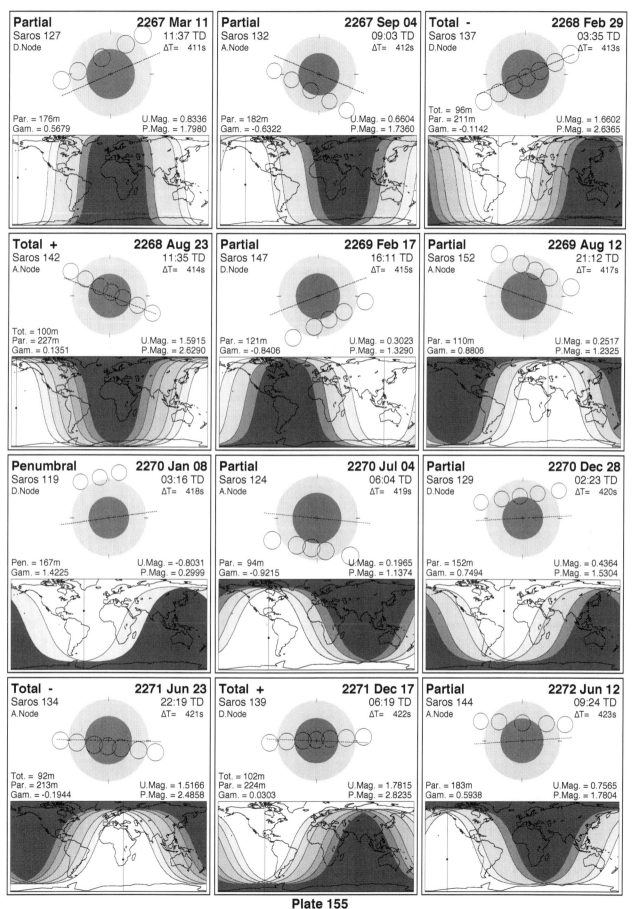

Partial	2267 Mar 11
Saros 127	11:37 TD
D.Node	ΔT= 411s
Par. = 176m	U.Mag. = 0.8336
Gam. = 0.5679	P.Mag. = 1.7980

Partial	2267 Sep 04
Saros 132	09:03 TD
A.Node	ΔT= 412s
Par. = 182m	U.Mag. = 0.6604
Gam. = -0.6322	P.Mag. = 1.7360

Total -	2268 Feb 29
Saros 137	03:35 TD
D.Node	ΔT= 413s
Tot. = 96m	
Par. = 211m	U.Mag. = 1.6602
Gam. = -0.1142	P.Mag. = 2.6365

Total +	2268 Aug 23
Saros 142	11:35 TD
A.Node	ΔT= 414s
Tot. = 100m	
Par. = 227m	U.Mag. = 1.5915
Gam. = 0.1351	P.Mag. = 2.6290

Partial	2269 Feb 17
Saros 147	16:11 TD
D.Node	ΔT= 415s
Par. = 121m	U.Mag. = 0.3023
Gam. = -0.8406	P.Mag. = 1.3290

Partial	2269 Aug 12
Saros 152	21:12 TD
A.Node	ΔT= 417s
Par. = 110m	U.Mag. = 0.2517
Gam. = 0.8806	P.Mag. = 1.2325

Penumbral	2270 Jan 08
Saros 119	03:16 TD
D.Node	ΔT= 418s
Pen. = 167m	U.Mag. = -0.8031
Gam. = 1.4225	P.Mag. = 0.2999

Partial	2270 Jul 04
Saros 124	06:04 TD
A.Node	ΔT= 419s
Par. = 94m	U.Mag. = 0.1965
Gam. = -0.9215	P.Mag. = 1.1374

Partial	2270 Dec 28
Saros 129	02:23 TD
D.Node	ΔT= 420s
Par. = 152m	U.Mag. = 0.4364
Gam. = 0.7494	P.Mag. = 1.5304

Total -	2271 Jun 23
Saros 134	22:19 TD
A.Node	ΔT= 421s
Tot. = 92m	
Par. = 213m	U.Mag. = 1.5166
Gam. = -0.1944	P.Mag. = 2.4858

Total +	2271 Dec 17
Saros 139	06:19 TD
D.Node	ΔT= 422s
Tot. = 102m	
Par. = 224m	U.Mag. = 1.7815
Gam. = 0.0303	P.Mag. = 2.8235

Partial	2272 Jun 12
Saros 144	09:24 TD
A.Node	ΔT= 423s
Par. = 183m	U.Mag. = 0.7565
Gam. = 0.5938	P.Mag. = 1.7804

Plate 155

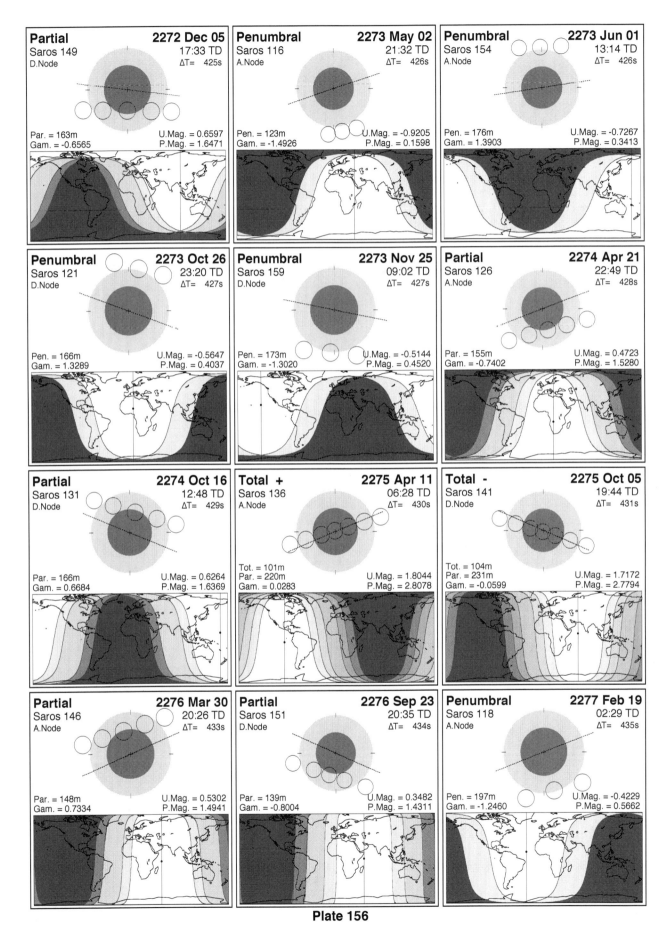

Partial   **2272 Dec 05**
Saros 149   17:33 TD
D.Node   ΔT= 425s
Par. = 163m   U.Mag. = 0.6597
Gam. = -0.6565   P.Mag. = 1.6471

Penumbral   **2273 May 02**
Saros 116   21:32 TD
A.Node   ΔT= 426s
Pen. = 123m   U.Mag. = -0.9205
Gam. = -1.4926   P.Mag. = 0.1598

Penumbral   **2273 Jun 01**
Saros 154   13:14 TD
A.Node   ΔT= 426s
Pen. = 176m   U.Mag. = -0.7267
Gam. = 1.3903   P.Mag. = 0.3413

Penumbral   **2273 Oct 26**
Saros 121   23:20 TD
D.Node   ΔT= 427s
Pen. = 166m   U.Mag. = -0.5647
Gam. = 1.3289   P.Mag. = 0.4037

Penumbral   **2273 Nov 25**
Saros 159   09:02 TD
D.Node   ΔT= 427s
Pen. = 173m   U.Mag. = -0.5144
Gam. = -1.3020   P.Mag. = 0.4520

Partial   **2274 Apr 21**
Saros 126   22:49 TD
A.Node   ΔT= 428s
Par. = 155m   U.Mag. = 0.4723
Gam. = -0.7402   P.Mag. = 1.5280

Partial   **2274 Oct 16**
Saros 131   12:48 TD
D.Node   ΔT= 429s
Par. = 166m   U.Mag. = 0.6264
Gam. = 0.6684   P.Mag. = 1.6369

Total +   **2275 Apr 11**
Saros 136   06:28 TD
A.Node   ΔT= 430s
Tot. = 101m
Par. = 220m   U.Mag. = 1.8044
Gam. = 0.0283   P.Mag. = 2.8078

Total -   **2275 Oct 05**
Saros 141   19:44 TD
D.Node   ΔT= 431s
Tot. = 104m
Par. = 231m   U.Mag. = 1.7172
Gam. = -0.0599   P.Mag. = 2.7794

Partial   **2276 Mar 30**
Saros 146   20:26 TD
A.Node   ΔT= 433s
Par. = 148m   U.Mag. = 0.5302
Gam. = 0.7334   P.Mag. = 1.4941

Partial   **2276 Sep 23**
Saros 151   20:35 TD
D.Node   ΔT= 434s
Par. = 139m   U.Mag. = 0.3482
Gam. = -0.8004   P.Mag. = 1.4311

Penumbral   **2277 Feb 19**
Saros 118   02:29 TD
A.Node   ΔT= 435s
Pen. = 197m   U.Mag. = -0.4229
Gam. = -1.2460   P.Mag. = 0.5662

Plate 156

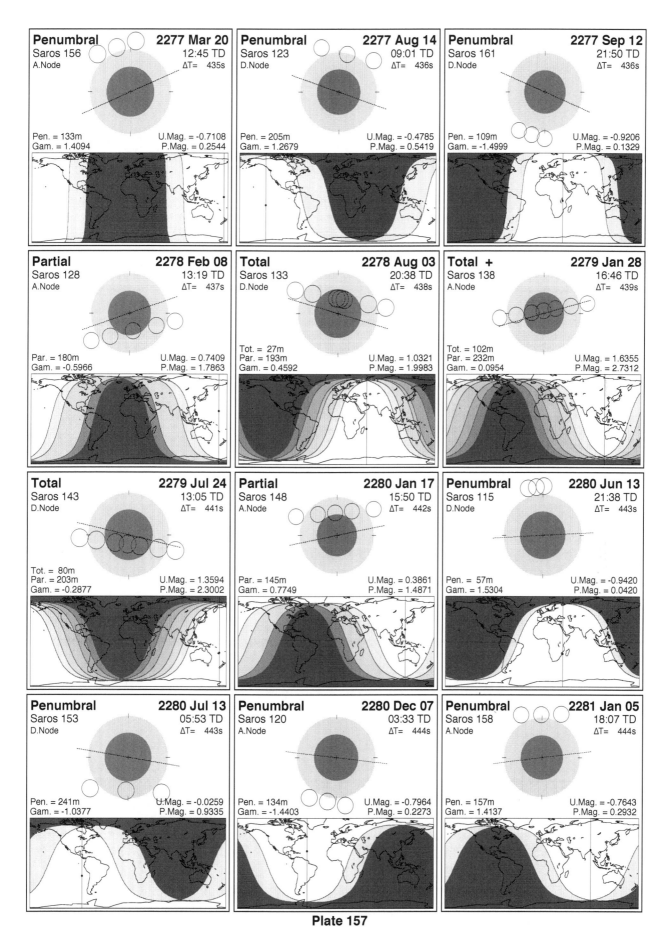

Penumbral   **2277 Mar 20**
Saros 156   12:45 TD
A.Node   ΔT= 435s
Pen. = 133m   U.Mag. = -0.7108
Gam. = 1.4094   P.Mag. = 0.2544

Penumbral   **2277 Aug 14**
Saros 123   09:01 TD
D.Node   ΔT= 436s
Pen. = 205m   U.Mag. = -0.4785
Gam. = 1.2679   P.Mag. = 0.5419

Penumbral   **2277 Sep 12**
Saros 161   21:50 TD
D.Node   ΔT= 436s
Pen. = 109m   U.Mag. = -0.9206
Gam. = -1.4999   P.Mag. = 0.1329

Partial   **2278 Feb 08**
Saros 128   13:19 TD
A.Node   ΔT= 437s
Par. = 180m   U.Mag. = 0.7409
Gam. = -0.5966   P.Mag. = 1.7863

Total   **2278 Aug 03**
Saros 133   20:38 TD
D.Node   ΔT= 438s
Tot. = 27m
Par. = 193m   U.Mag. = 1.0321
Gam. = 0.4592   P.Mag. = 1.9983

Total +   **2279 Jan 28**
Saros 138   16:46 TD
A.Node   ΔT= 439s
Tot. = 102m
Par. = 232m   U.Mag. = 1.6355
Gam. = 0.0954   P.Mag. = 2.7312

Total   **2279 Jul 24**
Saros 143   13:05 TD
D.Node   ΔT= 441s
Tot. = 80m
Par. = 203m   U.Mag. = 1.3594
Gam. = -0.2877   P.Mag. = 2.3002

Partial   **2280 Jan 17**
Saros 148   15:50 TD
A.Node   ΔT= 442s
Par. = 145m   U.Mag. = 0.3861
Gam. = 0.7749   P.Mag. = 1.4871

Penumbral   **2280 Jun 13**
Saros 115   21:38 TD
D.Node   ΔT= 443s
Pen. = 57m   U.Mag. = -0.9420
Gam. = 1.5304   P.Mag. = 0.0420

Penumbral   **2280 Jul 13**
Saros 153   05:53 TD
D.Node   ΔT= 443s
Pen. = 241m   U.Mag. = -0.0259
Gam. = -1.0377   P.Mag. = 0.9335

Penumbral   **2280 Dec 07**
Saros 120   03:33 TD
A.Node   ΔT= 444s
Pen. = 134m   U.Mag. = -0.7964
Gam. = -1.4403   P.Mag. = 0.2273

Penumbral   **2281 Jan 05**
Saros 158   18:07 TD
A.Node   ΔT= 444s
Pen. = 157m   U.Mag. = -0.7643
Gam. = 1.4137   P.Mag. = 0.2932

Plate 157

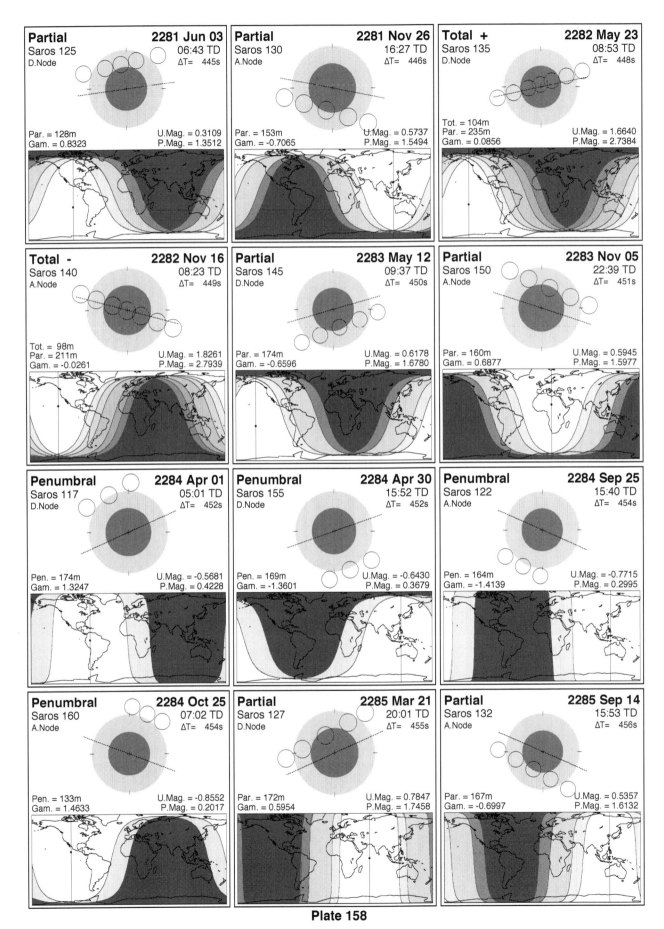

Partial   **2281 Jun 03**
Saros 125   06:43 TD
D.Node   ΔT= 445s
Par. = 128m   U.Mag. = 0.3109
Gam. = 0.8323   P.Mag. = 1.3512

Partial   **2281 Nov 26**
Saros 130   16:27 TD
A.Node   ΔT= 446s
Par. = 153m   U.Mag. = 0.5737
Gam. = -0.7065   P.Mag. = 1.5494

Total +   **2282 May 23**
Saros 135   08:53 TD
D.Node   ΔT= 448s
Tot. = 104m
Par. = 235m   U.Mag. = 1.6640
Gam. = 0.0856   P.Mag. = 2.7384

Total -   **2282 Nov 16**
Saros 140   08:23 TD
A.Node   ΔT= 449s
Tot. = 98m
Par. = 211m   U.Mag. = 1.8261
Gam. = -0.0261   P.Mag. = 2.7939

Partial   **2283 May 12**
Saros 145   09:37 TD
D.Node   ΔT= 450s
Par. = 174m   U.Mag. = 0.6178
Gam. = -0.6596   P.Mag. = 1.6780

Partial   **2283 Nov 05**
Saros 150   22:39 TD
A.Node   ΔT= 451s
Par. = 160m   U.Mag. = 0.5945
Gam. = 0.6877   P.Mag. = 1.5977

Penumbral   **2284 Apr 01**
Saros 117   05:01 TD
D.Node   ΔT= 452s
Pen. = 174m   U.Mag. = -0.5681
Gam. = 1.3247   P.Mag. = 0.4228

Penumbral   **2284 Apr 30**
Saros 155   15:52 TD
D.Node   ΔT= 452s
Pen. = 169m   U.Mag. = -0.6430
Gam. = -1.3601   P.Mag. = 0.3679

Penumbral   **2284 Sep 25**
Saros 122   15:40 TD
A.Node   ΔT= 454s
Pen. = 164m   U.Mag. = -0.7715
Gam. = -1.4139   P.Mag. = 0.2995

Penumbral   **2284 Oct 25**
Saros 160   07:02 TD
A.Node   ΔT= 454s
Pen. = 133m   U.Mag. = -0.8552
Gam. = 1.4633   P.Mag. = 0.2017

Partial   **2285 Mar 21**
Saros 127   20:01 TD
D.Node   ΔT= 455s
Par. = 172m   U.Mag. = 0.7847
Gam. = 0.5954   P.Mag. = 1.7458

Partial   **2285 Sep 14**
Saros 132   15:53 TD
A.Node   ΔT= 456s
Par. = 167m   U.Mag. = 0.5357
Gam. = -0.6997   P.Mag. = 1.6132

Plate 158

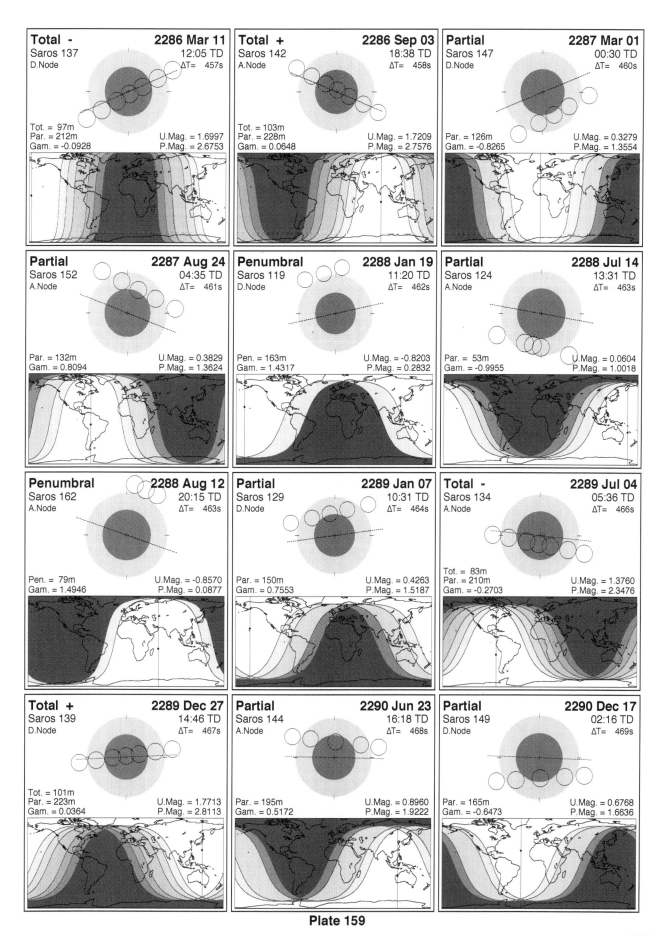

Total -	2286 Mar 11
Saros 137	12:05 TD
D.Node	ΔT= 457s

Tot. = 97m
Par. = 212m
Gam. = -0.0928
U.Mag. = 1.6997
P.Mag. = 2.6753

Total +	2286 Sep 03
Saros 142	18:38 TD
A.Node	ΔT= 458s

Tot. = 103m
Par. = 228m
Gam. = 0.0648
U.Mag. = 1.7209
P.Mag. = 2.7576

Partial	2287 Mar 01
Saros 147	00:30 TD
D.Node	ΔT= 460s

Par. = 126m
Gam. = -0.8265
U.Mag. = 0.3279
P.Mag. = 1.3554

Partial	2287 Aug 24
Saros 152	04:35 TD
A.Node	ΔT= 461s

Par. = 132m
Gam. = 0.8094
U.Mag. = 0.3829
P.Mag. = 1.3624

Penumbral	2288 Jan 19
Saros 119	11:20 TD
D.Node	ΔT= 462s

Pen. = 163m
Gam. = 1.4317
U.Mag. = -0.8203
P.Mag. = 0.2832

Partial	2288 Jul 14
Saros 124	13:31 TD
A.Node	ΔT= 463s

Par. = 53m
Gam. = -0.9955
U.Mag. = 0.0604
P.Mag. = 1.0018

Penumbral	2288 Aug 12
Saros 162	20:15 TD
A.Node	ΔT= 463s

Pen. = 79m
Gam. = 1.4946
U.Mag. = -0.8570
P.Mag. = 0.0877

Partial	2289 Jan 07
Saros 129	10:31 TD
D.Node	ΔT= 464s

Par. = 150m
Gam. = 0.7553
U.Mag. = 0.4263
P.Mag. = 1.5187

Total -	2289 Jul 04
Saros 134	05:36 TD
A.Node	ΔT= 466s

Tot. = 83m
Par. = 210m
Gam. = -0.2703
U.Mag. = 1.3760
P.Mag. = 2.3476

Total +	2289 Dec 27
Saros 139	14:46 TD
D.Node	ΔT= 467s

Tot. = 101m
Par. = 223m
Gam. = 0.0364
U.Mag. = 1.7713
P.Mag. = 2.8113

Partial	2290 Jun 23
Saros 144	16:18 TD
A.Node	ΔT= 468s

Par. = 195m
Gam. = 0.5172
U.Mag. = 0.8960
P.Mag. = 1.9222

Partial	2290 Dec 17
Saros 149	02:16 TD
D.Node	ΔT= 469s

Par. = 165m
Gam. = -0.6473
U.Mag. = 0.6768
P.Mag. = 1.6636

Plate 159

255

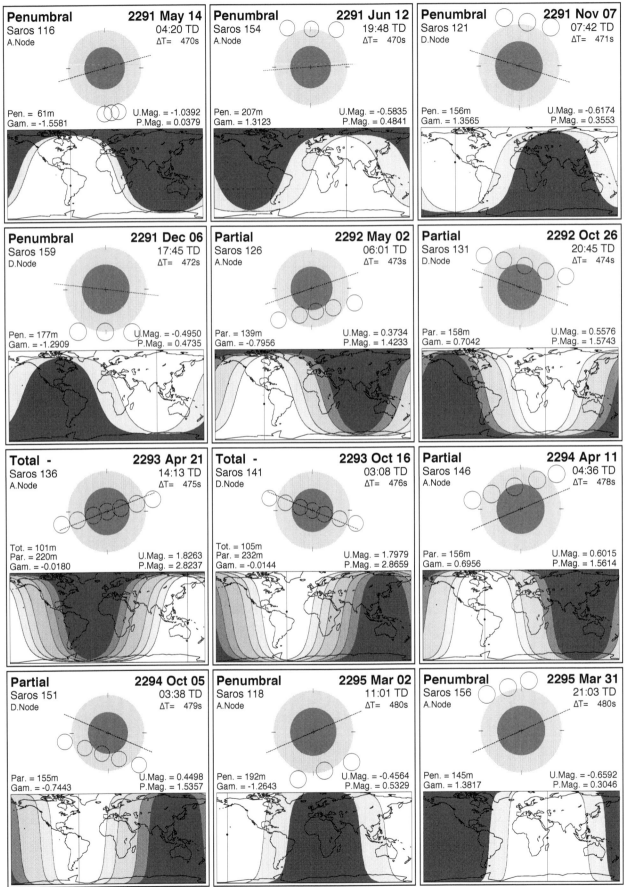

Penumbral   **2291 May 14**
Saros 116   04:20 TD
A.Node   ΔT= 470s

Pen. = 61m   U.Mag. = -1.0392
Gam. = -1.5581   P.Mag. = 0.0379

Penumbral   **2291 Jun 12**
Saros 154   19:48 TD
A.Node   ΔT= 470s

Pen. = 207m   U.Mag. = -0.5835
Gam. = 1.3123   P.Mag. = 0.4841

Penumbral   **2291 Nov 07**
Saros 121   07:42 TD
D.Node   ΔT= 471s

Pen. = 156m   U.Mag. = -0.6174
Gam. = 1.3565   P.Mag. = 0.3553

Penumbral   **2291 Dec 06**
Saros 159   17:45 TD
D.Node   ΔT= 472s

Pen. = 177m   U.Mag. = -0.4950
Gam. = -1.2909   P.Mag. = 0.4735

Partial   **2292 May 02**
Saros 126   06:01 TD
A.Node   ΔT= 473s

Par. = 139m   U.Mag. = 0.3734
Gam. = -0.7956   P.Mag. = 1.4233

Partial   **2292 Oct 26**
Saros 131   20:45 TD
D.Node   ΔT= 474s

Par. = 158m   U.Mag. = 0.5576
Gam. = 0.7042   P.Mag. = 1.5743

Total -   **2293 Apr 21**
Saros 136   14:13 TD
A.Node   ΔT= 475s

Tot. = 101m
Par. = 220m   U.Mag. = 1.8263
Gam. = -0.0180   P.Mag. = 2.8237

Total -   **2293 Oct 16**
Saros 141   03:08 TD
D.Node   ΔT= 476s

Tot. = 105m
Par. = 232m   U.Mag. = 1.7979
Gam. = -0.0144   P.Mag. = 2.8659

Partial   **2294 Apr 11**
Saros 146   04:36 TD
A.Node   ΔT= 478s

Par. = 156m   U.Mag. = 0.6015
Gam. = 0.6956   P.Mag. = 1.5614

Partial   **2294 Oct 05**
Saros 151   03:38 TD
D.Node   ΔT= 479s

Par. = 155m   U.Mag. = 0.4498
Gam. = -0.7443   P.Mag. = 1.5357

Penumbral   **2295 Mar 02**
Saros 118   11:01 TD
A.Node   ΔT= 480s

Pen. = 192m   U.Mag. = -0.4564
Gam. = -1.2643   P.Mag. = 0.5329

Penumbral   **2295 Mar 31**
Saros 156   21:03 TD
A.Node   ΔT= 480s

Pen. = 145m   U.Mag. = -0.6592
Gam. = 1.3817   P.Mag. = 0.3046

Plate 160

256

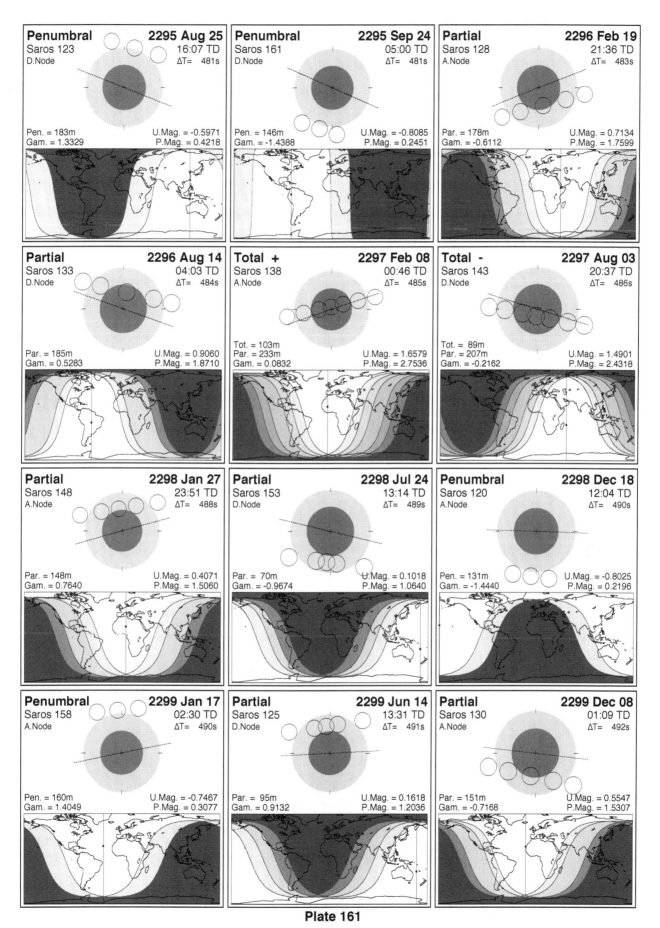

Penumbral   **2295 Aug 25**
Saros 123   16:07 TD
D.Node   ΔT= 481s
Pen. = 183m   U.Mag. = -0.5971
Gam. = 1.3329   P.Mag. = 0.4218

Penumbral   **2295 Sep 24**
Saros 161   05:00 TD
D.Node   ΔT= 481s
Pen. = 146m   U.Mag. = -0.8085
Gam. = -1.4388   P.Mag. = 0.2451

Partial   **2296 Feb 19**
Saros 128   21:36 TD
A.Node   ΔT= 483s
Par. = 178m   U.Mag. = 0.7134
Gam. = -0.6112   P.Mag. = 1.7599

Partial   **2296 Aug 14**
Saros 133   04:03 TD
D.Node   ΔT= 484s
Par. = 185m   U.Mag. = 0.9060
Gam. = 0.5283   P.Mag. = 1.8710

Total +   **2297 Feb 08**
Saros 138   00:46 TD
A.Node   ΔT= 485s
Tot. = 103m
Par. = 233m   U.Mag. = 1.6579
Gam. = 0.0832   P.Mag. = 2.7536

Total -   **2297 Aug 03**
Saros 143   20:37 TD
D.Node   ΔT= 486s
Tot. = 89m
Par. = 207m   U.Mag. = 1.4901
Gam. = -0.2162   P.Mag. = 2.4318

Partial   **2298 Jan 27**
Saros 148   23:51 TD
A.Node   ΔT= 488s
Par. = 148m   U.Mag. = 0.4071
Gam. = 0.7640   P.Mag. = 1.5060

Partial   **2298 Jul 24**
Saros 153   13:14 TD
D.Node   ΔT= 489s
Par. = 70m   U.Mag. = 0.1018
Gam. = -0.9674   P.Mag. = 1.0640

Penumbral   **2298 Dec 18**
Saros 120   12:04 TD
A.Node   ΔT= 490s
Pen. = 131m   U.Mag. = -0.8025
Gam. = -1.4440   P.Mag. = 0.2196

Penumbral   **2299 Jan 17**
Saros 158   02:30 TD
A.Node   ΔT= 490s
Pen. = 160m   U.Mag. = -0.7467
Gam. = 1.4049   P.Mag. = 0.3077

Partial   **2299 Jun 14**
Saros 125   13:31 TD
D.Node   ΔT= 491s
Par. = 95m   U.Mag. = 0.1618
Gam. = 0.9132   P.Mag. = 1.2036

Partial   **2299 Dec 08**
Saros 130   01:09 TD
A.Node   ΔT= 492s
Par. = 151m   U.Mag. = 0.5547
Gam. = -0.7168   P.Mag. = 1.5307

Plate 161

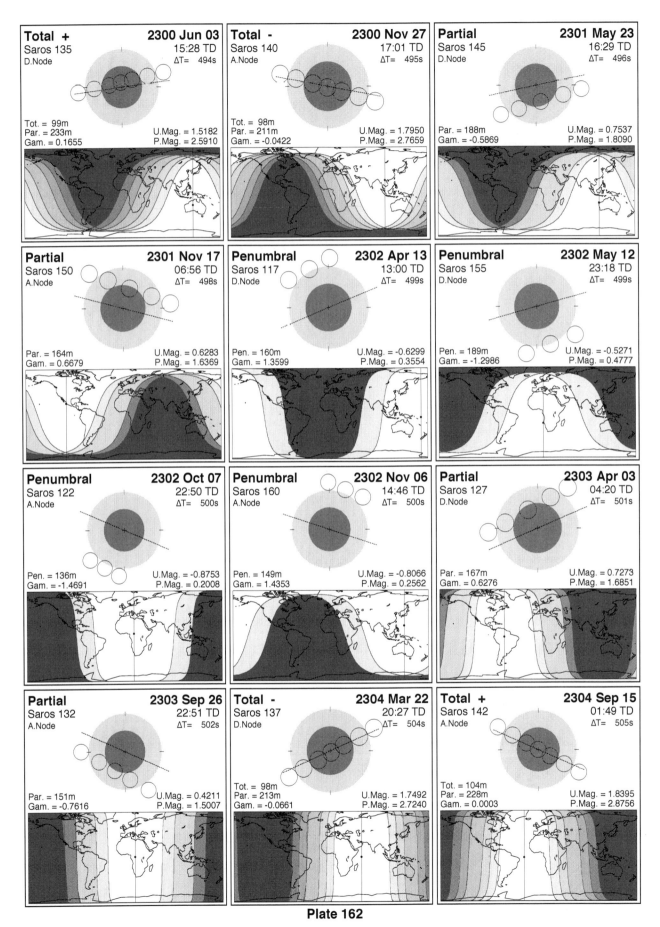

Total +   2300 Jun 03
Saros 135   15:28 TD
D.Node   ΔT= 494s
Tot. = 99m
Par. = 233m   U.Mag. = 1.5182
Gam. = 0.1655   P.Mag. = 2.5910

Total -   2300 Nov 27
Saros 140   17:01 TD
A.Node   ΔT= 495s
Tot. = 98m
Par. = 211m   U.Mag. = 1.7950
Gam. = -0.0422   P.Mag. = 2.7659

Partial   2301 May 23
Saros 145   16:29 TD
D.Node   ΔT= 496s
Par. = 188m   U.Mag. = 0.7537
Gam. = -0.5869   P.Mag. = 1.8090

Partial   2301 Nov 17
Saros 150   06:56 TD
A.Node   ΔT= 498s
Par. = 164m   U.Mag. = 0.6283
Gam. = 0.6679   P.Mag. = 1.6369

Penumbral   2302 Apr 13
Saros 117   13:00 TD
D.Node   ΔT= 499s
Pen. = 160m   U.Mag. = -0.6299
Gam. = 1.3599   P.Mag. = 0.3554

Penumbral   2302 May 12
Saros 155   23:18 TD
D.Node   ΔT= 499s
Pen. = 189m   U.Mag. = -0.5271
Gam. = -1.2986   P.Mag. = 0.4777

Penumbral   2302 Oct 07
Saros 122   22:50 TD
A.Node   ΔT= 500s
Pen. = 136m   U.Mag. = -0.8753
Gam. = -1.4691   P.Mag. = 0.2008

Penumbral   2302 Nov 06
Saros 160   14:46 TD
A.Node   ΔT= 500s
Pen. = 149m   U.Mag. = -0.8066
Gam. = 1.4353   P.Mag. = 0.2562

Partial   2303 Apr 03
Saros 127   04:20 TD
D.Node   ΔT= 501s
Par. = 167m   U.Mag. = 0.7273
Gam. = 0.6276   P.Mag. = 1.6851

Partial   2303 Sep 26
Saros 132   22:51 TD
A.Node   ΔT= 502s
Par. = 151m   U.Mag. = 0.4211
Gam. = -0.7616   P.Mag. = 1.5007

Total -   2304 Mar 22
Saros 137   20:27 TD
D.Node   ΔT= 504s
Tot. = 98m
Par. = 213m   U.Mag. = 1.7492
Gam. = -0.0661   P.Mag. = 2.7240

Total +   2304 Sep 15
Saros 142   01:49 TD
A.Node   ΔT= 505s
Tot. = 104m
Par. = 228m   U.Mag. = 1.8395
Gam. = 0.0003   P.Mag. = 2.8756

Plate 162

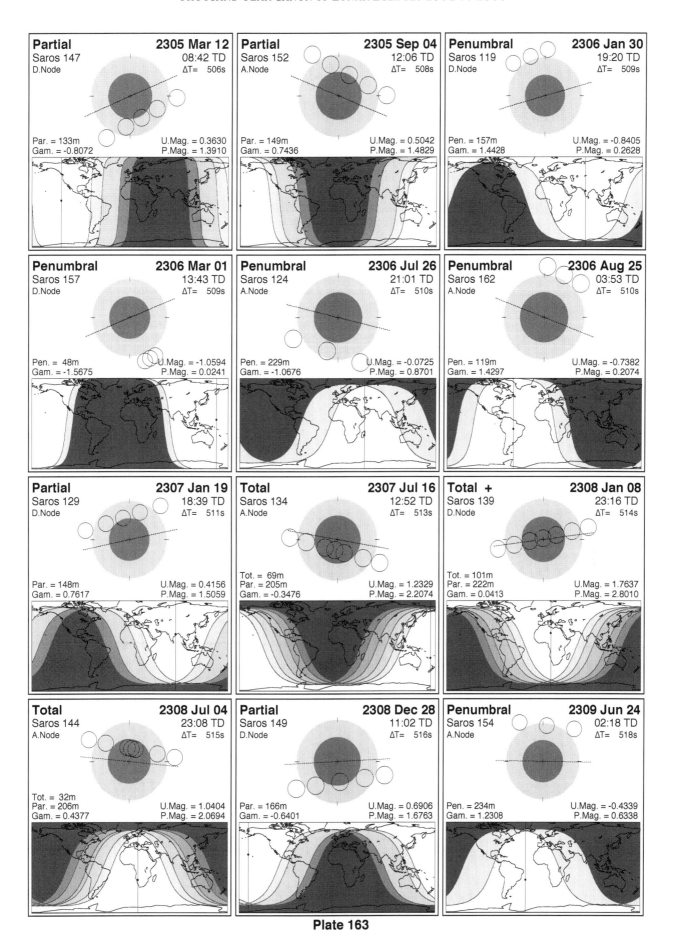

Partial	**2305 Mar 12**
Saros 147	08:42 TD
D.Node	ΔT= 506s
Par. = 133m	U.Mag. = 0.3630
Gam. = -0.8072	P.Mag. = 1.3910

Partial	**2305 Sep 04**
Saros 152	12:06 TD
A.Node	ΔT= 508s
Par. = 149m	U.Mag. = 0.5042
Gam. = 0.7436	P.Mag. = 1.4829

Penumbral	**2306 Jan 30**
Saros 119	19:20 TD
D.Node	ΔT= 509s
Pen. = 157m	U.Mag. = -0.8405
Gam. = 1.4428	P.Mag. = 0.2628

Penumbral	**2306 Mar 01**
Saros 157	13:43 TD
D.Node	ΔT= 509s
Pen. = 48m	U.Mag. = -1.0594
Gam. = -1.5675	P.Mag. = 0.0241

Penumbral	**2306 Jul 26**
Saros 124	21:01 TD
A.Node	ΔT= 510s
Pen. = 229m	U.Mag. = -0.0725
Gam. = -1.0676	P.Mag. = 0.8701

Penumbral	**2306 Aug 25**
Saros 162	03:53 TD
A.Node	ΔT= 510s
Pen. = 119m	U.Mag. = -0.7382
Gam. = 1.4297	P.Mag. = 0.2074

Partial	**2307 Jan 19**
Saros 129	18:39 TD
D.Node	ΔT= 511s
Par. = 148m	U.Mag. = 0.4156
Gam. = 0.7617	P.Mag. = 1.5059

Total	**2307 Jul 16**
Saros 134	12:52 TD
A.Node	ΔT= 513s
Tot. = 69m	
Par. = 205m	U.Mag. = 1.2329
Gam. = -0.3476	P.Mag. = 2.2074

Total +	**2308 Jan 08**
Saros 139	23:16 TD
D.Node	ΔT= 514s
Tot. = 101m	
Par. = 222m	U.Mag. = 1.7637
Gam. = 0.0413	P.Mag. = 2.8010

Total	**2308 Jul 04**
Saros 144	23:08 TD
A.Node	ΔT= 515s
Tot. = 32m	
Par. = 206m	U.Mag. = 1.0404
Gam. = 0.4377	P.Mag. = 2.0694

Partial	**2308 Dec 28**
Saros 149	11:02 TD
D.Node	ΔT= 516s
Par. = 166m	U.Mag. = 0.6906
Gam. = -0.6401	P.Mag. = 1.6763

Penumbral	**2309 Jun 24**
Saros 154	02:18 TD
A.Node	ΔT= 518s
Pen. = 234m	U.Mag. = -0.4339
Gam. = 1.2308	P.Mag. = 0.6338

Plate 163

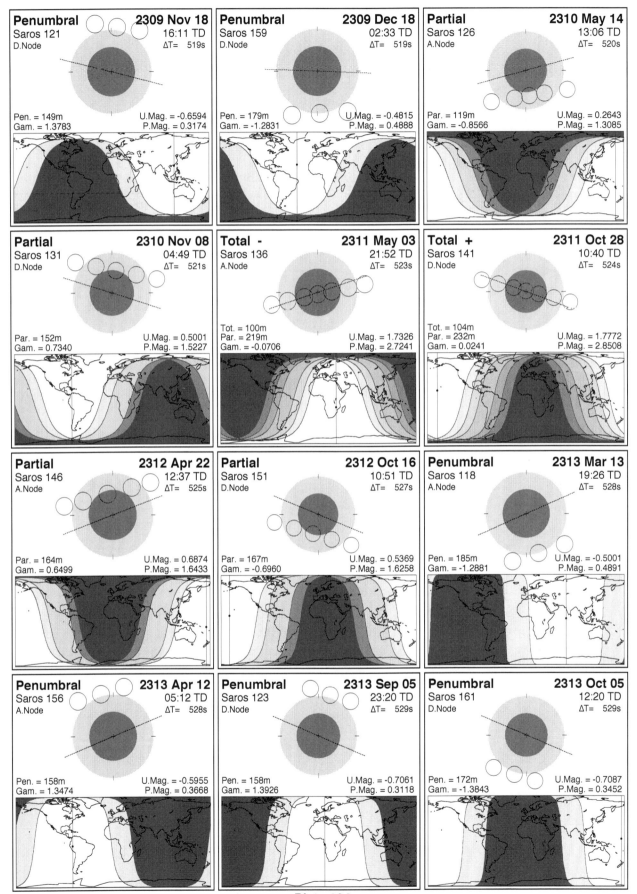

Penumbral **2309 Nov 18**
Saros 121 16:11 TD
D.Node ΔT= 519s
Pen. = 149m U.Mag. = -0.6594
Gam. = 1.3783 P.Mag. = 0.3174

Penumbral **2309 Dec 18**
Saros 159 02:33 TD
D.Node ΔT= 519s
Pen. = 179m U.Mag. = -0.4815
Gam. = -1.2831 P.Mag. = 0.4888

Partial **2310 May 14**
Saros 126 13:06 TD
A.Node ΔT= 520s
Par. = 119m U.Mag. = 0.2643
Gam. = -0.8566 P.Mag. = 1.3085

Partial **2310 Nov 08**
Saros 131 04:49 TD
D.Node ΔT= 521s
Par. = 152m U.Mag. = 0.5001
Gam. = 0.7340 P.Mag. = 1.5227

Total - **2311 May 03**
Saros 136 21:52 TD
A.Node ΔT= 523s
Tot. = 100m
Par. = 219m U.Mag. = 1.7326
Gam. = -0.0706 P.Mag. = 2.7241

Total + **2311 Oct 28**
Saros 141 10:40 TD
D.Node ΔT= 524s
Tot. = 104m
Par. = 232m U.Mag. = 1.7772
Gam. = 0.0241 P.Mag. = 2.8508

Partial **2312 Apr 22**
Saros 146 12:37 TD
A.Node ΔT= 525s
Par. = 164m U.Mag. = 0.6874
Gam. = 0.6499 P.Mag. = 1.6433

Partial **2312 Oct 16**
Saros 151 10:51 TD
D.Node ΔT= 527s
Par. = 167m U.Mag. = 0.5369
Gam. = -0.6960 P.Mag. = 1.6258

Penumbral **2313 Mar 13**
Saros 118 19:26 TD
A.Node ΔT= 528s
Pen. = 185m U.Mag. = -0.5001
Gam. = -1.2881 P.Mag. = 0.4891

Penumbral **2313 Apr 12**
Saros 156 05:12 TD
A.Node ΔT= 528s
Pen. = 158m U.Mag. = -0.5955
Gam. = 1.3474 P.Mag. = 0.3668

Penumbral **2313 Sep 05**
Saros 123 23:20 TD
D.Node ΔT= 529s
Pen. = 158m U.Mag. = -0.7061
Gam. = 1.3926 P.Mag. = 0.3118

Penumbral **2313 Oct 05**
Saros 161 12:20 TD
D.Node ΔT= 529s
Pen. = 172m U.Mag. = -0.7087
Gam. = -1.3843 P.Mag. = 0.3452

Plate 164

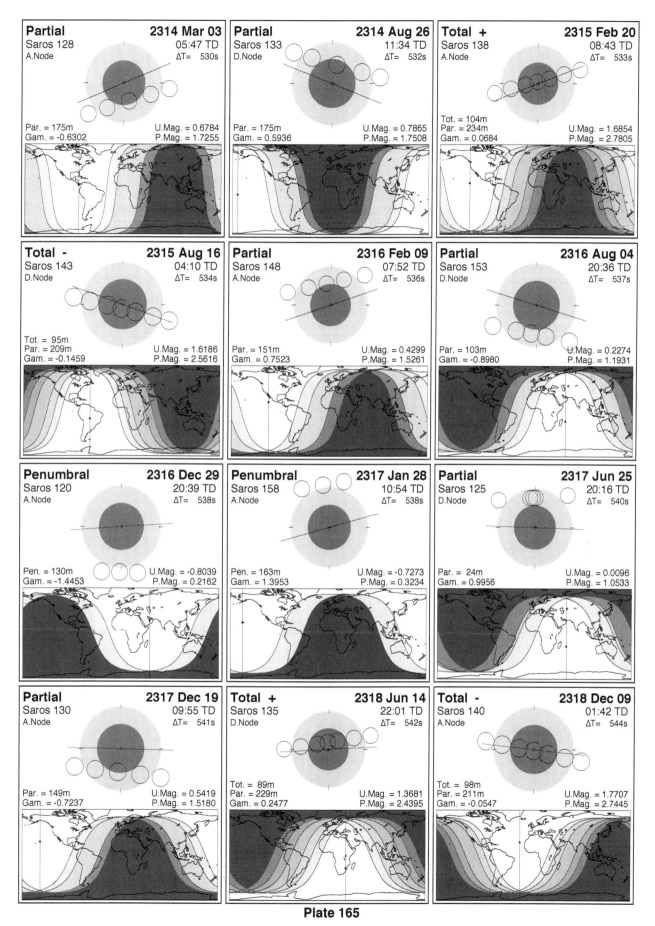

Partial 2314 Mar 03 Saros 128 05:47 TD A.Node ΔT= 530s Par. = 175m U.Mag. = 0.6784 Gam. = -0.6302 P.Mag. = 1.7255	**Partial** 2314 Aug 26 Saros 133 11:34 TD D.Node ΔT= 532s Par. = 175m U.Mag. = 0.7865 Gam. = 0.5936 P.Mag. = 1.7508	**Total +** 2315 Feb 20 Saros 138 08:43 TD A.Node ΔT= 533s Tot. = 104m Par. = 234m U.Mag. = 1.6854 Gam. = 0.0684 P.Mag. = 2.7805
Total - 2315 Aug 16 Saros 143 04:10 TD D.Node ΔT= 534s Tot. = 95m Par. = 209m U.Mag. = 1.6186 Gam. = -0.1459 P.Mag. = 2.5616	**Partial** 2316 Feb 09 Saros 148 07:52 TD A.Node ΔT= 536s Par. = 151m U.Mag. = 0.4299 Gam. = 0.7523 P.Mag. = 1.5261	**Partial** 2316 Aug 04 Saros 153 20:36 TD D.Node ΔT= 537s Par. = 103m U.Mag. = 0.2274 Gam. = -0.8980 P.Mag. = 1.1931
Penumbral 2316 Dec 29 Saros 120 20:39 TD A.Node ΔT= 538s Pen. = 130m U.Mag. = -0.8039 Gam. = -1.4453 P.Mag. = 0.2162	**Penumbral** 2317 Jan 28 Saros 158 10:54 TD A.Node ΔT= 538s Pen. = 163m U.Mag. = -0.7273 Gam. = 1.3953 P.Mag. = 0.3234	**Partial** 2317 Jun 25 Saros 125 20:16 TD D.Node ΔT= 540s Par. = 24m U.Mag. = 0.0096 Gam. = 0.9956 P.Mag. = 1.0533
Partial 2317 Dec 19 Saros 130 09:55 TD A.Node ΔT= 541s Par. = 149m U.Mag. = 0.5419 Gam. = -0.7237 P.Mag. = 1.5180	**Total +** 2318 Jun 14 Saros 135 22:01 TD D.Node ΔT= 542s Tot. = 89m Par. = 229m U.Mag. = 1.3681 Gam. = 0.2477 P.Mag. = 2.4395	**Total -** 2318 Dec 09 Saros 140 01:42 TD A.Node ΔT= 544s Tot. = 98m Par. = 211m U.Mag. = 1.7707 Gam. = -0.0547 P.Mag. = 2.7445

Plate 165

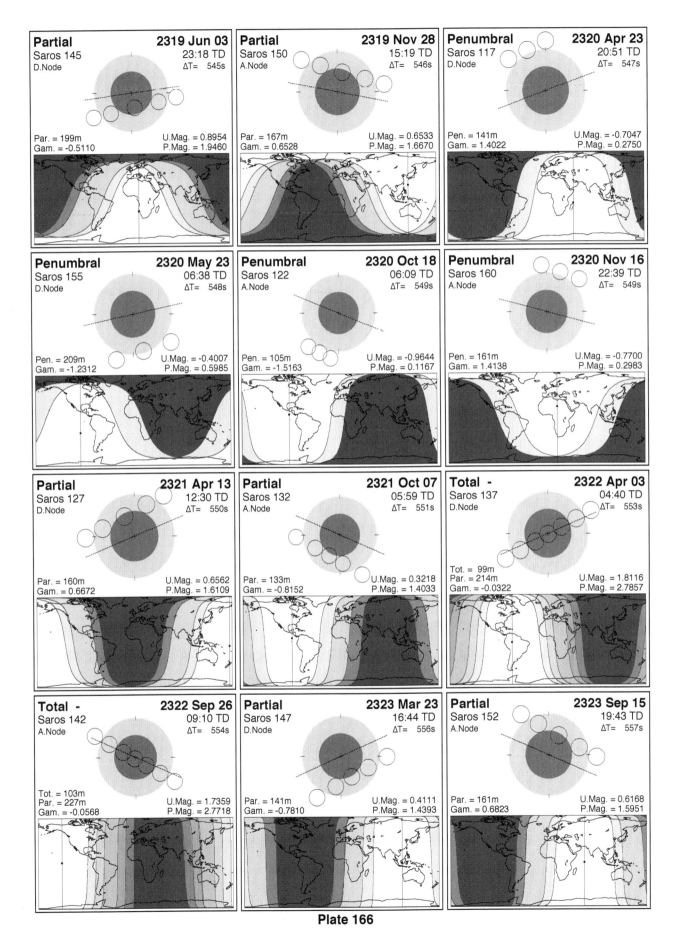

Partial   **2319 Jun 03**
Saros 145   23:18 TD
D.Node   ΔT= 545s
Par. = 199m   U.Mag. = 0.8954
Gam. = -0.5110   P.Mag. = 1.9460

Partial   **2319 Nov 28**
Saros 150   15:19 TD
A.Node   ΔT= 546s
Par. = 167m   U.Mag. = 0.6533
Gam. = 0.6528   P.Mag. = 1.6670

Penumbral   **2320 Apr 23**
Saros 117   20:51 TD
D.Node   ΔT= 547s
Pen. = 141m   U.Mag. = -0.7047
Gam. = 1.4022   P.Mag. = 0.2750

Penumbral   **2320 May 23**
Saros 155   06:38 TD
D.Node   ΔT= 548s
Pen. = 209m   U.Mag. = -0.4007
Gam. = -1.2312   P.Mag. = 0.5985

Penumbral   **2320 Oct 18**
Saros 122   06:09 TD
A.Node   ΔT= 549s
Pen. = 105m   U.Mag. = -0.9644
Gam. = -1.5163   P.Mag. = 0.1167

Penumbral   **2320 Nov 16**
Saros 160   22:39 TD
A.Node   ΔT= 549s
Pen. = 161m   U.Mag. = -0.7700
Gam. = 1.4138   P.Mag. = 0.2983

Partial   **2321 Apr 13**
Saros 127   12:30 TD
D.Node   ΔT= 550s
Par. = 160m   U.Mag. = 0.6562
Gam. = 0.6672   P.Mag. = 1.6109

Partial   **2321 Oct 07**
Saros 132   05:59 TD
A.Node   ΔT= 551s
Par. = 133m   U.Mag. = 0.3218
Gam. = -0.8152   P.Mag. = 1.4033

Total -   **2322 Apr 03**
Saros 137   04:40 TD
D.Node   ΔT= 553s
Tot. = 99m
Par. = 214m   U.Mag. = 1.8116
Gam. = -0.0322   P.Mag. = 2.7857

Total -   **2322 Sep 26**
Saros 142   09:10 TD
A.Node   ΔT= 554s
Tot. = 103m
Par. = 227m   U.Mag. = 1.7359
Gam. = -0.0568   P.Mag. = 2.7718

Partial   **2323 Mar 23**
Saros 147   16:44 TD
D.Node   ΔT= 556s
Par. = 141m   U.Mag. = 0.4111
Gam. = -0.7810   P.Mag. = 1.4393

Partial   **2323 Sep 15**
Saros 152   19:43 TD
A.Node   ΔT= 557s
Par. = 161m   U.Mag. = 0.6168
Gam. = 0.6823   P.Mag. = 1.5951

Plate 166

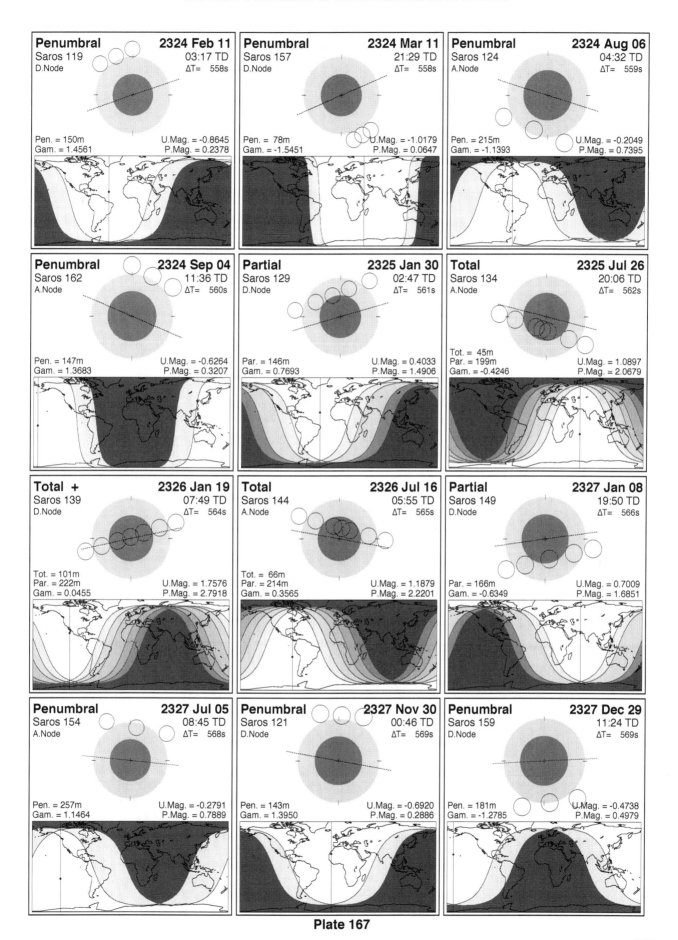

Penumbral	**2324 Feb 11**
Saros 119	03:17 TD
D.Node	ΔT= 558s
Pen. = 150m	U.Mag. = -0.8645
Gam. = 1.4561	P.Mag. = 0.2378

Penumbral	**2324 Mar 11**
Saros 157	21:29 TD
D.Node	ΔT= 558s
Pen. = 78m	U.Mag. = -1.0179
Gam. = -1.5451	P.Mag. = 0.0647

Penumbral	**2324 Aug 06**
Saros 124	04:32 TD
A.Node	ΔT= 559s
Pen. = 215m	U.Mag. = -0.2049
Gam. = -1.1393	P.Mag. = 0.7395

Penumbral	**2324 Sep 04**
Saros 162	11:36 TD
A.Node	ΔT= 560s
Pen. = 147m	U.Mag. = -0.6264
Gam. = 1.3683	P.Mag. = 0.3207

Partial	**2325 Jan 30**
Saros 129	02:47 TD
D.Node	ΔT= 561s
Par. = 146m	U.Mag. = 0.4033
Gam. = 0.7693	P.Mag. = 1.4906

Total	**2325 Jul 26**
Saros 134	20:06 TD
A.Node	ΔT= 562s
Tot. = 45m	U.Mag. = 1.0897
Par. = 199m	
Gam. = -0.4246	P.Mag. = 2.0679

Total +	**2326 Jan 19**
Saros 139	07:49 TD
D.Node	ΔT= 564s
Tot. = 101m	U.Mag. = 1.7576
Par. = 222m	
Gam. = 0.0455	P.Mag. = 2.7918

Total	**2326 Jul 16**
Saros 144	05:55 TD
A.Node	ΔT= 565s
Tot. = 66m	U.Mag. = 1.1879
Par. = 214m	
Gam. = 0.3565	P.Mag. = 2.2201

Partial	**2327 Jan 08**
Saros 149	19:50 TD
D.Node	ΔT= 566s
Par. = 166m	U.Mag. = 0.7009
Gam. = -0.6349	P.Mag. = 1.6851

Penumbral	**2327 Jul 05**
Saros 154	08:45 TD
A.Node	ΔT= 568s
Pen. = 257m	U.Mag. = -0.2791
Gam. = 1.1464	P.Mag. = 0.7889

Penumbral	**2327 Nov 30**
Saros 121	00:46 TD
D.Node	ΔT= 569s
Pen. = 143m	U.Mag. = -0.6920
Gam. = 1.3950	P.Mag. = 0.2886

Penumbral	**2327 Dec 29**
Saros 159	11:24 TD
D.Node	ΔT= 569s
Pen. = 181m	U.Mag. = -0.4738
Gam. = -1.2785	P.Mag. = 0.4979

Plate 167

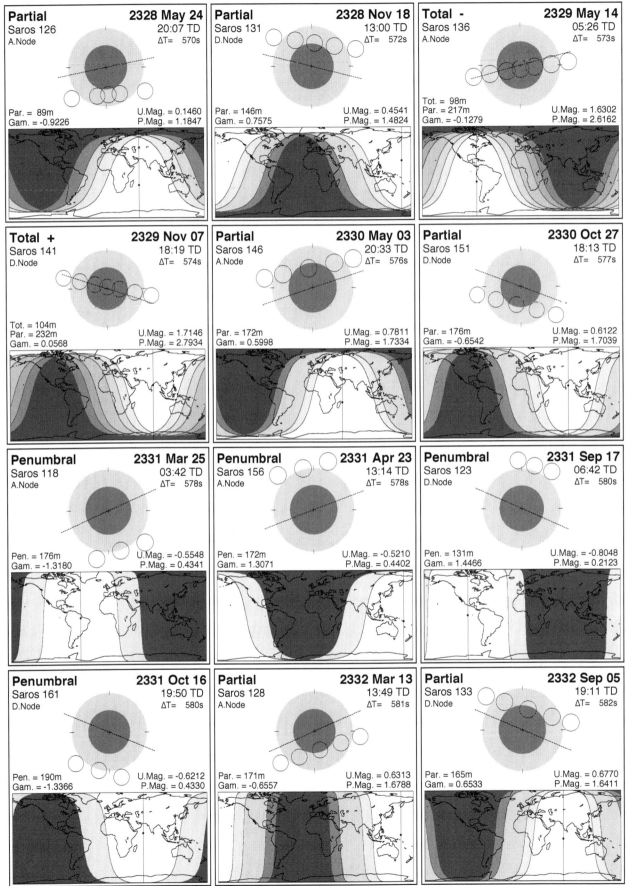

Partial **2328 May 24**	**Partial** **2328 Nov 18**	**Total -** **2329 May 14**
Saros 126 20:07 TD	Saros 131 13:00 TD	Saros 136 05:26 TD
A.Node ΔT= 570s	D.Node ΔT= 572s	A.Node ΔT= 573s
Par. = 89m U.Mag. = 0.1460	Par. = 146m U.Mag. = 0.4541	Tot. = 98m U.Mag. = 1.6302
Gam. = -0.9226 P.Mag. = 1.1847	Gam. = 0.7575 P.Mag. = 1.4824	Par. = 217m P.Mag. = 2.6162
		Gam. = -0.1279
Total + **2329 Nov 07**	**Partial** **2330 May 03**	**Partial** **2330 Oct 27**
Saros 141 18:19 TD	Saros 146 20:33 TD	Saros 151 18:13 TD
D.Node ΔT= 574s	A.Node ΔT= 576s	D.Node ΔT= 577s
Tot. = 104m	Par. = 172m U.Mag. = 0.7811	Par. = 176m U.Mag. = 0.6122
Par. = 232m U.Mag. = 1.7146	Gam. = 0.5998 P.Mag. = 1.7334	Gam. = -0.6542 P.Mag. = 1.7039
Gam. = 0.0568 P.Mag. = 2.7934		
Penumbral **2331 Mar 25**	**Penumbral** **2331 Apr 23**	**Penumbral** **2331 Sep 17**
Saros 118 03:42 TD	Saros 156 13:14 TD	Saros 123 06:42 TD
A.Node ΔT= 578s	A.Node ΔT= 578s	D.Node ΔT= 580s
Pen. = 176m U.Mag. = -0.5548	Pen. = 172m U.Mag. = -0.5210	Pen. = 131m U.Mag. = -0.8048
Gam. = -1.3180 P.Mag. = 0.4341	Gam. = 1.3071 P.Mag. = 0.4402	Gam. = 1.4466 P.Mag. = 0.2123
Penumbral **2331 Oct 16**	**Partial** **2332 Mar 13**	**Partial** **2332 Sep 05**
Saros 161 19:50 TD	Saros 128 13:49 TD	Saros 133 19:11 TD
D.Node ΔT= 580s	A.Node ΔT= 581s	D.Node ΔT= 582s
Pen. = 190m U.Mag. = -0.6212	Par. = 171m U.Mag. = 0.6313	Par. = 165m U.Mag. = 0.6770
Gam. = -1.3366 P.Mag. = 0.4330	Gam. = -0.6557 P.Mag. = 1.6788	Gam. = 0.6533 P.Mag. = 1.6411

Plate 168

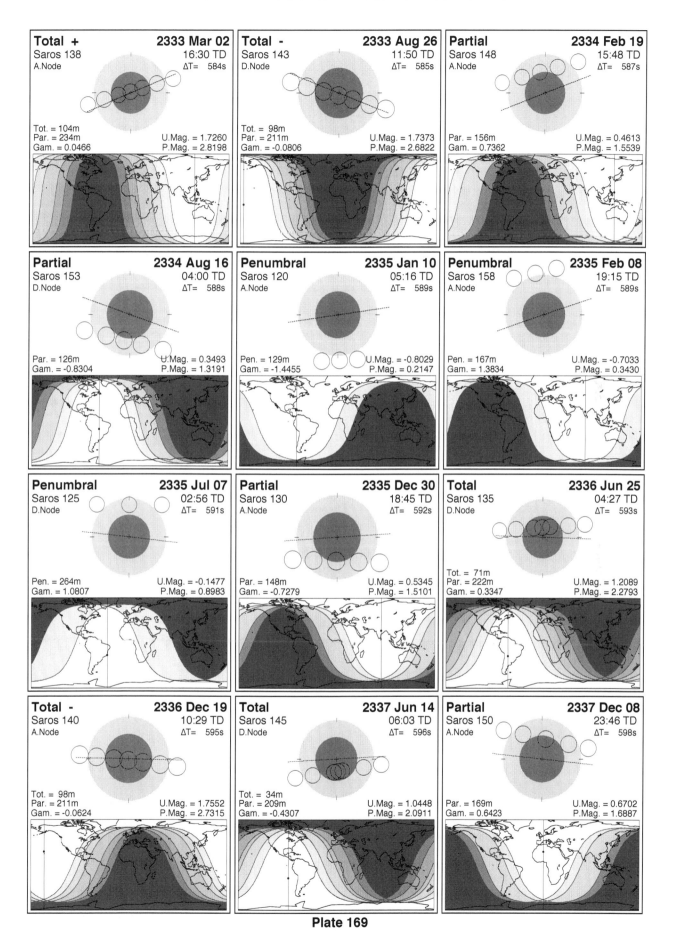

Total +	**2333 Mar 02**
Saros 138	16:30 TD
A.Node	ΔT= 584s
Tot. = 104m	
Par. = 234m	U.Mag. = 1.7260
Gam. = 0.0466	P.Mag. = 2.8198

Total −	**2333 Aug 26**
Saros 143	11:50 TD
D.Node	ΔT= 585s
Tot. = 98m	
Par. = 211m	U.Mag. = 1.7373
Gam. = −0.0806	P.Mag. = 2.6822

Partial	**2334 Feb 19**
Saros 148	15:48 TD
A.Node	ΔT= 587s
Par. = 156m	U.Mag. = 0.4613
Gam. = 0.7362	P.Mag. = 1.5539

Partial	**2334 Aug 16**
Saros 153	04:00 TD
D.Node	ΔT= 588s
Par. = 126m	U.Mag. = 0.3493
Gam. = −0.8304	P.Mag. = 1.3191

Penumbral	**2335 Jan 10**
Saros 120	05:16 TD
A.Node	ΔT= 589s
Pen. = 129m	U.Mag. = −0.8029
Gam. = −1.4455	P.Mag. = 0.2147

Penumbral	**2335 Feb 08**
Saros 158	19:15 TD
A.Node	ΔT= 589s
Pen. = 167m	U.Mag. = −0.7033
Gam. = 1.3834	P.Mag. = 0.3430

Penumbral	**2335 Jul 07**
Saros 125	02:56 TD
D.Node	ΔT= 591s
Pen. = 264m	U.Mag. = −0.1477
Gam. = 1.0807	P.Mag. = 0.8983

Partial	**2335 Dec 30**
Saros 130	18:45 TD
A.Node	ΔT= 592s
Par. = 148m	U.Mag. = 0.5345
Gam. = −0.7279	P.Mag. = 1.5101

Total	**2336 Jun 25**
Saros 135	04:27 TD
D.Node	ΔT= 593s
Tot. = 71m	
Par. = 222m	U.Mag. = 1.2089
Gam. = 0.3347	P.Mag. = 2.2793

Total −	**2336 Dec 19**
Saros 140	10:29 TD
A.Node	ΔT= 595s
Tot. = 98m	
Par. = 211m	U.Mag. = 1.7552
Gam. = −0.0624	P.Mag. = 2.7315

Total	**2337 Jun 14**
Saros 145	06:03 TD
D.Node	ΔT= 596s
Tot. = 34m	
Par. = 209m	U.Mag. = 1.0448
Gam. = −0.4307	P.Mag. = 2.0911

Partial	**2337 Dec 08**
Saros 150	23:46 TD
A.Node	ΔT= 598s
Par. = 169m	U.Mag. = 0.6702
Gam. = 0.6423	P.Mag. = 1.6887

Plate 169

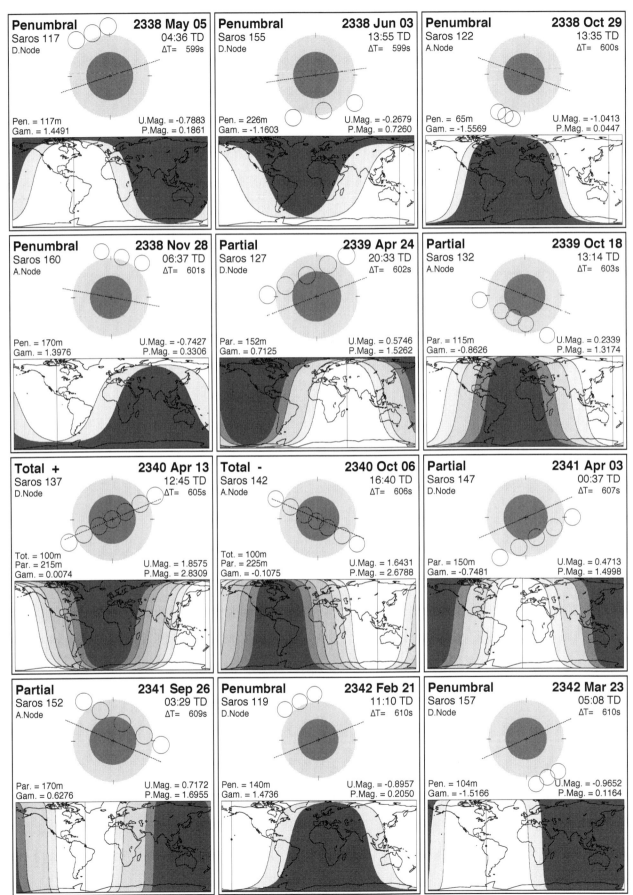

Penumbral   **2338 May 05**
Saros 117   04:36 TD
D.Node   ΔT= 599s
Pen. = 117m   U.Mag. = -0.7883
Gam. = 1.4491   P.Mag. = 0.1861

Penumbral   **2338 Jun 03**
Saros 155   13:55 TD
D.Node   ΔT= 599s
Pen. = 226m   U.Mag. = -0.2679
Gam. = -1.1603   P.Mag. = 0.7260

Penumbral   **2338 Oct 29**
Saros 122   13:35 TD
A.Node   ΔT= 600s
Pen. = 65m   U.Mag. = -1.0413
Gam. = -1.5569   P.Mag. = 0.0447

Penumbral   **2338 Nov 28**
Saros 160   06:37 TD
A.Node   ΔT= 601s
Pen. = 170m   U.Mag. = -0.7427
Gam. = 1.3976   P.Mag. = 0.3306

Partial   **2339 Apr 24**
Saros 127   20:33 TD
D.Node   ΔT= 602s
Par. = 152m   U.Mag. = 0.5746
Gam. = 0.7125   P.Mag. = 1.5262

Partial   **2339 Oct 18**
Saros 132   13:14 TD
A.Node   ΔT= 603s
Par. = 115m   U.Mag. = 0.2339
Gam. = -0.8626   P.Mag. = 1.3174

Total +   **2340 Apr 13**
Saros 137   12:45 TD
D.Node   ΔT= 605s
Tot. = 100m
Par. = 215m   U.Mag. = 1.8575
Gam. = 0.0074   P.Mag. = 2.8309

Total -   **2340 Oct 06**
Saros 142   16:40 TD
A.Node   ΔT= 606s
Tot. = 100m
Par. = 225m   U.Mag. = 1.6431
Gam. = -0.1075   P.Mag. = 2.6788

Partial   **2341 Apr 03**
Saros 147   00:37 TD
D.Node   ΔT= 607s
Par. = 150m   U.Mag. = 0.4713
Gam. = -0.7481   P.Mag. = 1.4998

Partial   **2341 Sep 26**
Saros 152   03:29 TD
A.Node   ΔT= 609s
Par. = 170m   U.Mag. = 0.7172
Gam. = 0.6276   P.Mag. = 1.6955

Penumbral   **2342 Feb 21**
Saros 119   11:10 TD
D.Node   ΔT= 610s
Pen. = 140m   U.Mag. = -0.8957
Gam. = 1.4736   P.Mag. = 0.2050

Penumbral   **2342 Mar 23**
Saros 157   05:08 TD
D.Node   ΔT= 610s
Pen. = 104m   U.Mag. = -0.9652
Gam. = -1.5166   P.Mag. = 0.1164

Plate 170

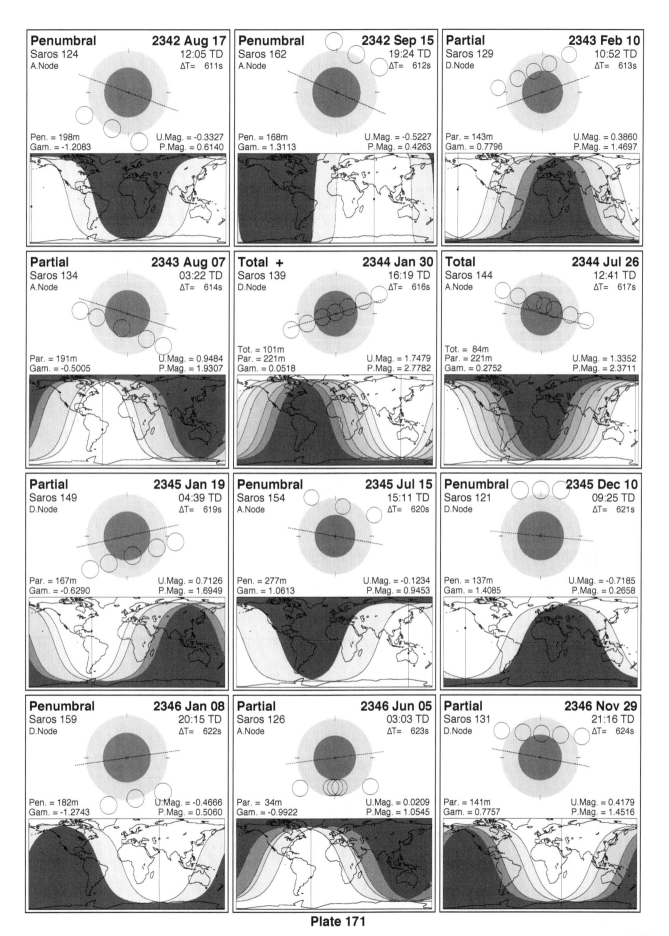

Plate 171

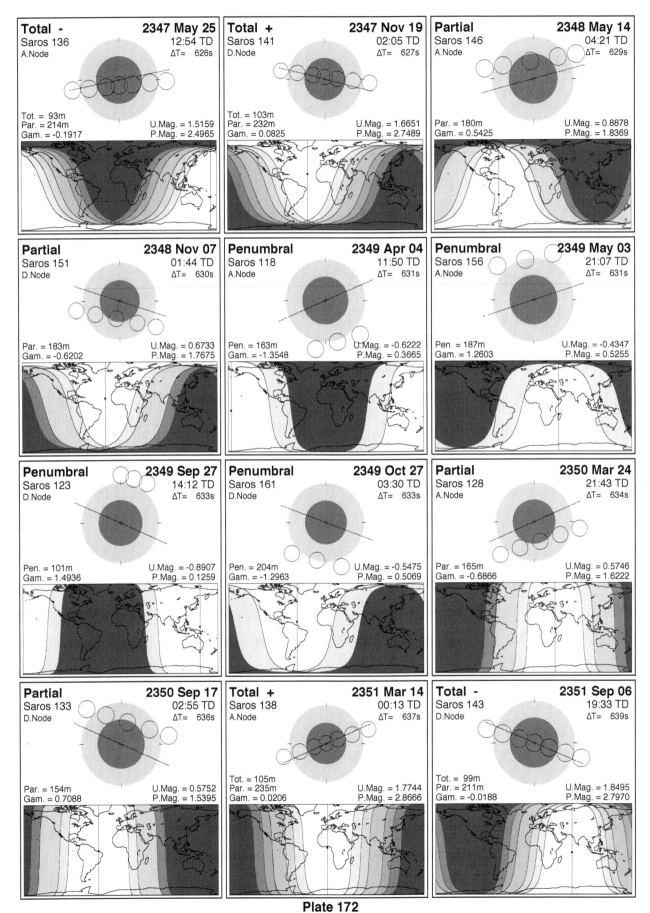

Total -   **2347 May 25**
Saros 136   12:54 TD
A.Node   ΔT= 626s
Tot. = 93m
Par. = 214m   U.Mag. = 1.5159
Gam. = -0.1917   P.Mag. = 2.4965

Total +   **2347 Nov 19**
Saros 141   02:05 TD
D.Node   ΔT= 627s
Tot. = 103m
Par. = 232m   U.Mag. = 1.6651
Gam. = 0.0825   P.Mag. = 2.7489

Partial   **2348 May 14**
Saros 146   04:21 TD
A.Node   ΔT= 629s
Par. = 180m   U.Mag. = 0.8878
Gam. = 0.5425   P.Mag. = 1.8369

Partial   **2348 Nov 07**
Saros 151   01:44 TD
D.Node   ΔT= 630s
Par. = 183m   U.Mag. = 0.6733
Gam. = -0.6202   P.Mag. = 1.7675

Penumbral   **2349 Apr 04**
Saros 118   11:50 TD
A.Node   ΔT= 631s
Pen. = 163m   U.Mag. = -0.6222
Gam. = -1.3548   P.Mag. = 0.3665

Penumbral   **2349 May 03**
Saros 156   21:07 TD
A.Node   ΔT= 631s
Pen. = 187m   U.Mag. = -0.4347
Gam. = 1.2603   P.Mag. = 0.5255

Penumbral   **2349 Sep 27**
Saros 123   14:12 TD
D.Node   ΔT= 633s
Pen. = 101m   U.Mag. = -0.8907
Gam. = 1.4936   P.Mag. = 0.1259

Penumbral   **2349 Oct 27**
Saros 161   03:30 TD
D.Node   ΔT= 633s
Pen. = 204m   U.Mag. = -0.5475
Gam. = -1.2963   P.Mag. = 0.5069

Partial   **2350 Mar 24**
Saros 128   21:43 TD
A.Node   ΔT= 634s
Par. = 165m   U.Mag. = 0.5746
Gam. = -0.6866   P.Mag. = 1.6222

Partial   **2350 Sep 17**
Saros 133   02:55 TD
D.Node   ΔT= 636s
Par. = 154m   U.Mag. = 0.5752
Gam. = 0.7088   P.Mag. = 1.5395

Total +   **2351 Mar 14**
Saros 138   00:13 TD
A.Node   ΔT= 637s
Tot. = 105m
Par. = 235m   U.Mag. = 1.7744
Gam. = 0.0206   P.Mag. = 2.8666

Total -   **2351 Sep 06**
Saros 143   19:33 TD
D.Node   ΔT= 639s
Tot. = 99m
Par. = 211m   U.Mag. = 1.8495
Gam. = -0.0188   P.Mag. = 2.7970

Plate 172

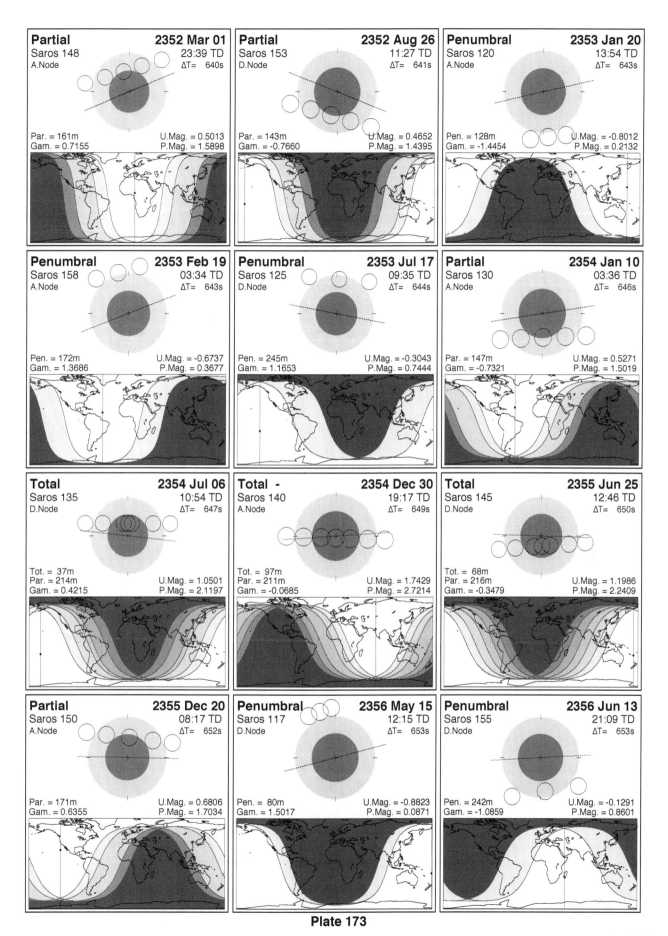

Partial **2352 Mar 01** Saros 148 23:39 TD A.Node ΔT= 640s Par. = 161m U.Mag. = 0.5013 Gam. = 0.7155 P.Mag. = 1.5898	**Partial** **2352 Aug 26** Saros 153 11:27 TD D.Node ΔT= 641s Par. = 143m U.Mag. = 0.4652 Gam. = -0.7660 P.Mag. = 1.4395	**Penumbral** **2353 Jan 20** Saros 120 13:54 TD A.Node ΔT= 643s Pen. = 128m U.Mag. = -0.8012 Gam. = -1.4454 P.Mag. = 0.2132
Penumbral **2353 Feb 19** Saros 158 03:34 TD A.Node ΔT= 643s Pen. = 172m U.Mag. = -0.6737 Gam. = 1.3686 P.Mag. = 0.3677	**Penumbral** **2353 Jul 17** Saros 125 09:35 TD D.Node ΔT= 644s Pen. = 245m U.Mag. = -0.3043 Gam. = 1.1653 P.Mag. = 0.7444	**Partial** **2354 Jan 10** Saros 130 03:36 TD A.Node ΔT= 646s Par. = 147m U.Mag. = 0.5271 Gam. = -0.7321 P.Mag. = 1.5019
Total **2354 Jul 06** Saros 135 10:54 TD D.Node ΔT= 647s Tot. = 37m Par. = 214m U.Mag. = 1.0501 Gam. = 0.4215 P.Mag. = 2.1197	**Total -** **2354 Dec 30** Saros 140 19:17 TD A.Node ΔT= 649s Tot. = 97m Par. = 211m U.Mag. = 1.7429 Gam. = -0.0685 P.Mag. = 2.7214	**Total** **2355 Jun 25** Saros 145 12:46 TD D.Node ΔT= 650s Tot. = 68m Par. = 216m U.Mag. = 1.1986 Gam. = -0.3479 P.Mag. = 2.2409
Partial **2355 Dec 20** Saros 150 08:17 TD A.Node ΔT= 652s Par. = 171m U.Mag. = 0.6806 Gam. = 0.6355 P.Mag. = 1.7034	**Penumbral** **2356 May 15** Saros 117 12:15 TD D.Node ΔT= 653s Pen. = 80m U.Mag. = -0.8823 Gam. = 1.5017 P.Mag. = 0.0871	**Penumbral** **2356 Jun 13** Saros 155 21:09 TD D.Node ΔT= 653s Pen. = 242m U.Mag. = -0.1291 Gam. = -1.0859 P.Mag. = 0.8601

Plate 173

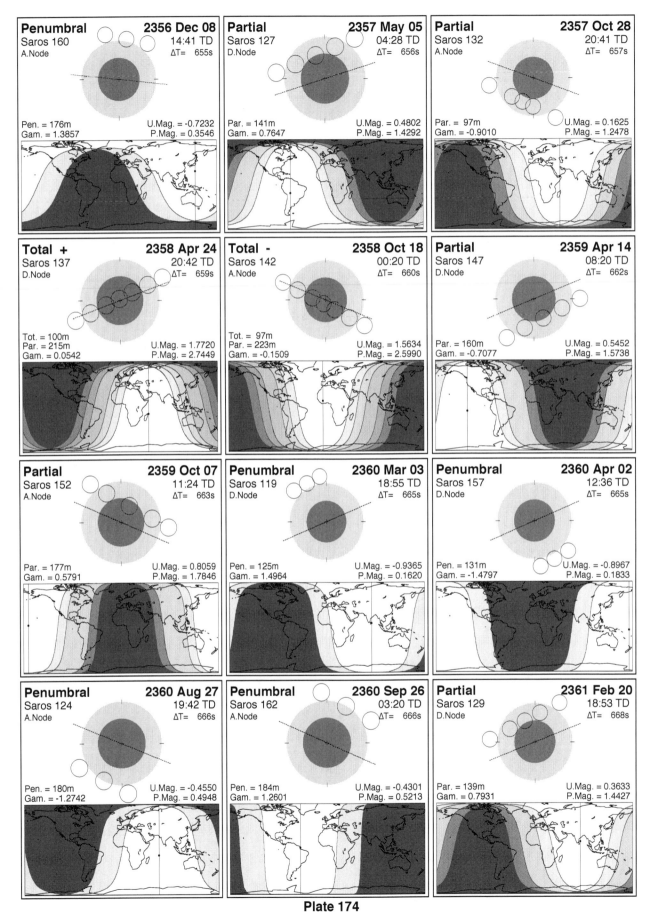

Penumbral   **2356 Dec 08**
Saros 160   14:41 TD
A.Node   ΔT= 655s
Pen. = 176m   U.Mag. = -0.7232
Gam. = 1.3857   P.Mag. = 0.3546

Partial   **2357 May 05**
Saros 127   04:28 TD
D.Node   ΔT= 656s
Par. = 141m   U.Mag. = 0.4802
Gam. = 0.7647   P.Mag. = 1.4292

Partial   **2357 Oct 28**
Saros 132   20:41 TD
A.Node   ΔT= 657s
Par. = 97m   U.Mag. = 0.1625
Gam. = -0.9010   P.Mag. = 1.2478

Total +   **2358 Apr 24**
Saros 137   20:42 TD
D.Node   ΔT= 659s
Tot. = 100m
Par. = 215m   U.Mag. = 1.7720
Gam. = 0.0542   P.Mag. = 2.7449

Total -   **2358 Oct 18**
Saros 142   00:20 TD
A.Node   ΔT= 660s
Tot. = 97m
Par. = 223m   U.Mag. = 1.5634
Gam. = -0.1509   P.Mag. = 2.5990

Partial   **2359 Apr 14**
Saros 147   08:20 TD
D.Node   ΔT= 662s
Par. = 160m   U.Mag. = 0.5452
Gam. = -0.7077   P.Mag. = 1.5738

Partial   **2359 Oct 07**
Saros 152   11:24 TD
A.Node   ΔT= 663s
Par. = 177m   U.Mag. = 0.8059
Gam. = 0.5791   P.Mag. = 1.7846

Penumbral   **2360 Mar 03**
Saros 119   18:55 TD
D.Node   ΔT= 665s
Pen. = 125m   U.Mag. = -0.9365
Gam. = 1.4964   P.Mag. = 0.1620

Penumbral   **2360 Apr 02**
Saros 157   12:36 TD
D.Node   ΔT= 665s
Pen. = 131m   U.Mag. = -0.8967
Gam. = -1.4797   P.Mag. = 0.1833

Penumbral   **2360 Aug 27**
Saros 124   19:42 TD
A.Node   ΔT= 666s
Pen. = 180m   U.Mag. = -0.4550
Gam. = -1.2742   P.Mag. = 0.4948

Penumbral   **2360 Sep 26**
Saros 162   03:20 TD
A.Node   ΔT= 666s
Pen. = 184m   U.Mag. = -0.4301
Gam. = 1.2601   P.Mag. = 0.5213

Partial   **2361 Feb 20**
Saros 129   18:53 TD
D.Node   ΔT= 668s
Par. = 139m   U.Mag. = 0.3633
Gam. = 0.7931   P.Mag. = 1.4427

Plate 174

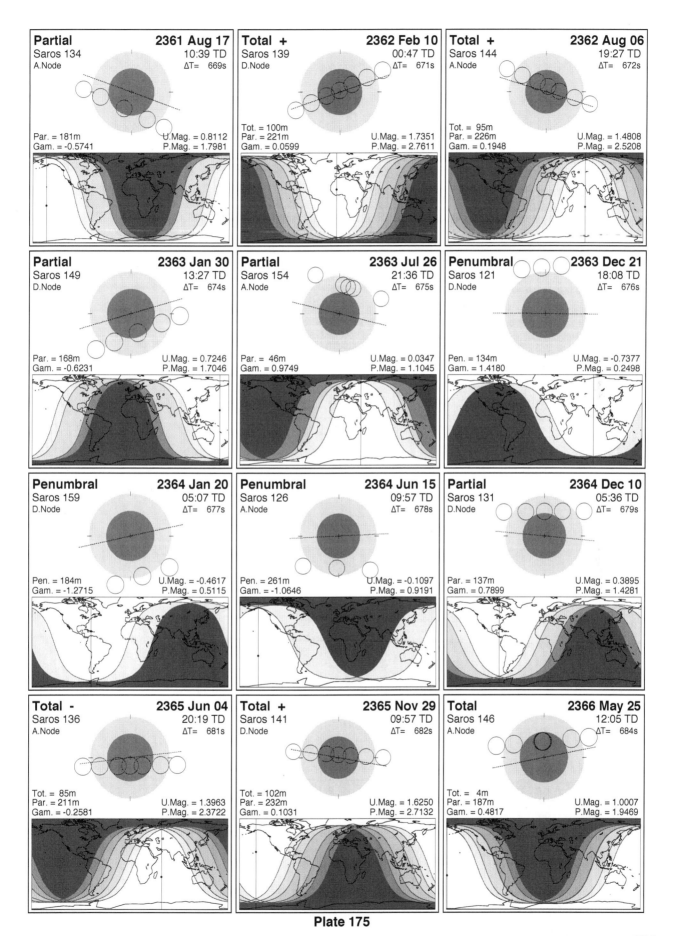

Partial   **2361 Aug 17**
Saros 134   10:39 TD
A.Node   ΔT= 669s

Par. = 181m   U.Mag. = 0.8112
Gam. = -0.5741   P.Mag. = 1.7981

Total +   **2362 Feb 10**
Saros 139   00:47 TD
D.Node   ΔT= 671s
Tot. = 100m
Par. = 221m   U.Mag. = 1.7351
Gam. = 0.0599   P.Mag. = 2.7611

Total +   **2362 Aug 06**
Saros 144   19:27 TD
A.Node   ΔT= 672s
Tot. = 95m
Par. = 226m   U.Mag. = 1.4808
Gam. = 0.1948   P.Mag. = 2.5208

Partial   **2363 Jan 30**
Saros 149   13:27 TD
D.Node   ΔT= 674s

Par. = 168m   U.Mag. = 0.7246
Gam. = -0.6231   P.Mag. = 1.7046

Partial   **2363 Jul 26**
Saros 154   21:36 TD
A.Node   ΔT= 675s

Par. = 46m   U.Mag. = 0.0347
Gam. = 0.9749   P.Mag. = 1.1045

Penumbral   **2363 Dec 21**
Saros 121   18:08 TD
D.Node   ΔT= 676s

Pen. = 134m   U.Mag. = -0.7377
Gam. = 1.4180   P.Mag. = 0.2498

Penumbral   **2364 Jan 20**
Saros 159   05:07 TD
D.Node   ΔT= 677s

Pen. = 184m   U.Mag. = -0.4617
Gam. = -1.2715   P.Mag. = 0.5115

Penumbral   **2364 Jun 15**
Saros 126   09:57 TD
A.Node   ΔT= 678s

Pen. = 261m   U.Mag. = -0.1097
Gam. = -1.0646   P.Mag. = 0.9191

Partial   **2364 Dec 10**
Saros 131   05:36 TD
D.Node   ΔT= 679s

Par. = 137m   U.Mag. = 0.3895
Gam. = 0.7899   P.Mag. = 1.4281

Total -   **2365 Jun 04**
Saros 136   20:19 TD
A.Node   ΔT= 681s
Tot. = 85m
Par. = 211m   U.Mag. = 1.3963
Gam. = -0.2581   P.Mag. = 2.3722

Total +   **2365 Nov 29**
Saros 141   09:57 TD
D.Node   ΔT= 682s
Tot. = 102m
Par. = 232m   U.Mag. = 1.6250
Gam. = 0.1031   P.Mag. = 2.7132

Total   **2366 May 25**
Saros 146   12:05 TD
A.Node   ΔT= 684s
Tot. = 4m
Par. = 187m   U.Mag. = 1.0007
Gam. = 0.4817   P.Mag. = 1.9469

Plate 175

271

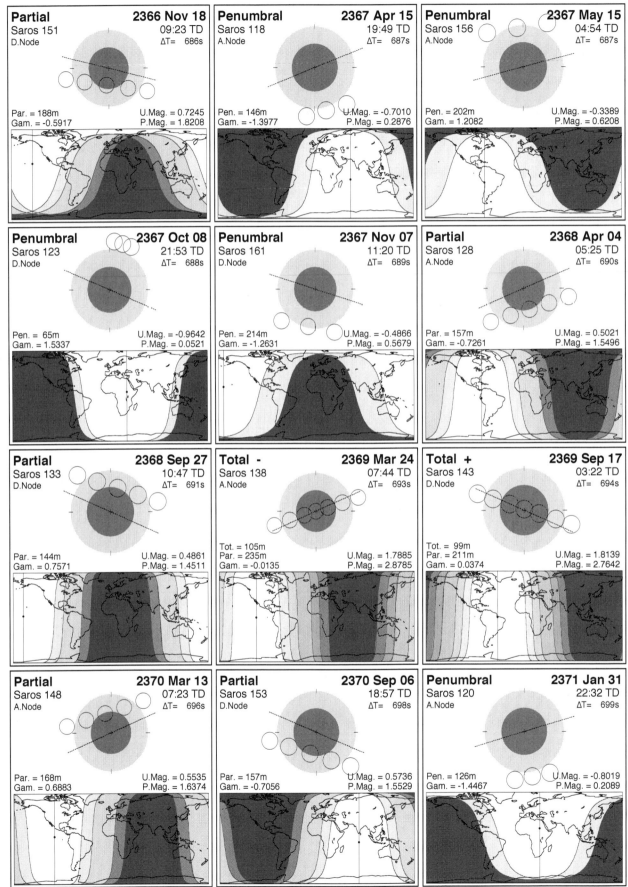

Partial   **2366 Nov 18**
Saros 151   09:23 TD
D.Node   ΔT= 686s
Par. = 188m   U.Mag. = 0.7245
Gam. = -0.5917   P.Mag. = 1.8208

Penumbral   **2367 Apr 15**
Saros 118   19:49 TD
A.Node   ΔT= 687s
Pen. = 146m   U.Mag. = -0.7010
Gam. = -1.3977   P.Mag. = 0.2876

Penumbral   **2367 May 15**
Saros 156   04:54 TD
A.Node   ΔT= 687s
Pen. = 202m   U.Mag. = -0.3389
Gam. = 1.2082   P.Mag. = 0.6208

Penumbral   **2367 Oct 08**
Saros 123   21:53 TD
D.Node   ΔT= 688s
Pen. = 65m   U.Mag. = -0.9642
Gam. = 1.5337   P.Mag. = 0.0521

Penumbral   **2367 Nov 07**
Saros 161   11:20 TD
D.Node   ΔT= 689s
Pen. = 214m   U.Mag. = -0.4866
Gam. = -1.2631   P.Mag. = 0.5679

Partial   **2368 Apr 04**
Saros 128   05:25 TD
A.Node   ΔT= 690s
Par. = 157m   U.Mag. = 0.5021
Gam. = -0.7261   P.Mag. = 1.5496

Partial   **2368 Sep 27**
Saros 133   10:47 TD
D.Node   ΔT= 691s
Par. = 144m   U.Mag. = 0.4861
Gam. = 0.7571   P.Mag. = 1.4511

Total -   **2369 Mar 24**
Saros 138   07:44 TD
A.Node   ΔT= 693s
Tot. = 105m
Par. = 235m   U.Mag. = 1.7885
Gam. = -0.0135   P.Mag. = 2.8785

Total +   **2369 Sep 17**
Saros 143   03:22 TD
D.Node   ΔT= 694s
Tot. = 99m
Par. = 211m   U.Mag. = 1.8139
Gam. = 0.0374   P.Mag. = 2.7642

Partial   **2370 Mar 13**
Saros 148   07:23 TD
A.Node   ΔT= 696s
Par. = 168m   U.Mag. = 0.5535
Gam. = 0.6883   P.Mag. = 1.6374

Partial   **2370 Sep 06**
Saros 153   18:57 TD
D.Node   ΔT= 698s
Par. = 157m   U.Mag. = 0.5736
Gam. = -0.7056   P.Mag. = 1.5529

Penumbral   **2371 Jan 31**
Saros 120   22:32 TD
A.Node   ΔT= 699s
Pen. = 126m   U.Mag. = -0.8019
Gam. = -1.4467   P.Mag. = 0.2089

Plate 176

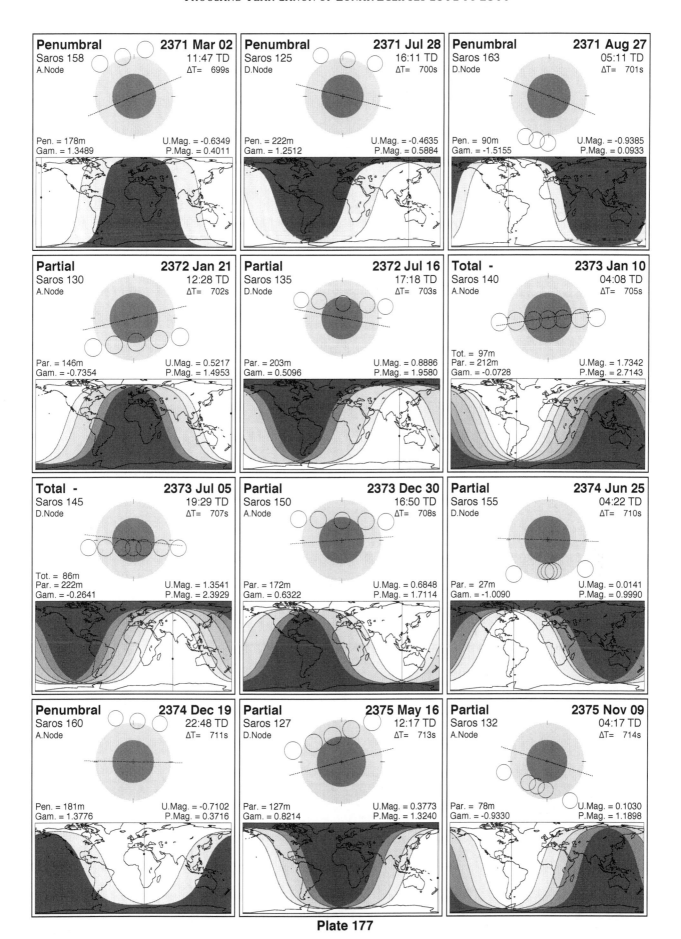

Penumbral 2371 Mar 02 Saros 158 11:47 TD A.Node ΔT= 699s Pen. = 178m U.Mag. = -0.6349 Gam. = 1.3489 P.Mag. = 0.4011	**Penumbral** 2371 Jul 28 Saros 125 16:11 TD D.Node ΔT= 700s Pen. = 222m U.Mag. = -0.4635 Gam. = 1.2512 P.Mag. = 0.5884	**Penumbral** 2371 Aug 27 Saros 163 05:11 TD D.Node ΔT= 701s Pen. = 90m U.Mag. = -0.9385 Gam. = -1.5155 P.Mag. = 0.0933
Partial 2372 Jan 21 Saros 130 12:28 TD A.Node ΔT= 702s Par. = 146m U.Mag. = 0.5217 Gam. = -0.7354 P.Mag. = 1.4953	**Partial** 2372 Jul 16 Saros 135 17:18 TD D.Node ΔT= 703s Par. = 203m U.Mag. = 0.8886 Gam. = 0.5096 P.Mag. = 1.9580	**Total -** 2373 Jan 10 Saros 140 04:08 TD A.Node ΔT= 705s Tot. = 97m Par. = 212m U.Mag. = 1.7342 Gam. = -0.0728 P.Mag. = 2.7143
Total - 2373 Jul 05 Saros 145 19:29 TD D.Node ΔT= 707s Tot. = 86m Par. = 222m U.Mag. = 1.3541 Gam. = -0.2641 P.Mag. = 2.3929	**Partial** 2373 Dec 30 Saros 150 16:50 TD A.Node ΔT= 708s Par. = 172m U.Mag. = 0.6848 Gam. = 0.6322 P.Mag. = 1.7114	**Partial** 2374 Jun 25 Saros 155 04:22 TD D.Node ΔT= 710s Par. = 27m U.Mag. = 0.0141 Gam. = -1.0090 P.Mag. = 0.9990
Penumbral 2374 Dec 19 Saros 160 22:48 TD A.Node ΔT= 711s Pen. = 181m U.Mag. = -0.7102 Gam. = 1.3776 P.Mag. = 0.3716	**Partial** 2375 May 16 Saros 127 12:17 TD D.Node ΔT= 713s Par. = 127m U.Mag. = 0.3773 Gam. = 0.8214 P.Mag. = 1.3240	**Partial** 2375 Nov 09 Saros 132 04:17 TD A.Node ΔT= 714s Par. = 78m U.Mag. = 0.1030 Gam. = -0.9330 P.Mag. = 1.1898

Plate 177

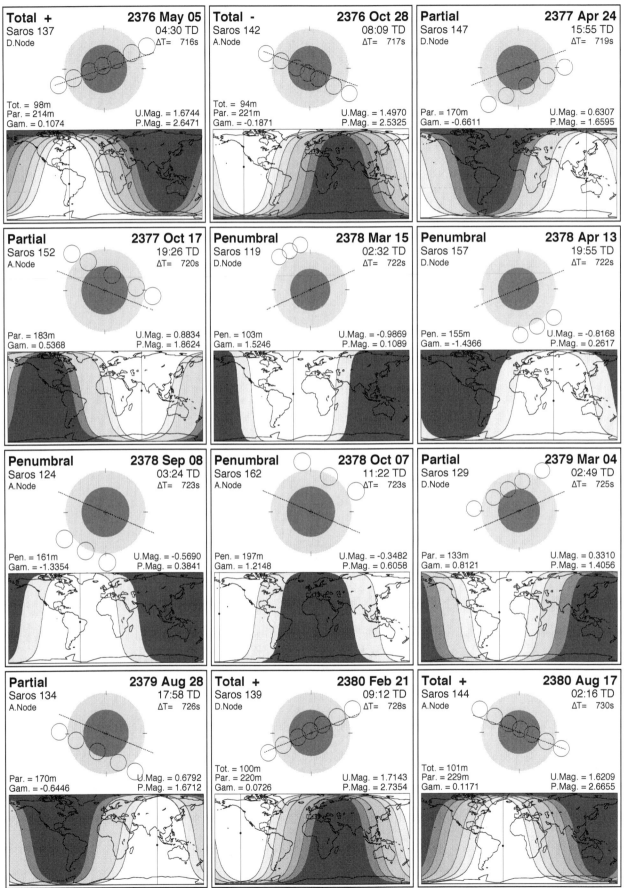

Total +   **2376 May 05**
Saros 137   04:30 TD
D.Node   ΔT= 716s
Tot. = 98m
Par. = 214m   U.Mag. = 1.6744
Gam. = 0.1074   P.Mag. = 2.6471

Total -   **2376 Oct 28**
Saros 142   08:09 TD
A.Node   ΔT= 717s
Tot. = 94m
Par. = 221m   U.Mag. = 1.4970
Gam. = -0.1871   P.Mag. = 2.5325

Partial   **2377 Apr 24**
Saros 147   15:55 TD
D.Node   ΔT= 719s
Par. = 170m   U.Mag. = 0.6307
Gam. = -0.6611   P.Mag. = 1.6595

Partial   **2377 Oct 17**
Saros 152   19:26 TD
A.Node   ΔT= 720s
Par. = 183m   U.Mag. = 0.8834
Gam. = 0.5368   P.Mag. = 1.8624

Penumbral   **2378 Mar 15**
Saros 119   02:32 TD
D.Node   ΔT= 722s
Pen. = 103m   U.Mag. = -0.9869
Gam. = 1.5246   P.Mag. = 0.1089

Penumbral   **2378 Apr 13**
Saros 157   19:55 TD
D.Node   ΔT= 722s
Pen. = 155m   U.Mag. = -0.8168
Gam. = -1.4366   P.Mag. = 0.2617

Penumbral   **2378 Sep 08**
Saros 124   03:24 TD
A.Node   ΔT= 723s
Pen. = 161m   U.Mag. = -0.5690
Gam. = -1.3354   P.Mag. = 0.3841

Penumbral   **2378 Oct 07**
Saros 162   11:22 TD
A.Node   ΔT= 723s
Pen. = 197m   U.Mag. = -0.3482
Gam. = 1.2148   P.Mag. = 0.6058

Partial   **2379 Mar 04**
Saros 129   02:49 TD
D.Node   ΔT= 725s
Par. = 133m   U.Mag. = 0.3310
Gam. = 0.8121   P.Mag. = 1.4056

Partial   **2379 Aug 28**
Saros 134   17:58 TD
A.Node   ΔT= 726s
Par. = 170m   U.Mag. = 0.6792
Gam. = -0.6446   P.Mag. = 1.6712

Total +   **2380 Feb 21**
Saros 139   09:12 TD
D.Node   ΔT= 728s
Tot. = 100m
Par. = 220m   U.Mag. = 1.7143
Gam. = 0.0726   P.Mag. = 2.7354

Total +   **2380 Aug 17**
Saros 144   02:16 TD
A.Node   ΔT= 730s
Tot. = 101m
Par. = 229m   U.Mag. = 1.6209
Gam. = 0.1171   P.Mag. = 2.6655

Plate 178

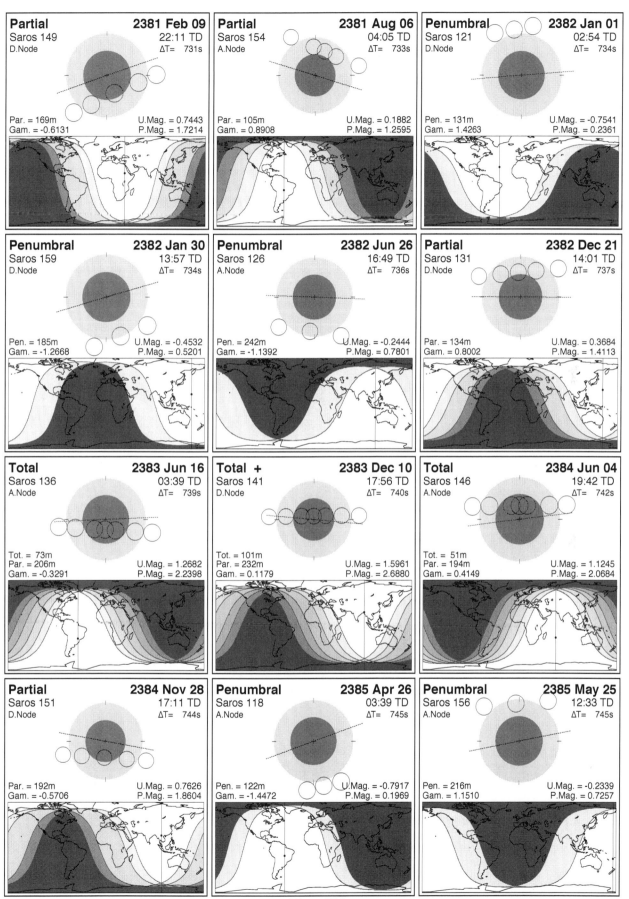

Partial	2381 Feb 09
Saros 149	22:11 TD
D.Node	ΔT= 731s
Par. = 169m	U.Mag. = 0.7443
Gam. = -0.6131	P.Mag. = 1.7214

Partial	2381 Aug 06
Saros 154	04:05 TD
A.Node	ΔT= 733s
Par. = 105m	U.Mag. = 0.1882
Gam. = 0.8908	P.Mag. = 1.2595

Penumbral	2382 Jan 01
Saros 121	02:54 TD
D.Node	ΔT= 734s
Pen. = 131m	U.Mag. = -0.7541
Gam. = 1.4263	P.Mag. = 0.2361

Penumbral	2382 Jan 30
Saros 159	13:57 TD
D.Node	ΔT= 734s
Pen. = 185m	U.Mag. = -0.4532
Gam. = -1.2668	P.Mag. = 0.5201

Penumbral	2382 Jun 26
Saros 126	16:49 TD
A.Node	ΔT= 736s
Pen. = 242m	U.Mag. = -0.2444
Gam. = -1.1392	P.Mag. = 0.7801

Partial	2382 Dec 21
Saros 131	14:01 TD
D.Node	ΔT= 737s
Par. = 134m	U.Mag. = 0.3684
Gam. = 0.8002	P.Mag. = 1.4113

Total	2383 Jun 16
Saros 136	03:39 TD
A.Node	ΔT= 739s
Tot. = 73m	
Par. = 206m	U.Mag. = 1.2682
Gam. = -0.3291	P.Mag. = 2.2398

Total +	2383 Dec 10
Saros 141	17:56 TD
D.Node	ΔT= 740s
Tot. = 101m	
Par. = 232m	U.Mag. = 1.5961
Gam. = 0.1179	P.Mag. = 2.6880

Total	2384 Jun 04
Saros 146	19:42 TD
A.Node	ΔT= 742s
Tot. = 51m	
Par. = 194m	U.Mag. = 1.1245
Gam. = 0.4149	P.Mag. = 2.0684

Partial	2384 Nov 28
Saros 151	17:11 TD
D.Node	ΔT= 744s
Par. = 192m	U.Mag. = 0.7626
Gam. = -0.5706	P.Mag. = 1.8604

Penumbral	2385 Apr 26
Saros 118	03:39 TD
A.Node	ΔT= 745s
Pen. = 122m	U.Mag. = -0.7917
Gam. = -1.4472	P.Mag. = 0.1969

Penumbral	2385 May 25
Saros 156	12:33 TD
A.Node	ΔT= 745s
Pen. = 216m	U.Mag. = -0.2339
Gam. = 1.1510	P.Mag. = 0.7257

Plate 179

275

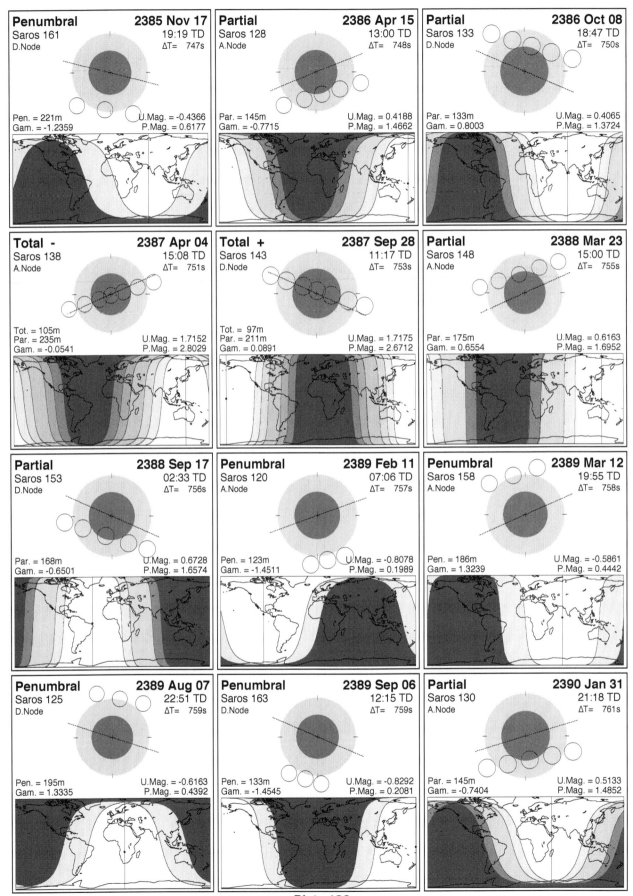

Penumbral **2385 Nov 17**	
Saros 161	19:19 TD
D.Node	ΔT= 747s
Pen. = 221m	U.Mag. = -0.4366
Gam. = -1.2359	P.Mag. = 0.6177

Partial **2386 Apr 15**	
Saros 128	13:00 TD
A.Node	ΔT= 748s
Par. = 145m	U.Mag. = 0.4188
Gam. = -0.7715	P.Mag. = 1.4662

Partial **2386 Oct 08**	
Saros 133	18:47 TD
D.Node	ΔT= 750s
Par. = 133m	U.Mag. = 0.4065
Gam. = 0.8003	P.Mag. = 1.3724

Total - **2387 Apr 04**	
Saros 138	15:08 TD
A.Node	ΔT= 751s
Tot. = 105m	
Par. = 235m	U.Mag. = 1.7152
Gam. = -0.0541	P.Mag. = 2.8029

Total + **2387 Sep 28**	
Saros 143	11:17 TD
D.Node	ΔT= 753s
Tot. = 97m	
Par. = 211m	U.Mag. = 1.7175
Gam. = 0.0891	P.Mag. = 2.6712

Partial **2388 Mar 23**	
Saros 148	15:00 TD
A.Node	ΔT= 755s
Par. = 175m	U.Mag. = 0.6163
Gam. = 0.6554	P.Mag. = 1.6952

Partial **2388 Sep 17**	
Saros 153	02:33 TD
D.Node	ΔT= 756s
Par. = 168m	U.Mag. = 0.6728
Gam. = -0.6501	P.Mag. = 1.6574

Penumbral **2389 Feb 11**	
Saros 120	07:06 TD
A.Node	ΔT= 757s
Pen. = 123m	U.Mag. = -0.8078
Gam. = -1.4511	P.Mag. = 0.1989

Penumbral **2389 Mar 12**	
Saros 158	19:55 TD
A.Node	ΔT= 758s
Pen. = 186m	U.Mag. = -0.5861
Gam. = 1.3239	P.Mag. = 0.4442

Penumbral **2389 Aug 07**	
Saros 125	22:51 TD
D.Node	ΔT= 759s
Pen. = 195m	U.Mag. = -0.6163
Gam. = 1.3335	P.Mag. = 0.4392

Penumbral **2389 Sep 06**	
Saros 163	12:15 TD
D.Node	ΔT= 759s
Pen. = 133m	U.Mag. = -0.8292
Gam. = -1.4545	P.Mag. = 0.2081

Partial **2390 Jan 31**	
Saros 130	21:18 TD
A.Node	ΔT= 761s
Par. = 145m	U.Mag. = 0.5133
Gam. = -0.7404	P.Mag. = 1.4852

Plate 180

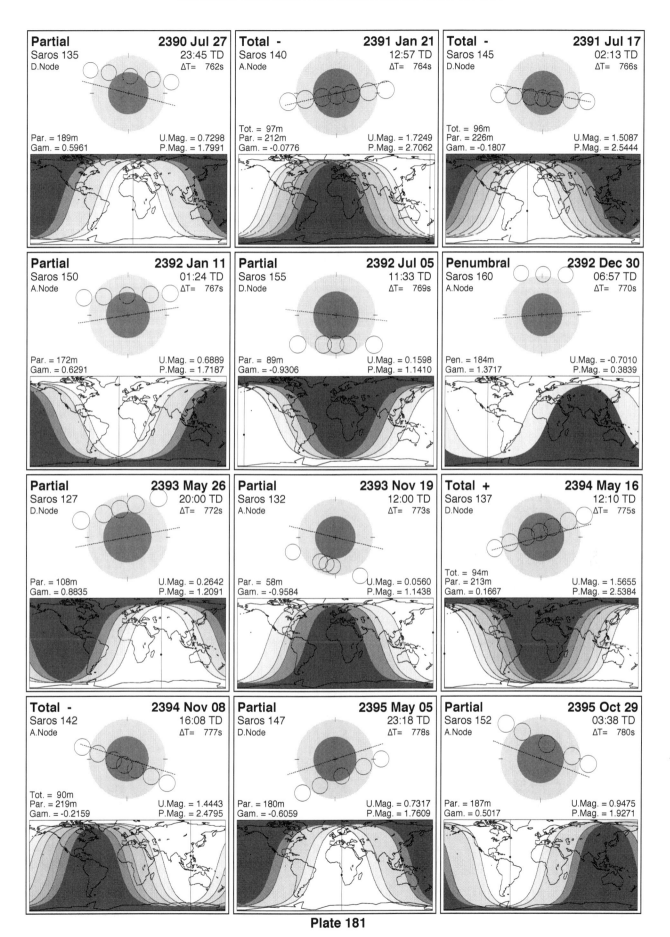

Partial	2390 Jul 27
Saros 135	23:45 TD
D.Node	ΔT= 762s
Par. = 189m	U.Mag. = 0.7298
Gam. = 0.5961	P.Mag. = 1.7991

Total -	2391 Jan 21
Saros 140	12:57 TD
A.Node	ΔT= 764s
Tot. = 97m	
Par. = 212m	U.Mag. = 1.7249
Gam. = -0.0776	P.Mag. = 2.7062

Total -	2391 Jul 17
Saros 145	02:13 TD
D.Node	ΔT= 766s
Tot. = 96m	
Par. = 226m	U.Mag. = 1.5087
Gam. = -0.1807	P.Mag. = 2.5444

Partial	2392 Jan 11
Saros 150	01:24 TD
A.Node	ΔT= 767s
Par. = 172m	U.Mag. = 0.6889
Gam. = 0.6291	P.Mag. = 1.7187

Partial	2392 Jul 05
Saros 155	11:33 TD
D.Node	ΔT= 769s
Par. = 89m	U.Mag. = 0.1598
Gam. = -0.9306	P.Mag. = 1.1410

Penumbral	2392 Dec 30
Saros 160	06:57 TD
A.Node	ΔT= 770s
Pen. = 184m	U.Mag. = -0.7010
Gam. = 1.3717	P.Mag. = 0.3839

Partial	2393 May 26
Saros 127	20:00 TD
D.Node	ΔT= 772s
Par. = 108m	U.Mag. = 0.2642
Gam. = 0.8835	P.Mag. = 1.2091

Partial	2393 Nov 19
Saros 132	12:00 TD
A.Node	ΔT= 773s
Par. = 58m	U.Mag. = 0.0560
Gam. = -0.9584	P.Mag. = 1.1438

Total +	2394 May 16
Saros 137	12:10 TD
D.Node	ΔT= 775s
Tot. = 94m	
Par. = 213m	U.Mag. = 1.5655
Gam. = 0.1667	P.Mag. = 2.5384

Total -	2394 Nov 08
Saros 142	16:08 TD
A.Node	ΔT= 777s
Tot. = 90m	
Par. = 219m	U.Mag. = 1.4443
Gam. = -0.2159	P.Mag. = 2.4795

Partial	2395 May 05
Saros 147	23:18 TD
D.Node	ΔT= 778s
Par. = 180m	U.Mag. = 0.7317
Gam. = -0.6059	P.Mag. = 1.7609

Partial	2395 Oct 29
Saros 152	03:38 TD
A.Node	ΔT= 780s
Par. = 187m	U.Mag. = 0.9475
Gam. = 0.5017	P.Mag. = 1.9271

Plate 181

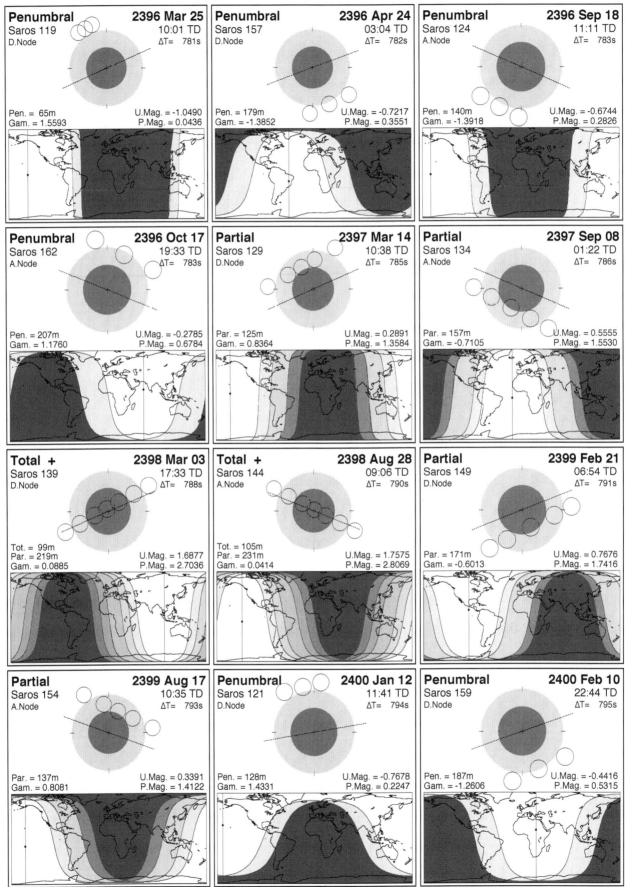

Penumbral **2396 Mar 25** Saros 119 10:01 TD D.Node ΔT= 781s Pen. = 65m U.Mag. = -1.0490 Gam. = 1.5593 P.Mag. = 0.0436	**Penumbral** **2396 Apr 24** Saros 157 03:04 TD D.Node ΔT= 782s Pen. = 179m U.Mag. = -0.7217 Gam. = -1.3852 P.Mag. = 0.3551	**Penumbral** **2396 Sep 18** Saros 124 11:11 TD A.Node ΔT= 783s Pen. = 140m U.Mag. = -0.6744 Gam. = -1.3918 P.Mag. = 0.2826
Penumbral **2396 Oct 17** Saros 162 19:33 TD A.Node ΔT= 783s Pen. = 207m U.Mag. = -0.2785 Gam. = 1.1760 P.Mag. = 0.6784	**Partial** **2397 Mar 14** Saros 129 10:38 TD D.Node ΔT= 785s Par. = 125m U.Mag. = 0.2891 Gam. = 0.8364 P.Mag. = 1.3584	**Partial** **2397 Sep 08** Saros 134 01:22 TD A.Node ΔT= 786s Par. = 157m U.Mag. = 0.5555 Gam. = -0.7105 P.Mag. = 1.5530
Total + **2398 Mar 03** Saros 139 17:33 TD D.Node ΔT= 788s Tot. = 99m Par. = 219m U.Mag. = 1.6877 Gam. = 0.0885 P.Mag. = 2.7036	**Total +** **2398 Aug 28** Saros 144 09:06 TD A.Node ΔT= 790s Tot. = 105m Par. = 231m U.Mag. = 1.7575 Gam. = 0.0414 P.Mag. = 2.8069	**Partial** **2399 Feb 21** Saros 149 06:54 TD D.Node ΔT= 791s Par. = 171m U.Mag. = 0.7676 Gam. = -0.6013 P.Mag. = 1.7416
Partial **2399 Aug 17** Saros 154 10:35 TD A.Node ΔT= 793s Par. = 137m U.Mag. = 0.3391 Gam. = 0.8081 P.Mag. = 1.4122	**Penumbral** **2400 Jan 12** Saros 121 11:41 TD D.Node ΔT= 794s Pen. = 128m U.Mag. = -0.7678 Gam. = 1.4331 P.Mag. = 0.2247	**Penumbral** **2400 Feb 10** Saros 159 22:44 TD D.Node ΔT= 795s Pen. = 187m U.Mag. = -0.4416 Gam. = -1.2606 P.Mag. = 0.5315

Plate 182

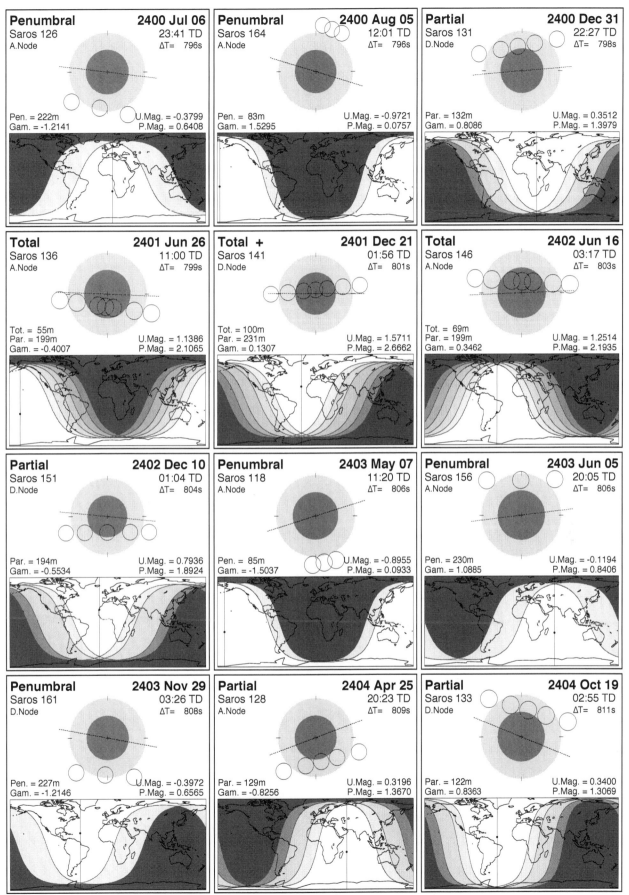

Penumbral   **2400 Jul 06**
Saros 126   23:41 TD
A.Node   ΔT= 796s
Pen. = 222m   U.Mag. = -0.3799
Gam. = -1.2141   P.Mag. = 0.6408

Penumbral   **2400 Aug 05**
Saros 164   12:01 TD
A.Node   ΔT= 796s
Pen. = 83m   U.Mag. = -0.9721
Gam. = 1.5295   P.Mag. = 0.0757

Partial   **2400 Dec 31**
Saros 131   22:27 TD
D.Node   ΔT= 798s
Par. = 132m   U.Mag. = 0.3512
Gam. = 0.8086   P.Mag. = 1.3979

Total   **2401 Jun 26**
Saros 136   11:00 TD
A.Node   ΔT= 799s
Tot. = 55m
Par. = 199m   U.Mag. = 1.1386
Gam. = -0.4007   P.Mag. = 2.1065

Total +   **2401 Dec 21**
Saros 141   01:56 TD
D.Node   ΔT= 801s
Tot. = 100m
Par. = 231m   U.Mag. = 1.5711
Gam. = 0.1307   P.Mag. = 2.6662

Total   **2402 Jun 16**
Saros 146   03:17 TD
A.Node   ΔT= 803s
Tot. = 69m
Par. = 199m   U.Mag. = 1.2514
Gam. = 0.3462   P.Mag. = 2.1935

Partial   **2402 Dec 10**
Saros 151   01:04 TD
D.Node   ΔT= 804s
Par. = 194m   U.Mag. = 0.7936
Gam. = -0.5534   P.Mag. = 1.8924

Penumbral   **2403 May 07**
Saros 118   11:20 TD
A.Node   ΔT= 806s
Pen. = 85m   U.Mag. = -0.8955
Gam. = -1.5037   P.Mag. = 0.0933

Penumbral   **2403 Jun 05**
Saros 156   20:05 TD
A.Node   ΔT= 806s
Pen. = 230m   U.Mag. = -0.1194
Gam. = 1.0885   P.Mag. = 0.8406

Penumbral   **2403 Nov 29**
Saros 161   03:26 TD
D.Node   ΔT= 808s
Pen. = 227m   U.Mag. = -0.3972
Gam. = -1.2146   P.Mag. = 0.6565

Partial   **2404 Apr 25**
Saros 128   20:23 TD
A.Node   ΔT= 809s
Par. = 129m   U.Mag. = 0.3196
Gam. = -0.8256   P.Mag. = 1.3670

Partial   **2404 Oct 19**
Saros 133   02:55 TD
D.Node   ΔT= 811s
Par. = 122m   U.Mag. = 0.3400
Gam. = 0.8363   P.Mag. = 1.3069

Plate 183

279

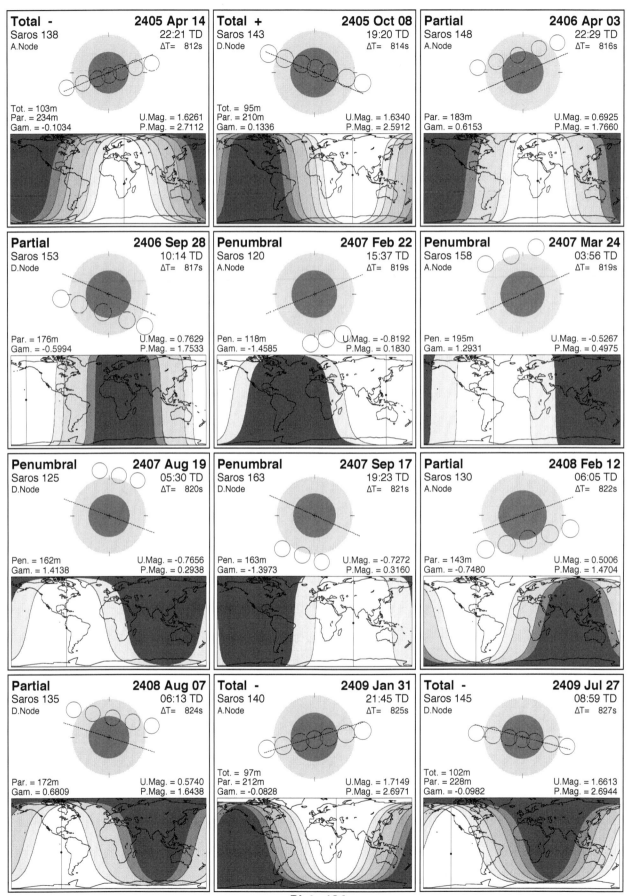

Total - 2405 Apr 14	**Total +** 2405 Oct 08	**Partial** 2406 Apr 03
Saros 138 22:21 TD	Saros 143 19:20 TD	Saros 148 22:29 TD
A.Node ΔT= 812s	D.Node ΔT= 814s	A.Node ΔT= 816s
Tot. = 103m	Tot. = 95m	Par. = 183m
Par. = 234m U.Mag. = 1.6261	Par. = 210m U.Mag. = 1.6340	Gam. = 0.6153 U.Mag. = 0.6925
Gam. = -0.1034 P.Mag. = 2.7112	Gam. = 0.1336 P.Mag. = 2.5912	P.Mag. = 1.7660
Partial 2406 Sep 28	**Penumbral** 2407 Feb 22	**Penumbral** 2407 Mar 24
Saros 153 10:14 TD	Saros 120 15:37 TD	Saros 158 03:56 TD
D.Node ΔT= 817s	A.Node ΔT= 819s	A.Node ΔT= 819s
Par. = 176m U.Mag. = 0.7629	Pen. = 118m U.Mag. = -0.8192	Pen. = 195m U.Mag. = -0.5267
Gam. = -0.5994 P.Mag. = 1.7533	Gam. = -1.4585 P.Mag. = 0.1830	Gam. = 1.2931 P.Mag. = 0.4975
Penumbral 2407 Aug 19	**Penumbral** 2407 Sep 17	**Partial** 2408 Feb 12
Saros 125 05:30 TD	Saros 163 19:23 TD	Saros 130 06:05 TD
D.Node ΔT= 820s	D.Node ΔT= 821s	A.Node ΔT= 822s
Pen. = 162m U.Mag. = -0.7656	Pen. = 163m U.Mag. = -0.7272	Par. = 143m U.Mag. = 0.5006
Gam. = 1.4138 P.Mag. = 0.2938	Gam. = -1.3973 P.Mag. = 0.3160	Gam. = -0.7480 P.Mag. = 1.4704
Partial 2408 Aug 07	**Total -** 2409 Jan 31	**Total -** 2409 Jul 27
Saros 135 06:13 TD	Saros 140 21:45 TD	Saros 145 08:59 TD
D.Node ΔT= 824s	A.Node ΔT= 825s	D.Node ΔT= 827s
Par. = 172m U.Mag. = 0.5740	Tot. = 97m	Tot. = 102m
Gam. = 0.6809 P.Mag. = 1.6438	Par. = 212m U.Mag. = 1.7149	Par. = 228m U.Mag. = 1.6613
	Gam. = -0.0828 P.Mag. = 2.6971	Gam. = -0.0982 P.Mag. = 2.6944

Plate 184

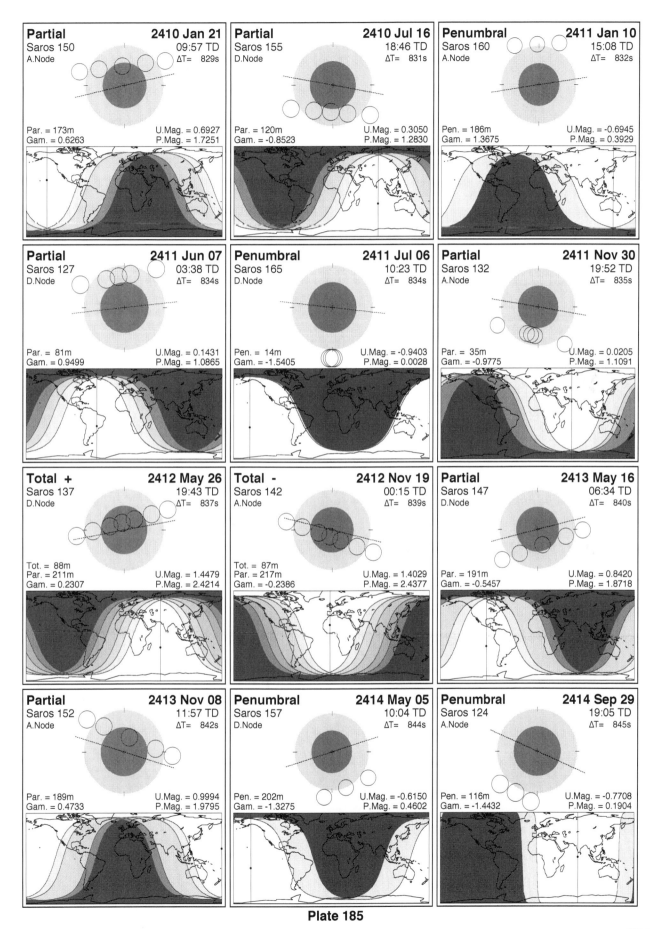

Partial	2410 Jan 21
Saros 150	09:57 TD
A.Node	ΔT= 829s

| Par. = 173m | U.Mag. = 0.6927 |
| Gam. = 0.6263 | P.Mag. = 1.7251 |

Partial	2410 Jul 16
Saros 155	18:46 TD
D.Node	ΔT= 831s

| Par. = 120m | U.Mag. = 0.3050 |
| Gam. = -0.8523 | P.Mag. = 1.2830 |

Penumbral	2411 Jan 10
Saros 160	15:08 TD
A.Node	ΔT= 832s

| Pen. = 186m | U.Mag. = -0.6945 |
| Gam. = 1.3675 | P.Mag. = 0.3929 |

Partial	2411 Jun 07
Saros 127	03:38 TD
D.Node	ΔT= 834s

| Par. = 81m | U.Mag. = 0.1431 |
| Gam. = 0.9499 | P.Mag. = 1.0865 |

Penumbral	2411 Jul 06
Saros 165	10:23 TD
D.Node	ΔT= 834s

| Pen. = 14m | U.Mag. = -0.9403 |
| Gam. = -1.5405 | P.Mag. = 0.0028 |

Partial	2411 Nov 30
Saros 132	19:52 TD
A.Node	ΔT= 835s

| Par. = 35m | U.Mag. = 0.0205 |
| Gam. = -0.9775 | P.Mag. = 1.1091 |

Total +	2412 May 26
Saros 137	19:43 TD
D.Node	ΔT= 837s

Tot. = 88m	
Par. = 211m	U.Mag. = 1.4479
Gam. = 0.2307	P.Mag. = 2.4214

Total -	2412 Nov 19
Saros 142	00:15 TD
A.Node	ΔT= 839s

Tot. = 87m	
Par. = 217m	U.Mag. = 1.4029
Gam. = -0.2386	P.Mag. = 2.4377

Partial	2413 May 16
Saros 147	06:34 TD
D.Node	ΔT= 840s

| Par. = 191m | U.Mag. = 0.8420 |
| Gam. = -0.5457 | P.Mag. = 1.8718 |

Partial	2413 Nov 08
Saros 152	11:57 TD
A.Node	ΔT= 842s

| Par. = 189m | U.Mag. = 0.9994 |
| Gam. = 0.4733 | P.Mag. = 1.9795 |

Penumbral	2414 May 05
Saros 157	10:04 TD
D.Node	ΔT= 844s

| Pen. = 202m | U.Mag. = -0.6150 |
| Gam. = -1.3275 | P.Mag. = 0.4602 |

Penumbral	2414 Sep 29
Saros 124	19:05 TD
A.Node	ΔT= 845s

| Pen. = 116m | U.Mag. = -0.7708 |
| Gam. = -1.4432 | P.Mag. = 0.1904 |

Plate 185

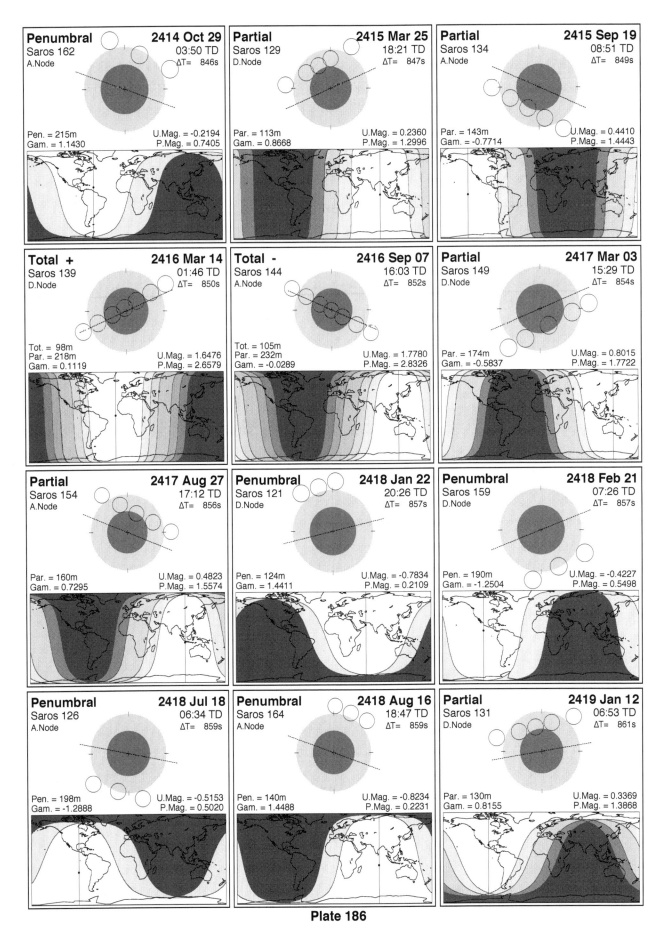

Penumbral   **2414 Oct 29**
Saros 162   03:50 TD
A.Node   ΔT= 846s

Pen. = 215m   U.Mag. = -0.2194
Gam. = 1.1430   P.Mag. = 0.7405

Partial   **2415 Mar 25**
Saros 129   18:21 TD
D.Node   ΔT= 847s

Par. = 113m   U.Mag. = 0.2360
Gam. = 0.8668   P.Mag. = 1.2996

Partial   **2415 Sep 19**
Saros 134   08:51 TD
A.Node   ΔT= 849s

Par. = 143m   U.Mag. = 0.4410
Gam. = -0.7714   P.Mag. = 1.4443

Total +   **2416 Mar 14**
Saros 139   01:46 TD
D.Node   ΔT= 850s

Tot. = 98m
Par. = 218m   U.Mag. = 1.6476
Gam. = 0.1119   P.Mag. = 2.6579

Total -   **2416 Sep 07**
Saros 144   16:03 TD
A.Node   ΔT= 852s

Tot. = 105m
Par. = 232m   U.Mag. = 1.7780
Gam. = -0.0289   P.Mag. = 2.8326

Partial   **2417 Mar 03**
Saros 149   15:29 TD
D.Node   ΔT= 854s

Par. = 174m   U.Mag. = 0.8015
Gam. = -0.5837   P.Mag. = 1.7722

Partial   **2417 Aug 27**
Saros 154   17:12 TD
A.Node   ΔT= 856s

Par. = 160m   U.Mag. = 0.4823
Gam. = 0.7295   P.Mag. = 1.5574

Penumbral   **2418 Jan 22**
Saros 121   20:26 TD
D.Node   ΔT= 857s

Pen. = 124m   U.Mag. = -0.7834
Gam. = 1.4411   P.Mag. = 0.2109

Penumbral   **2418 Feb 21**
Saros 159   07:26 TD
D.Node   ΔT= 857s

Pen. = 190m   U.Mag. = -0.4227
Gam. = -1.2504   P.Mag. = 0.5498

Penumbral   **2418 Jul 18**
Saros 126   06:34 TD
A.Node   ΔT= 859s

Pen. = 198m   U.Mag. = -0.5153
Gam. = -1.2888   P.Mag. = 0.5020

Penumbral   **2418 Aug 16**
Saros 164   18:47 TD
A.Node   ΔT= 859s

Pen. = 140m   U.Mag. = -0.8234
Gam. = 1.4488   P.Mag. = 0.2231

Partial   **2419 Jan 12**
Saros 131   06:53 TD
D.Node   ΔT= 861s

Par. = 130m   U.Mag. = 0.3369
Gam. = 0.8155   P.Mag. = 1.3868

Plate 186

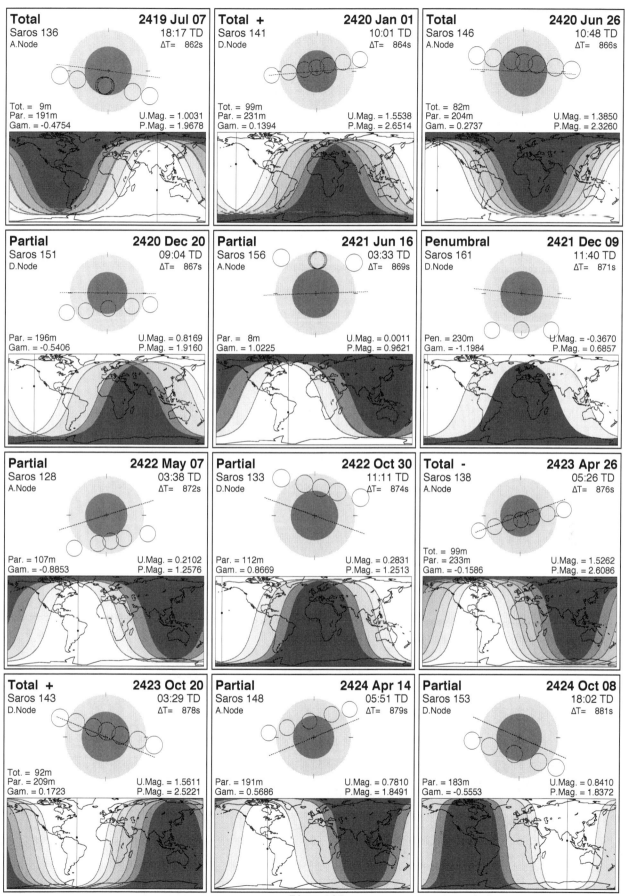

Total   2419 Jul 07
Saros 136   18:17 TD
A.Node   ΔT= 862s

Tot. = 9m
Par. = 191m   U.Mag. = 1.0031
Gam. = -0.4754   P.Mag. = 1.9678

Total +   2420 Jan 01
Saros 141   10:01 TD
D.Node   ΔT= 864s

Tot. = 99m
Par. = 231m   U.Mag. = 1.5538
Gam. = 0.1394   P.Mag. = 2.6514

Total   2420 Jun 26
Saros 146   10:48 TD
A.Node   ΔT= 866s

Tot. = 82m
Par. = 204m   U.Mag. = 1.3850
Gam. = 0.2737   P.Mag. = 2.3260

Partial   2420 Dec 20
Saros 151   09:04 TD
D.Node   ΔT= 867s

Par. = 196m   U.Mag. = 0.8169
Gam. = -0.5406   P.Mag. = 1.9160

Partial   2421 Jun 16
Saros 156   03:33 TD
A.Node   ΔT= 869s

Par. = 8m   U.Mag. = 0.0011
Gam. = 1.0225   P.Mag. = 0.9621

Penumbral   2421 Dec 09
Saros 161   11:40 TD
D.Node   ΔT= 871s

Pen. = 230m   U.Mag. = -0.3670
Gam. = -1.1984   P.Mag. = 0.6857

Partial   2422 May 07
Saros 128   03:38 TD
A.Node   ΔT= 872s

Par. = 107m   U.Mag. = 0.2102
Gam. = -0.8853   P.Mag. = 1.2576

Partial   2422 Oct 30
Saros 133   11:11 TD
D.Node   ΔT= 874s

Par. = 112m   U.Mag. = 0.2831
Gam. = 0.8669   P.Mag. = 1.2513

Total -   2423 Apr 26
Saros 138   05:26 TD
A.Node   ΔT= 876s

Tot. = 99m
Par. = 233m   U.Mag. = 1.5262
Gam. = -0.1586   P.Mag. = 2.6086

Total +   2423 Oct 20
Saros 143   03:29 TD
D.Node   ΔT= 878s

Tot. = 92m
Par. = 209m   U.Mag. = 1.5611
Gam. = 0.1723   P.Mag. = 2.5221

Partial   2424 Apr 14
Saros 148   05:51 TD
A.Node   ΔT= 879s

Par. = 191m   U.Mag. = 0.7810
Gam. = 0.5686   P.Mag. = 1.8491

Partial   2424 Oct 08
Saros 153   18:02 TD
D.Node   ΔT= 881s

Par. = 183m   U.Mag. = 0.8410
Gam. = -0.5553   P.Mag. = 1.8372

Plate 187

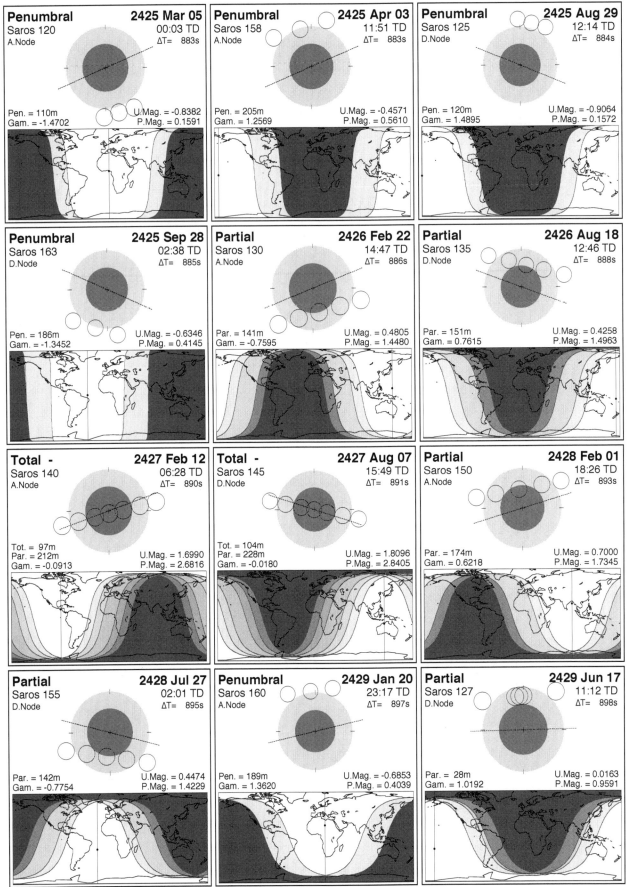

Penumbral   **2425 Mar 05**
Saros 120   00:03 TD
A.Node   ΔT= 883s
Pen. = 110m   U.Mag. = -0.8382
Gam. = -1.4702   P.Mag. = 0.1591

Penumbral   **2425 Apr 03**
Saros 158   11:51 TD
A.Node   ΔT= 883s
Pen. = 205m   U.Mag. = -0.4571
Gam. = 1.2569   P.Mag. = 0.5610

Penumbral   **2425 Aug 29**
Saros 125   12:14 TD
D.Node   ΔT= 884s
Pen. = 120m   U.Mag. = -0.9064
Gam. = 1.4895   P.Mag. = 0.1572

Penumbral   **2425 Sep 28**
Saros 163   02:38 TD
D.Node   ΔT= 885s
Pen. = 186m   U.Mag. = -0.6346
Gam. = -1.3452   P.Mag. = 0.4145

Partial   **2426 Feb 22**
Saros 130   14:47 TD
A.Node   ΔT= 886s
Par. = 141m   U.Mag. = 0.4805
Gam. = -0.7595   P.Mag. = 1.4480

Partial   **2426 Aug 18**
Saros 135   12:46 TD
D.Node   ΔT= 888s
Par. = 151m   U.Mag. = 0.4258
Gam. = 0.7615   P.Mag. = 1.4963

Total -   **2427 Feb 12**
Saros 140   06:28 TD
A.Node   ΔT= 890s
Tot. = 97m
Par. = 212m   U.Mag. = 1.6990
Gam. = -0.0913   P.Mag. = 2.6816

Total -   **2427 Aug 07**
Saros 145   15:49 TD
D.Node   ΔT= 891s
Tot. = 104m
Par. = 228m   U.Mag. = 1.8096
Gam. = -0.0180   P.Mag. = 2.8405

Partial   **2428 Feb 01**
Saros 150   18:26 TD
A.Node   ΔT= 893s
Par. = 174m   U.Mag. = 0.7000
Gam. = 0.6218   P.Mag. = 1.7345

Partial   **2428 Jul 27**
Saros 155   02:01 TD
D.Node   ΔT= 895s
Par. = 142m   U.Mag. = 0.4474
Gam. = -0.7754   P.Mag. = 1.4229

Penumbral   **2429 Jan 20**
Saros 160   23:17 TD
A.Node   ΔT= 897s
Pen. = 189m   U.Mag. = -0.6853
Gam. = 1.3620   P.Mag. = 0.4039

Partial   **2429 Jun 17**
Saros 127   11:12 TD
D.Node   ΔT= 898s
Par. = 28m   U.Mag. = 0.0163
Gam. = 1.0192   P.Mag. = 0.9591

Plate 188

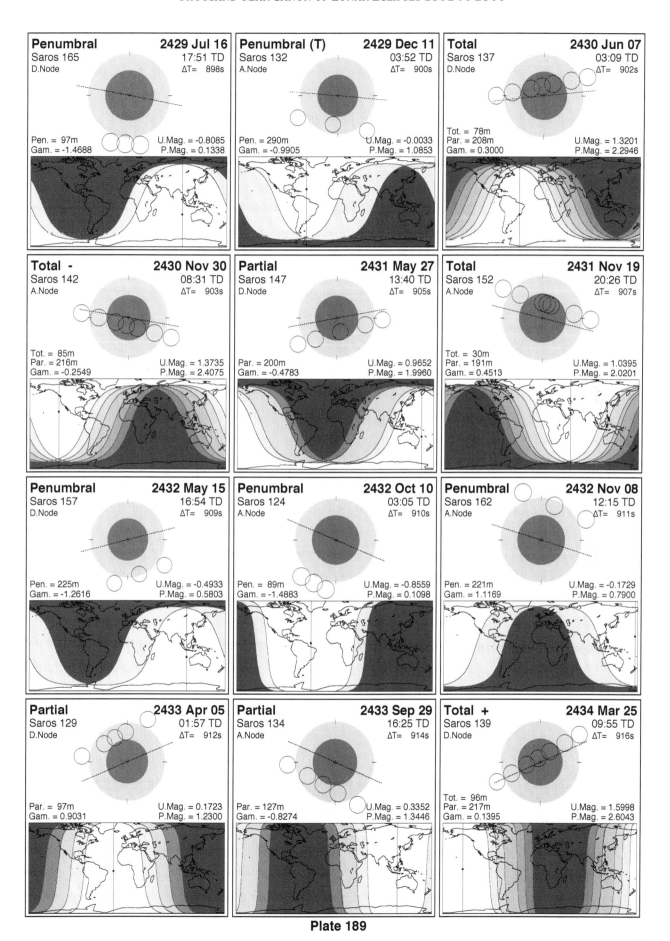

Penumbral	2429 Jul 16
Saros 165	17:51 TD
D.Node	ΔT= 898s
Pen. = 97m	U.Mag. = -0.8085
Gam. = -1.4688	P.Mag. = 0.1338

Penumbral (T)	2429 Dec 11
Saros 132	03:52 TD
A.Node	ΔT= 900s
Pen. = 290m	U.Mag. = -0.0033
Gam. = -0.9905	P.Mag. = 1.0853

Total	2430 Jun 07
Saros 137	03:09 TD
D.Node	ΔT= 902s
Tot. = 78m	
Par. = 208m	U.Mag. = 1.3201
Gam. = 0.3000	P.Mag. = 2.2946

Total -	2430 Nov 30
Saros 142	08:31 TD
A.Node	ΔT= 903s
Tot. = 85m	
Par. = 216m	U.Mag. = 1.3735
Gam. = -0.2549	P.Mag. = 2.4075

Partial	2431 May 27
Saros 147	13:40 TD
D.Node	ΔT= 905s
Par. = 200m	U.Mag. = 0.9652
Gam. = -0.4783	P.Mag. = 1.9960

Total	2431 Nov 19
Saros 152	20:26 TD
A.Node	ΔT= 907s
Tot. = 30m	
Par. = 191m	U.Mag. = 1.0395
Gam. = 0.4513	P.Mag. = 2.0201

Penumbral	2432 May 15
Saros 157	16:54 TD
D.Node	ΔT= 909s
Pen. = 225m	U.Mag. = -0.4933
Gam. = -1.2616	P.Mag. = 0.5803

Penumbral	2432 Oct 10
Saros 124	03:05 TD
A.Node	ΔT= 910s
Pen. = 89m	U.Mag. = -0.8559
Gam. = -1.4883	P.Mag. = 0.1098

Penumbral	2432 Nov 08
Saros 162	12:15 TD
A.Node	ΔT= 911s
Pen. = 221m	U.Mag. = -0.1729
Gam. = 1.1169	P.Mag. = 0.7900

Partial	2433 Apr 05
Saros 129	01:57 TD
D.Node	ΔT= 912s
Par. = 97m	U.Mag. = 0.1723
Gam. = 0.9031	P.Mag. = 1.2300

Partial	2433 Sep 29
Saros 134	16:25 TD
A.Node	ΔT= 914s
Par. = 127m	U.Mag. = 0.3352
Gam. = -0.8274	P.Mag. = 1.3446

Total +	2434 Mar 25
Saros 139	09:55 TD
D.Node	ΔT= 916s
Tot. = 96m	
Par. = 217m	U.Mag. = 1.5998
Gam. = 0.1395	P.Mag. = 2.6043

Plate 189

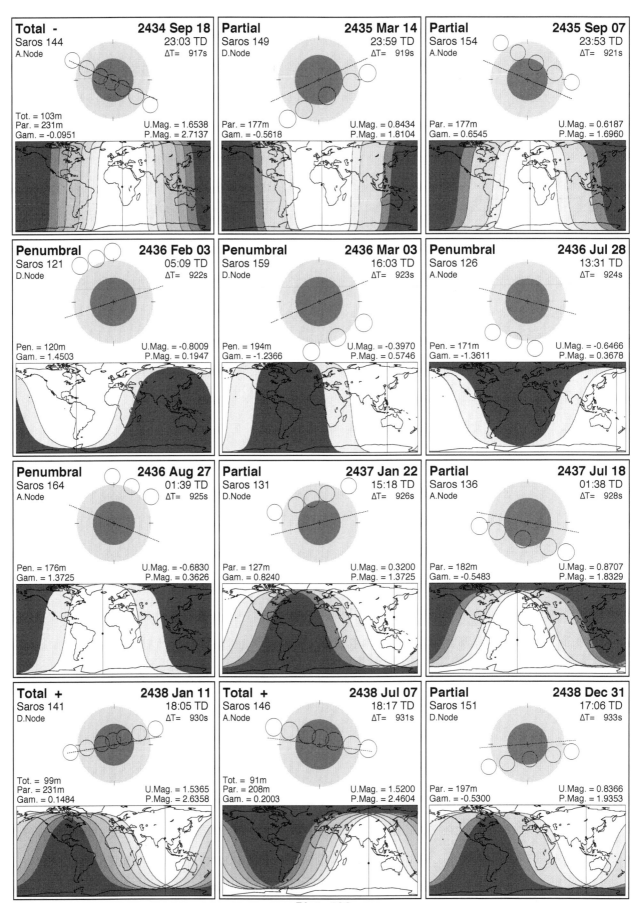

Total - **2434 Sep 18** Saros 144 23:03 TD A.Node ΔT= 917s Tot. = 103m Par. = 231m U.Mag. = 1.6538 Gam. = -0.0951 P.Mag. = 2.7137	**Partial** **2435 Mar 14** Saros 149 23:59 TD D.Node ΔT= 919s Par. = 177m U.Mag. = 0.8434 Gam. = -0.5618 P.Mag. = 1.8104	**Partial** **2435 Sep 07** Saros 154 23:53 TD A.Node ΔT= 921s Par. = 177m U.Mag. = 0.6187 Gam. = 0.6545 P.Mag. = 1.6960
Penumbral **2436 Feb 03** Saros 121 05:09 TD D.Node ΔT= 922s Pen. = 120m U.Mag. = -0.8009 Gam. = 1.4503 P.Mag. = 0.1947	**Penumbral** **2436 Mar 03** Saros 159 16:03 TD D.Node ΔT= 923s Pen. = 194m U.Mag. = -0.3970 Gam. = -1.2366 P.Mag. = 0.5746	**Penumbral** **2436 Jul 28** Saros 126 13:31 TD A.Node ΔT= 924s Pen. = 171m U.Mag. = -0.6466 Gam. = -1.3611 P.Mag. = 0.3678
Penumbral **2436 Aug 27** Saros 164 01:39 TD A.Node ΔT= 925s Pen. = 176m U.Mag. = -0.6830 Gam. = 1.3725 P.Mag. = 0.3626	**Partial** **2437 Jan 22** Saros 131 15:18 TD D.Node ΔT= 926s Par. = 127m U.Mag. = 0.3200 Gam. = 0.8240 P.Mag. = 1.3725	**Partial** **2437 Jul 18** Saros 136 01:38 TD A.Node ΔT= 928s Par. = 182m U.Mag. = 0.8707 Gam. = -0.5483 P.Mag. = 1.8329
Total + **2438 Jan 11** Saros 141 18:05 TD D.Node ΔT= 930s Tot. = 99m Par. = 231m U.Mag. = 1.5365 Gam. = 0.1484 P.Mag. = 2.6358	**Total +** **2438 Jul 07** Saros 146 18:17 TD A.Node ΔT= 931s Tot. = 91m Par. = 208m U.Mag. = 1.5200 Gam. = 0.2003 P.Mag. = 2.4604	**Partial** **2438 Dec 31** Saros 151 17:06 TD D.Node ΔT= 933s Par. = 197m U.Mag. = 0.8366 Gam. = -0.5300 P.Mag. = 1.9353

Plate 190

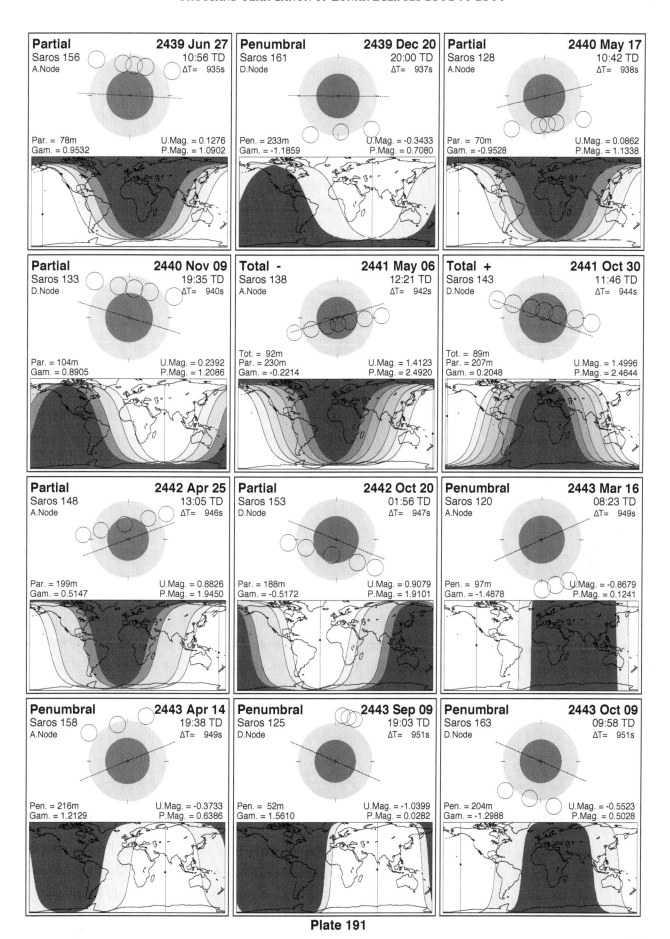

Partial	2439 Jun 27
Saros 156	10:56 TD
A.Node	ΔT= 935s
Par. = 78m	U.Mag. = 0.1276
Gam. = 0.9532	P.Mag. = 1.0902

Penumbral	2439 Dec 20
Saros 161	20:00 TD
D.Node	ΔT= 937s
Pen. = 233m	U.Mag. = -0.3433
Gam. = -1.1859	P.Mag. = 0.7080

Partial	2440 May 17
Saros 128	10:42 TD
A.Node	ΔT= 938s
Par. = 70m	U.Mag. = 0.0862
Gam. = -0.9528	P.Mag. = 1.1338

Partial	2440 Nov 09
Saros 133	19:35 TD
D.Node	ΔT= 940s
Par. = 104m	U.Mag. = 0.2392
Gam. = 0.8905	P.Mag. = 1.2086

Total -	2441 May 06
Saros 138	12:21 TD
A.Node	ΔT= 942s
Tot. = 92m	
Par. = 230m	U.Mag. = 1.4123
Gam. = -0.2214	P.Mag. = 2.4920

Total +	2441 Oct 30
Saros 143	11:46 TD
D.Node	ΔT= 944s
Tot. = 89m	
Par. = 207m	U.Mag. = 1.4996
Gam. = 0.2048	P.Mag. = 2.4644

Partial	2442 Apr 25
Saros 148	13:05 TD
A.Node	ΔT= 946s
Par. = 199m	U.Mag. = 0.8826
Gam. = 0.5147	P.Mag. = 1.9450

Partial	2442 Oct 20
Saros 153	01:56 TD
D.Node	ΔT= 947s
Par. = 188m	U.Mag. = 0.9079
Gam. = -0.5172	P.Mag. = 1.9101

Penumbral	2443 Mar 16
Saros 120	08:23 TD
A.Node	ΔT= 949s
Pen. = 97m	U.Mag. = -0.8679
Gam. = -1.4878	P.Mag. = 0.1241

Penumbral	2443 Apr 14
Saros 158	19:38 TD
A.Node	ΔT= 949s
Pen. = 216m	U.Mag. = -0.3733
Gam. = 1.2129	P.Mag. = 0.6386

Penumbral	2443 Sep 09
Saros 125	19:03 TD
D.Node	ΔT= 951s
Pen. = 52m	U.Mag. = -1.0399
Gam. = 1.5610	P.Mag. = 0.0282

Penumbral	2443 Oct 09
Saros 163	09:58 TD
D.Node	ΔT= 951s
Pen. = 204m	U.Mag. = -0.5523
Gam. = -1.2988	P.Mag. = 0.5028

Plate 191

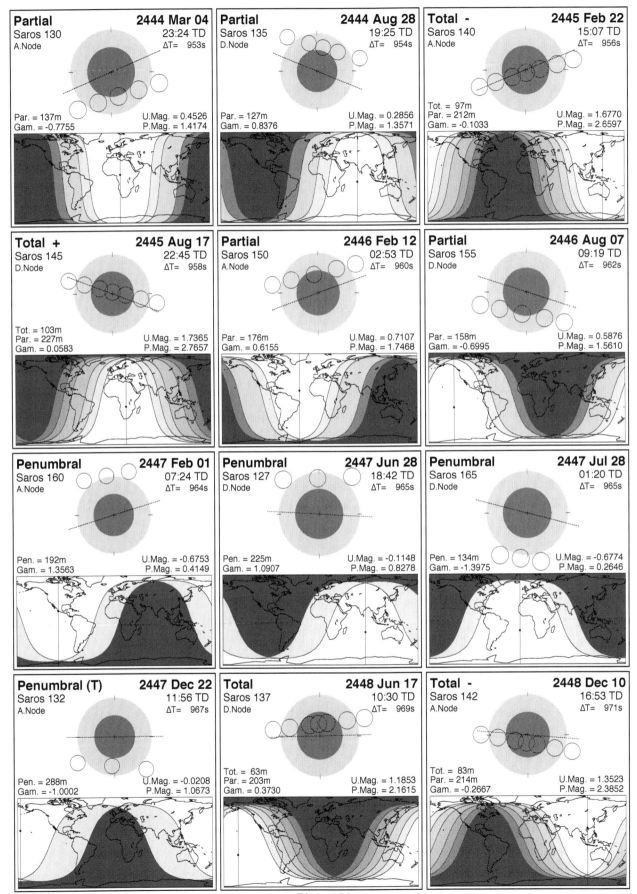

Partial	**2444 Mar 04**
Saros 130	23:24 TD
A.Node	ΔT= 953s
Par. = 137m	U.Mag. = 0.4526
Gam. = -0.7755	P.Mag. = 1.4174

Partial	**2444 Aug 28**
Saros 135	19:25 TD
D.Node	ΔT= 954s
Par. = 127m	U.Mag. = 0.2856
Gam. = 0.8376	P.Mag. = 1.3571

Total -	**2445 Feb 22**
Saros 140	15:07 TD
A.Node	ΔT= 956s
Tot. = 97m	
Par. = 212m	U.Mag. = 1.6770
Gam. = -0.1033	P.Mag. = 2.6597

Total +	**2445 Aug 17**
Saros 145	22:45 TD
D.Node	ΔT= 958s
Tot. = 103m	
Par. = 227m	U.Mag. = 1.7365
Gam. = 0.0583	P.Mag. = 2.7657

Partial	**2446 Feb 12**
Saros 150	02:53 TD
A.Node	ΔT= 960s
Par. = 176m	U.Mag. = 0.7107
Gam. = 0.6155	P.Mag. = 1.7468

Partial	**2446 Aug 07**
Saros 155	09:19 TD
D.Node	ΔT= 962s
Par. = 158m	U.Mag. = 0.5876
Gam. = -0.6995	P.Mag. = 1.5610

Penumbral	**2447 Feb 01**
Saros 160	07:24 TD
A.Node	ΔT= 964s
Pen. = 192m	U.Mag. = -0.6753
Gam. = 1.3563	P.Mag. = 0.4149

Penumbral	**2447 Jun 28**
Saros 127	18:42 TD
D.Node	ΔT= 965s
Pen. = 225m	U.Mag. = -0.1148
Gam. = 1.0907	P.Mag. = 0.8278

Penumbral	**2447 Jul 28**
Saros 165	01:20 TD
D.Node	ΔT= 965s
Pen. = 134m	U.Mag. = -0.6774
Gam. = -1.3975	P.Mag. = 0.2646

Penumbral (T)	**2447 Dec 22**
Saros 132	11:56 TD
A.Node	ΔT= 967s
Pen. = 288m	U.Mag. = -0.0208
Gam. = -1.0002	P.Mag. = 1.0673

Total	**2448 Jun 17**
Saros 137	10:30 TD
D.Node	ΔT= 969s
Tot. = 63m	
Par. = 203m	U.Mag. = 1.1853
Gam. = 0.3730	P.Mag. = 2.1615

Total -	**2448 Dec 10**
Saros 142	16:53 TD
A.Node	ΔT= 971s
Tot. = 83m	
Par. = 214m	U.Mag. = 1.3523
Gam. = -0.2667	P.Mag. = 2.3852

Plate 192

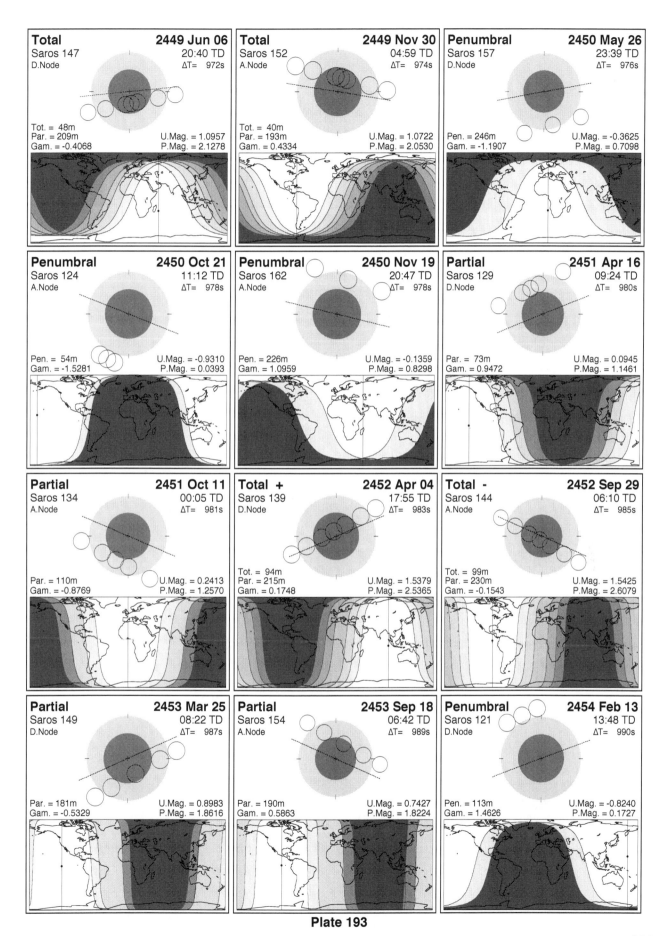

Total	2449 Jun 06
Saros 147	20:40 TD
D.Node	ΔT= 972s
Tot. = 48m	
Par. = 209m	U.Mag. = 1.0957
Gam. = -0.4068	P.Mag. = 2.1278

Total	2449 Nov 30
Saros 152	04:59 TD
A.Node	ΔT= 974s
Tot. = 40m	
Par. = 193m	U.Mag. = 1.0722
Gam. = 0.4334	P.Mag. = 2.0530

Penumbral	2450 May 26
Saros 157	23:39 TD
D.Node	ΔT= 976s
Pen. = 246m	U.Mag. = -0.3625
Gam. = -1.1907	P.Mag. = 0.7098

Penumbral	2450 Oct 21
Saros 124	11:12 TD
A.Node	ΔT= 978s
Pen. = 54m	U.Mag. = -0.9310
Gam. = -1.5281	P.Mag. = 0.0393

Penumbral	2450 Nov 19
Saros 162	20:47 TD
A.Node	ΔT= 978s
Pen. = 226m	U.Mag. = -0.1359
Gam. = 1.0959	P.Mag. = 0.8298

Partial	2451 Apr 16
Saros 129	09:24 TD
D.Node	ΔT= 980s
Par. = 73m	U.Mag. = 0.0945
Gam. = 0.9472	P.Mag. = 1.1461

Partial	2451 Oct 11
Saros 134	00:05 TD
A.Node	ΔT= 981s
Par. = 110m	U.Mag. = 0.2413
Gam. = -0.8769	P.Mag. = 1.2570

Total +	2452 Apr 04
Saros 139	17:55 TD
D.Node	ΔT= 983s
Tot. = 94m	
Par. = 215m	U.Mag. = 1.5379
Gam. = 0.1748	P.Mag. = 2.5365

Total -	2452 Sep 29
Saros 144	06:10 TD
A.Node	ΔT= 985s
Tot. = 99m	
Par. = 230m	U.Mag. = 1.5425
Gam. = -0.1543	P.Mag. = 2.6079

Partial	2453 Mar 25
Saros 149	08:22 TD
D.Node	ΔT= 987s
Par. = 181m	U.Mag. = 0.8983
Gam. = -0.5329	P.Mag. = 1.8616

Partial	2453 Sep 18
Saros 154	06:42 TD
A.Node	ΔT= 989s
Par. = 190m	U.Mag. = 0.7427
Gam. = 0.5863	P.Mag. = 1.8224

Penumbral	2454 Feb 13
Saros 121	13:48 TD
D.Node	ΔT= 990s
Pen. = 113m	U.Mag. = -0.8240
Gam. = 1.4626	P.Mag. = 0.1727

Plate 193

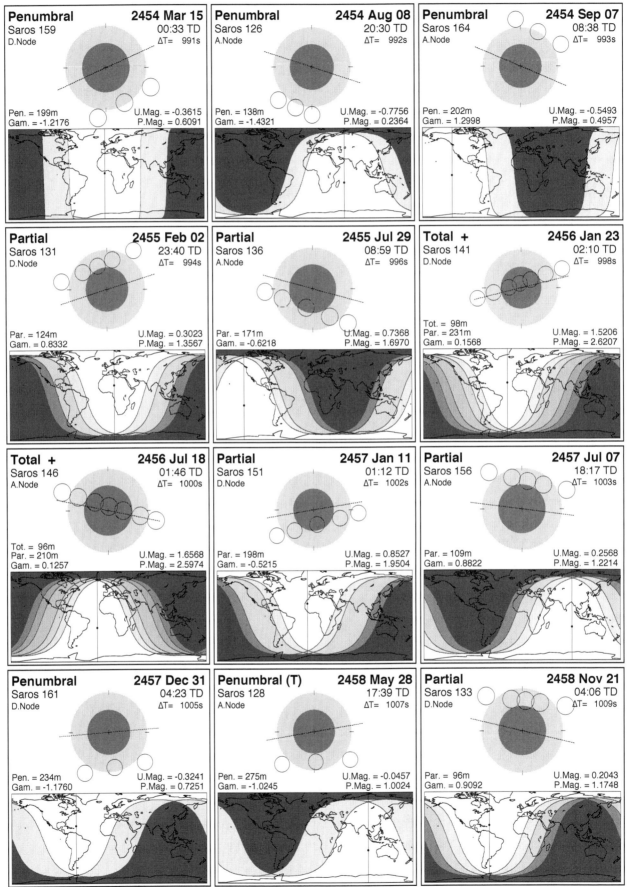

Penumbral   **2454 Mar 15**
Saros 159   00:33 TD
D.Node   ΔT= 991s
Pen. = 199m   U.Mag. = -0.3615
Gam. = -1.2176   P.Mag. = 0.6091

Penumbral   **2454 Aug 08**
Saros 126   20:30 TD
A.Node   ΔT= 992s
Pen. = 138m   U.Mag. = -0.7756
Gam. = -1.4321   P.Mag. = 0.2364

Penumbral   **2454 Sep 07**
Saros 164   08:38 TD
A.Node   ΔT= 993s
Pen. = 202m   U.Mag. = -0.5493
Gam. = 1.2998   P.Mag. = 0.4957

Partial   **2455 Feb 02**
Saros 131   23:40 TD
D.Node   ΔT= 994s
Par. = 124m   U.Mag. = 0.3023
Gam. = 0.8332   P.Mag. = 1.3567

Partial   **2455 Jul 29**
Saros 136   08:59 TD
A.Node   ΔT= 996s
Par. = 171m   U.Mag. = 0.7368
Gam. = -0.6218   P.Mag. = 1.6970

Total +   **2456 Jan 23**
Saros 141   02:10 TD
D.Node   ΔT= 998s
Tot. = 98m
Par. = 231m   U.Mag. = 1.5206
Gam. = 0.1568   P.Mag. = 2.6207

Total +   **2456 Jul 18**
Saros 146   01:46 TD
A.Node   ΔT= 1000s
Tot. = 96m
Par. = 210m   U.Mag. = 1.6568
Gam. = 0.1257   P.Mag. = 2.5974

Partial   **2457 Jan 11**
Saros 151   01:12 TD
D.Node   ΔT= 1002s
Par. = 198m   U.Mag. = 0.8527
Gam. = -0.5215   P.Mag. = 1.9504

Partial   **2457 Jul 07**
Saros 156   18:17 TD
A.Node   ΔT= 1003s
Par. = 109m   U.Mag. = 0.2568
Gam. = 0.8822   P.Mag. = 1.2214

Penumbral   **2457 Dec 31**
Saros 161   04:23 TD
D.Node   ΔT= 1005s
Pen. = 234m   U.Mag. = -0.3241
Gam. = -1.1760   P.Mag. = 0.7251

Penumbral (T)   **2458 May 28**
Saros 128   17:39 TD
A.Node   ΔT= 1007s
Pen. = 275m   U.Mag. = -0.0457
Gam. = -1.0245   P.Mag. = 1.0024

Partial   **2458 Nov 21**
Saros 133   04:06 TD
D.Node   ΔT= 1009s
Par. = 96m   U.Mag. = 0.2043
Gam. = 0.9092   P.Mag. = 1.1748

Plate 194

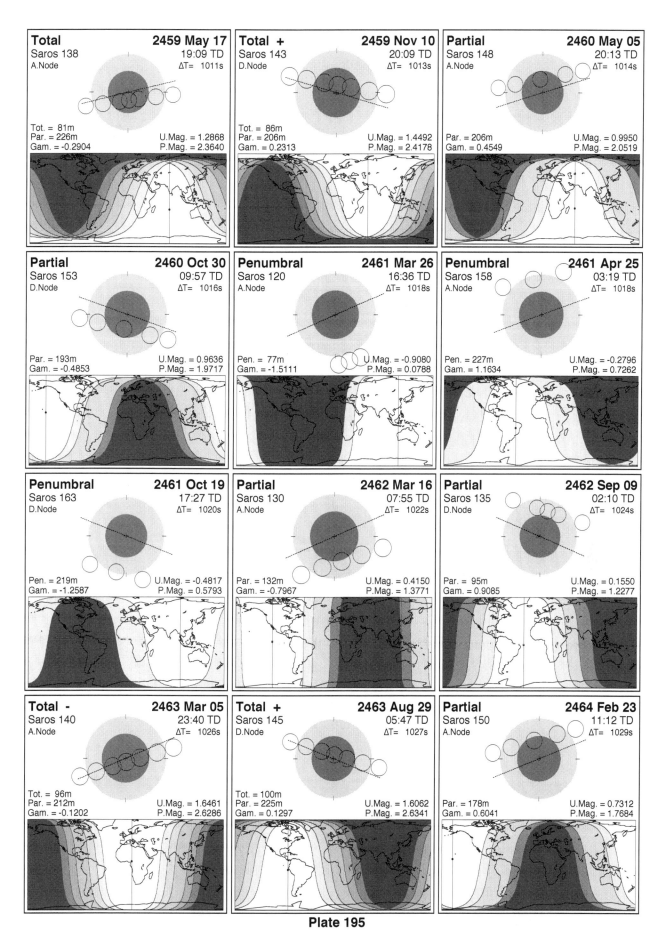

Total	2459 May 17
Saros 138	19:09 TD
A.Node	ΔT= 1011s
Tot. = 81m	
Par. = 226m	U.Mag. = 1.2868
Gam. = -0.2904	P.Mag. = 2.3640

Total +	2459 Nov 10
Saros 143	20:09 TD
D.Node	ΔT= 1013s
Tot. = 86m	
Par. = 206m	U.Mag. = 1.4492
Gam. = 0.2313	P.Mag. = 2.4178

Partial	2460 May 05
Saros 148	20:13 TD
A.Node	ΔT= 1014s
Par. = 206m	U.Mag. = 0.9950
Gam. = 0.4549	P.Mag. = 2.0519

Partial	2460 Oct 30
Saros 153	09:57 TD
D.Node	ΔT= 1016s
Par. = 193m	U.Mag. = 0.9636
Gam. = -0.4853	P.Mag. = 1.9717

Penumbral	2461 Mar 26
Saros 120	16:36 TD
A.Node	ΔT= 1018s
Pen. = 77m	U.Mag. = -0.9080
Gam. = -1.5111	P.Mag. = 0.0788

Penumbral	2461 Apr 25
Saros 158	03:19 TD
A.Node	ΔT= 1018s
Pen. = 227m	U.Mag. = -0.2796
Gam. = 1.1634	P.Mag. = 0.7262

Penumbral	2461 Oct 19
Saros 163	17:27 TD
D.Node	ΔT= 1020s
Pen. = 219m	U.Mag. = -0.4817
Gam. = -1.2587	P.Mag. = 0.5793

Partial	2462 Mar 16
Saros 130	07:55 TD
A.Node	ΔT= 1022s
Par. = 132m	U.Mag. = 0.4150
Gam. = -0.7967	P.Mag. = 1.3771

Partial	2462 Sep 09
Saros 135	02:10 TD
D.Node	ΔT= 1024s
Par. = 95m	U.Mag. = 0.1550
Gam. = 0.9085	P.Mag. = 1.2277

Total -	2463 Mar 05
Saros 140	23:40 TD
A.Node	ΔT= 1026s
Tot. = 96m	
Par. = 212m	U.Mag. = 1.6461
Gam. = -0.1202	P.Mag. = 2.6286

Total +	2463 Aug 29
Saros 145	05:47 TD
D.Node	ΔT= 1027s
Tot. = 100m	
Par. = 225m	U.Mag. = 1.6062
Gam. = 0.1297	P.Mag. = 2.6341

Partial	2464 Feb 23
Saros 150	11:12 TD
A.Node	ΔT= 1029s
Par. = 178m	U.Mag. = 0.7312
Gam. = 0.6041	P.Mag. = 1.7684

Plate 195

291

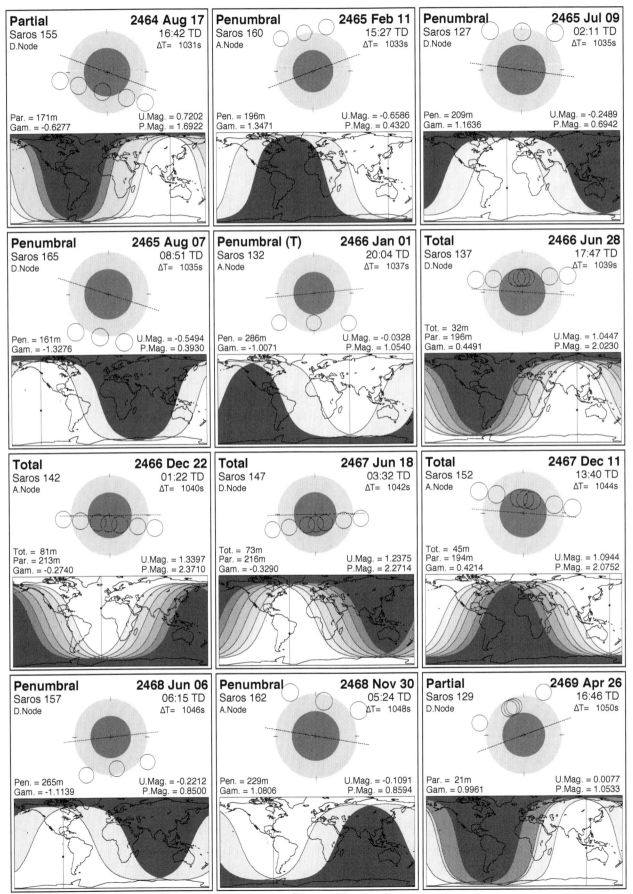

Partial **2464 Aug 17**	
Saros 155 16:42 TD	
D.Node ΔT= 1031s	
Par. = 171m U.Mag. = 0.7202	
Gam. = -0.6277 P.Mag. = 1.6922	

Penumbral   **2465 Feb 11**
Saros 160   15:27 TD
A.Node   ΔT= 1033s
Pen. = 196m   U.Mag. = -0.6586
Gam. = 1.3471   P.Mag. = 0.4320

Penumbral   **2465 Jul 09**
Saros 127   02:11 TD
D.Node   ΔT= 1035s
Pen. = 209m   U.Mag. = -0.2489
Gam. = 1.1636   P.Mag. = 0.6942

Penumbral   **2465 Aug 07**
Saros 165   08:51 TD
D.Node   ΔT= 1035s
Pen. = 161m   U.Mag. = -0.5494
Gam. = -1.3276   P.Mag. = 0.3930

Penumbral (T)   **2466 Jan 01**
Saros 132   20:04 TD
A.Node   ΔT= 1037s
Pen. = 286m   U.Mag. = -0.0328
Gam. = -1.0071   P.Mag. = 1.0540

Total   **2466 Jun 28**
Saros 137   17:47 TD
D.Node   ΔT= 1039s
Tot. = 32m
Par. = 196m   U.Mag. = 1.0447
Gam. = 0.4491   P.Mag. = 2.0230

Total   **2466 Dec 22**
Saros 142   01:22 TD
A.Node   ΔT= 1040s
Tot. = 81m
Par. = 213m   U.Mag. = 1.3397
Gam. = -0.2740   P.Mag. = 2.3710

Total   **2467 Jun 18**
Saros 147   03:32 TD
D.Node   ΔT= 1042s
Tot. = 73m
Par. = 216m   U.Mag. = 1.2375
Gam. = -0.3290   P.Mag. = 2.2714

Total   **2467 Dec 11**
Saros 152   13:40 TD
A.Node   ΔT= 1044s
Tot. = 45m
Par. = 194m   U.Mag. = 1.0944
Gam. = 0.4214   P.Mag. = 2.0752

Penumbral   **2468 Jun 06**
Saros 157   06:15 TD
D.Node   ΔT= 1046s
Pen. = 265m   U.Mag. = -0.2212
Gam. = -1.1139   P.Mag. = 0.8500

Penumbral   **2468 Nov 30**
Saros 162   05:24 TD
A.Node   ΔT= 1048s
Pen. = 229m   U.Mag. = -0.1091
Gam. = 1.0806   P.Mag. = 0.8594

Partial   **2469 Apr 26**
Saros 129   16:46 TD
D.Node   ΔT= 1050s
Par. = 21m   U.Mag. = 0.0077
Gam. = 0.9961   P.Mag. = 1.0533

Plate 196

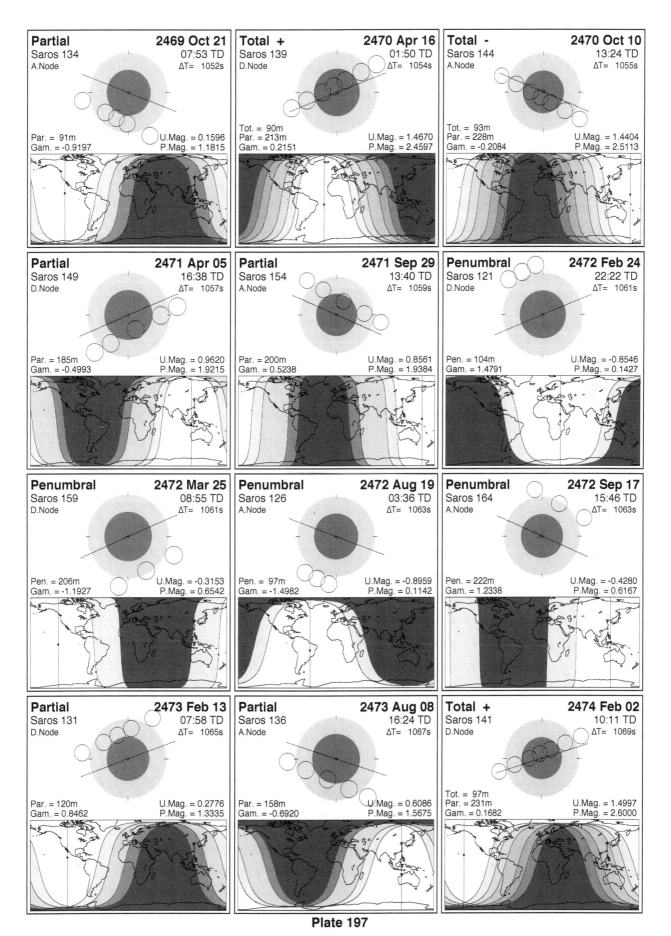

Partial — **2469 Oct 21**
Saros 134 — 07:53 TD
A.Node — ΔT= 1052s
Par. = 91m — U.Mag. = 0.1596
Gam. = -0.9197 — P.Mag. = 1.1815

Total + — **2470 Apr 16**
Saros 139 — 01:50 TD
D.Node — ΔT= 1054s
Tot. = 90m
Par. = 213m — U.Mag. = 1.4670
Gam. = 0.2151 — P.Mag. = 2.4597

Total - — **2470 Oct 10**
Saros 144 — 13:24 TD
A.Node — ΔT= 1055s
Tot. = 93m
Par. = 228m — U.Mag. = 1.4404
Gam. = -0.2084 — P.Mag. = 2.5113

Partial — **2471 Apr 05**
Saros 149 — 16:38 TD
D.Node — ΔT= 1057s
Par. = 185m — U.Mag. = 0.9620
Gam. = -0.4993 — P.Mag. = 1.9215

Partial — **2471 Sep 29**
Saros 154 — 13:40 TD
A.Node — ΔT= 1059s
Par. = 200m — U.Mag. = 0.8561
Gam. = 0.5238 — P.Mag. = 1.9384

Penumbral — **2472 Feb 24**
Saros 121 — 22:22 TD
D.Node — ΔT= 1061s
Pen. = 104m — U.Mag. = -0.8546
Gam. = 1.4791 — P.Mag. = 0.1427

Penumbral — **2472 Mar 25**
Saros 159 — 08:55 TD
D.Node — ΔT= 1061s
Pen. = 206m — U.Mag. = -0.3153
Gam. = -1.1927 — P.Mag. = 0.6542

Penumbral — **2472 Aug 19**
Saros 126 — 03:36 TD
A.Node — ΔT= 1063s
Pen. = 97m — U.Mag. = -0.8959
Gam. = -1.4982 — P.Mag. = 0.1142

Penumbral — **2472 Sep 17**
Saros 164 — 15:46 TD
A.Node — ΔT= 1063s
Pen. = 222m — U.Mag. = -0.4280
Gam. = 1.2338 — P.Mag. = 0.6167

Partial — **2473 Feb 13**
Saros 131 — 07:58 TD
D.Node — ΔT= 1065s
Par. = 120m — U.Mag. = 0.2776
Gam. = 0.8462 — P.Mag. = 1.3335

Partial — **2473 Aug 08**
Saros 136 — 16:24 TD
A.Node — ΔT= 1067s
Par. = 158m — U.Mag. = 0.6086
Gam. = -0.6920 — P.Mag. = 1.5675

Total + — **2474 Feb 02**
Saros 141 — 10:11 TD
D.Node — ΔT= 1069s
Tot. = 97m
Par. = 231m — U.Mag. = 1.4997
Gam. = 0.1682 — P.Mag. = 2.6000

Plate 197

293

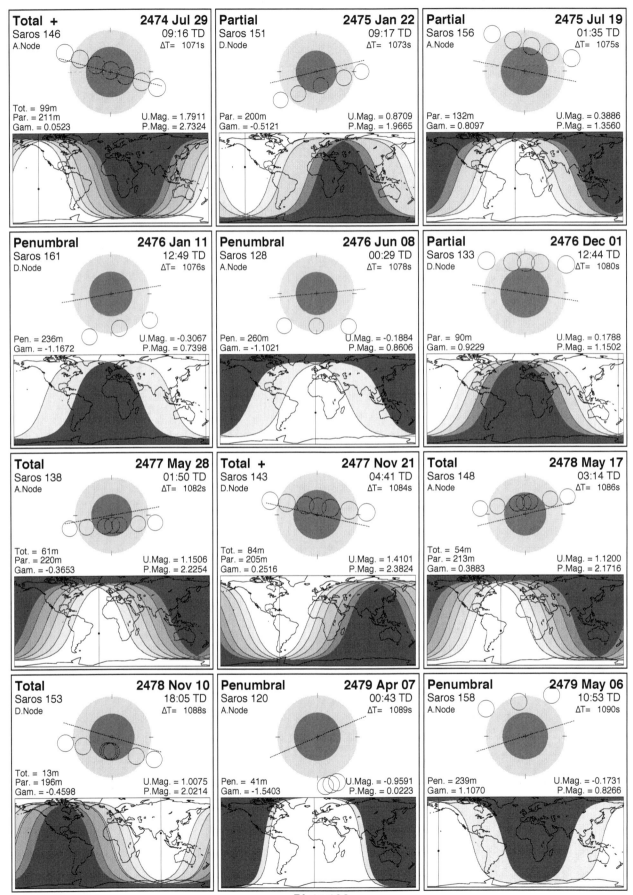

Total + 2474 Jul 29 Saros 146 09:16 TD A.Node ΔT= 1071s Tot. = 99m Par. = 211m U.Mag. = 1.7911 Gam. = 0.0523 P.Mag. = 2.7324	**Partial** 2475 Jan 22 Saros 151 09:17 TD D.Node ΔT= 1073s Par. = 200m U.Mag. = 0.8709 Gam. = -0.5121 P.Mag. = 1.9665	**Partial** 2475 Jul 19 Saros 156 01:35 TD A.Node ΔT= 1075s Par. = 132m U.Mag. = 0.3886 Gam. = 0.8097 P.Mag. = 1.3560
Penumbral 2476 Jan 11 Saros 161 12:49 TD D.Node ΔT= 1076s Pen. = 236m U.Mag. = -0.3067 Gam. = -1.1672 P.Mag. = 0.7398	**Penumbral** 2476 Jun 08 Saros 128 00:29 TD A.Node ΔT= 1078s Pen. = 260m U.Mag. = -0.1884 Gam. = -1.1021 P.Mag. = 0.8606	**Partial** 2476 Dec 01 Saros 133 12:44 TD D.Node ΔT= 1080s Par. = 90m U.Mag. = 0.1788 Gam. = 0.9229 P.Mag. = 1.1502
Total 2477 May 28 Saros 138 01:50 TD A.Node ΔT= 1082s Tot. = 61m Par. = 220m U.Mag. = 1.1506 Gam. = -0.3653 P.Mag. = 2.2254	**Total +** 2477 Nov 21 Saros 143 04:41 TD D.Node ΔT= 1084s Tot. = 84m Par. = 205m U.Mag. = 1.4101 Gam. = 0.2516 P.Mag. = 2.3824	**Total** 2478 May 17 Saros 148 03:14 TD A.Node ΔT= 1086s Tot. = 54m Par. = 213m U.Mag. = 1.1200 Gam. = 0.3883 P.Mag. = 2.1716
Total 2478 Nov 10 Saros 153 18:05 TD D.Node ΔT= 1088s Tot. = 13m Par. = 196m U.Mag. = 1.0075 Gam. = -0.4598 P.Mag. = 2.0214	**Penumbral** 2479 Apr 07 Saros 120 00:43 TD A.Node ΔT= 1089s Pen. = 41m U.Mag. = -0.9591 Gam. = -1.5403 P.Mag. = 0.0223	**Penumbral** 2479 May 06 Saros 158 10:53 TD A.Node ΔT= 1090s Pen. = 239m U.Mag. = -0.1731 Gam. = 1.1070 P.Mag. = 0.8266

Plate 198

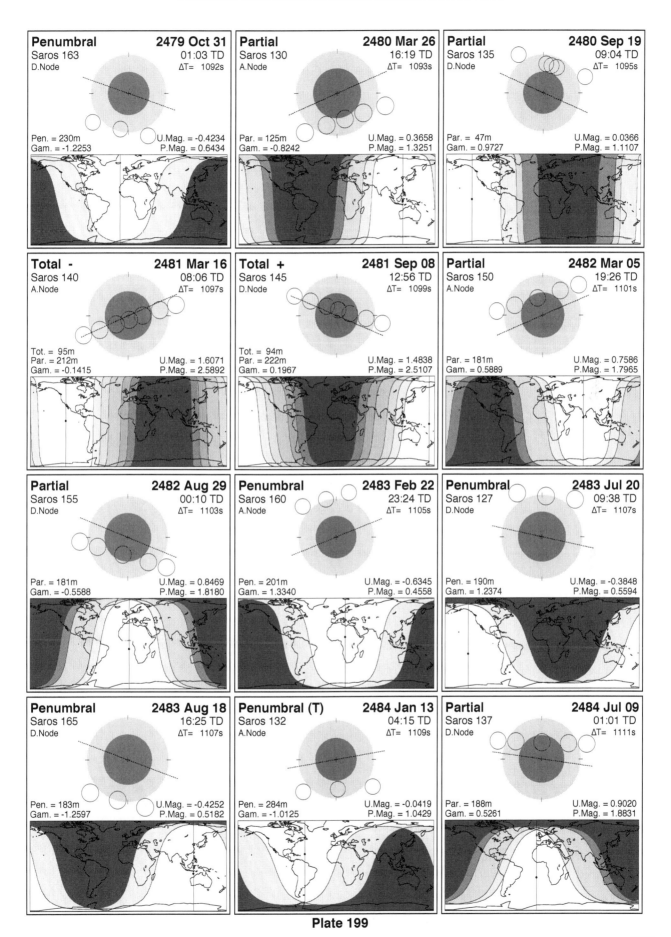

Penumbral **2479 Oct 31**	**Partial** **2480 Mar 26**	**Partial** **2480 Sep 19**
Saros 163 01:03 TD	Saros 130 16:19 TD	Saros 135 09:04 TD
D.Node ΔT= 1092s	A.Node ΔT= 1093s	D.Node ΔT= 1095s
Pen. = 230m U.Mag. = -0.4234	Par. = 125m U.Mag. = 0.3658	Par. = 47m U.Mag. = 0.0366
Gam. = -1.2253 P.Mag. = 0.6434	Gam. = -0.8242 P.Mag. = 1.3251	Gam. = 0.9727 P.Mag. = 1.1107
Total - **2481 Mar 16**	**Total +** **2481 Sep 08**	**Partial** **2482 Mar 05**
Saros 140 08:06 TD	Saros 145 12:56 TD	Saros 150 19:26 TD
A.Node ΔT= 1097s	D.Node ΔT= 1099s	A.Node ΔT= 1101s
Tot. = 95m	Tot. = 94m	
Par. = 212m U.Mag. = 1.6071	Par. = 222m U.Mag. = 1.4838	Par. = 181m U.Mag. = 0.7586
Gam. = -0.1415 P.Mag. = 2.5892	Gam. = 0.1967 P.Mag. = 2.5107	Gam. = 0.5889 P.Mag. = 1.7965
Partial **2482 Aug 29**	**Penumbral** **2483 Feb 22**	**Penumbral** **2483 Jul 20**
Saros 155 00:10 TD	Saros 160 23:24 TD	Saros 127 09:38 TD
D.Node ΔT= 1103s	A.Node ΔT= 1105s	D.Node ΔT= 1107s
Par. = 181m U.Mag. = 0.8469	Pen. = 201m U.Mag. = -0.6345	Pen. = 190m U.Mag. = -0.3848
Gam. = -0.5588 P.Mag. = 1.8180	Gam. = 1.3340 P.Mag. = 0.4558	Gam. = 1.2374 P.Mag. = 0.5594
Penumbral **2483 Aug 18**	**Penumbral (T)** **2484 Jan 13**	**Partial** **2484 Jul 09**
Saros 165 16:25 TD	Saros 132 04:15 TD	Saros 137 01:01 TD
D.Node ΔT= 1107s	A.Node ΔT= 1109s	D.Node ΔT= 1111s
Pen. = 183m U.Mag. = -0.4252	Pen. = 284m U.Mag. = -0.0419	Par. = 188m U.Mag. = 0.9020
Gam. = -1.2597 P.Mag. = 0.5182	Gam. = -1.0125 P.Mag. = 1.0429	Gam. = 0.5261 P.Mag. = 1.8831

Plate 199

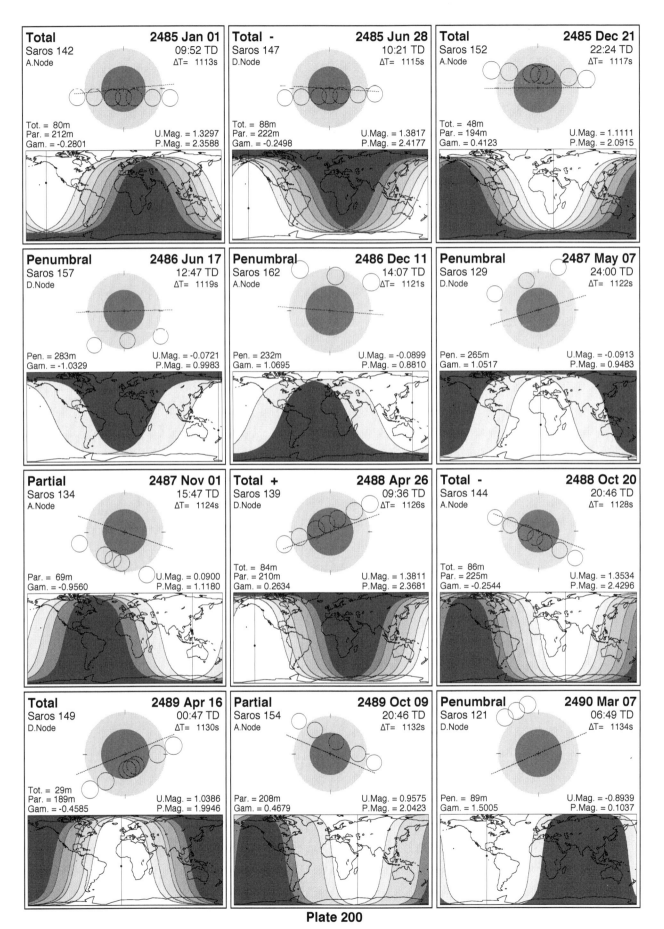

Total   **2485 Jan 01**
Saros 142   09:52 TD
A.Node   ΔT= 1113s
Tot. = 80m
Par. = 212m
Gam. = -0.2801   U.Mag. = 1.3297
P.Mag. = 2.3588

Total -   **2485 Jun 28**
Saros 147   10:21 TD
D.Node   ΔT= 1115s
Tot. = 88m
Par. = 222m
Gam. = -0.2498   U.Mag. = 1.3817
P.Mag. = 2.4177

Total   **2485 Dec 21**
Saros 152   22:24 TD
A.Node   ΔT= 1117s
Tot. = 48m
Par. = 194m
Gam. = 0.4123   U.Mag. = 1.1111
P.Mag. = 2.0915

Penumbral   **2486 Jun 17**
Saros 157   12:47 TD
D.Node   ΔT= 1119s
Pen. = 283m
Gam. = -1.0329   U.Mag. = -0.0721
P.Mag. = 0.9983

Penumbral   **2486 Dec 11**
Saros 162   14:07 TD
A.Node   ΔT= 1121s
Pen. = 232m
Gam. = 1.0695   U.Mag. = -0.0899
P.Mag. = 0.8810

Penumbral   **2487 May 07**
Saros 129   24:00 TD
D.Node   ΔT= 1122s
Pen. = 265m
Gam. = 1.0517   U.Mag. = -0.0913
P.Mag. = 0.9483

Partial   **2487 Nov 01**
Saros 134   15:47 TD
A.Node   ΔT= 1124s
Par. = 69m
Gam. = -0.9560   U.Mag. = 0.0900
P.Mag. = 1.1180

Total +   **2488 Apr 26**
Saros 139   09:36 TD
D.Node   ΔT= 1126s
Tot. = 84m
Par. = 210m
Gam. = 0.2634   U.Mag. = 1.3811
P.Mag. = 2.3681

Total -   **2488 Oct 20**
Saros 144   20:46 TD
A.Node   ΔT= 1128s
Tot. = 86m
Par. = 225m
Gam. = -0.2544   U.Mag. = 1.3534
P.Mag. = 2.4296

Total   **2489 Apr 16**
Saros 149   00:47 TD
D.Node   ΔT= 1130s
Tot. = 29m
Par. = 189m
Gam. = -0.4585   U.Mag. = 1.0386
P.Mag. = 1.9946

Partial   **2489 Oct 09**
Saros 154   20:46 TD
A.Node   ΔT= 1132s
Par. = 208m
Gam. = 0.4679   U.Mag. = 0.9575
P.Mag. = 2.0423

Penumbral   **2490 Mar 07**
Saros 121   06:49 TD
D.Node   ΔT= 1134s
Pen. = 89m
Gam. = 1.5005   U.Mag. = -0.8939
P.Mag. = 0.1037

Plate 200

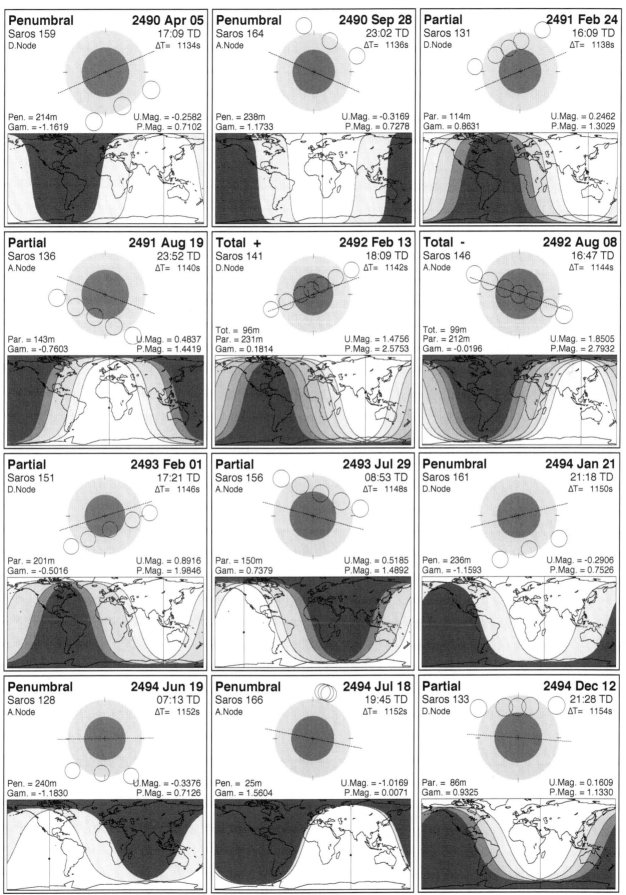

Penumbral	2490 Apr 05
Saros 159	17:09 TD
D.Node	ΔT= 1134s
Pen. = 214m	U.Mag. = -0.2582
Gam. = -1.1619	P.Mag. = 0.7102

Penumbral	2490 Sep 28
Saros 164	23:02 TD
A.Node	ΔT= 1136s
Pen. = 238m	U.Mag. = -0.3169
Gam. = 1.1733	P.Mag. = 0.7278

Partial	2491 Feb 24
Saros 131	16:09 TD
D.Node	ΔT= 1138s
Par. = 114m	U.Mag. = 0.2462
Gam. = 0.8631	P.Mag. = 1.3029

Partial	2491 Aug 19
Saros 136	23:52 TD
A.Node	ΔT= 1140s
Par. = 143m	U.Mag. = 0.4837
Gam. = -0.7603	P.Mag. = 1.4419

Total +	2492 Feb 13
Saros 141	18:09 TD
D.Node	ΔT= 1142s
Tot. = 96m	
Par. = 231m	U.Mag. = 1.4756
Gam. = 0.1814	P.Mag. = 2.5753

Total -	2492 Aug 08
Saros 146	16:47 TD
A.Node	ΔT= 1144s
Tot. = 99m	
Par. = 212m	U.Mag. = 1.8505
Gam. = -0.0196	P.Mag. = 2.7932

Partial	2493 Feb 01
Saros 151	17:21 TD
D.Node	ΔT= 1146s
Par. = 201m	U.Mag. = 0.8916
Gam. = -0.5016	P.Mag. = 1.9846

Partial	2493 Jul 29
Saros 156	08:53 TD
A.Node	ΔT= 1148s
Par. = 150m	U.Mag. = 0.5185
Gam. = 0.7379	P.Mag. = 1.4892

Penumbral	2494 Jan 21
Saros 161	21:18 TD
D.Node	ΔT= 1150s
Pen. = 236m	U.Mag. = -0.2906
Gam. = -1.1593	P.Mag. = 0.7526

Penumbral	2494 Jun 19
Saros 128	07:13 TD
A.Node	ΔT= 1152s
Pen. = 240m	U.Mag. = -0.3376
Gam. = -1.1830	P.Mag. = 0.7126

Penumbral	2494 Jul 18
Saros 166	19:45 TD
A.Node	ΔT= 1152s
Pen. = 25m	U.Mag. = -1.0169
Gam. = 1.5604	P.Mag. = 0.0071

Partial	2494 Dec 12
Saros 133	21:28 TD
D.Node	ΔT= 1154s
Par. = 86m	U.Mag. = 0.1609
Gam. = 0.9325	P.Mag. = 1.1330

Plate 201

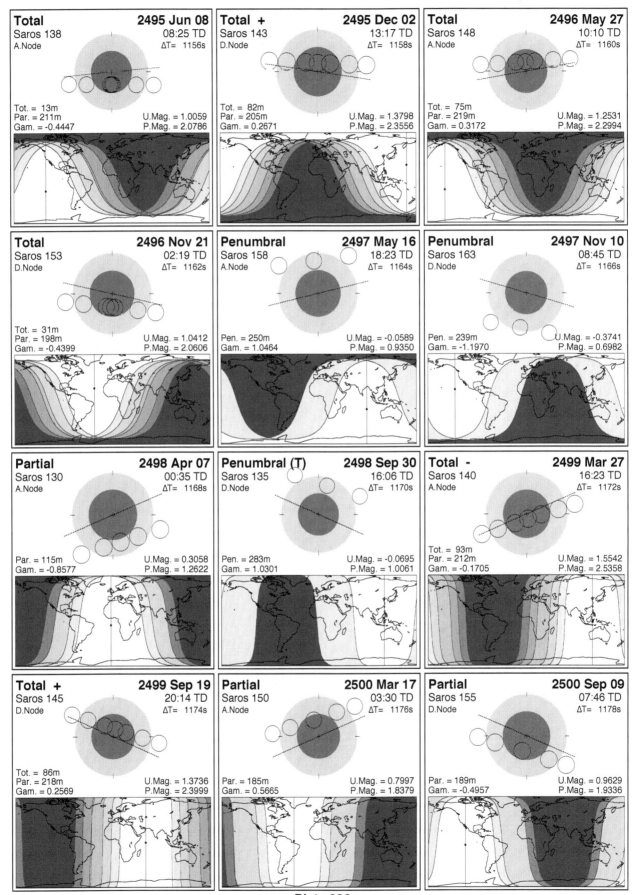

Total   **2495 Jun 08**
Saros 138   08:25 TD
A.Node   ΔT= 1156s
Tot. = 13m
Par. = 211m   U.Mag. = 1.0059
Gam. = -0.4447   P.Mag. = 2.0786

Total +   **2495 Dec 02**
Saros 143   13:17 TD
D.Node   ΔT= 1158s
Tot. = 82m
Par. = 205m   U.Mag. = 1.3798
Gam. = 0.2671   P.Mag. = 2.3556

Total   **2496 May 27**
Saros 148   10:10 TD
A.Node   ΔT= 1160s
Tot. = 75m
Par. = 219m   U.Mag. = 1.2531
Gam. = 0.3172   P.Mag. = 2.2994

Total   **2496 Nov 21**
Saros 153   02:19 TD
D.Node   ΔT= 1162s
Tot. = 31m
Par. = 198m   U.Mag. = 1.0412
Gam. = -0.4399   P.Mag. = 2.0606

Penumbral   **2497 May 16**
Saros 158   18:23 TD
A.Node   ΔT= 1164s
Pen. = 250m   U.Mag. = -0.0589
Gam. = 1.0464   P.Mag. = 0.9350

Penumbral   **2497 Nov 10**
Saros 163   08:45 TD
D.Node   ΔT= 1166s
Pen. = 239m   U.Mag. = -0.3741
Gam. = -1.1970   P.Mag. = 0.6982

Partial   **2498 Apr 07**
Saros 130   00:35 TD
A.Node   ΔT= 1168s
Par. = 115m   U.Mag. = 0.3058
Gam. = -0.8577   P.Mag. = 1.2622

Penumbral (T)   **2498 Sep 30**
Saros 135   16:06 TD
D.Node   ΔT= 1170s
Pen. = 283m   U.Mag. = -0.0695
Gam. = 1.0301   P.Mag. = 1.0061

Total -   **2499 Mar 27**
Saros 140   16:23 TD
A.Node   ΔT= 1172s
Tot. = 93m
Par. = 212m   U.Mag. = 1.5542
Gam. = -0.1705   P.Mag. = 2.5358

Total +   **2499 Sep 19**
Saros 145   20:14 TD
D.Node   ΔT= 1174s
Tot. = 86m
Par. = 218m   U.Mag. = 1.3736
Gam. = 0.2569   P.Mag. = 2.3999

Partial   **2500 Mar 17**
Saros 150   03:30 TD
A.Node   ΔT= 1176s
Par. = 185m   U.Mag. = 0.7997
Gam. = 0.5665   P.Mag. = 1.8379

Partial   **2500 Sep 09**
Saros 155   07:46 TD
D.Node   ΔT= 1178s
Par. = 189m   U.Mag. = 0.9629
Gam. = -0.4957   P.Mag. = 1.9336

Plate 202

Printed in Great Britain
by Amazon.co.uk, Ltd.,
Marston Gate.